FRANK R. MIELE, MSEE
President, Pegasus Lectures Inc.

VOLUME I

ULTRASOUND PHYSICS & INSTRUMENTATION

4TH EDITION

2006
Miele Enterprises, Inc.

A Cataloging In Publication Record is available from the Library of Congress

Printed in the United States of America

Last Digit is the print number: 9   8   7   6   5   4   3

ISBN: 978-1-933250-06-9   Volume 1
               978-1-933250-07-6   Volume 2
               978-1-933250-08-3   Set of Volume 1 and 2

Dedication

This book is dedicated to my wife Carol, my mother Graziella, my seven-year-old daughter Gina Luisa, my five-year-old daughter Cristiana Graziella, and in loving memory of my grandmother Gina Luisa: four generations of women who have shaped my life.

Of course I cannot forget my always smiling eight-month-old son Pietro Pio, my three-year-old son Franco Raffaello whose hugs redefine affection, or my eldest son Paul (forever Paulie to me), who loves to sit in on lectures and "help out." Finally, I must acknowledge my father Frank, whose tireless work and selflessness afforded me educational opportunities for which I feel blessed.

A special thanks to my friends and colleagues who took the time and made the effort as section reviewers and who provided quality images. Your time, suggestions, and expertise are much appreciated.

THANK YOU TO THE FOLLOWING 4TH EDITION SECTION REVIEWERS

Ali AbuRahma MD, RVT
Professor of Surgery, Chief of Vascular Surgery, and Medical Director of Vascular Laboratory
Robert C. Byrd Health Sciences Center of West Virginia University, Charleston, West Virginia

Catherine Carr-Hoefer RDMS, RDCS, RVT, RT, FSDMS
Assistant Director, Diagnostic Imaging, Radiology, Good Samaritan Regional Medical Center, Corvallis, Oregon

M. Robert De Jong RDMS, RDCS, RVT
Radiology Technical Manager, Ultrasound, The Johns Hopkins Medical Institutions, Baltimore, Maryland

Carol J. Gannon RN, RVT, RDCS, FSVU
Vice President, Pegasus Lectures, Inc., Dallas, Texas

Debra R. Goines BS, RVT, RDMS, RTR
Clinical Application Specialist, Mountain View, California

Mark J. Harry RDCS, RVT
Private Consultant, Cardiac Ultrasound Consulting,
Des Moines, Iowa

Janice D. Hickey MRT, RDMS, BSc.
Clinical Instructor, Department of Emergency Medicine, Lehigh Valley Hospital, Allentown, Pennsylvania

Bonnie Johnson RDMS, RVT, FSVU
Director, Vascular Laboratory Services, Division of Vascular Surgery, Stanford University Medical Center, Palo Alto, CA

Ann Marie Kupinski PhD, RVT, FSVU
Technical Director, Karmondy Vascular Laboratory, The Vascular Group, Albany, NY
Assistant Professor of Surgery, Albany Medical College, Albany, NY

Naresh Kumar MD
Medical Director, Whitby Cardiovascular Institute, Whitby, Ontario, Canada

Ronald Mucci, PhD
Signal Processing Engineer, Tiverton, Massachusetts

Marsha M. Neumyer BS, RVT, FSVU, FAIUM
CEO and International Director, Vascular Diagnostic Educational Services, Vascular Resource Associates, Harrisburg, Pennsylvania

Kathleen Palmieri RVT
Senior Consultant, Cardiovascular Technology Resources (A Division of KRP Accreditation Specialists, Inc.), Skaneateles, New York

Patrick Rafter MS
Electrical Engineer, Boston, Massachusetts

Terry Reynolds BS, RDCS
Director, School of Cardiac Ultrasound, Arizona Heart Institute, Phoenix, Arizona

William B. Schroedter BS, RVT, FSVU
Technical Director, Quality Vascular Imaging, Inc. , Venice, Florida

Robert Scissons RVT, FSVU
Technical Director, Bend Memorial Clinic Vascular Laboratory, Bend, Oregon

Franklin W. West RN, BSN, RVT, FSVU
Director of Professional Development, Pacific Vascular, Inc., Bothell, WA

THANK YOU TO THE FOLLOWING IMAGE CONTRIBUTORS

Bonnie Johnson RDMS, RVT, FSVU
Director, Vascular Laboratory Services, Division of Vascular Surgery, Stanford University Medical Center, Palo Alto, CA

M. Robert De Jong RDMS, RDCS, RVT
Radiology Technical Manager, Ultrasound, The Johns Hopkins Medical Institutions, Baltimore, Maryland

Jeffrey C. Hill BS, RDCS, FASE
Echocardiographic Laboratory, Division of Cardiology, University of Massachusetts Medical Center, Worcester, Massachusetts

Robert Scissons RVT, FSVU
Technical Director, Bend Memorial Clinic Vascular Laboratory, Bend, Oregon

Michael Stasik RVT
Senior Technologist, Cleveland Clinic Foundation, Cleveland, Ohio

David Tomberlin ARRT, RDCS, RVT
Lead Clinical Specialist, Cardiovascular, Dallas, Texas

Susan Whitelaw RVT, RDMS, RTR
Laboratory Supervisor, Cleveland Clinic Foundation, Cleveland, Ohio

Franklin W. West RN, BSN, RVT, FSVU
Director of Professional Development, Pacific Vascular, Inc., Bothell, WA

ATS Laboratories, Bridgeport, Connecticut

CIRS, Inc., Norfolk, Virginia

Flometrics, Inc., Solana Beach, California

GE Healthcare, Milwaukee, Wisconsin

Onda Corporation, Sunnyvale, California

Pacific Vascular, Inc., Bothell, Washington

Philips Medical Systems, Bothell, Washington

Precision Acoustics, Inc., United Kingdom

Siemens Ultrasound, Mountain View, California

and special thanks to Carol, Debbie, Eric, Halan, and Monica whose tireless efforts helped bring this book to fruition.

Preface

The greatest challenge with writing a textbook is that every reader brings a different level of knowledge, experience, and goals with him or her. For some people, this book represents their first exposure to ultrasound, and the book is to serve as a foundation on which to build. Others bring twenty or more years of experience and use this book as a way reinforcing the principles on which they perform their daily scans, or as a means to better understand new ultrasound techniques. Some are using this book in an ultrasound educational program, and others are using this book to prepare for a credentialing exam. Add to these differences in experience and goals the fact that some people experience dramatic feelings of fear and loathing just from hearing the word "physics" and you have a real conundrum when determining how to structure a textbook.

It should now be clear that the myriad goals and levels of experience make this a very challenging book to write. No one book can be everything to everyone. So instead, this book is really three books in one. Topics are divided into levels so that different level students can progress at a pace appropriate for their background, experience, and goals. Beginning students can follow Level 1 throughout the book, leaving Level 2 and Level 3 for when they have more ultrasound experience. More advanced students can choose to skip Level 1 and go right to Level 2, or use Level 1 as a refresher and use Level 2 as a means of preparing for the credentialing exams and advancing their knowledge. Level 3 is intended for those readers who really want to be challenged, or for content that is perhaps outside the areas generally tested on the credentialing exams. Extensive "Keypoints" sections are included at the conclusion of each chapter to both integrate concepts and serve as a study guide. The following is a description of each level:

Level 1:   **Ultrasound Physics Basics**
Level 1 material focuses on the underlying physics and basic concepts critical for developing skill in the use of diagnostic ultrasound. Level 1 presumes no knowledge other than the basic abilities that come from general schooling. This level also serves as a good refresher for people who have good ultrasound experience but weaker backgrounds in physics and basic mathematics.

Level 2:   **Exam Level Ultrasound Physics**
Level 2 material covers basic topics often outlined on the credentialing exams. Furthermore, Level 2 material is intended to generate a more profound understanding of the concepts so that the relationship of the physics fundamentals to the quality of the diagnostic ultrasound is understood. In other words, understanding Level 2 should not only prepare you for your board exams, but also result in better patient care.

Level 3:   **Advanced Ultrasound Physics Concepts and Applications**
Level 3 material contains advanced topics, newer ultrasound techniques, or even just higher level material for those people who want to be challenged. At times, Level 3 will also contain specific applications of the physics to a specialty area such as cardiac, vascular, or general ultrasound.

Animation and Image Library CD:

Throughout the book you will find CD-ROM icons that indicate additional content is available on the Animation and Image Library CD. Whenever possible, it is best to view the referenced CD content within the context of the correct topic.

Key concepts:

The keypoints serve as a chapter-by-chapter review of the fundamental principles. These sections serve both as a means of highlighting the main points as well as an exam review. Many of the keypoints included serve as the basis for exam questions, and as such should be reviewed by all exam candidates.

The Importance of Understanding the Structure of this Book

There are three reasons why understanding the structure of this book is so important:

1. So that you can customize how you use the book to your experience level and goals.
2. So that you have a clear indication of when you are knowledgeable to take a credentialing exam.
3. So that you have a systematic approach to increase your knowledge and clinical abilities from your current state.

In addition to serving as a core for an ultrasound physics program and a reference for your laboratory, this textbook has also been designed as an independent learning program to assist candidates preparing for their credentialing and board exams. Volume II, Appendix C contains a comprehensive Test Taking Strategies section to help improve your test taking skills including specific approaches detailing the incorporation of logic and reasoning skills for multiple choice exams. This section should be reviewed before and after reading the text. Volume II, Appendix M contains study suggestions, a study guide, and instructions for obtaining continuing medical education credits.

A Final Word about this Book's Structure:

There are many ultrasound physics books that either overshoot or undershoot the intended goals of the reader. In addition, there are books that are very easy to read, but stop short of building the knowledge necessary to demonstrate competence on a credentialing exam. More importantly, these books fall short of imbuing the reader with the knowledge necessary to improve patient care. There are other books that, although technically excellent, presume too much knowledge for most people such that the reader feels as if they are drowning from the very first page. By writing this book in three different levels, I am hoping to reach out to a wider audience, increasing knowledge for both the experienced and the neophyte in ultrasound. I have chosen to create a book that takes students through the first level and beyond with a clear path to the knowledge necessary to demonstrate competency at the credentialing exam level. I hope I have written a book that does not presume so much knowledge that students become overwhelmed and are afraid to utilize the text, but on the other hand pushes and challenges the student to continue learning. In essence, I have tried to write this book so that each level becomes appropriate as the reader's knowledge grows.

I believe the first step to knowledge is a true assessment of where you are, where you want to be, and what path you are willing to take to get there.

And so starts the journey ...

Frank R. Miele

Pegasus Lectures Physics and Instrumentation
Independent Learning Program

Jointly Sponsored by A. Webb Roberts Center for Continuing Medical Education of
Baylor Health Care System, Dallas
and Pegasus Lectures, Inc.

CME ENDURING MATERIAL INFORMATION

Faculty

Frank Miele, MSEE
President, Pegasus Lectures, Inc.

Frank graduated cum laude from Dartmouth College with a triple major in physics, mathematics, and engineering. While at Dartmouth, he was a Proctor Scholar and received citations for academic excellence in comparative literature, atomic physics and quantum mechanics, and real analysis. After completing his graduate work, Frank was awarded the Ruth Goodrich Prize for Academic Excellence. After co-teaching a course in digital electronics at Dartmouth, Frank was a research and design engineer and project leader, designing ultrasound equipment and electronics for more than ten years. In that role, Frank designed the hardware for the first parallel processing color Doppler system, created a Doppler system platform, designed HPRF Doppler, created the first released adaptive ultrasound processing technique, designed transcranial Doppler and transcranial imaging, worked on multiple transducer project teams, and performed extensive clinical trial testing and research.

Frank has been the vice president of Research and Development and chief scientist for a medical device company investigating ultrasound related hemodynamic based measurements. As a researcher and designer of ultrasound, he has lectured across the country to sonographers, physicians, engineers, and students on myriad topics. Frank has authored the Ultrasound & Physics Instrumentation Independent Learning Program, produced multiple educational videos, created exam simulation programs, as well as created the analysis algorithm method and apparatus for evaluating educational performance (patent pending). Frank has served as an author and Co-Chief editor for the ASCeXAM Simulation Review CD in conjunction with the American Society of Echocardiography. He has also served on the faculty for the Society of Vascular Ultrasound and Society of Vascular Surgery and is credited with several ultrasound and medical device patents, trade secrets, and publications.

Purpose and Target Audience

This activity is designed to familiarize physicians and sonographers with the physics and instrumentation concepts employed in diagnostic ultrasound and provide a method to prepare for ultrasound physics credentialing exams and/or accreditation. It will be of interest to, but not limited to, radiologists, cardiologists, neurologists, vascular surgeons, cardiovascular surgeons, anesthesiologists, and/or physicians providing interpretation of diagnostic ultrasound, preparing for accreditation, and/or desiring to improve their understanding of ultrasound physics.

Medium

Printed text
CD

Objectives

Upon completion of the activity, the participant should be able to:

- Define areas of strengths and weaknesses in their understanding of ultrasound physics.
- Comprehend the effect of system controls and transducer parameters on the diagnostic quality of an ultrasound image.
- Demonstrate improved understanding of ultrasound physics and how physics can affect the integrity of a diagnostic image.
- Demonstrate improved interpretative skills for diagnostic ultrasound, Doppler and hemodynamic variables.
- Demonstrate improved preparation for the ultrasound physics credentialing exam.

CME Credit

This activity has been planned and implemented in accordance with the Essential Areas and Policies of the Accreditation Council for Continuing Medical Education (ACCME) through the joint sponsorship of the A. Webb Roberts Center for Continuing Medical Education of the Baylor Health Care System, Dallas and Pegasus Lectures, Inc.

The A. Webb Roberts Center for Continuing Medical Education of Baylor Health Care System, Dallas designates this educational activity for a maximum of 35 Category 1 credits toward the AMA Physician's Recognition Award. Each physician should claim only those credits that he/she actually spent in the activity.

The A. Webb Roberts Center for Continuing Medical Education of Baylor Health Care System, Dallas is accredited by the ACCME to provide continuing medical education for physicians.

Faculty Disclosure

Frank Miele is the president of Pegasus Lectures, Inc. and owner of Miele Enterprises, LLC.

No unlabeled or investigational uses of a product or medical device are addressed in this CME activity.

Instructions

Participants must:
1. Read Volumes I & II of Ultrasound Physics and Instrumentation
2. Complete conceptual questions and exercises within Volumes I & II
   (Refer to study suggestions in Vol. II, Appendix M)
3. Complete the final exam and evaluation

Final Exam, Evaluation and Processing Fee

At the conclusion of this activity, participants must complete the final exam and the evaluation. A completed evaluation form must accompany the final exam. Please indicate on the evaluation form if you are a licensed or non-licensed physician. There is a $30 processing fee for AMA/PRA Category 1 credit. **The check for AMA/PRA credit should be made payable to: A. Webb Roberts Center.** Participants should send the original final exam for scoring (no copies accepted), the processing fee, the evaluation and any correspondence to:

Pegasus Lectures, Inc.
PO Box 157
Forney, TX 75126

Tel: 972-564-3056
Fax: 972-552-9186

NOTE: Participants must achieve a **75% pass rate** on the final exam to be awarded AMA/PRA CME credit. Feedback on exam scores will be provided. A CME certificate will be mailed directly to the participant from the A. Webb Roberts Center for Continuing Medical Education of Baylor Health Care System, Dallas.

Date of Original Release: May 2001
Date of Most Recent Update: October 2005

Estimated time to complete the educational activity: 35 hours

TABLE OF CONTENTS

VOLUME 1

Table of Contents

Pegasus Lectures, Inc.

Table of Contents

CHAPTER 4 - Pulsed Wave Operation

Pegasus Lectures, Inc.

Table of Contents

CHAPTER 5 - Transducers

Table of Contents

Table of Contents

VOLUME 2

CHAPTER 7 - Doppler

Table of Contents

CHAPTER 8 - Artifacts

Table of Contents

CHAPTER 10 - Contrast and Harmonics

Pegasus Lectures, Inc.

Table of Contents

Table of Contents

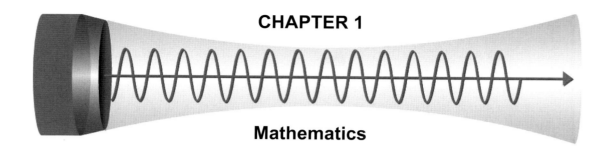

CHAPTER 1

Mathematics

Introduction

Without math, it is not possible to learn physics. Math is to physics what a paintbrush is to a painter or physical conditioning is to an athlete. The foundation of physics is mathematics. Therefore, to understand physics, and not just memorize facts, you must have at least a rudimentary understanding of mathematics.

Types of Math

Most people think of mathematics in terms of basic arithmetic and numerical manipulation. Whereas, this is certainly true, it is a very narrow view of mathematics. Mathematics is really an enormous field that includes many different topics. The field of mathematics includes many disciplines such as algebra, number theory, geometry, calculus, trigonometry, topology, and even logic and reasoning. Although you will not need to become an expert in any of these disciplines, the more you learn in mathematics, the easier it will be to understand physics.

How Much Math Will You Need?

Many people in the field of ultrasound will state that there is very little mathematics on the board exams. I do not agree. I think this disparity in opinions stems from the very narrow definition of mathematics as numerical calculations. It is true that there are very few numerical calculations on most of the credentialing exams, and certainly never such intensive calculations such that one would require a calculator. However, depending on the specific credentialing test and the test version, there are approximately twenty-five to forty percent of the questions that involve some form of mathematics.

As you will discover throughout this book, the mathematics included on the credentialing exams generally does not include performing many calculations, but rather asks relative relationships and logical conclusions from the mathematical relationships between variables. In other words, instead of asking you to calculate the resistance to flow for a fluid flowing through a vessel, you may be asked how the resistance to flow will change with changes in parameters that define the vessel. Instead of asking you to calculate a Doppler shift for a given transducer frequency, given a specific angle to flow and a blood flow velocity, you may be asked how the Doppler shift would change if a different transducer operating frequency were used given the same angle to flow and blood flow velocity. Answering this type of "relative" question involves math skills, which many students have not used for a long period of time, or worse, never developed. This last point is precisely why it is so critical for you to learn the basic mathematics, as outlined below.

To learn the basics of ultrasound (Level 1) you will need a proficiency in the basic mathematical functions. Specifically, you will need to:

- Be comfortable with the language of mathematics and translating English into mathematical functions.
- Add, subtract, multiply, and divide.
- Deal with fractions, percentages, and decimal notation.
- Understand exponential form and become fluent with the metric system.
- Understand the concept of reciprocals.
- Understand basic relationships of variables within an equation (proportionality and inverse).
- Perform algebraic manipulation of equations.

To master Level 2, you will need some higher-level math skills such as:

- Understand the difference between absolute and relative information.
- Understand the difference between linear and non-linear relationships.
- Recall or determine the equations commonly used in ultrasound physics and in hemodynamics.
- Understand the basic trigonometric functions of the sine and the cosine.
- Understand and apply the concepts of logarithms and decibels.
- Understand the basics of the binary system (relative to base 10).

To master Level 3, you will not necessarily need to develop many more math skills than suggested for Level 2. However, Level 3 presumes a more fluid working knowledge of the mathematics needed to master Level 2. The few additional mathematical topics that might help with Level 3 but are not necessarily required are:

- Some basic calculus.
- Understand rates of change (derivatives).
- Understanding integration.

How to Learn Mathematics

The good news is I have never encountered a student unable to master the mathematics necessary to pass the examination. The bad news is that learning this mathematics requires a structured approach, time, work, and patience.

A Structured Approach, Time, Work and Patience

Adults don't learn the same way children learn. Children tend not to be afraid of making a mistake in front of their peers. Adults, in comparison, live in fear and dread that someone will recognize that they are ignorant of even the slightest detail. I believe this approach of learning in fear puts an extraordinarily heavy and unfair burden upon adults in the position of student.

There is no way that anyone will understand everything just by reading the material once. Expecting to understand immediately is not only unreasonable, but puts a tremendous stress on the student. If you realize that learning is a process that only comes slowly over time through work and patience, you will not panic when something isn't clear the first time. It is not fair to yourself to lose self-esteem because you don't fully understand a concept the first time through the material. I often use the analogy that learning is like building a house. Before you can get to the fun part of decorating the interior with intricate art and furniture, you have to go through the backbreaking work of digging a hole in the ground, setting up forms, and building a foundation. Without a solid foundation, the house will never stand.

It is time to dig the hole and do the work necessary so that you can build the foundation.

1. Mathematic Basics

1.1 Numbers

In mathematics, there are many categorizations which group numbers together based on their similar properties. For example, there are counting numbers (the natural numbers), negative counting numbers (the negative natural numbers), the set of all the natural numbers, negative numbers and 0 (called the integers), numbers which can be expressed as the ratio of two integers (rational numbers), and numbers which cannot be expressed as the ratio of two integers (irrational numbers), etc.

Natural Numbers: 1, 2, 3, 4, …
Negative Natural Numbers: -1, -2, -3, -4, …
Integers: -5, -4, -3, -1, 0, 1, 2, 3, 4, 5, …
Rational Numbers: (all numbers which can be expressed as p/q where p and q are integers)
Irrational Numbers: (all numbers which cannot be expressed as p/q where p and q are integers)

For ultrasound physics, you will not need to know precise definitions of all of the various classifications of numbers. What you will need is a general ability to work with numbers including the basic mathematical operations of addition, subtraction, division, and multiplication.

1.2 Basic Mathematical Notation (symbols used in basic mathematics)

Addition	+	
Subtraction	−	
Multiplication	x	Example: m x f implies the variable m multiplied by the variable f.
	*	Example: t * v implies the variable t multiplied by the variable v.
	•	Example: c • v implies the variable c multiplied by the variable v.
	( )	Example: 3(7) implies the number 3 times the number 7.
No symbol		Example: 3z implies the number 3 multiplied by the variable z.
Division	/	Example: m / f implies the variable m divided by the variable f.
	÷	Example: j ÷ k implies the variable j divided by the variable k.
Equality	=	

Inequalities:

Greater than	>	Example: g > 3 is read as g is greater than the number 3.
Less than	<	Example: h < 6 is read as h is less than the number 6.
Greater than or equal to	≥	Example: k ≥ r is read as k is greater than or equal to r.
Less than or equal to	≤	Example: h ≤ 6 is read as h is less than or equal to 6.

*Note: Children generally learn to use the letter "x" to stand for multiplication. Once students reach algebra, there is generally a shift that occurs such that symbols other than "x" are often used to denote multiplication. This shift occurs since the letter x is generally used to stand for the unknown quantity in an algebraic expression. Since it is easy to confuse the "x" that stands for multiplication with the "x" that stands for a variable, other symbols become more commonly used. Therefore, there are many symbols used to indicate multiplication, such as: x, •, *, and sometimes ( ). All of these symbols will be used throughout this text and interchanged freely so as to accustom you to each of these notations.*

1.3 Basic Mathematical Definitions

Constant: A number which cannot change (Example: 3, 7, -14, 6 are all constants).

Natural constant: A number which reoccurs naturally in the universe in relation to a specific parameter (Example: pi (π) for circles).

Coefficient: A constant term used as a multiplier of a variable (Example: in the expression $7z^2$, the number 7 is the coefficient for the variable term z^2).

Variables: A physical quantity which can vary or change (Example: in the expression $3x^2$, the variable is represented by the letter x).

1.4 The Value of Estimating

The ability to estimate quickly is very handy in every day life. Learning to make good estimates comes from practice and a little bit of thinking. For example, if you were asked to solve the problem what is 19 times 20, and you were not allowed to use a calculator or paper and pencil, what would you do.

Approach 1: (rounding off: estimation)
Find a way of rounding off the numbers into two numbers you can easily multiply in your head. For example 19 x 20 is a little less than 20 x 20. Since 20 x 20 is 400, your first answer would be just a little less than 400.

Approach 2: (actual answer using estimation to simplify the math)
Start with Approach 1 and add one more step. Since 19 x 20 can be written as (20-1) x 20 which is the same as (20 x 20) – (1 x 20), you can actually solve this problem exactly in your head. As you solved in Approach 1, 20 x 20 is 400. Since the correct answer is actually 20 less than 400, the answer is 380.

In terms of ultrasound physics and hemodynamics, there are times when you should estimate the answer to a problem to make certain that you have not made a simple math calculation error. The best way to develop this ability is to put away the calculator and start practicing calculating and estimating in your head.

1.5 Exercises: Estimating

Answers Pg. 419

1. What is 24 x 6? (calculate both a rounded off answer and the actual answer)

2. What is 249 x 3? (calculate both a rounded off answer and the actual answer)

3. What is 12 ÷ 3.1? (calculate a rounded off answer only)

4. What is 199 ÷ 5? (calculate a rounded off answer only)

5. What is 37 x 11? (calculate both a rounded off answer and the actual answer)

2. Fractions, Decimal Form, and Percentages

One of the skills in mathematics that we learn earliest is how to deal with fractions and percentages. Unfortunately, the use of calculators has, for most people, caused this skill to deteriorate. Being able to deal with fractions and percentages is critical in physics and medicine.

A fraction consists of two parts: a number on top called the numerator, and a number on the bottom called the denominator. An increase in the numerator with no change to the denominator results in an increase in the fraction (see proportionality in Section 10.1).

$$\text{For the fraction defined as:} \quad Fraction = \frac{p}{q}.$$

$$*\text{An increase in } p \text{ implies an increase in } \frac{p}{q} : \left(\text{if } p \uparrow \Rightarrow \frac{p}{q} \uparrow \right).$$

Conversely, an increase in the denominator with no change to the numerator results in a decrease in the fraction (see inverse proportionality in Section 10.3).

$$\text{For the same fraction defined as:} \quad Fraction = \frac{p}{q}.$$

$$\text{An increase in } q \text{ implies a decrease in } \frac{p}{q} : \left(\text{if } q \uparrow \Rightarrow \frac{p}{q} \downarrow \right).$$

Often, a fraction is not written in its simplest form, implying that there is a multiplying factor which is common between the numerator and the denominator. In these cases, the fraction can be "simplified", or reduced to "simplest form" by dividing both the numerator and denominator by the common multiple.

◊ **Examples:**

$$\frac{4}{8} = \frac{4*1}{4*2} = \frac{4}{4}*\frac{1}{2} = 1*\frac{1}{2} = \frac{1}{2}$$

$$\frac{14}{200} = \frac{2*7}{2*100} = \frac{2}{2}*\frac{7}{100} = 1*\frac{7}{100} = \frac{7}{100}$$

$$\frac{120}{1200} = \frac{120*1}{120*10} = \frac{120}{120}*\frac{1}{10} = 1*\frac{1}{10} = \frac{1}{10}$$

Note: the symbol (⟹) stands for the word "implies."

Additionally, all fractions can be written in decimal form and as percentages. Converting from fractions to decimal form is simply the process of division. Converting from decimal form to percentages is just multiplication by 100%.

◊ **Examples:**

$$\frac{1}{1} = 1 = 100\% \qquad\qquad \frac{1}{2} = 0.5 = 50\%$$

$$\frac{1}{3} = 0.333 = 33.3\% \qquad\qquad \frac{1}{4} = 0.25 = 25\%$$

$$\frac{2}{1} = 2 = 200\% \qquad\qquad \frac{5}{2} = 2.5 = 250\%$$

Another way of thinking of fractions is how many times something occurs per hundred events. As such, it is easy to convert fractions to percentages when the denominator is a factor of 10. (You should notice that this process is equivalent to counting the number of decimal point shifts.)

◊ **Examples:**

$$\frac{7}{100} = 0.07 = 7\% \qquad\qquad \frac{2}{10} = \frac{20}{100} = 0.2 = 20\%$$

$$\frac{43}{1000} = \frac{4.3}{100} = 0.043 = 4.3\% \qquad\qquad \frac{16}{10} = \frac{160}{100} = 1.6 = 160\%$$

2.1 Exercises: Fractions and Percentages   Answers Pg. 419-420

Express each fraction in decimal form, and as a percentage.

1. $\dfrac{1}{1} =$ =
2. $\dfrac{1}{2} =$ =
3. $\dfrac{1}{3} =$ =
4. $\dfrac{1}{5} =$ =
5. $\dfrac{1}{6} =$ =
6. $\dfrac{1}{7} =$ =
7. $\dfrac{1}{8} =$ =
8. $\dfrac{1}{9} =$ =
9. $\dfrac{1}{10} =$ =
10. $\dfrac{1}{11} =$ =
11. $\dfrac{1}{20} =$ =
12. $\dfrac{1}{25} =$ =
13. $\dfrac{1}{30} =$ =

14. $\dfrac{1}{40} =$ =
15. $\dfrac{1}{50} =$ =
16. $\dfrac{1}{100} =$ =
17. $\dfrac{2}{100} =$ =
18. $\dfrac{1}{200} =$ =
19. $\dfrac{1}{2000} =$ =
20. $\dfrac{1}{1000} =$ =
21. $\dfrac{2}{1000} =$ =
22. $\dfrac{2}{50} =$ =
23. $\dfrac{2}{500} =$ =
24. $\dfrac{2}{5000} =$ =
25. $\dfrac{4}{5} =$ =

3. Reciprocals

In mathematics the reciprocal or inverse of any number is the other number which when the two numbers are multiplied gives unity (1).

◊ **Example:**   What is the reciprocal or inverse of the number two?

Because 2 * 1/2 = 1, the reciprocal or inverse of 2 is 1/2.

◊ **Example:**   What is the reciprocal of 8?

Because 8 * 1/8 = 1, 1/8 is the reciprocal of 8.

The property of reciprocals, although quite simple, is extremely powerful. The starting point is learning how to take the reciprocal of a number. Later in this chapter we will learn how to take the reciprocal of a variable, and the reciprocal of physical units. With this knowledge, as you will learn in Chapter 2, you will be able to convert easily between frequency and time. Once the basic understanding of reciprocals is in place, we will extrapolate the concept to include reciprocals within a question. This skill will prove very important since recognizing reciprocals cuts the number of ways of asking a question in half. For now, it is important that you master the basic concept of reciprocals. Once this skill is mastered, we will worry about extrapolating this technique to logic and reasoning skills for answering test questions.

3.1 Exercises: Reciprocals   **Answers Pg. 420**
Give the reciprocals of the following:

1. 3

2. 110

3. 1,284

4. 1 / 4

5. 1.268

6. 1/1,024

7. 1 / 31.926

4. Units

In mathematics, a unit is the reference for how a measurement of a physical quantity is made. Consider how distance is measured. There are many ways by which a distance could be measured. For example, the distance could be measured in inches, feet, yards, miles, meters, kilometers, knots (nautical distance), light years (based on how long it takes light to travel), etc. Each measurement system has its own unit or reference. Of course, the same distance measured by different measuring systems results in a different number of units. For example, if someone's height in inches is 60, their height in feet is 5, and their height in centimeters is approximately 152, which is equivalent to 1.52 meters. The person's height does not change, but depending on the unit (reference) the measurement result sure does change. Also notice that if you give someone's height without expressing the measurement unit, the answer is ambiguous. Clearly it does not make sense to say someone is 152 tall. You must express the units to make a measurement unambiguous.

Pegasus Lectures, Inc.

Invariably, at one point in your life as a student, you had a math or science teacher who would give you no credit if you did not express the units when answering a question which involved a calculation. Although you probably saw this as draconian (harsh and unfair punishment), there was a good reason. Learning to use units not only makes your answer unambiguous, but it also helps you determine what equation to use and if you have solved the problem correctly. For example, if you are asked to determine the wavelength of ultrasound in a particular medium, you know that the answer must have units of distance such as meters. The word "length" within the word wavelength makes this fact explicit. Therefore, if you write and solve an equation and the resulting unit comes out to be anything other than a unit of distance, you know you either remembered the equation incorrectly, or you made a mathematical error during your calculations.

Throughout the book, you will be learning the units used for the various measurements made in ultrasound. You will also find all of the units you need for ultrasound in Vol. 1, Appendix G.

5. Variables

Note that many times in mathematics, a physical quantity can change. The letter used to represent the physical quantity that can change is called a variable. In an equation, when you use a letter like: n, x, y, f, l, c, etc., you are using a shorthand so as not to have to write out the entire word(s) for which each symbol stands. Also, since the variable ultimately represents a number, you can treat these symbols like numbers in mathematical expressions.

◊ **Example:**   Let's say you have $4.00 to spend on apples and each apple costs $1.00. How many apples can you buy?

Mathematically: ($1.00) • (number of apples bought) = $4.00

For simplicity, instead of writing "number of apples bought" we will replace it with any letter we want, remembering that this letter really stands for the physical quantity: "number of apples bought". Let's assume that we let the letter "n" stand for the number of apples bought, the above expression is now shortened as follows:

$$(\$1.00) \bullet (n) = \$4.00$$

If we want to solve the equation to determine the value of n, we now follow the basic rules of manipulating an equation from algebra. In essence the basic rule for manipulating an equation is that whatever you do to one side of the equation, you must do to the other side of the equation for the equation to still hold true.

dividing both sides by $1.00

$$\left(\frac{\$1.00}{\$1.00}\right) \bullet (n) = \left(\frac{\$4.00}{\$1.00}\right)$$

$$(n) = 4/1 = 4$$

So you can buy 4 apples.

You should now make a distinction in your mind between variables and constants. As already defined, a variable is a letter which stands for a physical quantity which can change, or vary. A constant, is a fixed number which cannot change. Let's look at the following basic equation and identify the various components of the equation.

$$y = 3x + 2$$

In this equation there are two variables, specifically x and y. The number 2 is a constant. The number three is called a coefficient. Since a coefficient is fixed within an equation, you can also think of a coefficient as a constant term. In other words, the 3 and the 2 within the equation cannot change, but the values for x and y can change.

6. Applying Reciprocals

In Section 3 of this chapter we learned the general concept of reciprocals and how to take the reciprocal of a number (a constant). It is now time to learn how to take more complex reciprocals now that fractions, units, and variables have been introduced.

Reciprocal of a fraction:

◊ **Example:**   The reciprocal of 2/7 is 7/2

because: $\dfrac{2}{7} \bullet \dfrac{7}{2} = \dfrac{2 \bullet 7}{7 \bullet 2} = \dfrac{14}{14} = 1$

Reciprocal of a variable:

◊ **Example:**   Just as the reciprocal of 3 is 1/3

because: $\dfrac{3}{1} \bullet \dfrac{1}{3} = \dfrac{3 \bullet 1}{1 \bullet 3} = \dfrac{3}{3} = 1$

the reciprocal of x is 1/x

because: $\dfrac{x}{1} \bullet \dfrac{1}{x} = \dfrac{x \bullet 1}{1 \bullet x} = \dfrac{x}{x} = 1$

In some cases, the expressions will contain both variables and constants.

◊ **Example:**   The reciprocal of $14z^3$ is $1/14z^3$

because: $\left(\dfrac{14z^3}{1}\right) \bullet \left(\dfrac{1}{14z^3}\right) = \dfrac{14z^3 \bullet 1}{1 \bullet 14z^3} = \dfrac{14z^3}{14z^3} = 1$

6.1 Exercises: Applying Reciprocals   Answers Pg. 420-421

Determine the following reciprocals.

1. $\dfrac{9}{7}$

2. $\dfrac{32}{689}$

3. $\dfrac{1}{10}$

4. $\dfrac{1}{10,000}$

5. f

6. $\dfrac{1}{f}$

7. $(z+2)$

8. $\dfrac{1}{\lambda}$

9. π

10. $\dfrac{1}{T}$

11. $\dfrac{x}{10,000}$

12. $\dfrac{10,000}{z^3}$

13. $\dfrac{3x}{(z^2+19)}$

14. $\dfrac{\text{meters}}{\text{seconds}}$

15. $\dfrac{1}{\text{seconds}}$

16. $\dfrac{1}{\text{Hz}}$

17. $\dfrac{1}{10\ \text{Hz}}$

18. $\dfrac{3x}{\text{Hz}}$

7. Numbers Raised to a Power

7.1 Positive Powers

In the expression x^y, x is called the base and y is called the exponent or the power. For the moment, we will consider only the cases where y is an integer greater than zero. When the exponent is a positive integer, the exponent tells how many times the base is used as a factor (multiplication) with itself.

◊ **Example:** 2^3
the base is 2
the exponent is 3
(so 2 is used as a factor 3 times)
or $2^3 = 2 \cdot 2 \cdot 2 = 8$

◊ **Example:** $4^3 = 4 \cdot 4 \cdot 4 = 64$

◊ **Example:** $x^2 = x \cdot x$

There is a special name for the case where the exponent is 2 or 3.
If the exponent is 2, it is called a square.
If the exponent is 3, it is called a cube.
You can see why if you consider the following examples:

◊ **Example:**   Find the area of the square.

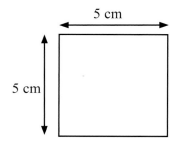

$$\begin{aligned}
\text{area} &= \text{width} \cdot \text{length} \\
&= 5 \text{ cm} \cdot 5 \text{ cm} \\
&= (5 \text{ cm})^2 \\
&= 25 \text{ cm}^2
\end{aligned}$$

◊ **Example:**   Find the volume of the cube *(recall for a cube the length = width = height)*.

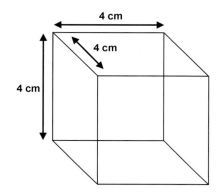

$$\begin{aligned}
\text{volume} &= \text{length} \cdot \text{ width } \cdot \text{height} \\
&= 4 \text{ cm} \cdot 4 \text{ cm} \cdot 4 \text{ cm} \\
&= (4 \text{ cm})^3 \\
&= 64 \text{ cm}^3
\end{aligned}$$

Any number raised to the 1st power (which means that the exponent = 1) is itself.

◊ **Example:** $5^1 = 5$

◊ **Example:** $26^1 = 26$

We have just seen how powers can be used to calculate the area of a square and volume of a cube. The following table illustrates the method of calculating the dimensional measurements associated with a square and circular object.

Important Calculations:

Dimensional Measurement	Square	Circle	Units
Perimeter (Circumference)	$x + x + x + x = 4x$	$2\pi r$	m^1
Area	$x \bullet x = x^2$	πr^2	m^2
Volume	$x \bullet x \bullet x = x^3$	$\frac{4}{3}\pi r^3$	m^3

Table 1:   **Dimensional Measurement of Squares and Circles**

Note that any time you see the variable "r" for radius, you should expect to see the natural constant π as a multiplier, where π approximately equals to 22/7 or:

$$\pi \text{ is a natural constant } \approx \frac{22}{7} \approx 3.14$$

7.2 Exercises: Numbers to a Positive Power   Answers Pg. 421
Simplify each expression:

1. 2^5 2. 6^2

3. 9^3 4. 10^1

5. 10^2 6. 10^3

7. 10^4 8. 10^5

9. $(1/10)^2$ 10. $(1/10)^1$

11. $(1/10)^5$ 12. $(3x)^3$

13. 0^2 14. 3^5

7.3 Numbers to a Negative Power

Although most people are pretty comfortable with positive integer exponents, negative exponents (and fractional exponents) are generally perceived as much more problematic. To understand what a negative exponent implies, it is first important to analyze the notational significance of a positive exponent. In essence, a positive exponent is a shorthand for expressing multiplication using the base. So if the exponent is a positive 3, then the base is used as a factor three times. Similarly, if the exponent is a positive 7, then the base is multiplied together (used as a factor) seven times. Therefore, if a positive exponent is a shorthand for multiplication, it should make sense that a negative exponent would serve as a shorthand for division. As we learned earlier, another way of expressing division is to multiply by a reciprocal. Therefore, a negative exponent (or power) tells how many times the reciprocal of the base is used as a multiplier.

◊ **Example:**

$5^{-3} = ?$

Base = 5

Exponent = -3 $\Rightarrow$ the reciprocal of the base of 5 is $\dfrac{1}{5}$

Therefore: $5^{-3} = \left(\dfrac{1}{5}\right)^3 = \left(\dfrac{1}{5}\right) \bullet \left(\dfrac{1}{5}\right) \bullet \left(\dfrac{1}{5}\right) = \dfrac{1}{125}$

◊ **Example:**

$3^{-2} = \left(\dfrac{1}{3}\right)^2 = \left(\dfrac{1}{3}\right) \bullet \left(\dfrac{1}{3}\right) = \dfrac{1}{9}$

◊ **Example:**

$4^{-2} = \left(\dfrac{1}{4}\right)^2 = \left(\dfrac{1}{4}\right) \bullet \left(\dfrac{1}{4}\right) = \dfrac{1}{16}$

◊ **Example:**

$\left(\dfrac{1}{2}\right)^{-3} = \left(\dfrac{2}{1}\right)^3 = \left(\dfrac{2}{1}\right) \bullet \left(\dfrac{2}{1}\right) \bullet \left(\dfrac{2}{1}\right) = 8$

◊ **Example:**

$2^{-3} = \left(\dfrac{1}{2}\right)^3 = \left(\dfrac{1}{2}\right) \bullet \left(\dfrac{1}{2}\right) \bullet \left(\dfrac{1}{2}\right) = \dfrac{1}{8}$

Understanding the notational meaning of a negative exponent, it should now become clear that x^{-y} is another way to write the expression $\dfrac{1}{x^y}$. In other words, x^y and x^{-y} are reciprocals. We will multiply x^y and x^{-y} together to show that these terms are reciprocals $x^y \bullet x^{-y} = x^y \bullet \dfrac{1}{x^y} = \dfrac{x^y}{x^y} = 1.$

7.4 Exercises: Numbers to a Negative and Positive Power   Answers Pg. 421-422

1. $2^{-2} =$

2. $3^{-4} =$

3. $3^4 =$

4. $5^{-1} =$

5. $3^2 =$

6. $\left(\dfrac{1}{2}\right)^2 =$

7. $\left(\dfrac{1}{2}\right)^{-2} =$ 8. $\dfrac{1}{3^2} =$

9. $\left(\dfrac{2}{3}\right)^{2} =$ 10. $\left(\dfrac{3}{2}\right)^{-2} =$

11. $\left(\dfrac{2}{3}\right)^{2} \bullet \left(\dfrac{2}{3}\right)^{-2} =$ 12. $3^2 \bullet \left(\dfrac{1}{3}\right)^{2}$

7.5 Numbers to the Zero Power and Exponent Rules

With respect to integer powers, we now know how to solve an expression to a positive power and an expression to a negative power. This leaves only the case where the exponent equals zero. Any number raised to the zero power, or the exponent = 0, is defined as 1.

◊   ***Example:*** $263^0 = 1$

◊   ***Example:*** $(1/10)^0 = 1$

◊   ***Example:*** $x^0 = 1$

The relationship of any number to the zero power equalling one is true because of the property of reciprocals. To demonstrate this point we will consider what happens when you multiply together two exponential expressions with the same base. In the process, we will also learn a very valuable rule on simplification when dealing with multiple exponential terms.

Consider the problem $10^3 \bullet 10^2 = ?$ The first term, 10^3, means that 10 will be used as a factor 3 times. The second term, 10^2, means that 10 will be used as a factor 2 more times. Clearly, in this problem 10 will be used as a factor a total of 5 times. Therefore, $10^3 \bullet 10^2$ is really the same as 10^{3+2}, or 10^5. In most algebra books you see this rule written formally in terms of abstract variables such as:

$$x^a \bullet x^b = x^{a+b}.$$

All this equation really says is that if x is used as a factor "a" times, and then it is used as a factor "b" more times, x would be used as a factor a total of "a + b" times.

So how does this expression relate to the fact that any number to the zero power equals one and the property of reciprocals? Consider the following problem:

What does $\quad 4^2 \times 4^{-2} = ?$

Solving the problem the long way: $4^2 \bullet 4^{-2} = (4 \bullet 4) \bullet \left(\dfrac{1}{4} \bullet \dfrac{1}{4}\right) = \dfrac{4 \bullet 4 \bullet 1 \bullet 1}{1 \bullet 1 \bullet 4 \bullet 4} = \dfrac{16}{16} = 1.$

But if we use the rule: $4^2 \bullet 4^{-2} = 4^{2-2} = 4^0.$

And since these are two different approaches to solving the same problem, the answer from the long approach must be the same as the answer to the shortcut approach, or: $4^0 = 1.$

In other words, when you multiply two reciprocals together the power becomes 0. Since the product of reciprocals is always 1, any number raised to the zero power must equal 1 (in essence the property of reciprocals).

The following are some examples which demonstrate how the above rule can be used to simplify problems.

◊ **Example:** $10^3 \cdot 10^2 = 10^{3+2} = 10^5$
proof:
$1,000 \cdot 100 = 100,000 = 10^5$

◊ **Example:** $10^{-2} \cdot 10^2 = 10^{-2+2} = 10^0 = 1$

◊ **Example:** $10^2/10^2 = 10^2 \cdot 10^{-2} = 10^{2-2} = 10^0 = 1$

◊ **Example:** $(1.2 \cdot 10^{-3}) \cdot (2 \cdot 10^9) = (1.2) \cdot (2) \cdot 10^{9-3} = 2.4 \cdot 10^6$

7.6 Exercises: Numbers to the Zero Power and Exponent Rules   Answers Pg. 422
Simplify the following expressions:

1. $3^3 \times 3^4 =$ 2. $4^2 \times 4^{-2} =$

3. $3^3 \times 3^2 =$ 4. $3^{-3} \times 3^4 =$

5. $3^3 \times 3^{-2} =$ 6. $3^{-3} \times 3^{-4} =$

7. $5^2 \times 5^{-2} =$ 8. $5^2 \times 5^{-4} =$

9. $\left(\dfrac{2}{3}\right)^{2} \times \left(\dfrac{2}{3}\right)^{-2} =$

10. $\left(\dfrac{x}{y}\right)^{3} \times \left(\dfrac{x}{y}\right)^{-2} =$

11. $\left(\dfrac{x}{y}\right)^{-3} \times \left(\dfrac{x}{y}\right)^{2} =$

12. $2^{3} \times 10^{2} =$

8. Exponential Form (Notation)

Exponential form, or notation, takes advantage of how easy it is to work with multiples of 10 when using the base 10 counting system. With a base of 10, the exponent tells you how many times to move the decimal point, whereas the + or – sign, as related to the exponent, tells you the direction to move the decimal point. A positive (+) exponent says move the decimal point to the right to make the number larger, while a negative (–) exponent indicates that the decimal point should be moved to the left, making the number smaller. In light of the last section dealing with the meaning of negative and positive exponents, these directions should make sense. A negative exponent implies division by multiples of 10 (multiplying by the reciprocal of the base) and hence leads to a smaller number. A positive exponent implies multiplication, by factors of 10, obviously resulting in larger numbers.

◇ **Example:** $1 \cdot 10^{2} = 1 \cdot 10 \cdot 10 = 1 \cdot (100) = 100$

$1 . 0\,0 \quad = 100$

(right 2)

◇ **Example:** $3 \cdot 10^{3} = 3 \cdot 10 \cdot 10 \cdot 10 \qquad = 3,000$

$3 . 0\,0\,0 \qquad\qquad = 3,000$

(right 3)

◇ **Example:** $2 \bullet 10^{-2} = 2 \bullet \left(\dfrac{1}{10}\right)^{2} = 2 \bullet \dfrac{1}{10} \bullet \dfrac{1}{10} = 2 \bullet \left(\dfrac{1}{100}\right) = \dfrac{2}{100}$

$= \dfrac{2}{100} = 0.02$

$0\,2\,.0 = 0.02$

(left 2)

◇ **Example:** $1.6 \bullet 10^{-6} = 1.6 \bullet \left(\dfrac{1}{10}\right)^{6} = 0\,0\,0\,0\,0\,0\,1\,.6 = 0.0000016$

(left 6)

◊ **Example:** $3 \bullet 10^4 = 3 . 0\ 0\ 0\ 0 = 30,000$

(right 4)

There are a few significant benefits to dealing with numbers in exponential form. First, when dealing with very large or very small numbers, it is quite common to lose track of the number of zeroes in the number and hence misinterpret the number. In exponential form, the number of zeroes is contained within the exponent. Second, when you have to multiply large or small numbers, exponential form makes the mathematics less cumbersome. In other words, with exponential form, you are much less likely to make a mistake representing where the decimal point should be.

8.1 Exercises: Exponential Notations   Answers Pg. 422

1. $1 \cdot 10^{-2} =$

2. $1 \cdot 10^2 =$

3. $3 \cdot 10^3 =$

4. $3 \cdot 10^{-3} =$

5. $1.68 \cdot 10^9 =$

6. $1.68 \cdot 10^{-9} =$

7. $\dfrac{1.68 \times 10^9}{1.68 \times 10^9} =$

8. $0.000016 = \underline{\hspace{1cm}} \cdot 10^{-6}$

9. $3,200,000 = \underline{\hspace{1cm}} \cdot 10^6$

10. $2.3 \cdot 10^0 =$

11. $\dfrac{6 \times 10^9}{2 \times 10^6} =$

12. $6 \times 10^9 \cdot 0.5 \times 10^{-9} =$

13. $6 \times 10^9 \cdot 0.5 \times 10^{-3} =$

14. $\dfrac{200 \times 10^7}{10 \times 10^2} \cdot 0.5 \times 10^{-3} =$

Note: Exponential notation is a shorthand way of writing large numbers, which takes advantage of how easy it is to work with the number 10 raised to a power.

◊ **Example:** $6,320,000,000,000,000 = 6.32 \cdot 10^{15}$

This form is much easier to both read and write.

You should also note that there is not necessarily a right way or a wrong way of writing a number. Every number can be written in an infinite number of ways as indicated in the following example.

◊ **Example:** $6.32 \cdot 10^{15} = 63.2 \cdot 10^{14} = 632 \cdot 10^{13} = 0.632 \cdot 10^{16}$

8.2 Deciding How to Write a Number

In general, we choose to write numbers such that there are a minimal number of digits before or after the decimal point. Furthermore, since our comma notation separates numbers by groupings of 3, we generally try to write the exponent in powers of 3 (+3, +6, +9, or -3, -6, -9, etc.). For example, instead of writing the number 0.0000047, we would more likely write 4.7×10^{-6}. Of course, 47×10^{-7}, and 0.47×10^{-5} are both correct and perfectly reasonable ways of writing this number. Similarly, instead of writing 6,000,000, we would more likely write 6×10^{6}. Again, this number is the same as 0.6×10^{7} or 60×10^{5}, and both forms are perfectly acceptable and reasonable ways to write the same number.

8.3 Exercises: Deciding How to Write a Number | Answers Pg. 423 |

Rewrite each number in exponential form:

1. 1,600,000 =

2. 9,000,000,000 =

3. 92,000,000 =

4. 0.00043 =

5. 0.0000045 =

6. 0.00000000091 =

7. 45,000 =

8. 0.000000046 =

9. The Metric System and Metric Abbreviations

9.1 Conversions for Metric and Non-metric Systems

As we have just discussed, there are some major advantages to using exponential form, especially when using a base of 10. The metric system is based on measuring physical quantities by taking advantage of these benefits. Since the metric system is based on powers of tens, converting between measurement units is a simple process of sliding the decimal point.

In comparison, converting between measurements in non-metric measuring systems, such as in the English system that is still commonly used in general practice in the United States, is a much more cumbersome and unwieldy process. Consider how the liquid measure of cups is converted to gallons. To convert, you must first know the conversion from cups to pints, then pints to quarts, and then quarts to gallons. In marked contrast, in the metric system, converting between milliliters and liters is a simple process of sliding the decimal point. Later in this chapter we discuss how to perform the conversion. Before learning to perform conversions, it is imperative that you first learn the definitions used in the metric system.

9.2 Metric Abbreviations

The metric abbreviations are based on exponential form using a base of 10. Instead of having to carry the entire mathematical expression with the power of ten written out, these powers of ten are abbreviated into a prefix. As shown in the table below, the ninth power of ten, (10^9), is abbreviated as giga. As suggested by the use of the word prefix, these abbreviations for powers of ten are then affixed to a unit such as Hz for frequency, liters for liquid measure, or meters for distance. So 1 GHz implies 1×10^9 Hz, or 1 billion Hertz.

The following chart displays the most commonly used metric abbreviations for ultrasound physics and ultrasound in general. There are certainly many more metric abbreviations which are not routinely used in ultrasound and hence not included in this table.

Prefixes (metric)		Number	Numerically	Mnemonic
G	(Giga) $= 10^9$	= billion	1,000,000,000	**g**ood
M	(Mega) $= 10^6$	= million	1,000,000	**m**others
k	(kilo) $= 10^3$	= thousand	1,000	**k**indly
h	(hecto) $= 10^2$	= hundred	100	**h**elp
da	(deca) $= 10^1$	= ten	10	**d**ads
d	(deci) $= 10^{-1}$	= tenth = 1/10	0.1	**d**evelop
c	(centi) $= 10^{-2}$	= hundredth = 1/100	0.01	**c**aring
m	(milli) $= 10^{-3}$	= thousandth = 1/1000	0.001	**m**others
μ	(micro) $= 10^{-6}$	= millionth = 1/1,000,000	0.000001	**u**nderstand
n	(nano) $= 10^{-9}$	= billionth = 1/1,000,000,000	0.000000001	**n**eed

Note: $G = 10^9 \Rightarrow reciprocal = 1/10^9 = 10^{-9} = n$

$k = 10^3 \Rightarrow reciprocal = 1/10^3 = 10^{-3} = m$

(The symbol $\Rightarrow$ means "implies")

You should note that some of the letters in this table come from the Greek alphabet. The use of Greek letters is common in physics and mathematics, perhaps because there are many more parameters that we need to measure than can be represented by 26 letters in the English alphabet. You should also note that these prefixes are "case sensitive." Being case sensitive means that a capital letter does not necessarily mean the same thing as a small (uncapitalized) letter. Note the difference between M which stands for mega and m which stands for milli. You must pay attention to the letter case, or your mathematics can be off by many factors of 10.

As already mentioned, these abbreviations are used to simplify writing numbers. Look at the following examples:

◊ **Example:**

3.2 M	represents	3,200,000
2.8 G	represents	2,800,000,000
1.9 m	represents	0.0019
23 m	represents	0.023

Note: Recall from the earlier section on exponential form that the exponent tells you how many places, and in which direction to move the decimal point.

The following two examples show how we can write out the abbreviated expressions in an unabbreviated form.

◊ **Example 1:** $3.2 \text{ M} = 3.2 \times 10^{6} \Rightarrow$ move decimal point 6 times to the right.

step 1: *add decimal point if not already displayed*

step 2: *add zeros as place holders* $3.2 \text{ M} = 0003.200000000000....M$

step 3: *replace prefix with meaning* $3.20000000....M = 3.20000000 \times 10^{6}$

step 4: *move decimal point* $3.20000000....M = 3\,2\,0\,0\,0\,0\,0.0$

(The +6 exponent indicates that the decimal point moves to the right 6 places)   **1 2 3 4 5 6**

step 5: *add commas to make number readable*   3,200,000.00

Answer: 3,200,000.00

◊ **Example 2:** $27 \mu = 27 \times 10^{-6}$

step 1: *add decimal point if not already displayed* 27.0μ

step 2: *add zeros as place holders* $27 \mu = ...00000027.0000...\mu$

step 3: *replace prefix with meaning* $...00000027.0000..\mu = ...00000027.0000...\times 10^{-6}$

step 4: *move decimal point:* $0\,0\,0\,0\,0\,0\,2\,7.0000...$

1 2 3 4 5 6

Answer: 0.000027

9.3 Exercises: Metric Abbreviations Answers Pg. 423-424

Give the numeric value of each expression.

1. 1.3 k =

2. 231 G =

3. 0.21 h =

4. 12.2 c =

5. 26.2 m =

6. 1.3 μ =

7. 42 n =

8. 0.02 M =

9.4 Abbreviations: Physical Units

As with any field, it is cumbersome to have to deal with long names. Hence, a series of abbreviations have been developed to make communication easier. Of course, the communication only becomes easier when there is a fluent understanding of the abbreviations and their physical meanings. This understanding will be developed in the next few chapters. For now, you need to begin the familiarization process. This list has also been included in Vol. 1, Appendix G for easy reference in subsequent chapters of the book.

Related to time:

P or T	Period (seconds)
PD	Pulse duration (the time for which the transmit pulse lasts)
PRP	Pulse repetition period (the time to transmit and receive an acoustic line of data)
Frame time	The time required to build up a frame = the time per acoustic line multiplied by the total number of lines in the frame.

Related to frequency:

f	Frequency (Hz)
f_0	Operating or transmit frequency of a transducer (for diagnostic ultrasound 2-12 MHz common)
PRF	Pulse repetition frequency = 1/PRP (typically less than 10 kHz)
Frame rate	The reciprocal of the frame time (typically less than 100 Hz)
Hz	Hertz = 1 cycle/second

Various parameters that have units of amplitude:

V	Volts: unit of electromotive force
m	Meters: unit of distance (metric system)
Z	Rayls: unit of acoustic impedance
R	Resistance, either electrical or to fluid flow
P	Pressure: mmHg, atm, dynes/cm^2, kg/m^2, etc.: unit of pressure (*not to be confused with P for period or P for power)

Related to power:

P	Power: units of Watts (*not to be confused with P for period or P for pressure)
W	Watts
I	Intensity = power/area = W/m² or W/cm²
dB	Decibels: a logarithmic power ratio

Related to distance:

d	distance (*not to be confused with D or d for diameter)
λ	Lambda: wavelength which has units of distance
SPL	Spatial Pulse Length
NZL	The distance from the transducer face to the focus of the transducer

Related to measure and circular dimensions:

ρ	Density = mass/volume : units of kg/m³
r	Radius of a circle: units of distance
d	Diameter of a circle = 2*radius: units of distance
A	Area: units of m²
Vol	Volume: units of m³
Q	Volumetric flow: units of volume per time, or m³/sec

Related to motion:

r	the general term usually used in the distance equation for the velocity. (*not to be confused with r for radius)
v	velocity of blood: units of m/sec
c	propagation speed of sound: units of m/sec

Related to hemodynamics:

P	Pressure: mmHg, atm, dynes/cm², kg/m², etc...,: units of pressure (*not to be confused with P for period or P for power)
ΔP	Pressure gradient (change in pressure = $P_2 - P_1$ where P_2 is the distal pressure and P_1 is the proximal pressure): units as above
Q	Volumetric flow: units of volume per time, or m³/sec
R	Resistance, either electrical or to fluid flow

Note: Caution must be used since many letters can stand for more than one physical quantity. Also pay attention since in some cases a capitalized letter indicates a different parameter than a lower case letter.

9.5 Combining Abbreviations

In an effort to further simplify writing measurable quantities, abbreviations can be combined. Note that the metric prefix always come first, followed by the physical unit.

◊ **Example:** 27.3 mW
= 27.3 milliWatts
= 27.3 x 10⁻³ Watts
= 0.0273 Watts

◊ **Example:** 4.3 cm
= 4.3 centimeters
= 4.3 x 10⁻² meters
= 0.043 meters

9.6 Exercises: Combining Abbreviations Answers Pg. 424

Using the method displayed in the previous examples, expand the following abbreviations.

1. 2.5 MHz

2. 1.6 kHz

3. 1.54 km/sec

4. 1.7 μsec

5. 100 cm

6. 100 mW/cm² (*convert to W/cm²*)

7. 1.8 ml (*convert to liters*)

8. 1,400 ml (*convert to liters*)

9.7 Reciprocals of Metric Units

As already mentioned, the metric table is developed using reciprocals, which facilitates performing mathematical calculations in your head. Consider the following problem:

What is the reciprocal of 10 MHz?

The reciprocal of 10 MHz is $\dfrac{1}{10 \text{ MHz}}$.

However, this is certainly not in the "simplest" form you would expect. Therefore, we would rewrite the answer as follows:

$$\frac{1}{10 \text{ MHz}} = \frac{1}{10} \bullet \frac{1}{M} \bullet \frac{1}{Hz} = 0.1 \bullet \mu \bullet \sec \ \left(\text{or simply: } 0.1 \ \mu\sec \right)$$

Note: By using the reciprocal relation of mega and micro, we were able to answer the question without expanding the mega into 10^6, performing division by 10^6, and then converting the answer back into units of microseconds, all the while running a very high probability of missing a decimal place somewhere in the process.

9.8 Exercises: Reciprocals of Metric Units Answers Pg. 424

Give the reciprocal of the following expressions.

1. 2.0 MHz

2. 1.0 kHz

3. 5 μsec

4. 0.1 msec

5. 10 GHz

6. 10 nsec

7. 0.1 GHz

8. 0.1 nsec

9.9 Converting Between Metric Units

Quite frequently, when you measure or calculate a physical quantity, the resulting number will be either very large or very small. In Section 8.1 and 8.2, we discussed the idea that although there is not necessarily a right or a wrong way of expressing numbers, in general, we prefer to write the numbers in a way that makes them appear as simple as possible. For example, using the English system for distance, presume you calculated that the distance between your house and your work to be 10,560 feet. Although this may be the correct distance, the numeric part of the expression is so large, that it is difficult to imagine how far this really is. If you convert this distance in feet to miles (by knowing the conversion that there are 5,280 feet per mile), you arrive at the equivalent expression of the distance being 2 miles. Now although these two answers are equivalent, 2 miles certainly appears to be a more readily comprehendible form. Luckily, since in medicine and physics we use the metric system, your conversions will not be as complicated as dividing by numbers such as 5,280 as was needed in the above example.

Another reason why you frequently need to convert between units is that when you solve an equation, you must make sure that the units are consistent. Once the mathematical expression is written in terms of consistent units, the expression can usually be greatly simplified.

◊ **Example 1:** How many days will it take to run 1 Gm if you run 10 km per day?

$$\#days = \frac{\text{total distance}}{\text{distance per day}}$$

so

$$\#days = \frac{1 \text{ Gm}}{10 \text{ km/day}}$$

Converting Gm into km

$$1 \text{ Gm} = 1 \times 10^9 \text{ meters}$$
$$= 1{,}000{,}000{,}000 \text{ meters}$$
$$= 1{,}000{,}000 \cdot \underline{10^3} \text{ meters}$$
$$= 1{,}000{,}000 \text{ \underline{k} meters}$$

$$\text{so \# days} = \frac{1{,}000{,}000 \text{ km}}{10 \text{ km/day}}$$

Answer   **100,000 days**
           or   **100 · 10³ days**
           or   **100 k days**

◊ **Example 2:** 12 nsec = how many μsec?

$$12 \text{ nsec} = 12 \cdot 10^{-9} \text{ sec}$$
$$= 0.000000012 \text{ sec}$$
$$= 0.012 \cdot 10^{-6} \text{ sec}$$

Answer   **0.012 μsec**

9.10 Another Approach to Conversions (a more intuitive approach)

Although the previous approach is mathematically pretty clear, it is frequently a little bit daunting for many people. We can accomplish the same conversions by using the rules about the mathematical relationships of proportionality and inverse proportionality that we have already learned.

Think of each measure of a physical quantity as consisting of two parts, a "numeric" part and the "units" part. (For example, 3 MHz has 3 as its numeric part and MHz as its units part.) If the goal is to convert an expression to having a different units part, then the numeric part must also change. Consider the following example:

Example: 12 donuts = ?? dozen

Let's start by comparing the units part. On the left side of the equation, the unit is a single donut. On the right side of the equation, the unit is a dozen. Since the unit is larger on the right than the left, the numeric part in front of the larger unit must be smaller than the numeric part in front of the smaller unit. This is graphically presented below using arrows:

12 donuts = ?? dozen

Because this is a non-metric example, we have to know that the conversion between dozens and donuts is 12 to 1, or that 12 donuts = 1 dozen.

With the metric system, this process is actually easier, as long as you know the metric table. Consider the following example:

◊ **Example 1:** How many meters are in 5.2 km?

Rewriting this mathematically we have: x m = 5.2 km

Comparing the units leads us to the following graphical representation

x m = 5.2 km

So we know that the number of meters in 5.2 km must be greater than 5.2 (which should make intuitive sense since a meter, m, is a shorter distance than a km). Now, assessing the prefix of the units, an m represents no decimal shifts (there is no prefix in front of the unit of meters) and a km represent 3 decimal shifts to the right. Therefore, there is a total of 3 decimal shifts between m and km. So the numerical part of the expression in front of m must be greater than 5.2 by 3 decimal point shifts or 5,200 m. This is shown graphically below:

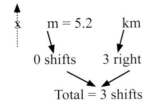

x   m = 5.2   km

0 shifts   3 right

Total = 3 shifts

So starting with 5.2, you must move the decimal point 3 times making the number bigger or, 5,200.

Therefore,

5,200 m = 5.2 km.

◊   ***Example 2***:   How many centimeters are in 3.2 km?

Rewriting this mathematically we have: x cm = 3.2 km

Comparing the units leads us to the following graphical representation

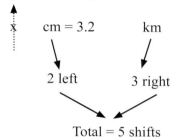

So we know that the number of cm in 3.2 km must be greater than 3.2 (which should make intuitive sense since a cm is a short distance and a km is a long distance relatively speaking). Now, assessing the prefix of the units, a cm represents 2 decimal shifts to the left and a km represents 3 decimal shifts to the right. Since these decimal shifts are in opposite directions, there are a total of 5 decimal shifts between cm and km. Therefore, the numerical part of the expression in front of cm must be greater than 3.2 by 5 decimal point shifts or 320,000 cm. This is shown graphically below:

x   cm = 3.2   km

2 left   3 right

Total = 5 shifts

So starting with 3.2, you must move the decimal point 5 times making the number bigger or, 320,000.
Therefore,

$$320,000 \text{ cm} = 3.2 \text{ km.}$$

◊   ***Example 3***: How many MHz equal 600 kHz?

Rewriting this mathematically we have: x MHz = 600 kHz

Comparing the units leads us to the following graphical representation

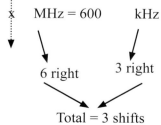

So we know that the number of MHz that is equivalent to 600 Hz must be less than 600 (which should make intuitive sense since a MHz is a bigger unit than a kHz). Now, assessing the prefix of the units, a MHz represents 6 decimal shifts to the right and a kHz represents 3 decimal shifts to the right. Since these decimal shifts are in the same direction, there are only 3 decimal shifts between MHz and kHz. Therefore, the numerical part of the expression in front of MHz must be smaller than 600 by 3 decimal point shifts or 0.600 MHz. This is shown graphically below:

x   MHz = 600   kHz

6 right   3 right

Total = 3 shifts

So starting with 600, you must move the decimal point 3 times making the number smaller or, 0.600. Therefore

$$0.600 \text{ MHz} = 600 \text{ kHz}.$$

Note: Whenever you complete a conversion, you should always apply the "common sense" test; "does the answer calculated make physical sense?" For example, if you were measuring the length of a table, the number of centimeters in the length should be greater than the number of meters in the length.

9.11 Exercises: Conversions Answers Pg. 424

1. 3 cm = ?? m

2. 3 MHz = ?? kHz

3. 2,000 μsec = ?? msec

4. 0.006 GHz = ?? MHz

5. 3,000 msec = ?? sec

6. 6,000,000 msec = ?? ksec

7. 920 cm = ?? km

8. 920 km = ?? cm

9.12 Exercises: Using Exponents Answers Pg. 425-426

1. $10^3 \cdot 10^2 =$

2. $10^2 \cdot 10^{-2} =$

3. $10^6/10^4 =$ (Hint - rewrite $1/10^4$ as 10^{-4})

4. $(2.3 \cdot 10^6) \cdot 10^3 =$

5. $(3.6 \cdot 10^3) \cdot 10^{-3} =$

6. $2 \cdot (1 \cdot 10^3)$

7. $100 \cdot (1 \cdot 10^2) =$

8. $10^{17} \cdot 10^{-6} =$

9. $10^{17}/10^6 =$

10. $(3 \cdot 10^4) \cdot (1 \cdot 10^{-2}) =$

11. $(3 \cdot 10^4)/(1 \cdot 10^2) =$

12. $10^4/10^{-2} =$

13. $10^4 \cdot 10^2 =$

14. 6 MHz / 2M =

15. 12 MHz / 4 kHz =

16. (1.54 km/sec) / (1.54 cm) =

17. $13 \ \mu sec \cdot 1540 \ m/sec =$ _____ m = _____ cm

18. $0.001540 \ m \ / \ \mu sec =$ _____ m/sec

19. $1.54 \ mm/\mu sec =$ _____ m/sec
     (Note: This is an important problem to be able to solve.)

20. $\dfrac{\dfrac{1}{1}}{\left(\dfrac{1}{sec} \right)}$

10. Proportionality and Inverse Proportionality

10.1 Direct Proportionality

Proportionality is one of the most important concepts in learning to interpret equations and apply mathematics. Proportionality is a general term which describes a relative relationship between two variables. There are two different types of proportional relationships described by mathematical equations: directly proportional and inversely proportional. When two variables are directly proportional, an increase in one variable results in an increase in the related variable. When two variables are inversely proportional, an increase in one variable results in a decrease in the related variable.

As with all languages (and mathematics clearly uses its own language) there are abbreviations and symbols used to shorten how we write frequently used terms. Just as the "=" sign stands for the concept of equivalence, the $\propto$ symbol is the mathematical shorthand for the concept of proportionality.

> The symbol for proportionality is: $\propto$

In addition to the two types of proportionality (direct and inverse) there are different rates at which both of these types of relationships can change. The concept of how fast one variable changes with respect to a related changing variable is perhaps the most important mathematical concept you will learn. This concept is critical since it relates directly to understanding not only ultrasound physics, but also sound interactions within the human body, vision and hearing, disease processes, the compensatory mechanisms of the body in response to disease and other stresses, and much more. In this first section, we will deal with the simpler cases of when the power of the two related variables are equal, leading to a simpler way of expressing the rate of change between the two related variables. In Level 2, the concept of unequal powers and the more complicated relationships will be introduced. As you will learn throughout ultrasound, understanding these relative relationships (especially the more complex, non-linear relationships) will be critical to providing high quality patient care and to passing your credentialing exams.

10.2 Direct Linear (Simple) Proportionality

This first example demonstrates direct linear proportionality. It is called a "linear" relationship because when you graph the two dependent variables against each other, the resulting plot is a straight line. When two variables have a linear relationship, a change of some percentage in one variable results in the exact same percentage change in the related variable.

For the purposes of this book, we will adopt the term simple proportionality to signify that the power of the two related variables are equal.

◊ **Example:** $y = 3 \cdot x \Rightarrow$ y is proportional to x.

Consider if:
$$x = 1 \Rightarrow y = 3 \cdot 1 = 3$$
$$x = 2 \Rightarrow y = 3 \cdot 2 = 6$$
$$x = 5 \Rightarrow y = 3 \cdot 5 = 15$$

So as **x** increases, **y** increases.
Similarly as **x** decreases, **y** decreases.
Symbolically we write: $y \propto x$.

Also note that both x and y increase or decrease at the same rate.

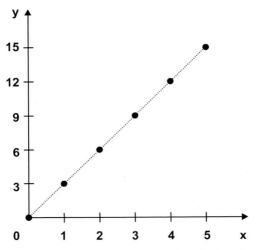

Fig. 1 **Linear Proportional Relationship**

In the real world, there are many examples of direct linear proportional relationships. For example, let's say that you work at a job where you are paid straight hourly rates (excluding overtime rates). If you double the number of hours you work, your pay will also double. If you decrease the number of hours you work by a factor of 13, your pay will also decrease by a factor of 13.

Another example of direct linear relationships is the relationship between time and distance traveled (assuming a fixed rate). For example, if you drive at a constant rate of 60 mph and you drive for triple the time, you will have traveled triple the distance.

10.3 Inverse (Simple) Proportionality
As the name suggests, inverse proportionality implies an "opposite" relationship between the two variables. In other words, when two variables are inversely related, an increase in one variable results in a decrease in the related variable. All inverse relationships are non-linear, implying that when you graph the relationship, the graph is not a straight line.

Again we will adopt the term simple inverse relationship to refer to any case where the powers of the two related variables are equal, and reserve discussion of the more complex cases when the powers are not equal for Level 2. Note that in the following example, the power for x and y is 1, and hence qualifies as a "simple" inverse relationship.

◊ **Example:** $y = 3/x \Rightarrow$ y is inversely proportional to x.

Consider if:

x = 1	$\Rightarrow$	y = 3/1 = 3
x = 2	$\Rightarrow$	y = 3/2 = 1.5
x = 5	$\Rightarrow$	y = 3/5 = 0.6

So an increase in **x** results in a decrease in **y**.
Similarly, a decrease in **x** results in an increase in **y**.

Note that stating "y is proportional to the inverse of x" is equivalent to stating "y is inversely proportional to x". Instead of creating a new symbol for inverse proportionality, we use the same proportional symbol and then we invert the variable.

$$\text{and} \quad x \propto \frac{1}{y}$$

$$\text{or} \quad y \propto \frac{1}{x}$$

With simple relationships, you can easily express the rate of change. For simple proportional relationships, an increase in one variable by a factor of x produces an increase in the related variable by a factor of x. For simple inverse relationships, an increase in one variable by a factor of x produces a corresponding decrease in the related variable by the same factor of x.

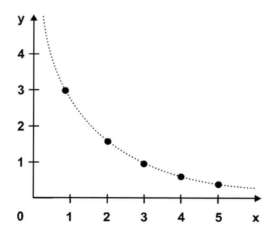

Fig. 2 **Inverse Proportional Relationship**

Note: The inverse operation of multiplication is division, just as the inverse of addition is subtraction. Therefore, multiplying by a reciprocal is exactly the same as division.

10.4 Exercises: Proportionality and Inverse Proportionality Answers Pg. 426-427

1. In the equation z = 3t, the relationship between z and t is _____ _____.

2. In the equation z = 3t, if t were to double, z would _____.

3. In the equation z = 3t, if t were increased by a factor of 36, z would _____ by a factor of _____.

4. In the equation z = 3t, if t were decreased by a factor of 4.3, z would _____ by a factor of _____.

5. In the equation m = 6j, the relationship between m and j is _____ _____.

6. In the equation m = 6j, if j were _____ by a factor of 6, m would increase by a factor of 6.

7. In the equation $m = \dfrac{5}{j}$, the relationship between m and j is _____ proportionality.

8. In the equation $m = \dfrac{5}{j}$, if j were _____ by a factor of 3, m would decrease by a factor of _____.

9. In the equation $m = \dfrac{5}{j}$, if j were _____ by a factor of ___, m would increase by a factor of 19.

10. In the equation $y = \dfrac{z}{k}$, if k were increased by a _____ of ___, y would decrease by a factor of 3.

11. In the equation $y = \dfrac{z}{k}$, if z were increased by a factor of 2, y would _____ by a _____ of _____.

12. In the equation $y = \dfrac{z}{k}$, y ∝ ___ and y is ∝ ___.

11. Distance Equation

The distance equation is generally well understood, since we use it virtually every day to calculate driving times. The equation is:

$$\text{Distance} = \text{rate} \cdot \text{time} .$$

◊ **Example:**   How far can you drive in two hours at 60 mph?

$$60 \cdot \frac{\text{miles}}{\text{hr}} \cdot 2 \text{ hr} = 120 \text{ miles}$$

◊ **Example:**   How far can you drive in two hours at 60 km/h?

$$60 \cdot \frac{\text{km}}{\text{hr}} \cdot 2 \text{ hr} = 120 \text{ km}$$

◊ **Example:**   How long will it take to drive 200 km if the speed limit is 100 km/h?

$$d = r * t$$

rewriting the equation for time yields:

$$t = \frac{d}{r}$$

$$t = \frac{200 \text{ km}}{100 \ \dfrac{\text{km}}{\text{hr}}}$$

$$t = 2 \text{ hr}$$

The same distance equation we use to calculate driving times is equally applicable to traveling ultrasound waves. Let's presume that ultrasound travels at a rate of 1540 m/sec in the body. Knowing the rate, we can easily calculate the time it will take sound to travel whatever distance required in the body. Consider the following problem:

How long would it take sound to travel 1 cm in the body?

Start by writing out the information given to solve the problem.

$$d = 1 \text{ cm}$$

$$r = 1540 \ \frac{\text{m}}{\text{sec}}$$

$$t = ?$$

Next, write out the equation needed to solve the problem.

$d = r \times t$.

Then rewrite the equation so that it is written in the form required.

$\dfrac{d}{r} = t$ (result from dividing both sides by "r" to get "t" alone).

Now plug in the numbers to solve the equation.

$$\frac{1 \text{ cm}}{1540 \ \dfrac{m}{sec}} = \frac{0.01 \text{ m}}{1540 \ \dfrac{m}{sec}} \quad \text{(convert to consistent units and cancel out)}$$

$$= \frac{0.01 \text{ sec}}{1540} = .00000649 \text{ sec} \approx 6.5 \times 10^{-6} \text{ sec} = 6.5 \times \mu\text{sec}.$$

Note: The unit of seconds is "under" two reciprocal bars and hence is equivalent to the unit of seconds being on the top of the expression.

How long would it take sound to travel 2 cm in the body?

From the equation, we know that the relationship between time and distance is direct proportionality. Therefore, if the distance traveled is doubled, the time is doubled, equal to 13 μsec.

It is very useful to remember the results of this calculation. As you will learn in Chapter 2, we generally presume that the propagation speed of sound in the body is approximately 1540 m/sec. Since we know that the relationship between distance and time is linearly proportional, if we remember the 6.5 μsec travel time per cm, we can always just scale this number to any distance required.

In Level 2, we will also stress a very important fact about how ultrasound imaging is performed. With ultrasound, we transmit sound into the body and then we receive the reflected signal. This means that if we want to image (view) a structure at a depth of 10 cm, the total travel for the ultrasound beam is not 10 cm, but rather 20 cm. This factor of 2, often referred to as the "roundtrip effect" must be taken into account when calculating real world ultrasound problems.

11.1 Exercises: Distance Equation   Answers Pg. 427

1. In the body, how long does it take sound to travel 2 cm?

2. In the body, how long does it take sound to travel 3 cm?

3. In the body, how long does it take sound to travel 4 cm?

4. In the body, how long does it take sound to travel 10 cm?

5. In the body, how long does it take sound to travel into the body 1 cm and then back out of the body?

6. In the body, how long does it take sound to travel into the body 10 cm and then back out of the body?

12. Math Terminology

12.1 The Language of Mathematics: Translating English into Mathematics

Perhaps the greatest difficulty is not mastering the mathematical concepts, but rather learning how to interpret the math from the language used to express the question. There are many terms commonly used which always, or nearly always, indicate the same mathematical function. If you are unfamiliar with the translation of these terms, it will always be difficult to answer a mathematically based question.

Below are some examples used to illustrate the English form of what are really mathematical expressions.

◊ **Example 1:** By what factor does the distance you travel increase, if your speed while traveling doubles?

◊ **Example 2:** What is ten percent of the number 354?

◊ **Example 3:** What is ten percent less than the number 354?

◊ **Example 4:** Assuming you are paid hourly, what happens to your pay if your working hours are reduced by a factor of four?

◊ **Example 5:** If you are paid $200 a week, and the tax is 25% of your pay, how much spending money do you have per week?

12.2 Mathematical Definition

So as to learn how to translate the English words into mathematical form, we will start with a simple list of definitions.

Factor:	implies multiplication (and division)
Increase:	to become larger
Decrease:	to become smaller
Reduce:	decreased, to become smaller
Less:	subtraction
More:	addition
Percent:	a fraction written relative to 100 representing the whole, or 1.
Of:	multiplication (and division)
Reciprocal:	inverted, the opposite
Doubles:	increased by a factor of 2 (multiply by 2)
Halves:	decreased by a factor of 2 (divide by 2)
Quadruples:	increase by a factor of 4 (multiply by 4)
Quarters:	decrease by a factor of 4 (divide by 4)

This above list generally seems quite simple until multiple terms are used together. The following table puts some of the definitions together in the ways in which they are commonly combined.

Increased by a factor of X	multiplied by X
Decreased by a factor of X	divided by X
Reduced by a factor of X	divided by X
X percent of Y	multiply Y by X/100
X percent less than Y	multiply Y by X/100 and then subtract the resulting value from Y
X percent more than Y	multiply Y by X/100 and then add the resulting value to Y
Reciprocal of X	1/X

Using these definitions, let's review the examples given above.

◊ **Example 1:** By what factor does the distance you travel increase if your speed of traveling doubles?

Since the distance traveled is directly related to the speed at which you travel, doubling the speed doubles the distance traveled. From our definitions, we know that doubling the distance is the same as saying that the distance increased by a factor of 2. Since the question asks for the factor of increase, the answer is 2.

◊ **Example 2:** What is ten percent of the number 354?

Recall that the term "percent of" implies multiplication. Since percent represents a fraction written relative to the number 100, ten percent = 10/100 = 1/10. So multiplying 354 by 1/10 yields 354/10 = 35.4

◊ **Example 3:** What is ten percent less than the number 354?

In Example 2 we calculated ten percent of 354. Notice that this question includes one more step. This question asks for ten percent <u>less</u> than 354. Since less implies subtraction, we need to subtract the ten percent of 354 from the number 354, or 354 – 35.4 = 318.6.

You should note that this question is really the same as asking what is ninety percent of the number 354. In other words, if you take away 10% of a number, what you have left is 90% of that number. To show this fact, let's perform the calculation.

$$\text{Ninety percent} = \frac{90}{100} = \frac{9}{10} = 0.9. \text{ So multiplying 354 by } 0.9 = 318.6.$$

Hence the same answer is achieved either way the problem is solved.

Note: We have just seen how the same question can be asked in a reciprocal manner. Ten percent reduction is the same as asking for ninety percent. The ability to recognize reciprocals in a question is critical to passing the credentialing exams.

Pegasus Lectures, Inc.

◊ **Example 4:** Assuming you are paid hourly, what happens to your pay if your working hours are reduced by a factor of four?

From the definitions, being "reduced by a factor of four" means divided by four. Since your pay is directly related to your working hours if you are paid hourly, reducing your hours by a factor of four means that your pay is also reduced by a factor of four, which is the same as saying that your pay is quartered, or that you receive only one fourth, or 25% of your original pay.

◊ **Example 5:** If you are paid $200 a week, and the tax is 25% of your pay, how much spending money do you have per week?

To answer the question you must understand that a tax implies that the money is taken away, or subtracted. In other words, you have to subtract 25% of the $200 you earn. First we must calculate 25% of 200. Since 25% = 25/100 = ¼ = 0.25, 25% of 200 = 200 multiplied by 0.25 = 50. So the tax is $50, and you get to spend $200 - $50 = $150.

You should also note that taking away 25% of the $200 is the same as leaving 75% of the $200. (These are reciprocal ways of stating the same information.) So this problem can also be solved by multiplying $200 by 0.75 = $150. Hopefully you are starting to realize that recognizing reciprocals can often simplify your life.

12.3 Exercises: Math Terminology
Answers Pg. 427-429

1. What is 1/4 of 100?

2. What is 1/5 of 100?

3. What is 1/3 of 333?

4. What is 1/9 of 81?

5. What is 1/4 as a percentage?

6. What is 1/5 as a percentage?

7. What is 1/3 as a percentage?

8. What is 1/9 as a percentage?

9. What is 25% of 100?

10. What is 20% of 100?

11. What is 33.3% of 333?

12. What is 11% of 81?

13.   What number is 11% less than 81?

14.   What number is 25% less than 100?

15.   What number is 20% less than 100?

16.   What number is 33.3% less than 333?

17.   Your salary is normally $100 per week. If you get a raise such that your salary is increased by a factor of 2, what is your new salary?

18.   Your salary is normally $100 per week. If you get demoted such that your salary is decreased by a factor of 2, what is your new salary?

19.   Your salary is normally $100 per week. If you get a raise such that your salary is increased by a factor of 4, what is your new salary?

20.   Your salary is normally $100 per week. If you get demoted such that your salary is decreased by a factor of 4, what is your new salary?

21.   If two variables are directly proportional, if one variable doubles, then the related variable _____ .

22.   If two variables are inversely proportional, if one variable doubles, then the related variable _____ .

23.   If two variables are directly proportional, if one variable increases by a factor of 17, then the related variable increases by a factor of _____ .

24.   If two variables are inversely proportional, if one variable decreases by a factor of 17, then the related variable _____ by a factor of 17.

25.   If your pay is decreased by 20%, what percentage of your pay is left?

26.   Given that you are paid hourly, if you work 20% more time, what percentage is the increase in your pay?

27.   If you double the speed you drive, by what factor have you reduced the time to drive the same distance?

28.   If you decrease the speed you drive by a factor of 19, by what factor have you increased the time to drive the same distance?

29.   Which is greater, 10% of 9 or 9% of 10?

30.   Which is greater 25% of 50 or 50% of 25?

31.   By what percentage did your pay increase if your initial pay was $75 and your new pay is $100?

13. Distance Equation Revisited

In Level 1, the general equation for distance was given and discussed both in terms of a traveling car and sound traveling in the body. For sound propagating in the body, we calculated that sound would require 6.5 µsec to travel 1 cm, presuming the propagation velocity of 1540 m/sec. With respect to diagnostic ultrasound, we must now consider two other points.

1)   For imaging, the sound must travel into and back out of the body (roundtrip effect).
2)   The propagation velocity might not always be the presumed 1540 m/sec.

13.1 The Roundtrip Effect

For medical imaging there are two fundamental modes which can be used, transmission mode, or reflection mode. A transmission modality is like x-ray, where the x-rays are transmitted through a patient and the change in transmission properties are recorded on film. In comparison, diagnostic ultrasound is a reflected modality, where the sound is transmitted into the patient, and the changes to the reflected beam are received and processed. The fact that ultrasound is a reflective mode dictates that the sound must travel twice as far as the distance to the structures we desire to image. This factor of 2 in flight (travel) time and flight path is referred to as the roundtrip effect. This effect is pictured below.

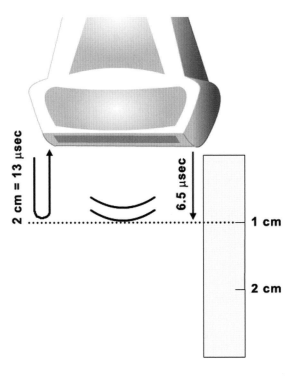

Fig. 3   **Imaging 1 cm Requires 13 µsec**

View Animation and Image Library CD

When we refer to imaging depth in ultrasound, we are speaking about the actual depth within the patient, not the total distance the sound beam must travel. Therefore, if the imaging depth is 2 cm, the total distance traveled by the ultrasound beam will be 4 cm. Similarly, if the imaging depth is 12 cm, then the total distance traveled by the ultrasound beam will be 24 cm. The calculation of 6.5 μsec per cm of travel still holds true assuming the propagation speed of 1540 m/sec. However, when the transit time for a sound beam is calculated, you must always pay attention to the wording of the question, paying particular attention as to whether or not you need to include the roundtrip effect. The table below illustrates this principle:

Imaging depth	Total distance	Time
0.5 cm	1 cm	6.5 μsec
1 cm	2 cm	13 μsec
2 cm	4 cm	26 μsec
3 cm	6 cm	39 μsec
4 cm	8 cm	52 μsec
5 cm	10 cm	65 μsec
8 cm	16 cm	104 μsec
10 cm	20 cm	130 μsec
15 cm	30 cm	195 μsec

Table 2:   **Propagation Times in the Body Assuming 1540 m/sec**

From this table, it should be clear that you have two choices. You can choose to remember the 6.5 μsec per cm of travel and then multiply by the total travel distance, or you can choose to remember the 13 μsec per cm of imaging depth and then multiply by the imaging depth instead. Obviously, these two methods are equivalent, but you must always make certain that you are interpreting the wording correctly so as not to be incorrect by a factor of two in your calculations:

The following examples should clarify this point for you.

◊   ***Example 1:***   How long does it take ultrasound to travel a distance of 3 cm in the body?

Since the question says "travel a distance of", the total travel distance is 3 cm. Since it takes 6.5 μsec per cm of travel, the total time would be 3 times 6.5 μsec, or 19.5 μsec.

Pegasus Lectures, Inc.

◊ **Example 2:** How long does it take ultrasound to image to a depth of 3 cm in the body?

Since the question says "image to a depth of 3 cm", the total distance traveled is 6 cm. Since it takes 6.5 μsec per cm of travel, the total time would be 6 times 6.5 μsec, or 39 μsec. Note that the same answer can be achieved by using 13 μsec per cm of imaging depth and multiplying by 3 cm, yielding the same answer of 39 μsec.

◊ **Example 3:** How long does it take ultrasound to travel down and back to a structure of 10 cm deep in the body?

Since the question says down and back to a structure 10 cm, the total distance traveled is 20 cm. Since it takes 6.5 μsec per cm of travel, the total time would be 20 times 6.5 μsec, or 130 μsec. Equivalently, using the imaging depth of 10 cm multiplied by 13 μsec, the same answer of 130 μsec is achieved.

13.2 When the Propagation Velocity of 1540 m/sec is Incorrect

As you will learn in Chapter 2, the speed of sound is not always 1540 m/sec. How fast sound travels is a function of various properties of the medium. If the speed of sound is not 1540 m/sec, you cannot use the pre-calculated rate of 6.5 μsec per cm of distance or 13 μsec per cm of imaging depth. Instead, you will need to use the distance equation and perform the calculation using the actual speed of sound for the medium in question.

◊ **Example 1:** If the speed of sound in air is 331 m/sec, how long will it take sound to travel 331 m?

$$c = 331 \ \frac{m}{sec}$$

$d = 331 \ m$

$t = ?$

Rewrite the distance equation in terms of time, or: $t = \dfrac{d}{r}$.

Plug the values given into the equation:

$$t = \frac{331 \ m}{331 \ \dfrac{m}{sec}} = 1 \ sec.$$

◊ **Example 2:** If the speed of sound in a medium is 1,000 m/sec, how long will it take sound to travel 420 m?

$$c = 1,000 \ \frac{m}{sec}$$

$d = 420 \ m$

$t = ?$

Rewrite the distance equation in terms of time, or: $t = \dfrac{d}{r}$.

Plug the values given into the equation:

$$t = \frac{420 \ m}{1,000 \ \dfrac{m}{sec}} = 0.42 \ sec.$$

If you assume a propagation speed that is incorrect, obviously, the calculated time will also be incorrect. This error occurs quite frequently in diagnostic ultrasound. The ultrasound system is designed to always presume a propagation velocity of 1540 m/sec. However, the propagation velocity can certainly vary within the body. As a result of this incorrect time estimate, the system will sometimes portray structures in a deeper or shallower location than reality. This error is referred to as speed error. Differences in propagation velocity from the assumed 1540 m/sec will be discussed in Chapter 2 and speed error will be discussed in more detail in Chapter 8. For now, it is important that you make sure you can calculate the distance equation correctly for various propagation velocities and various imaging depths.

13.3 Exercises: Distance Equation Revisited   Answers Pg. 429-430

1.   How far can ultrasound travel in soft tissue in 1 second? (Recall from Section 9.4 that we use the letter c to refer to the speed of sound. In Chapter 2, we learn that c = 1540 m/sec for soft tissue.)

2.   Given that 1 m is a little more than 3.25 ft., convert your answer above to feet.

3.   Given that there are 5,280 feet/mile, what is the closest approximation to how far ultrasound can travel in soft tissue in 1 second?
a) 0.001 miles
b) 0.1 miles
c) 1 mile
d) 1,000 miles

4.   How long does it take for an ultrasound pulse to travel:
a) 1 cm in soft tissue?
b) 1 cm and then return 1 cm to the transducer?
(Understanding this problem is absolutely critical.)

5.   If a system assumes a speed of 1540 m/sec, what is the maximum depth to which it can image in 130 μsec?
(Don't forget that the distance traveled = 2 • max depth since the pulse must return to the transducer.)
(Understanding this problem is also absolutely critical.)

6.   If a system assumes a speed of 1540 m/sec but the speed is really 2,000 m/sec, what is the maximum depth it can image in 130 μsec?

7.   Given the results of #5 and #6 which of the following is true?
a) objects in #6 will appear too deep
b) objects in #6 will appear too shallow
c) objects in #6 will appear in the same place as #5
d) since the time is the same, the distance is the same

14. Non-Linear Relationships

In Level 1 (Section 10.1) we discussed simple relative relationships between variables. In these cases, the powers of the related variables were always the same and always equal to 1. You will also note that only the operations of multiplication and division were expressed in the equations, never addition and subtraction. As a result, we were able to simply express that a change in one variable by a factor of x produced a corresponding change in the related variable by the same factor of x. When the relationship was proportionality, then both variables increased and decreased together. When the relationship was inversely related, the variables changed in inverse directions.

We now must discuss more complex relationships where the powers of the related variables are not always equal and not always equal to 1. As mentioned in Level 1, understanding and interpreting these more complex relationships will be the most important mathematical tool you will develop both for taking the exam and for truly understanding how ultrasound behaves in predicting the body's response to disease. As we progress through this book, you will learn that many of the equations which dictate the behavior of ultrasound and the behavior of the body with respect to disease will behave in these complex non-linear fashions.

14.1 Direct Non-Linear Proportionality

As discussed in Section 10.1, the word direct implies that both related variables change in the same direction, or an increase in one variable produces an increase in the related variable, and a decrease in one variable produces a decrease in the related variable. Quite frequently, the word direct is dropped and just assumed, so that the word direct is implied in the expression non-linear proportionality. In these complex cases where the powers of the two related variables are not equal, a change in one variable will produce a more significant change in the related variable. Unlike the simple case discussed in Section 10.2, a change in one variable by a factor of x produces a bigger change in the related variable than a factor of x. The following example demonstrates a non-linear proportionality.

◊ **Example:** $y = 3 \cdot x^2 \Rightarrow$ y is proportional to x^2
(Recall that the symbol ($\Rightarrow$) means "implies")
If $x = 1 \Rightarrow y = 3 \cdot (1)^2 = 3$
$x = 2 \Rightarrow y = 3 \cdot (2)^2 = 12$
$x = 5 \Rightarrow y = 3 \cdot (5)^2 = 75$

So an increase in x, results in a greater increase in y.
Similarly, a decrease in x results in a greater decrease in y, or $y \propto x^2$.

Note that for this example, a change in x by a factor of 2 results in a change in y by a factor of 2^2, or 4, clearly a non-linear relationship.

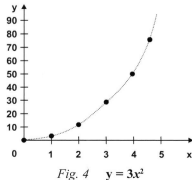

Fig. 4 $y = 3x^2$

14.2 Complex - Inverse Proportionality

As mentioned in Section 10.3, all inverse relationships are non-linear. However, when the power of the two variables are not equal and are not equal to one, then a much more complex non-linear relationship results. In the simple case when the powers are equal and equal to 1, an increase in one variable by a factor of x produces a corresponding decrease in the related variable by the same factor of x (and vice versa). For more complex inverse relationships, a change in one variable by a factor of x will produce a corresponding change in the opposite direction not by the same factor of x, but by a power of that factor x. In other words, small changes in one variable produce significantly greater changes in the related variable.

◊ **Example:**

$$y = 3/x^2 \quad \Rightarrow \quad \text{y is inversely proportional to } x^2.$$

If
$$x = 1 \quad \Rightarrow \quad y = 3/1^2 = 3$$
$$x = 2 \quad \Rightarrow \quad y = 3/2^2 = 3/4$$
$$x = 5 \quad \Rightarrow \quad y = 3/5^2 = 3/25$$

So if x increases a small amount, y decreases a much larger amount
or $y \propto 1/x^2$

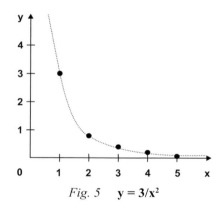

Fig. 5   **y = 3/x²**

15. Interpreting Relationships Within Linear and Non-Linear Equations

Remember that these mathematical concepts are powerful tools when understood well enough to be applied. In this section, we will develop the skills necessary to apply these concepts to general equations. We will start off with simple equations and work our way toward seemingly more complex equations. However, since the concepts to be applied are always the same, once you have adequate exposure and experience in these concepts, even more complex appearing equations will not present any greater challenge than apparently simple equations.

15.1 Assessing an Equation and Expressing the Relative Relationship

We have already seen that within an equation if two variables are in the numerator on opposite sides of the equal sign, that the variables are directly related. We have also seen that when two variables are on opposite sides of the equal sign, but one is in the numerator and the other is in the denominator, that the variables are inversely related. When the power is not equal to 1, all we have to do is keep the power with the variable to express the relative relation. Take for example the following made up equation:

$$g = \frac{h^2 d^3}{z}$$

From this equation we know that:

$$g \propto h^2$$

$$g \propto d^3$$

$$g \propto \frac{1}{z}$$

Determining the Dominance of the Variables

Although this sounds complicated, it is nothing more than looking at the powers of each of the variables and ranking them from largest to smallest. Higher powers imply greater dominance. Again consider the made up equation. In that equation the variable "d" has the highest power, followed by "h", and then by "z".

The value of knowing the dominance of variables is that you now have a way of assessing which variable has the greatest impact on the related variable (in this case the variable g).

Consider what would happen to the variable g, if h were doubled.

since $g \propto h^2 \Rightarrow$ a factor of 2 change in h results in a 2^2 change in g, or a factor of 4.

Consider what would happen to the variable g, if d were doubled.

since $g \propto d^3 \Rightarrow$ a factor of 2 change in d results in a 2^3 change in g, or a factor of 8.

Consider what would happen to the variable g, if z were doubled.

since $g \propto \frac{1}{z} \Rightarrow$ a factor of 2 change in z results in an inverse change in g by a factor of 2, or a factor of 0.5.

Clearly, very small changes in d result in very large changes in the related variable g, for this equation. Hence, d is the dominant variable.

Discussing Relative Changes

We have now arrived at the point in our mathematical review which is the crux of whether an individual passes the physics exam or does not. Not surprisingly, we are also at the point in our mathematical understanding of determining if an individual will be able to relate the physics equations with what is experienced in the world. Given an equation, and assessing the equation for relationships, it is now possible to determine how changes in one variable will influence a related variable. In case this point doesn't sound too important to you, consider that the value of an equation is its ability to predict how physical parameters will behave in the world. Quite frequently, we cannot directly measure the physical parameter that has the greatest importance to the well being of the patient. But we may be able to measure a parameter that is related to the parameter we really need to know and quantify. For example, let's say that you really want to determine how much blood flow occurs, but all you can measure is the size and shape of the vessel or blood flow path. If you have an equation that predicts how blood flow will change with changes in the vessel flow path, by measuring the vessel flow path, you can now predict what will happen hemodynamically to your patient.

Of course, this last step requires that you actually understand what the equation means, how the parameter that you measured relates to the parameter you really want to measure, and if there are any other parameters that have not been accounted for in your equation.

Perhaps the best way to determine if you understand how to assess relative changes between related variables is to try some practice questions.

15.2 Exercises: Assessing an Equation   Answers Pg. 430-431

Answer the following questions based on the made up equation: $w = \dfrac{2qkt^2 d^3 f^4}{3zm^3}$.

1. How would w change if q were increased by a factor of 7?

2. How would w change if q were decreased by a factor of 3?

3. How would w change if k were increased by a factor of 2?

4. How would w change if t were increased by a factor of 7?

5. How would w change if d were increased by a factor of 2?

6. How would w change if d were decreased by a factor of 3?

7. How would w change if f were increased by a factor of 2?

8. How would w change if f were halved?

9. How would w change if z were doubled?

10. How would w change if z were increased by a factor of 2?

11. How would w change if z were halved?

12. How would w change if z were decreased by a factor of 2?

13. How would w change if m were doubled?

14. How would w change if m were increased by a factor of 3?

15. How would w change if m were decreased by a factor of 3?

The concepts taught in this section will be tested very heavily on the exam. In the introduction to this chapter, it was stressed that although you would not have to perform intensive math calculations, you would be expected to determine and express the mathematical relationships between variables. Of course, on your boards they will not be worded "What is the mathematical relationship between the wavelength of an ultrasound wave and the frequency of the ultrasound wave?" Instead, you will be asked hypotheticals such as "How would the wavelength change if you changed your imaging transducer from a 3 MHz to a 6 MHz operating frequency?"

15.3 Exercises: Proportionality   Answers Pg. 431-432

The following exercises give you another opportunity to familiarize yourself with interpreting equation based questions. In this section, the questions are mostly phrased in terms of real world situations, some of which relate to ultrasound.

For question 1-5 use the equation: $f_{dop} = \left[\dfrac{2f_0 v}{c} \bullet \cos(\theta)\right]$.

1. f_{dop} is....

   a)   proportional to f_o
   b)   inversely proportional to f_o
   c)   proportional to the square of f_o
   d)   cannot be determined

2. f_{dop} is....

   a)   proportional to c
   b)   inversely proportional to c
   c)   proportional to the square of c
   d)   cannot be determined

3. f_{dop} is....

   a)   proportional to v
   b)   inversely proportional to v
   c)   proportional to the square of v
   d)   cannot be determined

4. f_{dop} is....

   a)   proportional to $\cos(\theta)$
   b)   inversely proportional to $\cos(\theta)$
   c)   proportional to the square of $\cos(\theta)$
   d)   cannot be determined

5.   If f_o is doubled...

   a) f_{dop} is halved
   b) f_{dop} is quadrupled
   c) f_{dop} is doubled
   d) f_{dop} is unchanged

6.   The price of diamonds is proportional to the square of the number of carats. If the price of diamond A is four times the price of diamond B then

   a)   diamond A is 1/2 the number of carats of diamond B
   b)   diamond A is 1/4 the number of carats of diamond B
   c)   diamond A is twice the number of carats of diamond B
   d)   diamond A is four times the number of carats of diamond B

7. If in problem #6, a one-carat diamond costs $2,000, then how much will a four-carat diamond cost?

8. Write out the general equation which relates the cost of a diamond, (C), and the number of carats, (n).
    Hint: $C = ($ $) \cdot (n)^{()}$

9. If power is proportional to amplitude squared, if you triple the amplitude you _____ the power by a factor of _____.

10. Intensity $\propto$ power $\propto$ (amplitude)^2. If you double the amplitude, how does the intensity change?

11. If the intensity is increased by a factor of 9, by how much has the power changed? By how much has the amplitude changed?

12. Intensity = power/area. If the area is increased by a factor of 2, the intensity is _____.

13. If the intensity remains constant but the beam area is increased, then the power must have _____.

14. If the intensity decreases by a factor of 16 for a fixed beam area, the power must have _____ by a factor of _____ and the amplitude must have _____ by a factor of _____.

16. Dealing with Percentage Change

16.1 Simple Calculations with Proportional Variables
For a variable that has changed, calculating a percentage change is performed by subtracting the old value of the variable (before the change) from the new value of the variable (after the change) and then dividing by the old value, or:

$$\% \text{ Change} = \frac{(\text{new value} - \text{old value})}{\text{old value}} \times 100\%.$$

◊ **Example 1:** By what percentage has the price of gas increased if the price changed from $2 per gallon to $2.50 per gallon?

$$\% \text{ Change gas price} = \frac{(\$2.50 - \$2.00)}{\$2.00} \times 100\% = \frac{0.50}{2.00} = \frac{0.25}{1.00} = .25 \text{ or } 25\%.$$

◊ **Example 2:** By what percentage has the cross-sectional area of a vessel changed if originally it was 1.0 cm^2 and with disease it became 0.8 cm^2?

$$\% \text{ Change vessel area} = \frac{\left(0.8 \text{ cm}^2 - 1.0 \text{ cm}^2\right)}{1.0 \text{ cm}^2} \times 100\% = \frac{-0.2}{1} = -.2 \text{ or } -20\%.$$

16.2 Calculations with Non-linearly Related Variables

Quite frequently, we are required to measure the change in a parameter over time and then express the percentage change in a non-linearly related variable. For example, you might measure the radius of a vessel at a first and follow up visit, and then express the percentage change in cross-sectional area or volume. Since the area and the volume are non-linearly related to the radius, the rate of change in the area term and volume term will be greater than the rate of change in the measured radius measurement.

The following general rules will work for all problems in which a percentage change must be calculated from a measure parameter and as such, are a much better approach than trying to memorize certain relationships.

16.3 Rules for Dealing with Percentage Change

1. Express the percentage change in the measured variable as a fraction (always new value in terms of old value).
2. Write the mathematical relationship between the related variables.
3. Apply the mathematical relationship to the fraction from step 1.
4. Convert the fraction back into a percentage.
5. Most importantly, watch out for reciprocals in the question.

16.4 Examples

The best way to solidify this percentage change concept is to see these steps applied in a few examples:

◊ **Example 1:** If the radius of a vessel is reduced by 10%, what is the percentage residual cross-sectional area?

We will solve this problem by following the steps as listed above.

Step 1: $\quad r_{new} = \dfrac{9}{10} r_{old}$ (always write new in terms of old)

Note: A 10% reduction in radius implies a 90% residual radius. Since we always write the new parameter in terms of the old parameter, we convert 90% to a fraction, not the 10%.

Step 2: $\quad area \propto r^2$

Step 3: $\quad area_{new} \propto r_{new}^2 = \left(\dfrac{9}{10} r_{old}\right)^2 = \dfrac{81}{100}\left(r_{old}\right)^2$

Step 4: $\quad \dfrac{81}{100}\left(r_{old}\right)^2 = 81\%$ of original (old area).

Therefore, the residual area with a 10% reduction in radius is 81%. As you can see, the non-linear relationship between radius and area results in a faster change in area than in radius.

Note: Since the calculation results in the new area as a percentage of the old (residual area) there is no step 5 to perform. Compare this example carefully with the next example.

◊ **Example 2:**   If the radius of a vessel is reduced by 10%, what is the percentage decrease in area?

Step 1: $r_{new} = \dfrac{9}{10} r_{old}$ (always write new in terms of old)

Step 2: $area \propto r^2$

Step 3: $area_{new} \propto r_{new}^2 = \left(\dfrac{9}{10} r_{old}\right)^2 = \dfrac{81}{100}(r_{old})^2$

Step 4: $\dfrac{81}{100}(r_{old})^2 = 81\%$ of original (old area).

Step 5: 100% - 81% = 19%.

Notice that this problem is really just the reciprocal of the first example. The most common mistake students make performing these calculations is ignoring the terminology which indicates a reciprocal calculation. In Example 2, the first clause of the problem did not change, but the second clause was the reciprocal of the second clause of Example 1.

◊ **Example 3:** If the residual vessel radius is 10%, what is the percentage residual area?

Step 1: $r_{new} = \dfrac{1}{10} r_{old}$ (always write new in terms of old)

Note: This problem gives the residual radius as 10%. Since the residual is an expression of the new in terms of the old already, no reciprocal is necessary in this step as was necessary in Example 1 and Example 2.

Step 2: $area \propto r^2$

Step 3: $area_{new} \propto r_{new}^2 = \left(\dfrac{1}{10} r_{old}\right)^2 = \dfrac{1}{100}(r_{old})^2$

Step 4: $\dfrac{1}{100}(r_{old})^2 = 1\%$ of original (old) area.

Note: Since the calculation results in the new area as a percentage of the old (residual area) there is no step 5 to perform. Compare this example with Example 4.

◊ **Example 4:**   If the residual vessel radius is 10%, what is the percentage decrease in area?

Now that we can recognize reciprocals in questions, it should be clear that this question is just the reciprocal of the previous example. Therefore, the first four steps are as just performed in Example 3, and all that is necessary is to calculate the change in area as the reciprocal of the residual area, or:

Step 5: 100% - 1% = 99%

17. Logarithms

Logarithms are an extremely powerful non-linear mathematical tool. Logarithms are particularly useful as a mathematical method to deal with relatively large numbers and relatively small numbers simultaneously.

Effectively, logarithms provide a mechanism to compress a large range of numbers into a smaller range. This functionality is critical in ultrasound since the range of signal amplitudes which are reflected from the body (the signal dynamic range) is enormous, especially relative to the range which can be displayed by a monitor and the range which can be interpreted by the human eye.

Logarithms are defined as the power to which a base must be raised to get the desired number. The following examples demonstrate how to mathematically solve a logarithm.

◊ **Example:** $\log_{10}(x) = 3 \Rightarrow 10^3 = x \Rightarrow x = 10 \cdot 10 \cdot 10 = 1,000$
Note: think circle when solving logarithms

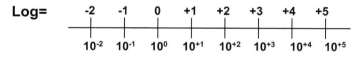

◊ **Example:** $\log_{10}(100) = x \Rightarrow 10^x = 100, \text{ since } 100 = 10^2$

$$10^x = 10^2$$
$$\text{or } x = 2$$

Note: If no base is given, the base of 10 is assumed $\Rightarrow$ (log x = 2) = $\log_{10}(x)$ = 2.

Visualizing and understanding logarithms:

Log=

-2	-1	0	+1	+2	+3	+4	+5
10^{-2}	10^{-1}	10^0	10^{+1}	10^{+2}	10^{+3}	10^{+4}	10^{+5}

Fig. 6   **Log Scale**

From the graphic representation of base 10 logarithms above, it should become clear that solving the logarithm of any power of 10 is the same as expressing the power to which 10 is raised. For example the log of 100 is 2 since 10 raised to the second power is 100. The log of one tenth is -1 since 10 raised to the -1 power is one tenth. The log of 10,000 is 4 since $10^4 = 10,000$.

As expressed in the first paragraph of this section, logarithms are really a non-linear compression scheme to help us deal with large ranges of numbers or data. When we graph data logarithmically, the logarithm of the data point is an indication of how much the data has been compressed to be displayed on that particular graph. For example, on a logarithmic graph, the number 100 has been compressed by 2 factors of 10 to be displayed. Similarly, the number 1,000 represents 3 "orders" of compression. Having studied reciprocals, we can now simply state that since a positive logarithm represents a compression of data, a negative logarithm must represent a decompression of data. Therefore, if a factor of 100 is 2 orders of compression, a factor of 1/100 represents 2 orders of decompression.

There is one logarithm you must memorize: the log (2) = 0.3. Knowing the logarithm of 2, as well as being able to solve for the log of any power of ten, will allow you to solve virtually any logarithm. This concept will become clear in the next section as we learn some nice properties associated with logarithms.

$$\log_{10}(2) = 0.3$$

Although you have to memorize the fact that the log of 2 is 0.3, we can show graphically why this logarithm should make sense.

Fig. 7   **Linear Scale**

Compare the graph from 1 to 10 above with the graph of the same range (from 1 to 10) below. The graph above is a linear graph. Notice how the spacing between numbers remains fixed, so that a number twice as big will be twice as far up on the graph. In comparison, the logarithmic graph presents each successive number closer to the previous number, indicating increasing compression with greater numbers. Clearly, if you double the number, you do not double the distance on the graph (a non-linear mapping).

You should also notice that the number 2 is a little less than a third of the way from the number 1 toward the number 10. This shows graphically why the log of 2 is 0.3.

Fig. 8   **Log Scale and the Log of 2**

17.1 Properties of Logarithms

One of the reasons why logarithms are a very powerful tool in mathematics is that logarithms convert multiplication into addition and division into subtraction.

$$\log(x * y) = \log(x) + \log(y)$$

and

$$\log\left(\frac{x}{y}\right) = \log(x) - \log(y)$$

This mathematical relationship should make sense to you. Since a logarithm is a compression scheme, compressing data by a factor of "x" times "y" is the same as compressing the data by a factor of x and then by a factor of "y." Again, recall that multiplication and division are inverse operations, so if logarithms convert multiplication into addition, it should be intuitive that logarithms convert division into subtraction. Note that the first example below is given to demonstrate why this mathematical relationship "makes sense." The next three examples demonstrate how this information can be used to calculate many logarithms that are not powers of 10. This is one of the reasons you memorized that the log(2) = 0.3.

◊ **Example 1:** $\log_{10}(1000) = \log_{10}(10 * 100) = \log_{10}(10) + \log_{10}(100) = 1 + 2 = 3$

◊ **Example 2:** $\log_{10}(20) = \log_{10}(2 * 10) = \log_{10}(2) + \log_{10}(10) = 0.3 + 1 = 1.3$

◊ **Example 3:** $\log_{10}(4) = \log_{10}(2 * 2) = \log_{10}(2) + \log_{10}(2) = 0.3 + 0.3 = 0.6$

◊ **Example 4:** $\log_{10}(5) = \log_{10}(10/2) = \log_{10}(10) - \log_{10}(2) = 1 - 0.3 = 0.7$

Notice that Examples 2, 3, and 4 all demonstrate how knowing the log of 2, in addition to knowing some properties of logarithms can help you solve many other logarithms.

17.2 Exercises: Logarithms Answers Pg. 432-433
Solve for x.

1. $\log_{10} x = 2$

2. $\log_x 10 = 1$

3. $\log_{10} 10 = x$

4. $\log_{10} 1,000 = x$

5. $\log_{10} x = 4$

6. $\log_6 36 = x$

7. $\log_6 x = 2$

8. $\log 100 = x$

18. Trigonometry

Trigonometry is a mathematical discipline that deals with the physical relationship between angles and dimensions of triangles. Many physical situations can be modeled using triangles and hence, by using trigonometry. For example, the height of an object can be calculated by measuring the length of its shadow, given that you know the angle of the light to the object. One of the easiest ways of learning trigonometry is to start with what is called the unit circle. A circle is actually a collection of all the various proportioned triangles which exist. When you look at the examples, this concept of a circle including all of the triangles should become clearer.

We will start with a unit circle. It is called a unit circle because the radius has a length of one, or one unit.

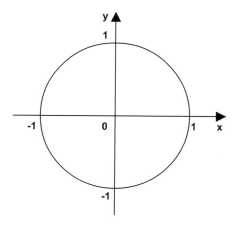

Fig. 9 **Unit Circle**

To determine the cosine (or cos) of an angle (θ), draw the angle onto the circle, and then project the intersection with the circle onto the x-axis.

◊ **Example:**   What is the cosine at θ = 60°?

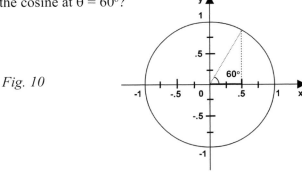

Fig. 10

Unit Circle

So cosine (60°) = 0.5

To determine the sine (or sin) of an angle (θ) - draw the angle onto the unit circle and project the intersection onto the y-axis.

◊ **Example:**   What is the sine (60°)?

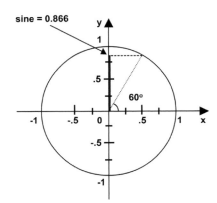

Fig. 11

Unit Circle

So the sine (60°) = 0.866

◊ **Example:**   What is the cosine (0°)?

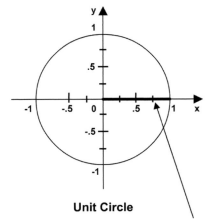

Fig. 12

Unit Circle

Intersection of angle with circle is already on axis, where x = 1, so cosine (0°) = **1**

◊ **Example:**   What is the cosine (90°)?

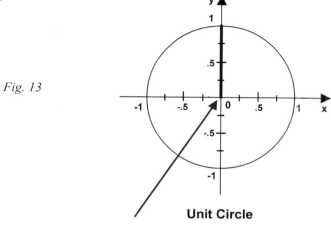

Fig. 13

Unit Circle

Projection of the intersection of the angle and the circle is at x = 0, so cosine (90°) = **0**.

View Animation and Image Library CD

The following table demonstrates the sines and cosines of the "basic" angles. The basic angles are just the angles which we easily recognized on a unit circle that can serve as reference points for other angles. Clearly using the technique just demonstrated, you can estimate the sine and cosine of any angle.

Angle (θ)	Cos (θ)	Sin(θ)
0°	1	0
30°	0.866	0.5
45°	0.707	0.707
60°	0.5	0.866
90°	0	1
120°	-0.50	0.866
135°	-0.707	0.707
150°	-0.866	0.50
180°	-1	0
210°	-0.866	-0.50
225°	-0.707	-0.707
240°	-0.50	-0.866
270°	0	-1

Table 3: **Cosine and Sine**

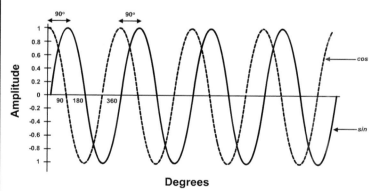

Fig. 14   **Graphical Representation of the Sine and Cosine Versus Angle**

Notice that the sine and cosine look the same on the graph except for a "phase" difference. The cosine leads the sine by 90°. You will learn more about "phase" later in this chapter in the section on wave addition.

Reconciling this approach with the classic explanation of trigonometry is relatively easy. In the table below are the definitions most people associate with trigonometry.

$$\cos(\theta) = \frac{\text{adjacent}}{\text{hypotenuse}}$$

$$\sin(\theta) = \frac{\text{opposite}}{\text{hypotenuse}}$$

$$\tan(\theta) = \frac{\sin(\theta)}{\cos(\theta)} = \frac{\text{opposite}}{\text{adjacent}}$$

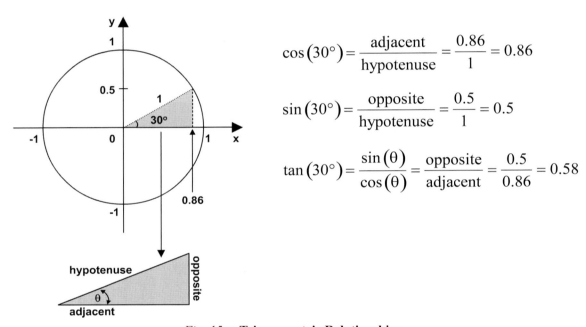

$$\cos(30°) = \frac{\text{adjacent}}{\text{hypotenuse}} = \frac{0.86}{1} = 0.86$$

$$\sin(30°) = \frac{\text{opposite}}{\text{hypotenuse}} = \frac{0.5}{1} = 0.5$$

$$\tan(30°) = \frac{\sin(\theta)}{\cos(\theta)} = \frac{\text{opposite}}{\text{adjacent}} = \frac{0.5}{0.86} = 0.58$$

Fig. 15   **Trigonometric Relationships**

For completeness:

The secant is the reciprocal of the cosine.

The cosecant is the reciprocal of the sine.

The cotangent is the reciprocal of the tangent.

By placing the triangle onto a unit circle, the hypotenuse = 1, which makes calculating the trigonometric functions easy. If you were given a right triangle for which the hypotenuse is not 1, you can calculate the cosine as the adjacent side divided by the hypotenuse. Similarly, you can calculate the sine as the opposite divided by the hypotenuse.

Pegasus Lectures, Inc.

18.1 Angles, Quadrants and Signs

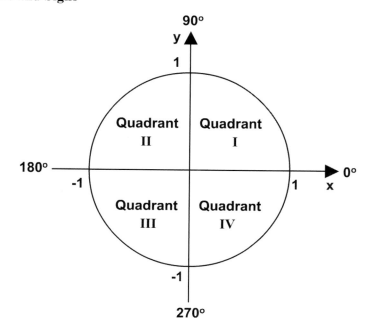

Fig. 16 **Quadrants of a circle**

One fourth of a circle is called a quadrant. The first quadrant of a circle is from 0° to 90°. The second quadrant is from 90° to 180°. The third quadrant is from 180° to 270°, and the fourth quadrant is from 270° to 360°. The quadrants of the unit circle are displayed in the above graph. You should know in which quadrants the cosine is negative and in which quadrants the cosine is positive. Similarly, you should know in which quadrants the sine is positive and in which quadrants the sine is negative. This is really quite simple to remember if you draw your unit circle and recall how the sine and cosine are determined. Since the cosine is the projection onto the x-axis, the cosine is positive in quadrant I and quadrant IV, and negative in quadrants II and III. In contrast, the sine is the projection onto the y-axis and hence is positive in quadrant I and II, and negative in quadrants III and IV.

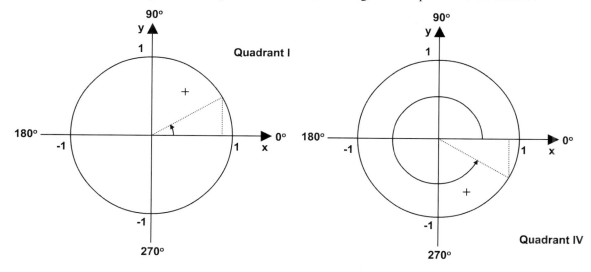

Fig. 17 **Cosine is Positive in Quadrant I and Quadrant IV**

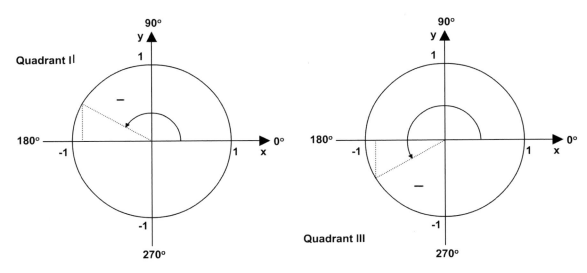

Fig. 18 **Cosine is Negative in Quadrant II and Quadrant III**

18.2 The Value of Knowing Basic Trigonometry in Ultrasound (and Medicine)

As was mentioned, one aspect of trigonometry is a mathematical approach to dealing with the ratios of sides of a various triangles. Why should you care about triangles and angles? The answer is that many parameters we would like to know, we cannot measure directly. Instead, we are forced to measure what is commonly referred to as a projection or "shadow" of the actual object. However, the length of the "shadow" can be affected by changing angles.

Consider how the length of a long bone would change on an x-ray as the angle to the bone changes with respect to its long axis. Although the bone does not vary in length over the time it takes to perform this test, the length of the projection of the bone will certainly vary. In other words, there are angle effects which affect your measurement accuracy.

The same phenomenon certainly occurs in ultrasound. As the angle between the ultrasound beam and a structure varies, the dimensions of the structure will vary in the image. Also, as you will learn in Chapter 7, when we measure blood velocity using Doppler, changes in Doppler angle (insonification angle) will produce changes in our measurement. Clearly, we would like to have some approach to eliminate, or at least minimize, the errors associated with these angle effects.

Trigonometry provides us with the mathematical tool to somewhat correct the "distortion" caused by angle affects, as well as a means by which to model how significant will be the error, and at what angles the error will be the greatest.

It is expected that you will be able to solve the sine and the cosine of all of the basic angles (0°, 30°, 45°, 60°, 90°, 120°, 135°, 150°, 180°, 270°, 360°). By knowing the sines and cosines of the basic angles you will be able to use these known values (fiducial points) to help you make relatively accurate estimates for the sines and cosines of every angle. It is not critical that you know cosines of angles to any great precision. Instead, what is more important is that you understand how the sine and cosine vary with angle.

Pegasus Lectures, Inc.

You will notice from the graph of the sine and cosine that these two functions are extremely non-linear in their behavior. As a result, you should expect that any measurement you make that depends on the sine or cosine of the angle will have very non-linear associated errors. This point is critical, since this information can then be used to help determine how measurements can be best made so as to minimize error and maximize clinical accuracy. For now, it is important that you learn the basics of trigonometry. In the Chapter 7, when discussing Doppler, the concepts of angular effects and trigonometry will be revisited and applied. In Level 3 of Chapter 7, there is a mathematical treatment of how to quantify the error associated with angular effects.

18.3 Exercises: Trigonometry   Answers Pg. 433-434

Using the large unit circle on the next page, find the:

1.	cos (30°)		11.	sin (30°)
2.	cos (45°)		12.	sin (45°)
3.	cos (60°)		13.	sin (60°)
4.	cos (0°)		14.	sin (0°)
5.	cos (90°)		15.	sin (90°)
6.	cos (180°)		16.	sin (180°)
7.	cos (135°)		17.	sin (135°)
8.	cos (270°)		18.	sin (270°)
9.	cos (360°)		19.	sin (360°)
10.	cos (225°)		20.	sin (225°)

21.   On the axis provided below, plot the cosine data as was already done for the sine data.

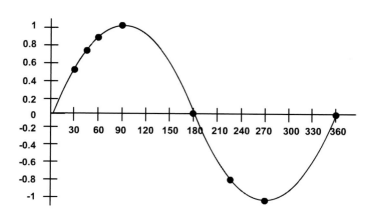

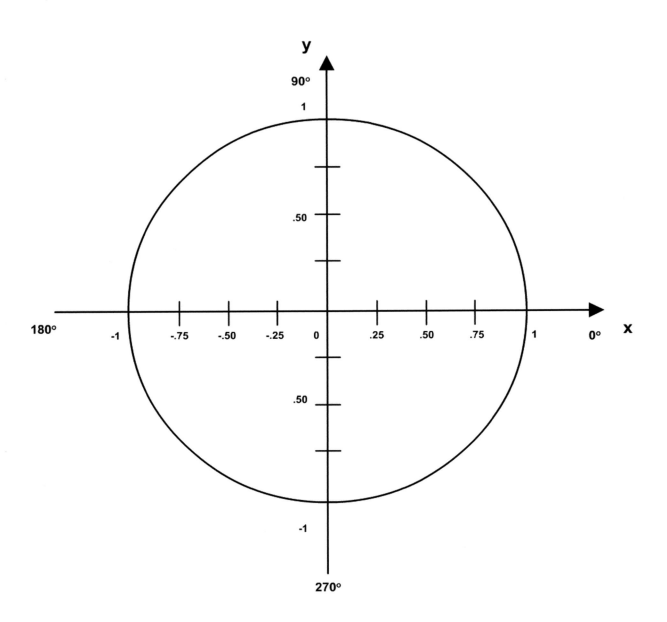

19. The Decimal System and the Binary System

19.1 Decimal (Base 10) and Binary (Base 2)

For daily use, our number system is base 10, or decimal. Base 10 means that there are ten digits (0 - 9) which are used to represent all numbers. Base 10 is very convenient, given the fact that we have ten fingers and ten toes, which essentially served as our first calculators. To facilitate learning how to use other base counting systems, it is usually easiest to review how the already familiar base 10 system works.

Look at the number $732_{10} \Rightarrow 732$

* Note: we normally do not write the subscripted 10; it is assumed.

Another way of writing 732_{10} is:

$$732 = 700 + 30 + 2$$
$$= 7(100) + 3(10) + 2$$
$$= 7(10)^2 + 3(10)^1 + 2(10)^0$$
(note powers of ten)

In table form 732 =

•••••	10^4	10^3	10^2	10^1	10^0	10^{-1}	10^{-2}	10^{-3}	•••••
	0	0	7	3	2	0	0	0	

Decimal point

2. Look at the number $6{,}327.64 = 6(10)^3 + 3(10)^2 + 2(10)^1 + 7(10)^0 + 6(10)^{-1} + 4(10)^{-2}$

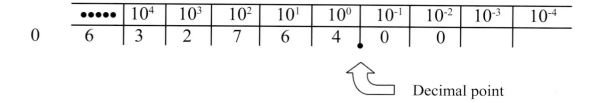

	•••••	10^4	10^3	10^2	10^1	10^0	10^{-1}	10^{-2}	10^{-3}	10^{-4}
0		6	3	2	7	6	4	0	0		

Decimal point

Do you think we would use decimal (base 10) if we had been born with 8 fingers? Base 8 works just like base 10 except you now can only use the eight digits (0 -7).

$$372_8 =$$
$$3(8)^2 + 7(8)^1 + 2(8)^0$$
$$3(64) + 7(8) + 2(1) = 250_{\text{base 10}}$$

••••	8^4	8^3	8^2	8^1	8^0	8^{-1}	8^{-2}	8^{-3}	8^{-4}	
0	0	3	7	2	0	0	0	0		

Octal point

In other words, there is absolutely nothing unique or special about the counting system of base 10. There are an infinite number of counting systems which could have been chosen; we chose base 10 because of convenience relative to our anatomy. Understanding how to use another base is really the same as understanding how to count in the base 10 system.

19.2 Exercises: Decimal Conversions   Answers Pg. 435

1.   Convert $432_{\text{base 8}}$ into decimal

2.   Convert $2,703_{\text{base 8}}$ into decimal

3.   Write the number $9_{\text{base 10}}$ in base 8

19.3 Binary
In our daily life, we are most familiar with the counting system using base 10, utilizing ten digits: 0, 1, 2, ..., 9. With electronics, a distinct voltage must be used for each digit. Imagine how difficult it would be to represent numbers electronically using base 10; there would have to be ten distinct voltage levels.

A commonly used base for electronics and computers is called binary, or base 2. The binary system functions exactly as all other base systems, except it only uses the digits 0 and 1. For binary, only two voltage levels are necessary to represent the digits. The digit 0 is represented by 0 Volts, and the digit 1 is usually represented by +5 Volts. As electronic devices become smaller with a desire to use less power, a lower voltage (3.5 Volts or less) is more often being used to represent the digit 1.

Memory, like your computer memory or RAM, is really the storage or encoding of voltages representing numbers in binary.

19.4 Converting from Binary to Base 10

We will start by considering how a binary number can be converted to base 10. Note that the binary system is based on powers (groupings) of twos just as the decimal system is based on powers or groupings of tens. Just as we wrote the base 10 number in a grid form, we will take the same approach with binary. Notice that instead of the 1's column, the 10's column, the 100's column, etc., we have the 1's column, the 2's column, the 4's column etc.

◊ **Example:** 1011_2 (binary)

2^3	2^2	2^1	2^0
1	0	1	1

$$= \quad 1\,(2)^3 \quad + \quad 0\,(2)^2 \quad + \quad 1\,(2)^1 \quad + \quad 1\,(2)^0$$
$$= \quad 1\,(8) \quad + \quad 0\,(4) \quad + \quad 1\,(2) \quad + \quad 1\,(1)$$
$$= \quad 8 \quad + \quad 0 \quad + \quad 2 \quad + \quad 1$$

> **so** $1011_2 = 11_{10}$

◊ **Example:** 1100_2 (binary)

2^3	2^2	2^1	2^0
1	1	0	0

$$= \quad 1\,(2)^3 \quad + \quad 1\,(2)^2 \quad + \quad 0\,(2)^1 \quad + \quad 0\,(2)^0$$
$$= \quad 1\,(8) \quad + \quad 1\,(4) \quad + \quad 0\,(2) \quad + \quad 0\,(1)$$
$$= \quad 8 \quad + \quad 4 \quad + \quad 0 \quad + \quad 0$$

> **so** $1100_2 = 12_{10}$

◊ **Example:** 1111_2 (binary)

2^3	2^2	2^1	2^0
1	1	1	1

$$= \quad 1\,(2)^3 \quad + \quad 1\,(2)^2 \quad + \quad 1\,(2)^1 \quad + \quad 1\,(2)^0$$
$$= \quad 1\,(8) \quad + \quad 1\,(4) \quad + \quad 1\,(2) \quad + \quad 1\,(1)$$
$$= \quad 8 \quad + \quad 4 \quad + \quad 2 \quad + \quad 1$$

> **so** $1111_2 = 15_{10}$

Note that in binary form, all even numbers end in a zero and all odd numbers end in a 1. This fact can be helpful to eliminate at least a few choices on an exam. For example, if you were asked:

Which of the following is the decimal equivalent of the binary number 10001?

    a)   18
    b)   17
    c)   16
    d)   15
    e)   14

You should know that the answer has to be an odd number since the binary number ends in the digit 1. Therefore, you can automatically eliminate the three even choices (A, C, and E), leaving you only two choices from which to choose. The correct answer is choice B since:

◊ **Example:** 10001_2 (binary)

2^4	2^3	2^2	2^1	2^0
1	0	0	0	1

$$
\begin{aligned}
&= \quad 1\,(2)^4 \quad + \quad 0\,(2)^3 \quad + \quad 0\,(2)^2 \quad + \quad 1\,(2)^1 \quad + \quad 1\,(2)^0 \\
&= \quad 1\,(16) \quad + \quad 0\,(8) \quad + \quad 0\,(4) \quad + \quad 1\,(2) \quad + \quad 1\,(1) \\
&= \quad 16 \quad + \quad 0 \quad + \quad 0 \quad + \quad 0 \quad + \quad 1
\end{aligned}
$$

$$\boxed{\text{so} \quad 10001_2 = 17_{10}}$$

19.4 Converting from Decimal to Binary

To convert from decimal to binary, you must successively remove the highest powers of 2 contained within the number you are converting. As an example, in the number 19, the highest power of 2 is the fourth power, or 16. This results in a 1 in the 16's column (2^4), with a three left over. The highest power in the remaining value of three is the first power, putting a 1 in the (2^1) column, and leaving a remainder of 1. The highest power of 2 in the remaining 1 is the zero power, putting a 1 in the (2^0) column. This process is shown graphically below.

◊ **Example:**   Write the number 19 in binary

$$
\begin{aligned}
19 = 16 + 2 + 1 \;=\; & \;1(2)^4 \;+\; 0(2)^3 \;+\; 0(2)^2 \;+\; 1(2)^1 \;+\; 1(2)^0 \\
= & \quad 1 \qquad 0 \qquad 0 \qquad 1 \qquad 1
\end{aligned}
$$

$$19_{10} = 10011_2$$

Note for the exam. It is much more common to have you convert a number from binary form to decimal form than from decimal form to binary form. I have included converting in the reverse direction only for completeness sake. Make certain to know the voltage representation of binary numbers: 0 Volts for 0 and +5 Volts for a 1.

19.6 Exercises: Binary   Answers Pg. 435-436

1. $101_2 =$ (Convert to base 10)

2. $(2_{10})^4 =$ (Convert to binary)

3. $8 =$ (Convert to binary)

4. $33 =$ (Convert to binary)

5. $10111_2 =$ (Convert to base 10)

6.   If 5 Volts represents a 1 and 0 Volts represents a 0, the memory cell:
      5V   5V   0V   0V   5V   0V   0V   5V

      a) would represent what number in binary?

      b) Convert your answer to decimal.

7.   How can you tell that the number 1021 is not in binary?

8.   Fill in the blanks
      0000   0001   1
      0000   0010   __
      0000   0011   __
      ____   ____   4
      0000   0101   5
      0000   0110   __
      0000   0111   7
      ____   ____   __
      0000   1001   __

20. Analog to Digital (A/D) Conversion

Most physical signals and movements in the world are analog. Analog signals are continuous in time and can exist in an infinite number of states. All biological signals are analog. If you monitor blood flow, EKGs, pressure waveforms, and back scattered energy in ultrasound, all of these signals will be analog. The following two figures demonstrate two different analog signals. The first graph represents a low frequency content signal, since it varies slowly with time. The second graph represents higher frequency signal content since the signal changes relatively quickly with respect to time.

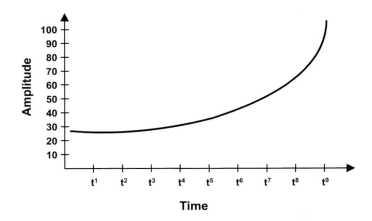

Fig. 19   **Slowly Varying Analog Signal**

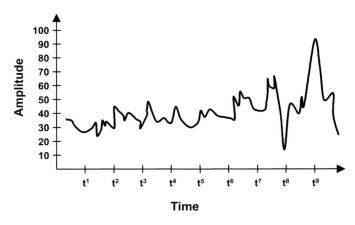

Fig. 20   **Quickly Varying Analog Signal**

For many reasons, continuous (analog) signals are difficult to process and store. Most biological signals and communication signals require significant processing, usually involving many steps. A special circuit must be designed to perform each of these processing steps when the signal is processed in the analog domain. If instead, these signals could be converted into discrete values represented as a time series of numbers (digital signals), then a single math processing circuit could be used to perform most of the processing steps. Thus there is a motivation to creating a specialized electronic circuit whose job it is to convert signals from continuous to discrete time values.

In order to convert the signals, an electronic circuit called an analog to digital converter (A/D) is used. In essence, an A/D converter takes periodic samples of the continuous analog signal and outputs numbers that are proportional to the signal at the moment of "sampling." The A/D converter uses a clock signal to tell it when to sample the signal. Every time the clock "ticks", the analog signal is sampled, and the digital number is stored as a binary number.

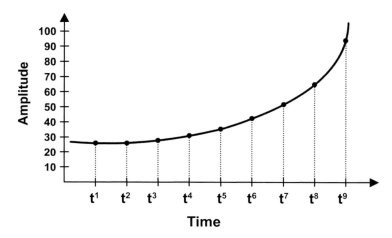

Fig. 21   **Graphical Representation of Sampling**

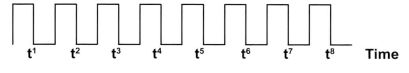

Fig. 22   **The Sampling Clock**

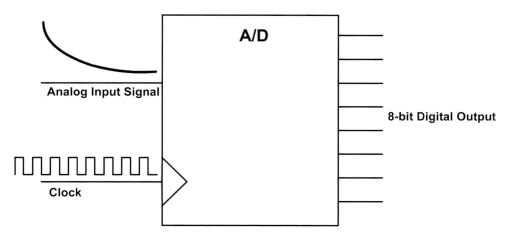

Fig. 23   **8-bit A/D Converter**

The digital signal is therefore just a list of binary numbers at discrete time intervals.

Note: In this example, the reconstructed signal looks relatively similar to the original analog signal. This faithful representation of the signal after conversion does not always hold. We will now consider a case in which the reconstructed signal will not faithfully represent the original analog signal.

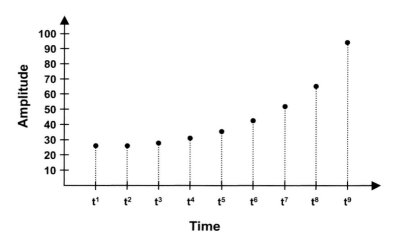

Fig. 24   **Graphical Representation of a Digital Signal**

Ultimately, once the signal has been detected, converted, and processed, it will need to be displayed. Even if the data sent to the display is in the digital format, a reconversion from digital to analog takes place such that the data displayed is analog. If all goes well, the "reconstructed signal" has retained the important information of the original analog signal.

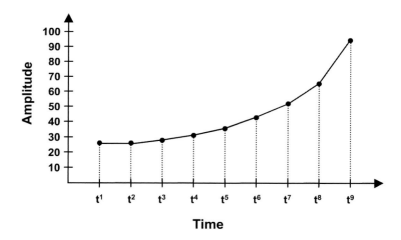

Fig. 25   **Reconstructed Signal**

Now let's repeat the sampling and reconstruction process on the "quickly varying analog signal" as was just done on the "slowly varying analog signal".

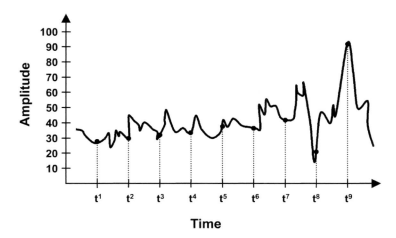

Fig. 26   **Sampling of a Quickly Varying Analog Signal**

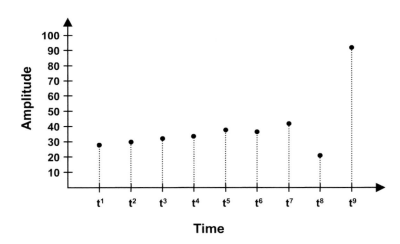

Fig. 27   **Graphical Representation of the Digital Signal**

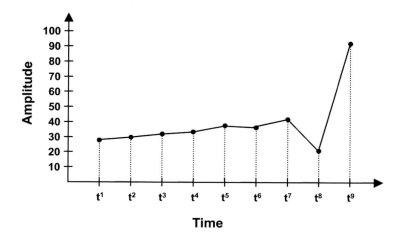

Fig. 28   **Reconstructed Signal**

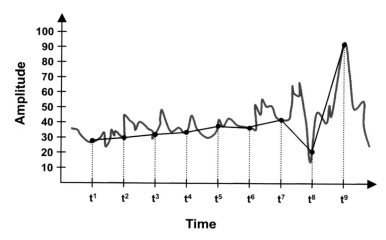

Fig. 29   **Reconstructed Versus Original Signal**

In this case notice how poorly this "reconstructed" signal reflects the variations of the original signal. Although the general shape is correct, there certainly are many quick changes within the original signal which are missing in the reconstructed signal. Clearly, in the process of sampling and reconstructing, much information has been lost. You should now consider why sampling at the same rate worked quite well for a more slowly varying signal (a signal with lower frequency content) than for a more quickly varying signal (a signal with higher frequency content).

In order to preserve the higher frequency energy within the quickly varying signal, the sampling rate must be increased. In essence, the faster a signal varies (the higher the frequency the signal), the faster the sampling rate must be to preserve the information within the signal. How fast the sampling must be to make an accurate reconstruction is called the Nyquist criterion (discussed in the next section).

All signals coming from the body are analog and must be received as analog signals. Therefore, the very first stage of all ultrasound systems must be analog. The reason for converting analog signals into digital signals in ultrasound, and most other electronic systems, is to make it easier to process the signals for measurements and display. For ultrasound, digitizing the signals makes it easier to perform scan conversion, analysis and measurement, post processing, and data storage.

21. Nyquist Criteria

As just discussed, when a signal changes faster (contains high frequency content), the sampling per time must be faster for an accurate reconstruction of the signal. Under-sampling a signal (sampling too slowly) results in a poor reconstruction which loses too much of the original information. For an accurate reconstruction, the minimum rate at which you must sample is called the Nyquist criterion. The Nyquist criterion states that the sampling frequency must be at least twice the highest frequency in the signal.

$$Nyquist: f(max) = \frac{f_{sampling}}{2}$$

One way of demonstrating the Nyquist criterion is to sample a sine wave and then to do a reconstruction. If the frequency of the reconstructed signal is not the same as the initial analog signal, Nyquist has been violated.

Example:

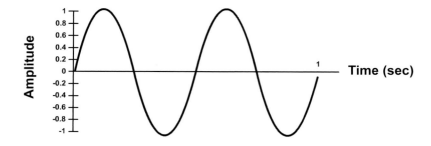

$$f_{signal} = 2 \text{ Hz}$$

Fig. 30   **Analog Signal**

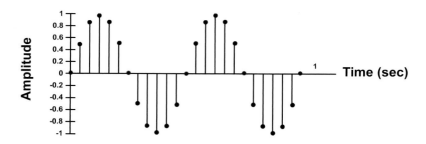

$$f_{sampling} = 25 \text{ Hz} \ (25 \text{ samples/sec})$$

Fig. 31   **Sampled Signal**

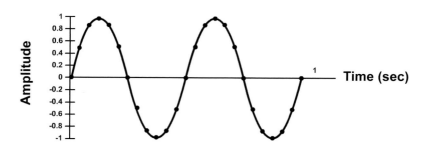

$$f_{reconstructed} = 2 \text{ Hz}$$

Fig. 32   **Reconstructed Signal**

In this example, the sampling rate satisfies the Nyquist criterion, since the sample rate of 25 Hz is faster than twice the signal frequency (2 x 2 Hz = 4 Hz). As a result, the reconstructed signal has the correct (same) frequency as the original signal.

◊   *Example:*

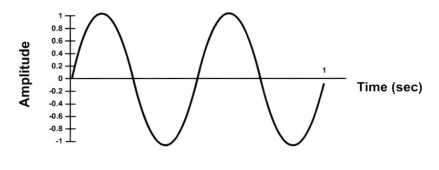

$$f_{signal} = 2 \text{ Hz}$$

Fig. 33   **Analog Signal**

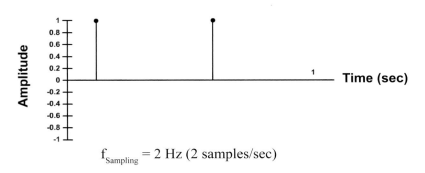

$$f_{Sampling} = 2 \text{ Hz (2 samples/sec)}$$

Fig. 34   **Sampled Signal**

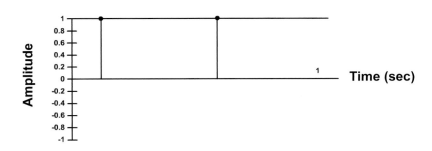

$$f_{reconstructed} = 0 \text{ Hz}$$

Fig. 35   **Reconstructed (Aliased) Signal**

Clearly, this example demonstrates a violation of the Nyquist criterion, because the sampling rate of 2 Hz is not at least twice 2 Hz, or equivalently 4Hz. The result was a reconstructed signal with the wrong frequency.

◊   *Example:*

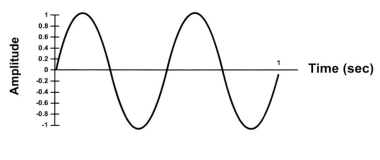

$$f_{signal} = 2 \text{ Hz}$$

Fig. 36   **Analog Signal**

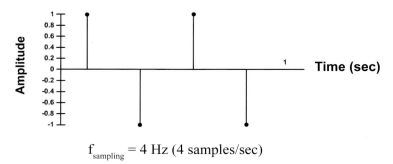

$$f_{sampling} = 4 \text{ Hz (4 samples/sec)}$$

Fig. 37   **Sampled Signal**

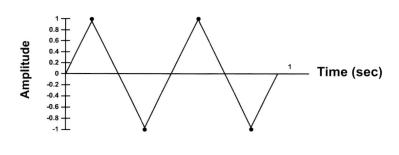

$$f_{reconstructed} = 2 \text{ Hz}$$

Fig. 38   **Reconstructed Signal**

In this example, the Nyquist criterion was satisfied.

View Animation and Image Library CD

◊ **Example:**   Watch what happens if you sample at the wrong frequency:

$$f_{signal} = 9 \text{ Hz}$$
$$f_{sampling} = 8 \text{ Hz}$$
$$f_{reconstructed} = 1 \text{ Hz}$$

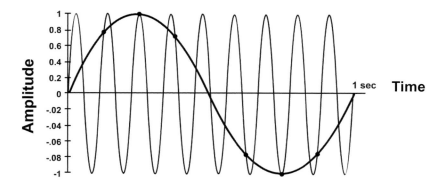

Fig. 39   **Aliasing**

Not only do you inaccurately recreate the original signal, but you create a signal at the wrong frequency. When the Nyquist criterion is violated, an artifact called aliasing occurs. You have most likely seen many examples of aliasing in life including old western movies in which the wagon wheels appear to spin in the wrong direction. In these films, the sample rate is related to the frame rate of the film. So when the frame rate of the film is not twice as fast as the frequency of the wheel, aliasing occurs, giving the appearance of the wheels varying speeds and even reversing.

For ultrasound, the concept of aliasing is important in order to understand temporal artifacts (ability to distinguish changes in time) in imaging and in order to understand limits in velocity detection in spectral and color Doppler. Temporal artifacts in imaging occur when the frame rate is not high enough with respect to changes that are occurring within the body. Doppler artifacts occur when the Doppler sampling rate is not fast enough with respect to the frequency shift which results from moving structures such as red blood cells. A further discussion of Nyquist as it relates to Doppler modalities and artifacts is in Chapter 7.

If there is one thing that aliasing should teach us it is that you can't necessarily trust everything you perceive with your senses. This fact is very important because quite frequently, the limiting factor in ultrasound is not the ultrasound equipment or the physics of sound interacting with the body, but rather the limitations of the human senses to perceive reality.

View Animation and Image Library CD

22. Addition of Waves

The final topic in this section relates to wave addition. As with most of the topics discussed within this math chapter, the full import of what is being taught will only be realized with progression through the book.

With respect to ultrasound, understanding wave addition is fundamental to understanding the operation of phased array transducers. Wave addition is needed to grasp the concept of how ultrasound beams are steered and focused electronically. You might at this point think that this information is not that critical since you most likely don't have plans to design an ultrasound system or an ultrasound transducer anytime soon. However, understanding wave addition is critical for a very different reason than you would most likely guess.

The ability to determine flow direction in spectral and color Doppler is contingent upon understanding how different image formats are produced by different transducer types. If you do not understand how an image is produced, you will never truly be able to determine the direction of blood flow. In addition, there are some artifacts associated with the inability to make waves add up "perfectly" to create an ideal beam. You will learn that this limitation results in a very real artifact called grating lobes. Again, the ability to understand this artifact is directly related to understanding how multiple waves add together from phased array transducers. These concepts will also be employed in advanced imaging techniques such as pulse inversion harmonics, compound imaging and color persistence.

22.1 Constructive Interference (In Phase Waves)
For now, we will content ourselves with just learning the basic principles of wave addition. Let us assume you directed two waves in the exact same direction, with exactly the same frequency and the same amplitude. You would naturally expect the resulting wave to be twice as big.

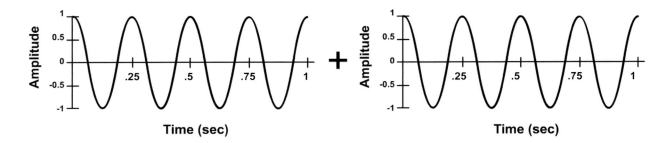

Fig. 40   **Two Waves Identical in Amplitude, Frequency, and Phase**

Note that these two signals are called "in phase" because both waves reach peaks and cross the zero line at the exact same time. In other words, if the peaks and zero-crossing always align, there is no phase difference between the waves, and the waves are called "in phase."

Adding two signals which are in phase results in "constructive interference." As the name suggests, constructive interference occurs when two waves interact so as to produce one larger wave. In this example, *Figure 40*, the two waves used are identical in frequency, amplitude, and phase. Since each wave has the same amplitude, the resulting wave has twice the amplitude of either wave individually. This effect of pure constructive interference is demonstrated in the following figure, *Figure 41*.

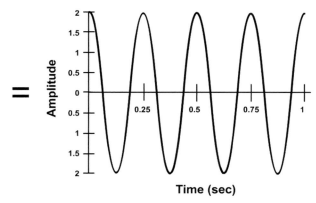

Fig. 41   **Constructive Interference From Two In Phase Waves**

22.2 Destructive Interference (Out of Phase Waves)

Now compare what would happen if you took the exact same two waves except shifted one of the waves in time so that the positive peaks of one wave aligned with the negative peaks of the other wave, as depicted in *Figure 42*.

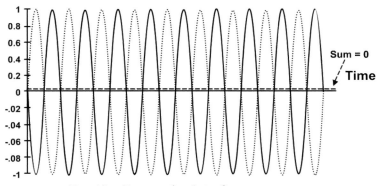

Fig. 42   **Destructive Interference**

When two waves are aligned such that the peak of one wave aligns with the minimum of the other wave, the waves have a phase difference of 180° and are said to be completely "out of phase."

Notice that the two completely out of phase waves interact and cancel each other out. When two waves are purely out of phase, the result is not surprisingly termed destructive interference. In this case, since the amplitudes were identical, the net result is a complete cancellation.

22.3 Partial Constructive (or Partially Destructive) Interference

We have just demonstrated the case in which two waves are perfectly aligned in time (perfectly in phase) and when two waves are perfectly out of phase. In the first case, pure constructive interference occurred whereas in the second case, pure destructive interference occurred. Consider the much more commonly occurring case where the waves are out of phase with respect to each other, but not perfectly out of phase (less than 180 degrees). Common sense tells you that we should expect an effect somewhere between constructive and destructive interference. The next example demonstrates what happens if you take the exact same two waves as in the previous examples, except shift one wave in time so that the positive peaks are neither completely aligned nor anti-aligned to the positive peaks of the second wave.

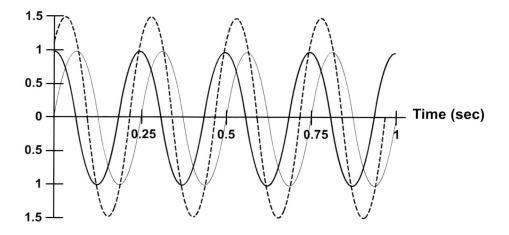

Fig. 43　**Partially Constructive Interference**

In this case, the two waves add only partially constructively, such that the new wave is not as "big" as when the two waves were in phase, and not as small as when the two waves were completely out of phase. This type of interference can also be called "partial destructive interference." Which term is used is inconsequential, but may reflect whether you are a pessimist or an optimist.

In this example, the two waves were created to be out of phase by 90 degrees (in fact they should look familiar to you as the sine and the cosine). Of course it is possible for the two waves to be out of phase by a phase shift such as 37 degrees or 98 degrees etc. As the phase shift gets smaller, approaching 0 degrees (or in phase), the interference becomes more and more constructive. Similarly, as the phase shift gets larger and larger (approaching 180 degrees) the interference becomes more and more destructive.

The examples given here demonstrate the concept of partially constructing interference using two waves. Of course this concept can be extrapolated to include many waves simultaneously. Pure constructive interference would occur when all of the waves were perfectly in phase. Pure destructive interference would occur when all of the waves were completely out of phase. In the ultrasound world, the much more likely scenario is not pure constructive or pure destructive interference, but rather a whole range of varying phase delays between the many waves resulting in partial constructive interference.

KEY CONCEPTS
Mathematics

- Most of the mathematics you will need for the exam involves relative expressions, not absolute calculations.

- You must be familiar with the concept of relationships between variables (proportionality and inverse proportionality).

- Understanding the difference between linear and non-linear relationships is critical.

   o   Linear relationships express the fact that two related variables change at the same rate.

   o   Non-linear relationships express the fact that small changes in one variable result in larger changes in the related variable.

- Understanding math terminology is another area which greatly affects scoring. You must be able to translate terms such as increase, decrease, factor, etc. into mathematical expressions.

- The property of reciprocals is used repeatedly throughout ultrasound physics.

- Knowing the metric table (and the reciprocal relationships within the table) greatly simplifies many calculations.

- The distance equation expresses a linear relationship between time and distance.

$$d = r \times t$$

- If you presume a propagation velocity of 1540 m/sec, it takes 6.5 microseconds for sound to travel 1 cm. To image 1 centimeter requires that the sound travel 2 cm (roundtrip effect) thereby requiring 13 microseconds.

$$ID\,(imaging\ depth) = 1\,cm \Rightarrow travel = 2\,cm \Rightarrow 13\,\mu sec$$

- You should remember the 13 microsecond per cm of imaging depth calculation. Because of the linear relationship, you can easily calculate the imaging time for any other depth by scaling. For example: to image 5 cm requires $5 \times 13\,\mu sec = 65\,\mu sec$.

- Logarithms provide a powerful tool to compress data non-linearly.

- You should know the log of any power of 10 and the log of 2. The log of any power of 10 is simply the power (exponent).

$$log\,(2) = 0.3$$

- You should know how to calculate the sine and the cosine of the basic angles including ($0°$, $30°$, $45°$, $60°$, $90°$, $120°$, $135°$, $150°$, $180°$, $270°$, $360°$).

- The cosine is the projection to the x-axis and hence, is positive in quadrants 1 and 4 and negative in quadrants 2 and 3.

- The sine is the projection to the y-axis and hence, is positive in quadrants 1 and 2 and negative in quadrants 3 and 4.

- The sine and the cosine are separated by a 90 degree phase shift.

- Any variable which is dependent on the sine or the cosine of an angle behaves non-linearly since the cosine and the sine are non-linear.

- The Nyquist criterion dictates that the sample rate must be at least twice as fast as a frequency to be detected. Sampling slower than the Nyquist criteria results in aliasing.

$$Nyquist : f(max) = \frac{f\ sampling}{2}$$

- Constructive interference occurs when two or more waves are in phase (0 degree phase shift) such that the maxima and minima of all waves align and add to create one larger wave.

- Destructive interference occurs when two waves are purely out of phase (180 degree phase shift) such that the maxima of one wave aligns with the minima of the other wave, causing a complete cancellation of the wave amplitude.

- Partial constructive interference (for optimists) or partial destructive interference (for pessimists) results when two or more waves are not completely in or out of phase. The result is a wave which is smaller than the sum of the individual amplitudes, but as not a great as the sum of all the individual amplitudes.

Note: See Appendix F: Physical Units and Appendix G: Equations for additional review.

CHAPTER 2

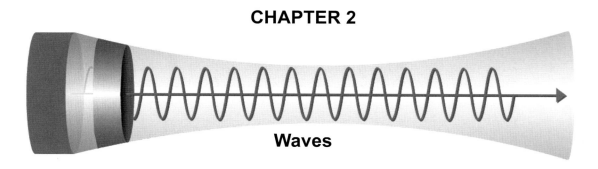

Waves

Introduction

It is unfortunate when students memorize a series of facts and topics with little understanding as to the direct relevance or application in their world. I believe it is always easier to understand a topic when you first understand the motivation for learning the material and the approach taken. As a result, we will learn the material of this chapter using an iterative approach. First we will discuss the reasons this material is important to anyone performing ultrasound related tests. In Level 1 we will discuss waves in general, developing the foundation for Level 2. In Level 2, many of the same topics will be again reviewed, but this time with specific reference to ultrasound, its application, and relation to topics to be discussed in later chapters. In this way, you will be exposed to the topic multiple times, reviewing and building a more solid foundation.

1. The Motivation for Studying Waves

So why do we need to study waves? The simple answer is diagnostic ultrasound is based on how sound waves interact with various structures within the body. Since changing parameters of the sound wave can lead to changes in the diagnostic quality of the clinical study performed, and since changing some of the parameters can also change the potential risk of causing bioeffects (biological changes that potentially cause harm to the patient), it is useful to discuss the various parameters of the ultrasound wave. Specifically, we will need to know what parameters can be changed by you the sonographer, what parameters cannot be changed, and how these parameters relate to the quality of the clinical study and the risk of bioeffects.

Note: Although the risk of bioeffects with ultrasound is very low, the potential does exist. Bioeffects will be discussed formerly in Chapter 9, and also throughout the entire text as related topics are covered.

2. Waves

2.1 Definition of a Wave
A wave is a mechanism which transfers energy from one location to another. If a wave is the result of a sudden impact or impulse of energy, it is generally referred to as a "shock wave." When a wave has a somewhat repetitious source, the wave is referred to as cyclical. Therefore, a wave with a repetitious source can be defined as a cyclical transfer of energy from one location to another location. The use of the term "cyclical" is useful since there is a clear indication that the energy of the wave results in changes that are repetitious. Since the term cycle refers to a single event or

phase, cyclical refers to the cycle repeating multiple times, relatively uniformly. For ultrasound, we will be concerned primarily with cyclical waves.

Since there are many different forms of energy that can be transported, there are many different types of waves. For the purpose of ultrasound, we are primarily concerned with acoustic (sound) energy. Therefore, we can greatly reduce the range of wave topics which need to be covered in depth to include only those topics most directly related to sound waves as applied to diagnostic ultrasound.

2.2 Examples of Waves

We will not need to go into depth about wave types other than sound waves. However, so as to get across basic principles of all waves, it is instructive to consider other types of waves beside sound waves. Think about what all of these different types of waves have in common:

- water in the ocean
- sound
- television signals
- light
- oscillation of a guitar string
- a bunch of people doing the "wave" at Fenway Park

All of these waves clearly transport energy from one location to another. Also, interpreting the characteristics of these waves will yield information about the source. For example, is the wave strong or weak, does it vary quickly, can it travel a long distance, can it penetrate through an object in its path, what effect does it have on the medium (material) which surrounds it?

3. Classification of Waves

3.1 Benefit to Classifications

Classification schemes are useful as a technique to subdivide large groups into smaller groups. The benefit of subdividing according to similar characteristics is a simplification in the amount of information that must be retained. In other words, if everyone of a certain group has the same characteristics, then there is no need to memorize the specific characteristics associated with each individual.

For example, colleges subdivide students according to the year of graduation and then subdivide each year into specific majors. By dividing the entire student body into years of graduation, the classification of freshman, sophomore, junior, or senior alone tells how much more time there is until the individual student will graduate. By further dividing the class into majors, the specific curriculum is somewhat defined, limiting the number of elective classes an individual student can take.

For waves, one useful classification is based on how the wave propagates (travels). The first classification distinction we will discuss is the concept of an electromagnetic wave versus a mechanical wave.

Pegasus Lectures, Inc.

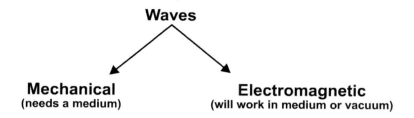

Fig. 1 **Classification of Waves**

3.2 Electromagnetic (EM) Waves

An electromagnetic wave is a transfer of energy through a varying electrical and magnetic field. Some examples of EM waves are:

- light
- heat
- X-rays
- gamma rays
- television signals

The mathematics that define and describe electromagnetic wave theory and propagation are very complex and are generally refined to as higher order mathematics. Fortunately, sound is not an electromagnetic wave, so you will not be required to know much more than the absolute basics about electromagnetic waves.

One of the defining characteristics of an electromagnetic wave is that it can travel both through a medium (a material such as air, water, tissue, metal, etc.) as well as through a vacuum (the absence of a medium such as space). You are not required to know much more about electromagnetic waves than this one defining characteristic. However, you should be very appreciative of the importance of this one characteristic. If electromagnetic waves could not travel through a vacuum like space, sunlight would not reach the earth and you would not exist to read this textbook which, without an author, would also not exist.

3.3 Mechanical Waves

As the name suggests, a mechanical wave requires a physical interaction. The term mechanical refers to the fact that there is a physical interaction between the wave and the medium through which the wave propagates. In other words, mechanical waves must have a medium, or the wave cannot exist. From the first list of waves, described in Section 2.2, ocean waves, sound, the vibration of a guitar string, and people at a ball park are all examples of mechanical waves.

The term mechanical as a classification is very useful since the word itself invokes some relationships critical for ultrasound. For example, the fact that the wave is mechanical indicates that the wave will interact with the tissue of the patient (the medium), and that the tissue of the patient will interact with the wave. As a result, we should expect potential changes in the patient as the wave propagates. Furthermore, we should also anticipate changes to the characteristics of the wave with propagation through the patient. In fact, each of these "interactions" are so important, that each will spawn an entire chapter: one chapter entitled bioeffects, and the other chapter entitled attenuation.

4. Conceptual Questions   Answers Pg. 437

1.   Electromagnetic waves
       a) do not transfer energy.
       b) cannot propagate through a medium.
       c) include sound waves.
       d) none of the above.

2.   Mechanical waves must have a _____ to propagate.

3.   Sound is a _____ wave.

4.   All waves transport _____.

5.   A mechanical wave implies an interaction between the wave and the _____.

5. Propagation of Mechanical Waves

As indicated in the diagram below, there are two distinct mechanisms by which a mechanical wave can propagate: in transverse mode or longitudinal mode. The word propagate implies that the wave "travels" from one location to another. However, the word travel does not adequately describe the concept of wave (energy) propagation. Wave propagation really implies that there is a change in the location of energy concentration per time. When the wave is being created, the highest energy associated with the wave is close to the source. With time, the energy interacts with the neighboring molecules of the medium, imparting momentum. With momentum, the higher energy molecules then interact with their neighboring molecules, imparting some of the energy, hence giving up some of their energy. In this manner, the wave "propagates" or "travels" away from the source.

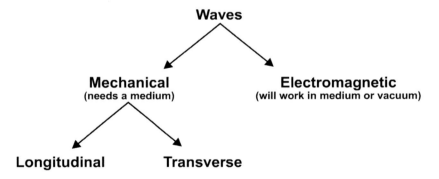

Fig. 2   **Further Classifying Waves**

5.1 Transverse Waves
As the prefix "trans" suggests, a transverse wave is a wave whose particles move "across" or perpendicular to the wave propagation direction. The term movement may be more accurately described as an oscillation, since the particles actually vibrate back and forth about the center position, as the wave propagates along its path. The following diagram illustrates how the particles of a transverse wave "oscillate" with the wave propagation.

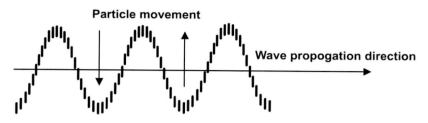

Fig. 3   **Transverse Waves**

In *Figure 3*, the wave is traveling from left to right (left side of the page toward the right side of the page), while the particles of the medium are oscillating back and forth about the mean or center position. For this drawing, each short line segment represents a particle of the medium, and the distance away from the center line of the image represents the distance the particles traveled.

As you are about to learn, sound is **NOT** a transverse wave.

Note: You may have already noticed a theme developing. Quite frequently, the terminology used in physics is very descriptive of the associated physical parameter. In other words, if you pay close attention to the meaning of the root words and prefixes, it becomes significantly easier to recall the definition of each term.

5.2 Longitudinal Waves

5.2.1 Definition and Depiction
For a longitudinal wave the particle motion is "along" the direction of the wave propagation.

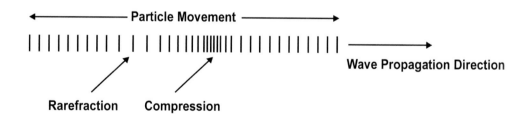

Fig. 4   **Longitudinal Waves**

In *Figure 4*, the short line segments again represent particles or molecules of the medium. When these line segments are drawn close together, it represents a high particle density. Conversely, when the line segments are far apart, it represents a lower particle density.

Sound is a longitudinal wave, which implies that sound travels through compresions and rarefactions of the medium. The following diagram shows the classification of sound within the broad category of waves.

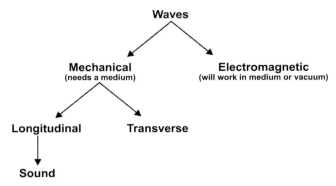

Fig. 5   **Sound is a Longitudinal, Mechanical Wave**

5.2.2 Developing a More Thorough Understanding of Longitudinal Waves

The description of a longitudinal wave is usually "a series of compressions and rarefactions which cause particles within the medium to vibrate back and forth, along, or in the same direction as the wave propagation direction." Instead of starting from this definition of sound as a longitudinal wave, we will take a more intuitive step-by-step approach to understanding the physical interactions which give rise to this definition and this terminology. More importantly, this intuitive approach should yield a much more thorough understanding of how sound interacts with the medium.

Recall that all waves transfer energy. For a longitudinal wave, the source of the wave imparts energy to the particles (molecules) of the medium in contact with the source. When this energy is imparted to the nearest particles, these particles begin to move. However, since these particles have neighbors in the direction which the wave was imparted, the higher energy particles encroach on the space of the lower energy neighbors. This collision results in two responses. First, some of the energy of the higher energy molecules is now transferred to the neighboring lower energy particles. Second, from the collision, the higher energy molecules reflect back towards the wave source. This process of colliding and imparting energy with neighbors, continues until all of the energy of the wave is eventually dissipated.

Now consider the moment when the higher energy molecules traveled and collided with their neighbors. During that collision period, in that neighborhood, there was a higher concentration of molecules than normal, referred to as a state of compression. After the collision occurred and the compressed molecules traveled away from each other, there was a decrease in molecular density relative to normal, referred to as rarefaction. Since this process continues repeatedly, we now have the definition of a longitudinal wave as a series of compressions and rarefactions. Since the particle motion is in the direction of the wave propagation, we now have the second part of the definition, "along", or in the same direction as the wave propagation.

5.3 Problems with Static Drawings of Waves

There are two major difficulties with static drawings of waves:

1)   Motion must be inferred by the person interpreting the picture.

Understanding the motion of a wave with respect to time is critical. On a static picture, distance and time appear along the same dimension of the graph (along the horizontal axis). As a result, it is easy to confuse the concept of distance measures for a wave with time measures for a wave. To rectify this problem, it is usually instructive to show physical waves in a dynamic state.

2)   Drawing a longitudinal wave is challenging and time consuming.

Although a sound wave propagates longitudinally, virtually every picture depicting a sound wave uses a transverse diagram. This depiction is particularly confusing when such painstaking efforts are made to point out differences between longitudinal and transverse wave propagation, the differences between transverse and longitudinal waves, and the definitive statement that sound is a longitudinal, not a transverse wave.

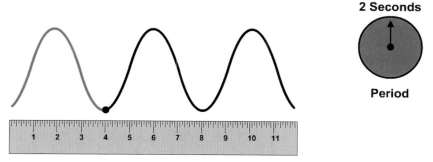

Fig. 6   **Case 1: Period = 2 seconds, Wavelength = 4 inches**

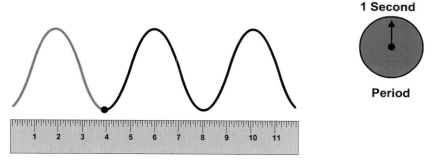

Fig. 7   **Case 2: Period = 1 second, Wavelength = 4 inches**

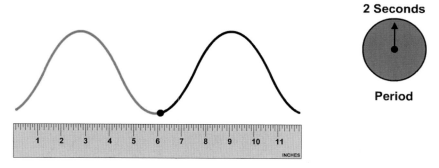

Fig. 8   **Case 3: Period = 2 seconds, Wavelength = 6 inches**

The general reason for drawing a sound wave using a transverse depiction is quite simple: transverse waves are easy to draw and longitudinal waves are not. Therefore, with only a few exceptions from this point on, sound waves, although longitudinal in nature, will be depicted using transverse drawings.

To fully appreciate a static drawing of a wave, you must pay close attention to the parameters being displayed. Between *Figure 6* and *Figure 7*, both waves travel the same distance but in different time periods. In contrast, *Figure 6* and *Figure 8* display waves that travel different distances in the same time period. An animation is included to help clarify the differences between time and distance.

 **View Animation and Image Library CD**

6. Variations in the Medium with Propagation (Acoustic Variables)

The fact that sound is a mechanical wave indicates a physical interaction with the medium. Therefore, it should not be surprising that the cyclical interaction of the wave with the medium can cause cyclical changes to certain parameters in the medium itself. In fact, careful reading of the description of how a longitudinal wave propagates indicates how some of these interactions occur, and even what these changes might be. The changes that occur to the medium are referred to as acoustic variables. Since the word variable refers to a changing quantity, and acoustic refers to sound, this nomenclature should be relatively easy to remember.

As displayed in the diagram, there are four quantities that vary with the propagation of sound. Specifically, these four variables are pressure, density, temperature, and particle motion.

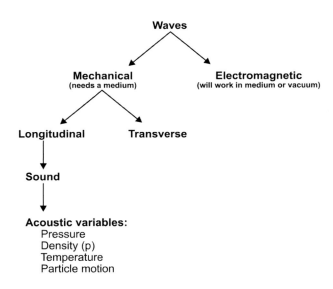

Fig. 9 **The Acoustic Variables**

6.1 Pressure
Pressure is defined as a concentration of force, or force per area. In the compression phase of the sound wave, the pressure increases. During the rarefaction phase of the pressure wave the pressure decreases. Clearly, the pressure varies cyclically as the wave propagates through the medium.

There are many different units commonly used to measure pressure. Some of the most common units are:

- Atmosphere (atm)
- Millimeters of mercury (mmHg)
- Pascals
- kg/m^2, (metric system)
- lbs/in^2 (English system)
- Dynes/cm^2

6.2 Density

6.2.1 The Equation for Density
The concept of density is quite familiar to most people. There are two parameters that combine to form the concept of density, specifically, the mass and the volume. Let's consider the following comparative situations:

Situation 1:
If there are two blocks of material identical in volume, but block A weighs more than block B, then block A has a higher density than block B.

This fact implies that the *density* $(\rho) \propto mass$.

Situation 2:
If there are two blocks of material identical in mass, but block A is much larger than block B, then block B has a higher density than block A.

This fact implies that the *density* $(\rho) \propto \dfrac{1}{volume}$.

Combining these two relationships together yields the equation:

$$density\ (\rho) = \frac{mass}{volume} \left(\frac{kg}{m^3} \right).$$

6.2.2 Density as an Acoustic Variable
From our description of how a longitudinal wave propagates, we know that there are periods of higher particle concentrations (higher density) and lower particle concentrations (lower density). Therefore, as the wave propagates through the medium, there are cyclical variations in the density of the medium. During compression, the density is increased, whereas during rarefaction, the density is decreased. Although the change in density may not be that great, as you will learn in later sections, this change in density can have dramatic effects, and will lead to a non-linear imaging technique called harmonic imaging.

6.3 Temperature

6.3.1 Generation of Heat
Not surprisingly, any mechanical system produces heat. As the wave vibrates the particles in the medium, some of wave energy is lost to heat within the medium. Locally, as the particles go from higher to lower concentrations the temperature will also fluctuate cyclically.

6.3.2 Measuring Temperature

There are three relatively well known temperature scales: Kelvin, Celsius, and Fahrenheit. Degrees Kelvin is the scale of choice for many physics applications including cryogenics and superconductors. Fortunately, this safely eliminates the need for further description in a physics book intended for application of ultrasound. The two remaining scales are both based on the freezing and boiling point of water molecules under standard conditions.

The conversion from Celsius to Fahrenheit can be easily derived by comparing the two known state transition points as follows:

	Celsius	Fahrenheit
Freezing	0 degrees	32 degrees
Boiling	100 degrees	212 degrees

Table 1: **Boiling and Freezing Points for Water**

In the Celsius scale, there is a difference of 100 degrees from freezing to boiling. For the Fahrenheit scale, the same transition occurs over a difference of 180 degrees. Therefore, a ratio is easily determined between Celsius and Fahrenheit:

$$\frac{Fahrenheit}{Celsius} = \frac{180°}{100°} = \frac{18}{10} = \frac{9}{5} \ or \ 1.8$$

Now we must also take into account the fact that the Fahrenheit scale references freezing to 32 degrees whereas the Celsius scale references freezing to 0 degrees. Therefore, the conversion can be written as:

$$Temperature \ in \ Fahrenheit = 1.8*(temperature \ in \ Celsius) + 32°$$

6.4 Particle Motion

Again referring to our description of wave propagation, we discussed particles of the medium being imparted with momentum and traveling into the locale of the nearest neighbors. In essence, the particles move (or more precisely, oscillate) back and forth about their original location, allowing the concentration of energy to propagate along the wave path. It is very important to note that the particles vibrate in their position and do not actually "travel" with the wave. The wave may travel a great distance, but ultimately, the particles should ultimately exist at or very close to their original starting location, depending on the elastic properties of the medium.

7. Conceptual Questions   Answers Pg. 437-438

1.   If a wave needs a medium to propagate it is a _____ wave.

2.   If a wave does not need a medium to propagate it is a(n) _____ wave.

3.   Which of the following is not an example of an electromagnetic wave? (more than one might apply)

a) x-rays
b) light
c) sound
d) heat
e) television signals

4.   All waves are a(n) _____ transfer most often through cyclical variations.

a) particle
b) energy
c) voltage
d) temperature

5.   The naming of waves as mechanical is due to the physical interaction between the wave and the medium. The interaction produces four specific possible changes called _____ variables:

1) _____
2) _____
3) _____
4) _____

6.   All of the following are acceptable units of pressure except

a) Pa (Pascals)
b) lb/in^2
c) kg/m^2
d) lb/ft
e) atm (atmospheres)
f) mmHg (millimeters of mercury)

7.   Density is defined as

a) mass/volume: kg/m^3
b) mass/volume: kg/m^2
c) volume/mass: m^3/kg
d) mass · volume: m^{3}kg

8.   The freezing point of water is at 0° Celsius, what is the freezing point in Fahrenheit?

9.   The boiling of water is 212° F, what is the boiling point in Celsius?

10.   Sound is a _____ , _____ wave.

a) longitudinal, electromagnetic
b) longitudinal, mechanical
c) transverse, electromagnetic
d) transverse, mechanical

11.   For a longitudinal wave, the energy is transported by a series of _____ and _____ of the medium particles.

   a) compression, heating
   b) rarefactions, reflections
   c) reflections refractions
   d) compressions, rarefactions

8. Wave Characteristics and Parameters

8.1 General
There are many parameters of a wave which can be used to specify the wave characteristics. As we will learn in Level 2 and in later chapters, understanding these parameters is important since changing any of these ultimately may change the quality of a clinical ultrasound study, or potentially change the risks to the patient associated with bioeffects. For now, it is enough to learn the parameters and their physical meanings.

8.2 Four Basic Parameters and the Many Associated Parameters
There are four basic wave parameters which we will need to either be able to calculate or measure:

Basic four parameters:

Frequency/Period	$\Rightarrow$	Determined by the wave source
Wavelength	$\Rightarrow$	Determined by both the wave source and properties of the medium
Propagation Velocity	$\Rightarrow$	Determined by the properties of the medium
Amplitude	$\Rightarrow$	Determined by the wave source initially, changes as wave propagates

Note: You should have noticed that the frequency and the period are grouped together as one parameter. The reason is that time and frequency are reciprocals. Therefore, the frequency and the period specify the same information, just in reciprocal form. This fact was first introduced to you in Chapter 1.

Related to these four parameters is a group of related parameters, as listed below. It is imperative to develop a thorough understanding of the four basic parameters since they serve as the foundation for understanding the entire list of associated parameters.

Related parameters:
- power
- attenuation and attenuation rate
- reflection
- penetration
- speed of sound
- intensity (and intensity limits)
- absorption
- refraction
- sound vs. ultrasound (definition)
- acoustic impedance

Note: These related parameters will be discussed in Level 2 and/or in later chapters. They are introduced here as a motivation for learning the fundamental parameters.

8.3 Frequency (f) and Period (P)

8.3.1 General

Frequency is a measure of how often an event occurs per time. The unit for frequency is cycles/second, commonly referred to as Hertz, abbreviated as (Hz). You should realize that to be a measure of frequency, there must be a time reference. For example, all of the following are acceptable measures of a frequency:

- once per day
- occurrences per year (# of events implied)
- once per eternity (# of events implied)
- 3 times per minute

However, "17 times" is NOT an acceptable measure of frequency. Frequency is a rate, so without the time reference, 17 times is just a number of occurrences. From the number 17 times, it is unclear if what is implied is 17 times per second, or 17 times per minute, or 17 times per lifetime.

8.3.2 Frequency of a Sound Wave

The frequency of a sound wave refers to the number of compression or rarefaction cycles that occur per time. If there were only one compression cycle in a second, then the frequency of the wave would be 1 Hz. If there are 20,000 compression cycles per second, then the frequency is 20,000 Hz or equivalently, 20 kHz.

8.3.3 Graphical Depiction of Frequency

As we mentioned earlier in this chapter, although sound is a longitudinal wave, it is significantly easier to depict the wave in terms of transverse characteristics. Therefore, although we have accurately described the frequency of a sound wave as the number of compression cycles per second, we will depict a cycle using a transverse drawing as in the following diagram. In order to relate the transverse depiction with the actual characteristics of the sound wave, we will imagine that a peak corresponds to a compression and that the minimum corresponds to rarefaction.

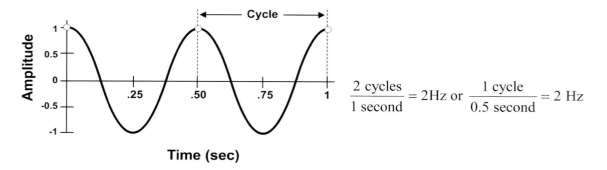

$$\frac{2 \text{ cycles}}{1 \text{ second}} = 2\text{Hz} \quad or \quad \frac{1 \text{ cycle}}{0.5 \text{ second}} = 2 \text{ Hz}$$

Fig. 10   **Transverse Depiction of a 2 Hz Wave**

When there are more compressions per time, the frequency increases, as depicted in *Figure 11*.

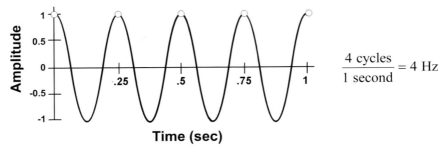

$$\frac{4 \text{ cycles}}{1 \text{ second}} = 4 \text{ Hz}$$

Fig. 11   Transverse Depiction of a 4 Hz Wave

8.3.4 Determining the Frequency

The frequency of a wave is determined by the source of the wave. If the source creates many compressions per second, then the wave will have a high frequency. If the source produces fewer cycles per second, then the wave will have a lower frequency. The medium does not determine the frequency of the wave. For ultrasound, the source is considered to be a combination of the transducer, the ultrasound system, and the user.

◊   **Examples:**   If a 10 MHz wave traverses a tissue-blood boundary, it is still a 10 MHz wave.

A 10 MHz transducer produces a 10 MHz wave in both water and soft tissue.

8.3.5 The Relationship Between Time (Period) and Frequency

The word period refers to time, so the period refers to the time between repeating events, or equivalently, the time per cycle. Notice that this definition is the reciprocal of the definition for frequency. Therefore, if you are given the frequency, no other information is required to calculate a period. Conversely, if you are given the period, no additional information is required to calculate the frequency.

$$Period = \frac{1}{Frequency}.$$

The following examples demonstrate how to convert a frequency to a period, serving as a review of the exercises you performed in Chapter 1. Notice that knowledge of the metric table makes the process significantly simpler.

◊   **Examples:**

Frequency/Period
10 Hz $\Rightarrow 1/(10 \text{ Hz}) = 0.1$ seconds
5 Hz $\Rightarrow 1/(5 \text{ Hz}) = 0.2$ seconds
12 kHz $\Rightarrow 1/(12 \text{ kHz}) = 0.083$ msec
2 MHz $\Rightarrow 1/(2 \text{ MHz}) = 0.5$ μsec $= 500$ nsec

$$\left(units = \frac{1}{Hz} = \frac{1}{\left(\dfrac{1}{seconds}\right)} = \frac{seconds}{1} = seconds \right)$$

This reciprical relationship between time and frequency always holds true. Therefore, whenever you are asked to convert a measurement from a time based measurement to a frequency based measurement (or vice versa) you will simply calculate the reciprocal. As you will notice from the examples below, it does not matter what the modifying term is before the basic measurement of time or frequency, the reciprocal nature never changes.

◊ **Examples:**

$$Payment\ period\ =\ \frac{1}{payment\ frequency}$$

$$Transmit\ period\ =\ \frac{1}{transmit\ frequency}$$

$$Pulse\ repetition\ frequency\ =\ \frac{1}{pulse\ repetiton\ period}$$

$$Work\ frequency\ =\ \frac{1}{work\ period}$$

$$Frame\ time\ =\ \frac{1}{frame\ (rate)\ frequency}$$

8.3.6 Interpreting the Period

For a sound wave, the period represents the time that transpires between the occurrence of one compression and the occurrence of the next compression. The period can be equivalently expressed as the time between the occurrence of one rarefaction until the occurrence of the next rarefaction.

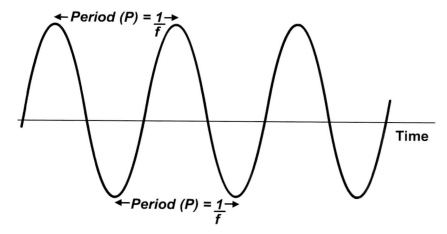

Fig. 12   **Depiction of the Period as the Reciprocal of the Frequency**

Note that the horizontal axis in Figure 12 represents time, not distance. Although an imperfect depiction, as already discussed, it is not possible to demonstrate motion in a static picture.

8.4 Propagation Velocity

8.4.1 Defining Speed and Velocity

The rate at which the wave propagates through the medium is termed the propagation velocity. In general physics, the term velocity is used distinctly from the term "speed." Specifically, speed is a "scalar" quantity, referring only to the rate of travel. In contrast, the velocity is a "vector" quantity, referring to both the speed and a direction of travel. For sound in the body, the assumption is generally made that all sound propagates in a relatively straight path, hence making the distinction between these terms less significant. Therefore, you will hear the propagation velocity also referred to as the propagation speed or the speed of sound in the medium. Whereas the term velocity is more precise, there is little information lost in using the terminology of speed in this case. Therefore, to get you accustomed and comfortable with either terminology, both terms will be randomly intermixed throughout the book.

8.4.2 Units and Graphical Representation

Since the "propagation velocity" is a "velocity" term, the units are distance per time. In the metric system, a velocity is specified as meters/sec, or m/sec. *Figure 13* and *14* graphically demonstrates how a velocity can be measured by comparing physical location with respect to time. If there is a long distance in a short time between the first and second measured locations, the velocity is very high. Conversely if there is a short distance in a long time between the first and second measured locations, the velocity is very low.

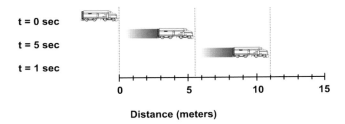

Fig. 13   **The train has traveled 11 meters in 10 seconds, so its velocity is 1.1 m/sec.**

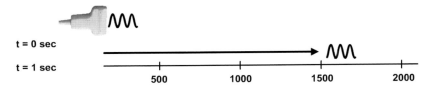

Fig. 14   **Sound has traveled 1500 meters in 1 second, so it has a propagation velocity of 1500 m/sec.**

Note: In both Figure 13 and 14, the horizontal axis represents a measure of distance, not time.

8.4.3 What Determines the Speed of Sound

The propagation velocity is determined by the properties of the medium and is virtually unrelated to the frequency of the wave. Whereas the frequency can have slight effects on the propagation velocity, the effects are so small that we will consider them negligible. In other words, the propagation velocity for a 10 MHz wave and a 2 kHz wave will be virtually the same traveling through the same medium.

Pegasus Lectures, Inc.

Since the speed of sound is dependent on the medium, different mediums have different propagation speeds. In Level 2, the precise properties which affect the propagation speed and a table of propagation speeds will be given. For now, it is important to become accustomed with the variables used, the units, and the physical meaning of each of these parameters.

8.4.4 Graphical Depiction of Propagation Speed for Sound Waves

When many cycles are drawn in a wave, it is quite easy to confuse the frequency of the wave with the concept of propagation velocity. Study the following scenarios carefully to avoid making these mistakes. As you will see, understanding the propagation velocity will simplify other related concepts such as the wavelength, an artifact called speed error, and the Doppler effect.

Scenario 1:

In *Figure 15*, both wave A and wave B start at the same location and travel the same distance in 1 second. Therefore both waves are traveling at the same speed. However, wave A has 3 cycles in one second (3 Hz) whereas wave B has 6 cycles in one second (6 Hz). Therefore these two waves are of different frequencies.

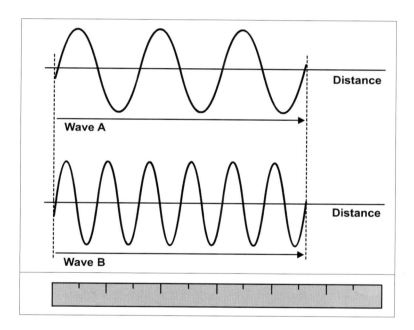

Fig. 15   **Same Propagation Speeds but Different Frequencies**

Scenario 2:

In *Figure 16*, both wave A and wave B have 3 cycles per second (3 Hz) and both waves start at the same location. However, although both waves start at the same location, but wave B travels a shorter distance than wave A, during the same 1 second time period.

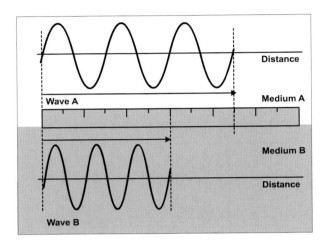

Fig. 16   **Same Frequencies but Different Propagation Speeds**

In this case, both wave A and B are the same frequency. However, since wave B traveled a shorter distance per time than wave A, wave B is in a lower propagation velocity medium than wave A.

 **View Animation and Image Library CD**

8.5 Wavelength

8.5.1 Definition
The letter used to represent the variable of wavelength is the Greek letter lamda (λ). As the name suggests, a wavelength refers to a physical distance. Specifically, the wavelength is the physical distance from one peak compression to the next peak compression. Similarly, the wavelength can be measured as the distance from one rarefaction to the next rarefaction, or, from any point on the cyclical wave to the next point where the cycle repeats. This definition of wavelength is depicted in *Figure 17*.

Pegasus Lectures, Inc.

8.5.2 Graphical Representation

◊ **Example 1:**

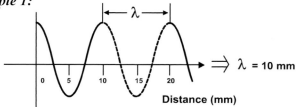

$\Rightarrow$ λ = 10 mm

Fig. 17 **Longer Wavelength**

◊ **Example 2:**

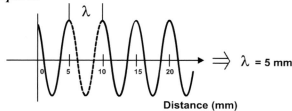

$\Rightarrow$ λ = 5 mm

Fig. 18 **Shorter Wavelength**

8.5.3 Distinguishing the Wavelength from the Period

Again we must stress how important it is for you to pay attention to the labels on the axes of any graph of data. For a still image, the depiction of the period and the depiction of the wavelength appear identical. For static images, the only way of distinguishing between the two very different parameters is to label the data indicating whether the physical unit is time or distance. *Figure 19* demonstrates the difference between the depiction of the period and the depiction of the wavelength. Although Wave A and Wave B look identical, Wave A is a depiction of the period and Wave B is a depiction of the wavelength.

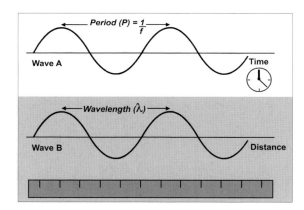

Fig. 19 **Understanding the Difference Between the Period and the Wavelength**

View Animation and Image Library CD

8.5.4 What Determines the Wavelength

The wavelength changes with changes in the frequency of the wave and with changes in the propagation velocity of the wave. In other words, the wavelength depends on characteristics of both the source and the medium. The illustrations of *Figure 20* and *Figure 21* demonstrate how the wavelength varies with change in the frequency of the wave, and with change to the propagation velocity of the wave.

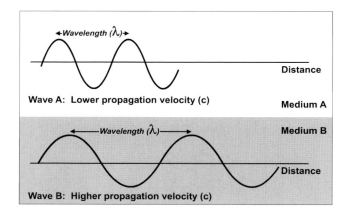

Fig. 20   **Wavelength Dependence on Propagation Velocity**

Scenario 1:

Referring to *Figure 20*, waves A and B are both the same frequency since both waves have 2 cycles per second (2 Hz). However, wave B travels a greater distance than wave A during 1 second, so medium B has a higher propagation velocity than medium A. From *Figure 20*, it is clear that wave B also has a longer wavelength. Therefore, as the propagation velocity increases, the wavelength also increases, or mathematically we can say that the wavelength and the propagation velocity are proportional:

$$\lambda \propto c.$$

View Animation and Image Library CD

Scenario 2:

Referring to *Figure 21*, waves A and B are in the same medium and hence, have the same propagation velocity. However, wave A has three cycles per second, whereas wave B has only two cycles per second. Wave A represents a higher frequency wave than wave B. From *Figure 21*, it is clear that wave B has a longer wavelength. Therefore, as the frequency decreases, the wavelength increases, or mathematically we can say that the wavelength and the frequency are inversely proportional:

$$\lambda \propto \frac{1}{f}.$$

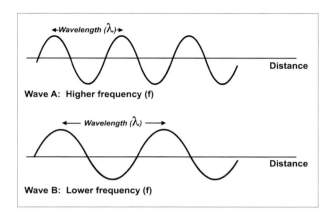

Fig. 21 **Wavelength Dependence on Frequency**

 **View Animation and Image Library CD**

8.5.5 The Wavelength Equation

The two relative expressions just derived can be combined into one equation, or:

$$\lambda = \frac{c}{f}.$$

This equation is referred to, not surprisingly, as the wavelength equation. Because of its importance in diagnostic ultrasound, we will be reviewing the wavelength equation in more depth in Level 2 and then persistently throughout the rest of this text. You must commit this equation to memory.

8.5.6 Different Ways of Remembering the Wavelength Equation

Beside brute force memorization, there are at least two other means by which you can recall the all important wavelength equation. The first of these two approaches is to go through the mental thought experiments just demonstrated in Section 8.5.4 above. This approach is very useful since it forces you to think about the physical relationships between the wavelength and the frequency and between the wavelength and the propagation velocity.

The other approach is to use the units to help you recall the equation. Consider the units for frequency, propagation velocity, and wavelength:

Frequency (f) = Wavelength (λ) • Propagation Velocity (c)

f	λ	c
$\left(\dfrac{1}{sec}\right)$	m	$\dfrac{m}{sec}$

Visually, it should be obvious that multiplying $\left(\dfrac{1}{sec}\right) * m = \dfrac{m}{sec}$, or, $f * \lambda = c$. This is the same equation we derived, just written in terms of c instead of lambda.

8.6 Amplitude

8.6.1 Definition
In simplest terms, the amplitude of a physical quantity is defined as the strength, volume, or size of that physical quantity. For example, when listening to music, the amplitude of the music is determined by the volume knob. If you increase the volume on the stereo, the music becomes louder, meaning the amplitude becomes higher. In more formal terms, the amplitude is defined as the maximum variation of a variable from its mean value.

8.6.2 Units
The measure of amplitude can be applied to many different physical quantities such as pressure, density, temperature, distance, electropotential energy, etc. As a result, the unit associated with an amplitude measurement is dependent on the parameter that is being measured. Earlier in this chapter, we were exposed to many different units for amplitude when we discussed the acoustic variables.

Just as there are parameters which change when a sound wave propagates through a medium (the acoustic variables), there is an electrical variable which varies with the propagation of an electrical wave, more commonly referred to as the voltage. Not surprisingly, the unit for voltage is Volts.

8.6.3 Graphical Representation
Since Volts is a unit for amplitude, we can use *Figure 22* of a varying electrical signal as an illustration of amplitude. In this case, the amplitude is measured as 2 Volts.

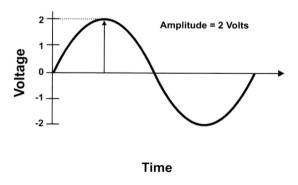

Fig. 22   **Measuring the Amplitude**

8.6.4 Calculating the Amplitude

Using the formal definition of amplitude, it is relatively intuitive how to measure or calculate the amplitude of a cyclically varying signal. Since the definition of the amplitude is the maximum variation of a variable from its mean, the following steps can be employed to determine the equation for the amplitude:

1) Start by identifying the mean.
2) Graphically display the "maximum variation" or farthest point of the signal from the mean (the arrow in the figure below).
3) Label the maximum.
4) The difference between these two values is the amplitude. Mathematically, a difference implies subtraction.

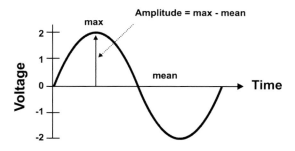

Fig. 23   **Defining the Amplitude Equation**

Now you should notice that the wave depicted is symmetric about the baseline, therefore, the distance from the top of the wave (the maximum) to the middle point of the wave (the mean) is the same as the distance from the bottom point of the wave to the mean. Therefore the amplitude can be defined as the distance from the mean to the maximum, or the distance from the minimum to the the mean. This fact is illustrated in *Figure 24*.

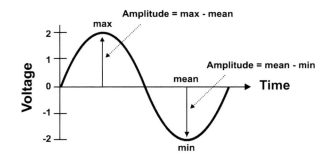

Fig. 24   **Defining the Amplitude Equation**

You should also notice that there is yet one more method of calculating the amplitude from the following graph. Again, since the wave is symmetric about the mean, the amplitude can also be derived by taking half of the total distance from the maximum to the minimum, as illustrated in *Figure 25*.

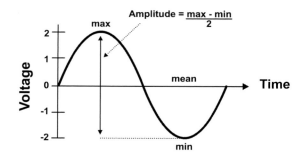

Fig. 25 **Defining the Amplitude Equation**

Therefore, there are "three" methods of calculating the amplitude which we will combine together into this one form:

$$Amplitude = (max - mean) = (mean - min) = \frac{max - min}{2}.$$

We will use some examples to further illustrate how to calculate the amplitude.

◊ **Example 1:**

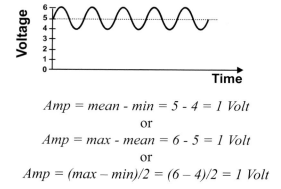

Amp = mean - min = 5 - 4 = 1 Volt
or
Amp = max - mean = 6 - 5 = 1 Volt
or
Amp = (max – min)/2 = (6 – 4)/2 = 1 Volt

◊ **Example 2:**

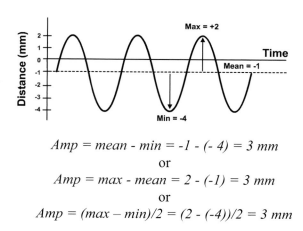

Amp = mean - min = -1 - (- 4) = 3 mm
or
Amp = max - mean = 2 - (-1) = 3 mm
or
Amp = (max – min)/2 = (2 - (-4))/2 = 3 mm

9. Conceptual Questions Answers Pg. 439-441

1. Repetitious waves are a _____ transfer of _____ .

2. Cyclical means
    a) periodic or repetitive.
    b) in a circle.
    c) linear.

3. The major classifications of waves are _____ and _____ .

4. An electromagnetic wave does not need a _____ to propagate.

5. Examples of electromagnetic waves are
    a) TV, microwave, and sound.
    b) music, ultrasound, and ocean waves.
    c) x-rays, light, and microwaves.

6. A _____ wave needs a medium to propagate.

7. There can be no _____ waves in a vacuum.

8. A vacuum is the absence of a _____ .

9. There is no sound in a _____, since there is no medium.

10. Two classifications of mechanical waves are _____ and _____ .

11. In a _____ wave, particle motion is perpendicular or "transverse" to the wave direction.

12. In a _____ wave, the particle motion is back and forth in the same direction as the wave propagation.

13. Sound is a _____, mechanical wave.

14. A longitudinal wave has areas of _____ and compression.

15. An area of _____ is where the particles are farther apart than the normal state.

16. An area of _____ is where the particles are closer together than the normal state.

17. Not all waves need a _____ to propagate; _____ waves can operate in a vacuum.

18. _____ is a way of specifying how fast a wave is cyclically varying.

19. The unit for frequency is_____, which is an abbreviation for cycles per _____ .

20. Frequency has units which are the inverse of _____, or one divided by _____, also called Hz.

21.   The number of times a longitudinal wave reaches maximum compression and rarefaction per time is called the _____ .

22.   The reciprocal of frequency is the _____ .

23.   The period has units of _____ .

24.   The reciprocal of the _____ is frequency. Frequency has units of Hertz.

25.   The _____ is the time between cycles of peak compression in a longitudinal wave, such as sound.

26.   The _____ between cycles of peak compression is the same as the time between cycles of peak rarefaction.

27.   The _____ is the_____ between cycles of peak rarefaction.

28.   Frequency and period are _____ .

29.   The units for _____ and period are reciprocals.

30.   Hertz and _____ (or seconds) are inversely related.

31.   Since frequency and period are inversely related, if the frequency increases the period _____.

32.   A shorter period means a higher _____ .

33.   A lower _____ means a longer period.

34.   The _____ is the physical measure of distance between wave peaks (maxima) or similarly wave (minima).

35.   Wavelength is a measure of _____ and therefore in the metric system has units of _____ .

36.   The period is a measure of _____ between peaks whereas the _____ is a measure of distance between peaks.

37.   Frequency and _____ are related through the wave propagation velocity.

38.   The propagation _____ has units of meters/second.

39.   The _____ _____ is a measure of how fast a wave will travel.

40.   The propagation velocity, (c), equals the frequency, (f), times the _____ or $f \cdot \lambda = c$.

41.   For a given propagation velocity, if the frequency increases, the _____ must decrease.

Pegasus Lectures, Inc.

42. For a given propagation velocity, if the frequency _____, the _____ must increase.

43. Frequency and wavelength have an _____ relationship.

44. If the propagation velocity changes and the frequency is not changed the _____ must change.

45. To determine the _____, the frequency and the propagation velocity must be known.

46. The frequency, wavelength and propagation velocity are related together by the equation: _____ .

47. The _____ of a signal is a measure of how big or loud it is.

48. The _____ is determined as the maximum variation from the mean.

49. The _____ is the same as the average.

50. The _____ = $\dfrac{maximum + minimum}{2}$.

51. If the maximum is 20 and the minimum is 10, the mean is _____ .

52. The difference between the maximum and the mean is the same as the difference between the mean and the _____ .

53. Since the amplitude equals the difference between the maximum and the mean, the _____ also equals the difference between the _____ and the minimum.

54. If the _____ of an ultrasound echo increases, the B-mode image will get brighter.

55. If the _____ of a Doppler echo _____, the Doppler audio will get louder.

56. Amplitude is used to measure any wave variable. For sound waves, the units of amplitude will be any measure of the four _____ variables.

57. For electrical waves, _____ is used to measure parameters of electric variables such as voltage.

58. Some possible units of _____ are Pascals, degrees Celsius, meters, kg/m³.

59. A wave which has a physical interaction with the _____ is called a mechanical wave.

60. A change within the _____ caused by a wave is called a variable.

61. For an acoustic wave, the changes caused to the medium are called _____ variables.

62. There are _____ acoustic variables.

63.   The four acoustic variables are:
       1) _____
       2) _____
       3) _____
       4) _____ .

64.   Units of _____ are: Pascals, Atmospheres, mmHg, kg/m^2, lbs/in^2.

65.   Units of _____ are: meters, feet, miles, yards, etc.

66.   Units of _____ are: degrees Celsius, degrees Fahrenheit, degrees Kelvin.

67.   Units of _____ are mass/volume such as Kg/m^3 and lbs/ft^3.

68.   Changes in acoustic variables are the result of the mechanical interaction of the acoustic wave and
       the _____ .

10. Exercises   Answers Pg. 441-443

1.   What is the frequency, in Hertz, of something that occurs 60 times in one minute?

2.   What is the frequency, in Hertz, of something that occurs 60 times in 0.5 seconds?

3.   What is the frequency, in Hertz, of something that occurs 60 times in 0.1 seconds?

4.   What is the frequency, in Hertz, of something that occurs 60 times in 1 hour?

5.   What determines the frequency of operation for ultrasound?
       a) medium
       b) pulser
       c) patient
       d) wavelength

6.   How much will the frequency change if the propagation velocity changes by a factor of 2?

7.   If the frequency is 1 MHz, what is the period?

8.   If the period is 0.5 μsec, what is the frequency?

9.   Which two of the following give the same information?
       a) frequency = 10 kHz
       b) frequency = 3 kHz
       c) period = 0.1 msec
       d) period = 10 ksec

10.   Since the period and the frequency are reciprocals, the period multiplied by the frequency equals
       _____ .

11.   What determines the period for ultrasound?
        a) medium
        b) pulser
        c) patient
        d) wavelength

12.   How much will the period change if the propagation velocity changes by a factor of 2?

13.   If ultrasound travels 662 meters through air in 2 seconds, what is the propagation velocity of sound in air in m/sec?

14.   How far can a car travel in 2 hours driving at 60 mph?

15.   How far can an ultrasound beam travel in soft tissue in 1 second? ($c_{soft\ tissue}$ = 1540 m/sec)

16.   How long would it take a car traveling 30 mph to travel 45 miles?

17.   How long would it take ultrasound in soft tissue to travel to a target 1 cm deep and back to the transducer?

18.   The speed of sound
        a) changes with frequency.
        b) changes with period.
        c) depends on inertia and elasticity of medium.

19.   The wavelength has units of
        a) time.
        b) events/time.
        c) distance/time.
        d) distance.

20.   If the propagation velocity is unchanged but the frequency changes, the wavelength
        a) will change.
        b) will remain constant.
        c) can't be determined.

21.   If the frequency is unchanged but the propagation velocity changes, the wavelength
        a) changes.
        b) remains constant.
        c) can't be determined.

22.   Which of the following will not result in a change in wavelength?
        a) change in period
        b) change in medium stiffness
        c) change in medium density
        d) change in amplitude of transmit signal.

11. Relating Wave Characteristics to Application and Relevance in Diagnostic Ultrasound

In Level 1, we developed the rudimentary understanding of waves as a general phenomenon. Although all of the material covered in Level 1 is applicable, there was no effort made to relate these concepts and parameters with actual scanning. This approach is intentional since a foundation must be built before we can hope for an understanding of greater complexity.

The task is now to relate those general parameters of Level 1 with the relevance to diagnostic ultrasound and ultimately the importance of how well you can control system parameters to perform a good clinical study. The wave parameters discussed and the concepts taught in this chapter are the foundation to all later chapters. Therefore, we will need to make a great effort to ensure that a thorough understanding is developed. To facilitate this understanding, this section will include many numerical examples. Additionally, you should make certain to complete all of the conceptual questions and exercises as a means of testing your readiness to progress on to Level 2 of later chapters.

12. Wave Characteristics and Parameters

12.1 Frequency and Period
Perhaps the wave parameter first thought of when scanning a patient is the operating, or transmit frequency. Specifically, the operating frequency refers to the frequency at which the transducer crystal vibrates. This vibrational frequency is then coupled into the body as a sound wave, compressing and decompressing (rarefaction of) the tissue.

◊ **Example:** If a 2 MHz transducer is used, the sound wave compresses and decompresses the tissue 2 million times per second. Since the period is the reciprocal of the frequency, a 2 MHz wave has a period of

$$Period = \frac{1}{f} = \frac{1}{2\ MHz} = 0.5\ \mu sec.$$

12.2 The General Term Frequency
In reality, the term "frequency" is a general term which can refer to any periodic event. There are many different frequencies such as the operating or transmit frequency (as we just described), the pulse repetition frequency, the frame frequency (usually called the frame rate), the Doppler shifted frequency, etc. If the term frequency is used in ultrasound without any qualifying words like "pulse repetition", "frame", or "Doppler", then it is generally presumed that the frequency being referenced is the operating frequency.

12.2.1 Classifications of Sound

What Sound is Not
Although many people would define "sound" as something that can be heard, this definition is unequivocally ambiguous. Even from person to person there is variation as to what frequencies can be heard. Also, with age, hearing decreases, especially at the higher frequency ranges. What is heard by one person may not be heard by another. Therefore, without any significant discussion of physics, this definition is already flawed.

Sound is a longitudinal mechanical wave of virtually any frequency. It is useful to further define sound into various classifications.

The Human Audible Range
The human audible range is usually defined as any sound wave with a frequency between 20 Hz to 20 kHz. In reality, very few adults can hear frequencies anywhere even close to 20 kHz. In general, the highest frequencies heard by most adults is below 17 kHz and quite frequently well below 15 kHz. Not surprisingly, humans classify sound ranges according to the human audible range. By adding a prefix to the word sound, we can then specify a specific range of frequencies. For example, the prefix "infra" means "below" so infrasound is sound below human hearing, or below 20 Hz. The prefix "ultra" means "above" so ultrasound is any sound above human hearing, or above 20 kHz.

At this point you must make a distinction between ultrasound and diagnostic ultrasound. Diagnostic ultrasound is a subset of ultrasound. Specifically, diagnostic ultrasound refers to the range of frequencies useful for diagnostic ultrasound.

The Diagnostic Range (Non-invasive)
The diagnostic range is usually specified as the range of frequencies from 2 MHz to about 10 or 12 MHz. Clearly from these numbers, interpreting the terminology "diagnostic range" requires certain assumptions. When the term "diagnostic frequencies" or "diagnostic range" is used there is generally a tacit assumption that only non-invasive, transcutaneous ultrasound is being referenced. There are certainly applications of diagnostic ultrasound that utilize higher frequencies than 12 MHz, and there are certainly diagnostic applications that utilize frequencies lower than 2 MHz. We will further discuss these points later in this section.

Classifications of Sound
Putting the information of the last few paragraphs together in one table yields:

Infrasound	0 Hz - 20 Hz (below human audible)
Audible	20 Hz - 20 kHz (human audible)
Ultrasound	>20 kHz (above human audible)
Diagnostic	2 MHz - 12 MHz (approximate useful diagnostic range)

Table 2: **Defining Sound Ranges**

Figure 26 presents these data graphically.

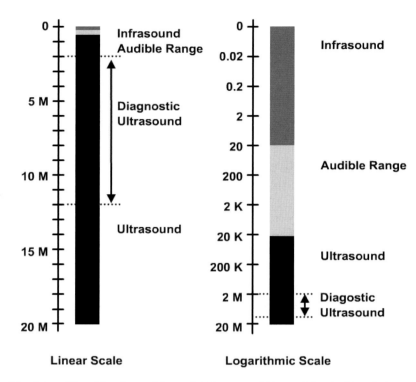

Fig. 26 **Classification of Sound (Linear and Logarithmic Graphs)**

Note: The two scales in Figure 26 give the exact same information. Recall that logarithmic graphs are good for dealing with a large dynamic range. Because of the large dynamic range of these data, notice how the logarithmic scale presentation is much easier to decipher than the linear scale presentation.

Why 2 MHz to 12 MHz?

In general, conventional diagnostic ultrasound does not commonly use frequencies much below 2 MHz because of poor detail resolution. From the wavelength equation, we know that a lower frequency results in a longer wavelength. We will learn in later chapters that longer wavelengths result in a decrease in ability to resolve structures close together and to discern fine detail. At some point, the resolution is considered so poor that there is little reason to acquire data. The frequency of 2 MHz, is generally the limit of acceptable resolution. However, there are exceptions. Some newer harmonic techniques will transmit at frequencies lower than 2 MHz and receive at frequencies near 2 MHz. Also, there are some applications of Doppler which do not require high resolution, but do require extraordinary sensitivity, which will utilize frequencies slightly below 2 MHz. (generally around 1.6 or 1.8 MHz)

The upper limit of 10 MHz or 12 MHz is dictated by the inability of higher frequency sound to penetrate deep into the patient. In Chapter 3, the concept of attenuation will be fully discussed. For now, you should realize that the diagnostic frequency range really demonstrates one of the classic trade-offs on diagnostic ultrasound: resolution versus penetration.

Pegasus Lectures, Inc.

Just as there are exceptions to using frequencies below 2 MHz, there are obvious exceptions to using frequencies above 12 MHz. For small parts imaging, if the imaging is very superficial, it is now common to exceed the 10 or 12 MHz range. Additionally, invasive ultrasound is diagnostic ultrasound and often exceeds this range.

12.2.2 Intravascular Ultrasound (Frequencies Above the Typical Diagnostic Range)

An example of when even higher frequencies are used for diagnostic ultrasound is intravascular ultrasound. Intravascular ultrasound (IVUS) began in the late 1980's and, depending on the application, uses frequencies as high as 30 to 40 MHz. The primary goal of intravascular ultrasound is to assess vessel walls and help characterize plaque morphology. The transducer is either a single rotated element or a very small phased array. The transducer contained within a sheath is attached to the end of a catheter, usually less than 1 mm in diameter. The high frequencies are desirable for maximal resolution. Since the imaging depths are so shallow, and since there is no air interface, these high frequencies are tenable. The following image of *Figure 27*, demonstrates an IVUS image from a coronary artery.

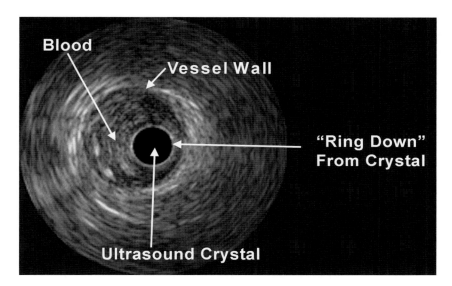

Fig. 27   **Intravascular Ultrasound (IVUS) Image of a Coronary Artery**

12.2.3 Therapeutic Ultrasound (Physiotherapy and HIFU)

Therapeutic ultrasound (physiotherapy) has been in use for many years, and has been increasing in efficacy. Therapeutic ultrasound is used to increase blood flow and manage several soft tissue conditions such as muscle spasm, tendonitis, and bursitis. Additionally, therapeutic ultrasound is used to reduce joint contractures, scar tissue, and pain as well as promoting wound healing. The typical frequency range for therapeutic ultrasound is between 0.5 MHz and 3.0 MHz, and most commonly, a frequency close to 1 MHz is used. Beam intensities range from about 0.25 W/cm^2 to as high as 2.5 W/cm^2 resulting in tissue temperature rises as high as 4 degrees Celsius up to depths of about 5 cm.

In recent years, the term therapeutic ultrasound has also started to include some very exciting acoustic surgical techniques based on using high intensity ultrasound. High-intensity focused ultrasound (HIFU) has shown promise for selective destruction of tissue volumes such as cancerous lesions in the liver, kidney, breast, and prostate. By using extremely high intensity beams, large temperature increases are possible. By focusing the beam, the energy can be concentrated on the diseased tissue while sparing the healthy surrounding tissue. The frequencies commonly used for HIFU are from 0.5 MHz to about 10 MHz with transmit intensities as high as 1,500 W/cm^2. These high intensities can raise the local temperature above 56 degrees Celsius, and are allowed to exist for a few seconds. There is even some hope that HIFU may eventually be used within the skull.

12.2.4 Relation to Future Topics

As mentioned at the beginning of this chapter, one of the goals is to help the student learn the material in the context of why each piece matters and of how the pieces interrelate. The following list indicates the various topics which will build from the concepts and discussion contained in this section on frequency:

1) penetration
2) types of reflection
3) resolution
4) harmonics
5) appropriate transducer selection for imaging and for Doppler

12.3 Propagation Velocity

12.3.1 General

In Level 1, we discussed the meaning of the propagation velocity, and that the propagation velocity is primarily determined by the properties of the medium through which the wave is propagating. Perhaps one of the most maligned topics in ultrasound physics has been the discussion of exactly what properties of the medium affect the propagation velocity and how. In an effort to simplify the topic, it is frequently oversimplified such that what the student memorizes no longer agrees with what is observed when scanning a patient. For anyone who then tries to apply what they are learning with what they are clinically seeing there is a very disconcerting disconnect.

12.3.2 Terminology: Elasticity, Compressibility, Stiffness, and Bulk Modulus

There are many terms that are commonly used when referring to the properties of the medium that determine the propagation velocity. Many of the terms are related and although each has a specific, differentiating physics meaning, for the purposes of diagnostic ultrasound, some of these differences can be ignored. We will begin by discussing some of the terminology.

12.3.2.1 Elasticity

The term elasticity refers to the ability of a solid object to return to its original shape after distortion by a force. For example, if a mechanical vibration distorts a crystal's dimensions, the elasticity is a measure of that crystal material's ability to return to its original "un-deformed" shape.

12.3.2.2 Compressibility

The compressibility of a material is a measure of how much the volume of the material changes for a given distorting force (pressure). A high compressibility implies that the material can be compressed to a much smaller volume than a low compressibility material, for the same given force (pressure). For the purposes of ultrasound, it is generally presumed that a compressible material is elastic and vice versa.

12.3.2.3 Stiffness (Inelasticity)

In ultrasound, the term "stiffness" is commonly used to imply the inverse of elasticity or compressibility. Therefore, a stiff material is a material which cannot be compressed much. Since the prefix "in" means not, an inelastic material is a material which is "not" elastic and hence, stiff.

12.3.2.4 Bulk Modulus

The bulk modulus is formally defined as the decrease in the ratio of the stress to the strain, where the stress is defined as the change in the pressure applied, and the strain is defined as the percent change in volume which occurs as a result of the stress (as pictured in *Figure 28*). With that behind us, for the purposes of ultrasound, we will simply relate the bulk modulus as meaning the inverse of the compressibility. Therefore, a low compressibility material would have a high bulk modulus.

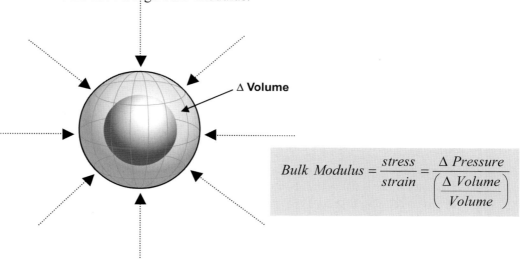

$$Bulk\ Modulus = \frac{stress}{strain} = \frac{\Delta\ Pressure}{\left(\dfrac{\Delta\ Volume}{Volume}\right)}$$

Fig. 28   **Changing Volume with Pressure**

12.3.2.5 Table Relating Terminology

The following table should help put all of these terms into perspective.

High Bulk Modulus	incompressible	inelastic	stiff
Low Bulk Modulus	compressible	elastic	not stiff

Table 3:   **Bulk Modulus and Related Terms**

Note: Although technically these terms are not completely equivalent, for the purposes of ultrasound, the lack of rigor is acceptable.

12.3.3 The Propagation Velocity Analogy

It has already been stated that the propagation velocity is determined by properties of the medium, and not by the frequency of the wave. We will use a classic physics analogy to determine what parameters of the medium will affect the propagation velocity.

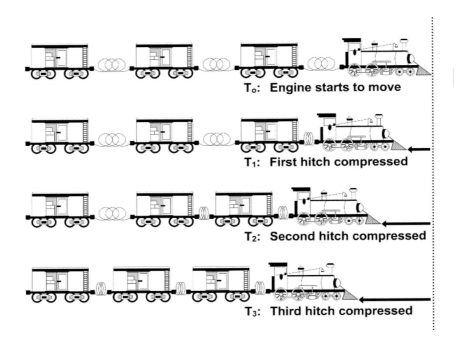

T_o: Engine starts to move

T_1: First hitch compressed

T_2: Second hitch compressed

T_3: Third hitch compressed

Fig. 29 **Train in Reverse and Compression**

Consider a situation in which a long train is sitting in a station and needs to go in reverse. From time zero of *Figure 29* (T_o) you will notice that the hitch between each pair of cars is drawn as an uncompressed spring. As depicted in the diagram, at time T_o, the train starts to back up. Because there is slack in the hitch between the engine and the first car there is a time delay from when the engine first starts to move and when the first car starts to move (time T_1). Once the first car starts to move, there is another time delay until the slack between the first and second car is removed. Once the slack is compressed out, (time T_2), the second car starts to move. In this manner, the longitudinal compression wave travels from the engine until it reaches the last car of the train, resulting in movement of the last car. Before the train started to move, you could consider the train as compressible because of the slack between each car. Once the train starts moving, you would hear a series of "clangs" that represents the time when the slack between each hitch has been compressed out and the train becomes a rigid object.

The speed with which the wave propagates from one car to the next is clearly dependent on the amount of slack between each car. If there is a lot of slack, then the speed will be slow, as more time is required for the previous car to move a greater distance to compress out the slack. This concept is depicted in *Figure 30*.

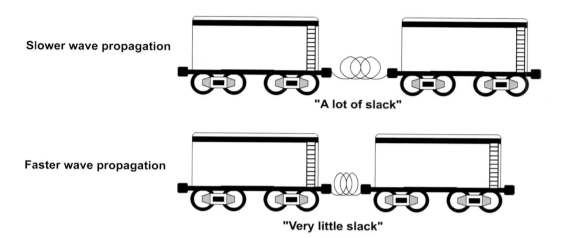

Slower wave propagation

"A lot of slack"

Faster wave propagation

"Very little slack"

Fig. 30   **Compressibility and Propagation Velocity**

You can also imagine that the time required to compress out the slack between the hitches will depend on the mass of each car. If the train is unloaded, each car will be easier to accelerate, and the car will begin to move more quickly. Instead, if the train is heavily loaded, more time will be required to accelerate each car and the wave velocity through the train will be slower.

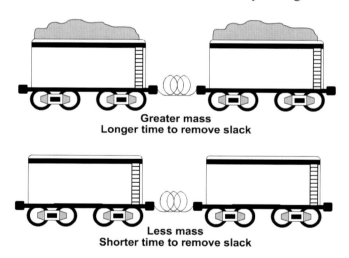

Greater mass
Longer time to remove slack

Less mass
Shorter time to remove slack

Fig. 31   **Mass and Propagation Velocity**

Interestingly, if you carefully analyze this analogy, it will become clear that the velocity of the train engine is actually slower than the wave propagation velocity. Referring to *Figure 32*, notice that in the time it took the engine to move the short distance of 3 meters, the wave has propagated from the engine of the train to the end of the fourth car or 30 meters. Let's imagine that this propagation occurred over a 1 second time period. The velocity of the train is therefore 3 meters/second whereas the wave propagation velocity is 30 meters/second. For this example, the wave propagation velocity is actually 10 times greater than the velocity of the train.

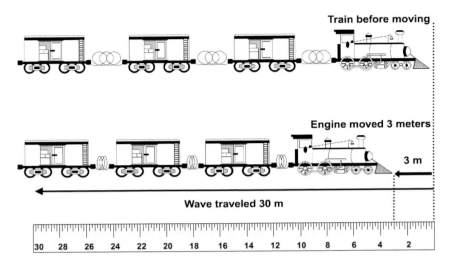

Fig. 32   **Wave Velocity Versus Train Velocity**

View Animation and Image Library CD

12.3.4 Relating the Analogy to the Speed of Sound

In our train analogy, the train cars represent the molecules of a medium, and the compressible hitches between the cars represent the molecular bonds. From our analogy, the "slack" in the hitches is analogous to the compressibility of the medium, and the mass of the train cars is analogous to the density of the medium.

From our analogy, we know that an increase in density results in a decrease in propagation velocity, presuming that the slack in the hitches was not changed. We would therefore expect to see an inverse relationship between the propagation velocity and the density of the material.

$$propagation\ velocity\ (c) \propto \frac{1}{density\ (\rho)}.$$

However, this is not the entire story. As we will see, unlike the analogy, a change in density in a material usually results in a change in the compressibility of the material as well.

From our analogy, we also know that if the slack between the train cars (the compressibility) is increased, the propagation velocity will decrease, presuming that there is no change in the density (train load). We would therefore expect an inverse relationship between the propagation velocity and the compressibility of a material. Again, this is not the whole story.

$$propagation\ velocity\ (c) \propto \frac{1}{compressibility}.$$

In both cases of our analogy, a presumption was made that a change in one parameter did not affect the other parameter. Specifically, it was presumed that changing the density did not affect the compressibility, and that a change in compressibility did not affect the density. This is where the analogy breaks down. Let's modify our analogy slightly so that it better reflects reality. Let's imagine that if a train is designed to be very heavily loaded, it is likely that the hitches will be designed with less compressibility (similar to how heavy duty vehicles have stiffer shock absorbers). Now, when a train has a heavier load, it also is less compressible and we must consider that the two effects work in opposite directions. This modification now more closely reflects what generally occurs in the real world. For the materials commonly found in the body, a change in density is accompanied by a much greater change in the compressibility.

View Animation and Image Library CD

12.3.5 Putting the Pieces Together to Create the Equation

We have determined that the speed of sound is determined principally by two parameters, the density of the material, and what we have referred to as the compressibility of the material (also related to the stiffness of the material or the bulk modulus of the material). In physics, the most precise way of defining the relationship is to use the bulk modulus (related to the inverse of the compressibility). So we know:

$$propagation\ velocity\ (c) \propto \frac{1}{density\ (\rho)}$$

and

$$propagation\ velocity\ (c) \propto \frac{1}{compressibility} \Rightarrow (c) \propto \beta_{modulus}.$$

Without proof, we will just state that the relationship between the propagation velocity and both the density and the modulus is a square root. Therefore we have:

$$c = \sqrt{\frac{\beta_{modulus}}{\rho}}.$$

In other words, as the bulk modulus of a material increases, the propagation velocity increases. As the density increases, the propagation velocity decreases.

12.3.7 Propagation Velocities for Various Materials

The following table lists the approximate propagation velocities for a range of materials from gases to solids.

Medium	Propagation Velocity
Gases	
Air (0 degrees C)	331 m/sec
Air (25 degrees C)	347 m/sec
Helium (0 degrees C)	972 m/sec
Hydrogen (0 degrees C)	1286 m/sec
Liquids	
Methyl alcohol (0 degrees C)	1130 m/sec
Methyl alcohol (25 degrees C)	1145 m/sec
Water (0 degrees C)	1405 m/sec
Mercury (25 degrees C)	1450 m/sec
Water (25 degrees C)	1495 m/sec
Ocean water (25 degrees C)	1530 m/sec
Solids	
Lead	1322 m/sec
Rubber	1600 m/sec
Gold	3240 m/sec
Copper	3560 m/sec
Brass	4700 m/sec
Aluminum	5100 m/sec
Stainless steel	5790 m/sec
Diamond	12000 m/sec

Table 4: **Propagation Velocities**

12.3.8 Discussion of Values in the Materials Table

As you can see from the above table, the propagation velocity for gases tends to be the lowest of the three states. In general, the propagation velocity for most gases is below 1,000 m/sec. From the table, it is clear that the propagation velocity in a gas changes with temperature. As the temperature increases, the propagation velocity increases. The propagation velocity for fluids is generally higher than for gases, and usually above 1,000 m/sec but lower than 2,000 m/sec. The propagation velocity for fluids also shows temperature dependence.

For solids, there is a very large range of propagation velocities. More compressible materials like rubber have much lower propagation velocities than very stiff materials like diamonds. You should notice that the propagation velocity in most metals tends to be above 3000 m/sec. This fact should not be too surprising given the high stiffness of metals. The one clear exception given in the table is the material of lead. Although lead is relatively dense, it has a low bulk modulus, resulting in a relatively low propagation velocity (in comparison with other metals). This low bulk modulus of lead is not too surprising when you consider how lead can be easily molded (deformed) and shaped.

Because metal objects are sometimes introduced into the body (needles for biopsy, prosthetic valves, stents), it is recommended that you remember that the velocity in metals tends to be relatively high.

12.3.9 What Affects Velocity Most in the Body
From the equation of Section 12.3.5, and from *Table 4*, it is easy to be misled with respect to expectations for propagation velocities in the body. From the equation, since the propagation velocity is dependent on the square root of both the bulk modulus and the density, you might presume that both parameters have equal effects. Similarly, since most people think of the body as comprised of solids, you might presume the presence of high propagation velocities in the body is more consistent with the upper end of the propagation table. This thought process is where the biggest mistakes are made. Because of the high fluid content, most tissues in the body (excluding lung and bone) tend to behave more like fluids than solids. In reality, for most materials found in the body, materials that are slightly denser have a significantly higher bulk modulus (much less compressible, or much stiffer). Therefore, materials that are denser generally have much higher propagation velocities than materials that are less dense. This seems to contradict the relationship that is stated above that the propagation velocity is inversely related to the density. However, just as we had to adjust out train analogy, we need to adjust our thinking. If it were possible to increase the density without increasing the stiffness of a tissue, then the relationship would hold as anticipated. Since for tissues in the body, increased density always implies an increase in bulk modulus, more dense tissues generally have higher propagation velocities.

12.3.10 Propagation Velocities in the Body
The following table lists the approximate propagation velocity for sound through many different biological materials.

Medium	Propagation Velocity
Air (25 degrees C)	347 m/sec
Lung	500 m/sec
Fat	1440 m/sec
Water (25 degrees C)	1495 m/sec
Brain	1510 m/sec
"Soft Tissue"	average 1540 m/sec
Liver	1560 m/sec
Kidney	1560 m/sec
Blood	1560 m/sec
Muscle	1570 m/sec
Bone	4080 m/sec

Table 5:   **Propagation Velocities in the Body**

The following table *(Table 6)*, demonstrates the relationship that generally exists for tissue in the body.

$\uparrow \rho \Rightarrow$ *Bulk modulus increases (incompressible, inelastic, stiff)* $\Rightarrow$ *increases c*
$\downarrow \rho \Rightarrow$ *Bulk modulus decreases (compressible, elastic, not stiff)* $\Rightarrow$ *decreases c*

Table 6: **Relating Density (ρ), Bulk Modulus and Propagation Velocity (c) in the Body**

12.3.11 Discussion of Values in the Biological Table

As you can see from *Table 5*, the propagation velocities of the "biomaterials" (excluding bone and lung) are generally close to the propagation velocity of sound in water. Lung, comprised primarily of low density air, is very compressible and has a propagation velocity very close to air. Similarly, the higher density bone is very incompressible. As a result of the high bulk modulus, the propagation velocity in bone is very high in comparison to other biological materials such as liver, kidney, or brain. The propagation velocity in water (at 25 degrees C) is close to 1500 m/sec. You will notice that many tissues have propagation velocities which, as a percentage, vary only slightly from this value. The propagation velocity for "soft tissue" is actually an approximate average velocity in the body presuming that the sound does not propagate through an air filled cavity, a fluid-filled cavity, or bone. In reality, there is no specific tissue that comprises "soft tissue".

In the materials table (*Table 4* of section 12.3.7) we saw that the propagation velocity for gases and fluids varies with temperature. Although the propagation velocity in tissue varies with temperature, the normal range of variance is very small. We can therefore ignore temperature variation on propagation velocity in the body with very little introduction of error.

12.3.12 The Propagation Velocity Assumed by the Ultrasound System

All ultrasound systems assume a propagation velocity of 1540 m/sec to determine depth of structures. By measuring the time between the transmit event and the returning echoes, depth can be calculated using the distance equation. Given that the propagation velocity is assumed (1540 m/sec), and the time of travel (time of flight) is measured, the distance can be calculated. Since ultrasound is based on reflection, the distance traveled is actually twice the depth of the structure causing the reflection (sound travels to the structure and reflects back to the transducer, commonly referred to as the "roundtrip effect"). Therefore, by solving the distance equation and accounting for the roundtrip effect, the depth of structures in the body can be depicted in an ultrasound image.

Of course, the accuracy of the depth depiction is predicated on the assumed velocity of 1540 m/sec. When the velocity is other than 1540 m/sec, the depth prediction is not accurate (referred to as speed error artifact). Fortunately, the variance in propagation velocities, as a percentage, for most tissues varies relatively little and the associated errors are not too significant. However, whenever the propagation velocity varies more significantly, as occurs when scanning air filled regions, large fluid-filled cavities, bone, and virtually any man-made object in the body, the errors can become more dramatic.

12.3.13 Relation to Future Topics

Knowledge of the propagation velocity through various materials in ultrasound is important for many reasons. Principally, the propagation velocity affects:

1) the depth prediction accuracy (speed error artifact)
2) the wavelength (and hence any parameter affected by the wavelength)
3) axial resolution
4) refraction and refraction related artifact

12.4 Wavelength

12.4.1 The Equation and its Importance

In Section 1 we learned that the wavelength is determined principally by two parameters, the frequency of the wave, and the propagation velocity of the wave through the medium. With respect to ultrasound, the wave frequency is the transducer frequency, often referred to as the operating frequency.

The wavelength equation is one of two fundamental equations which dictate diagnostic ultrasound behavior. As we will learn in Chapter 3, the wavelength, in part, determines the type of reflection that occurs. Also, as we will learn in Chapter 4, the wavelength affects the resolution of the image in the axial direction (along the axis of the beam). Since both of these aspects of ultrasound are so critical, it is expected that you will be very familiar with the equation, what affects the wavelength, and how to calculate the wavelength.

12.4.2 Control of the Wavelength

Since the wavelength affects two critical parameters for ultrasound (reflection type and resolution), it should make sense that we will want to analyze how the wavelength can be controlled.

When we developed the equation, we considered how changes in frequency and changes in propagation velocity affect the wavelength. Increasing the propagation velocity causes the wave to be "stretched out", increasing the wavelength (proportionality). Increasing the frequency dictates that there are more cycles for the same time period, or a shortening of the wavelength (inverse proportionality).

Recall that the propagation velocity is determined strictly by the properties of the medium. The operating frequency is determined strictly by the source. Therefore, one of the two parameters which determines the wavelength, the propagation velocity, is completely out of the control of the sonographer when imaging. Ironically, although the frequency is "chosen" by the user, the real world issue of penetration tends to restrict how much freedom the sonographer gets to exercise. As a result, with conventional ultrasound modalities, the sonographer has only a little control over the very important parameter of the wavelength.

12.4.3 Calculating the Wavelength

Calculating the wavelength from the wavelength equation is facilitated greatly by a thorough understanding of the metric table. The reduction in calculation complexity is illustrated by the following examples.

◊ **Example 1:** Calculate the wavelength for a 10 MHz operating frequency presuming a medium of "soft tissue".

$$f = 10 \; MHz$$
$$c = 1540 \; m / \sec$$
$$\lambda = ?$$

Using the equation: $\lambda = \dfrac{c}{f} = \dfrac{1540 \; m}{10 \; MHz * \sec} = \dfrac{154 \; m}{1 \; M \dfrac{1}{\sec} * \sec} = 154 \; \mu m$

(Recall that the metric table is based on reciprocals. A mega (M) in the denominator is equivalent to a micro (μ) in the numerator.)

◊ **Example 2:** Calculate the wavelength for a 2 MHz operating frequency presuming a medium of bone.

$$f = 2 \; MHz$$
$$c = 4080 \; m / \sec$$
$$\lambda = ?$$

Using the equation: $\lambda = \dfrac{c}{f} = \dfrac{4080 \; m}{2 \; MHz * \sec} = \dfrac{2040 \; m}{1 \; M \dfrac{1}{\sec} * \sec} = 2040 \; \mu m$

◊ **Example 3:** Calculate the wavelength (λ) in soft tissue using a 5 MHz transducer.

$$f = 5 \; MHz$$
$$c = 1540 \; m / \sec$$
$$\lambda = ?$$

Using the equation: $\lambda = \dfrac{c}{f} = \dfrac{1540 \; m}{5 \; MHz * \sec} = \dfrac{1540 \; m}{5 \; M \dfrac{1}{\sec} * \sec} = 308 \; \mu m$

Pegasus Lectures, Inc.

12.4.4 Relation to Future Topics

As already mentioned, the wavelength is a critical parameter and will be discussed throughout the book in relation to many other topics. Specifically, the wavelength will be important for the following topics:

1. types of reflection and signal strength
2. types of reflection and artifacts
3. resolution
4. harmonics

12.5 Amplitude

In addition to the formal definition of the maximum variation from its mean, we learned in Level 1 that the amplitude is a measure of size or loudness. The term "amplitude" is general, and can be used in reference to measuring changes in the four acoustic variables or for measuring changes in the electrical variable of electromotive force (voltage). Although the term amplitude can be used to assess the degree of change in any of the four acoustic variables, since these changes are relatively small, this application of amplitude is rarely made. Usually, when referring to amplitude in ultrasound, the term is being used to refer to the transmit voltage which drives the transducer crystal elements.

12.5.1 Control of Electrical Amplitude and Transmit Gain

The control of the transmitted signal amplitude is achieved through the "transmit power" setting control on the ultrasound system. As discussed in the upcoming sections, although amplitude and power are different, there is a relationship between these two parameters. As a result, the control of the transmitted signal amplitude generally has many names depending on the equipment manufacturer. Some examples are acoustic power, output power, transmit, transmit gain, power gain, transmit voltage, acoustic amplitude, output intensity, acoustic intensity, and the acoustic output.

Although these many different names can be confusing, the confusion can be minimized by realizing that all of these terms (in one form or another) express the concept of how big the output signal is in terms of an amplitude or power related term. When the "transmit power" setting is increased, the amplitude of the transmit voltage which drives the transducer is increased.

12.5.1.1 Effect on Acoustic Pressure Field

As will be discussed in Chapter 5, a higher amplitude drive signal (voltage) to the transducer results in a greater mechanical distortion of the transducer crystal. This increase in distortion implies a strong acoustic wave in the body. For a longitudinal wave such as sound, a higher amplitude wave implies a greater degree of compression and a greater degree of rarefaction. For our transverse depiction of a sound wave, this increase in amplitude is displayed as a taller wave, where the taller peak represents a higher compression, and the lower peak represents a greater rarefaction.

12.5.1.2 Relationship to Acoustic Power

The electrical voltage signal is a relatively easy parameter to physically measure. In comparison, measuring the acoustic amplitude of the pressure field is considerably more challenging. In the chapter on quality assurance (Chapter 11) the techniques for measuring acoustic pressure fields will be discussed. For now, it will suffice to know that the process is complex, difficult, and time consuming. Ultimately, it is desirable to have some way of relating a change in the transmit voltage (amplitude) to the possible benefits and risks to the patient.

For electrical signals, the power is proportional to the voltage of the signal (amplitude) squared. Power is defined as a measure of the rate at which energy is transferred or the rate at which work is performed and has units of Watts. If a transducer is run at a higher power, it should not be too surprising that the acoustic energy produced (the wave) will also have a higher power. This fact is important for at least two major reasons:

1. a higher power is related to a stronger ultrasound signal (improved signal-to-noise ratio),
2. a higher power is also related to an increase risk of bioeffects on the patient.

In other words, driving the transducer with a higher transmit voltage will produce higher power waves which potentially can produce better images because of increased penetration, but with a potential increase in the risk of bioeffects.

Since both of these parameters are of great interest to us, we would like to have an easy method of assessing relative improvement in the signal and relative increased risk from bioeffects. Recalling that it is very challenging to measure the acoustic pressure field, we will instead look for a relationship between the acoustic power and the transmit voltage. Since a higher voltage implies a higher electrical power, and a higher electrical power implies a higher acoustic power, we will relate the acoustic power to the electrical voltage as:

$$Power \propto (Voltage)^2$$
or, in general,

$$Power \propto (Amplitude)^2$$

This non-linear relationship is important since it expresses the fact that a small increase in transmit voltage produces much faster changes in the rate of delivery of acoustic energy into the patient. In terms of increased sensitivity, when stronger signals are desirable, this relationship is obviously good news. In terms of increased risk of bioeffects, this relationship is clearly not so great. (You will learn in Chapter 9 that the risk of bioeffects, although possible, have never been confirmed with appropriate use of ultrasound).

The following example will help demonstrate the relationship between amplitude measurements and power measurements.

◊ **Example 1:**   If the amplitude is increased by a factor of 5, what happens to the power?

$$Power \propto (Amplitude)^2$$
$$Original\ Power \propto (Original\ Amplitude)^2$$
$$New\ Power \propto (5 \times Original\ Amplitude)^2$$

So the new power is 5^2, or 25 times the original power.

◊ **Example 2:**   If the transmit voltage is increased by a factor of 6, what happens to the power?

$$Power \propto (Amplitude)^2$$
$$Original\ Power \propto (Original\ Amplitude)^2$$
$$New\ Power \propto (6 \times Original\ Amplitude)^2$$

So the new power is 6^2, or 36 times the original power.

Note that voltage is a measure of amplitude.

◊ **Example 3:**   If the amplitude is decreased by a factor of 3, what happens to the power?

$$Power \propto (Amplitude)^2$$
$$Original\ Power \propto (Original\ Amplitude)^2$$
$$New\ Power \propto (\frac{1}{3} \times Original\ Amplitude)^2$$

So the new power is $\left(\frac{1}{3}\right)^2$, or $\frac{1}{9}$ times the original power.

Note: Stating that the new power is 1/9 the original power is mathematically the same as stating that the power has decreased by a factor of 9.

12.5.1.3 Relationship to Acoustic Intensity

Although assessing relative changes in acoustic power based on changes in the electrical amplitude is easier than directly measuring the acoustic power, the power is not the best indicator of sensitivity or of the risk of bioeffects. Power is a general statement about the rate at which work is performed (energy transferred). However, for ultrasound it is possible to spread this energy transfer over a large region or a small region of the body. Clearly, if the same amount of energy is spread over a large region, neither the sensitivity nor the risk of bioeffects will be as high as when the energy is distributed over a smaller region. This fact leads to the definition of another related parameter referred to as the intensity.

The intensity is a measure of the concentration of force (power) per area. To determine the equation we will develop the mathematical relationship through a few scenarios.

Scenario 1:

Assume there are two flashlights with identical beams, but flashlight A has a much brighter bulb (higher power) than flashlight B. Which flashlight beam has a higher intensity?

Clearly the higher power results in a more intense beam, given that both flashlights have the same beam shape. Therefore, the relationship between the intensity and the power is proportional or:

$$Intensity \propto Power.$$

Scenario 2:

Assume there are two flashlights with identical bulbs (same power), but flashlight A spreads the light over a broader beam (larger beam area) than flashlight B. Which flashlight beam has a higher intensity?

Since the power for flashlight A is spread over a larger area, the beam is more diffuse, and hence, has a lower intensity. As the beam area increases, for the same power, the intensity decreases which is an inverse proportionality, or:

$$Intensity \propto \frac{1}{Beam\ Area}.$$

By combining the two relationships into one equation, we have:

$$Intensity = \frac{Power}{Beam\ Area}.$$

Since the unit for power is Watts, and the units for area in the metric system is based on meters squared, the unit for intensity is $\frac{Watts}{m^2}$. However, since square meters is relatively enormous in comparison with normal beam areas for ultrasound, the units for are are usually expressed using the prefix of centimeters, or $\frac{Watts}{cm^2}$.

The following examples are provided to further illustrate the relationships between amplitude, power, and intensity.

◊ **Example 1:**   If the power is increased by a factor of 5, what happens to the beam intensity?

$$Intensity \propto Power$$
$$Original\ Intensity \propto Original\ Power$$
$$New\ Intensity \propto 5 \times Original\ Power$$
So the new intensity is 5 times the original intensity

Note: As with all relative math questions, an assumption is made that no other variable is changed. In this case, the presumption is that the beam area is not changed as the power is changed.

Pegasus Lectures, Inc.

◊ **_Example 2:_** If the transmit voltage is increased by a factor of 6, what happens to the beam intensity?

$$Intensity \propto Power \propto (Amplitude)^2$$

$$Original\ Intensity \propto (Original\ Amplitude)^2$$

$$New\ Intensity \propto (6 \times Original\ Amplitude)^2$$

So the new intensity is 6^2, or 36 times the original intensity.

Note: That the power is proportional to the amplitude squared. Since the intensity equals the power divided by the area, the intensity is also proportional to the amplitude squared.

Mathematically, we can write:

$$Intensity = \frac{Power}{Beam\ Area} \propto \frac{(Amplitude)^2}{Beam\ Area}.$$

◊ **_Example 3._** If the beam area is doubled, what happens to the intensity?

$$Intensity \propto \frac{1}{Beam\ Area}$$

$$Original\ Intensity \propto \frac{1}{Original\ Beam\ Area}$$

$$New\ Intensity \propto \frac{1}{2 \times Beam\ Area}$$

So the new intensity is $\frac{1}{2}$ original intensity.

Note: Stating the intensity is half of the original intensity is the same as stating that the intensity has been decreased by a factor of 2.

12.5.2 Relation to Future Topics
The concepts related to amplitude, power, and intensity are pervasive in ultrasound. Following is a partial list of the topics which are related:

1) common intensity measurements and risk of bioeffects
2) mechanical index and cavitation
3) receiver gain and compensation (TGCs)
4) attenuation
5) sensitivity
6) signal-to-noise ratio
7) non-linear effects and harmonics

13. Decibels (dB)

13.1 The Need for Decibels
We have just learned that the acoustic intensity is proportional to the power, and that the power is proportional to the square of the amplitude. In Chapter 3 we will learn that the rate at which the signal intensity decreases while traveling through the body (attenuation) is very non-linear. Non-linear attenuation almost guarantees that the range of signals intensities will be very large since the wave at shallow depths will have a much higher intensity than the wave at deeper depths. As a result of the very non-linear attenuation, we will have a need for a non-linear means by which to assess the changes in signal intensity or power.

13.2 The Definition of Decibels
In Chapter 1, we learned a powerful non-linear mathematical tool which is very useful for compressing large ranges of data. That tool is the logarithm. The tool we will use to refer to relative changes in signal power (or intensity) is called decibels. A decibel is defined as a logarithmic power ratio. Since you have already learned how to calculate a logarithm, converting from a ratio to decibels is relatively straight forward.

Notice that in the definition we used the term "power ratio". A ratio implies division of two numbers. Specifically, the power ratio entails taking the ratio of an initial and a final power. In ultrasound, this power is produced by driving a transducer with an excitation voltage. The acoustic power into the patient can be changed by changing the transmit voltage through the power output control. Within the patient, the power changes as the sound travels and interacts with the tissue. Therefore, we can see that there are two distinct mechanisms by which the power is changed.

13.3 The Equation for Decibels
In terms of the power ratio used to calculate decibels, the initial power is the acoustic power before whichever change occurs (changing the power control or attenuation in the body). Obviously, the final power is the resulting acoustic power after the change has occurred (after changing the power control knob or the attenuation from traveling in the body). Putting the definition of decibels into equation form we have:

$$\underline{\text{Power form}}$$
$$dB \triangleq 10 * log\left(\frac{P_f}{P_i}\right).$$

Where:
$$P_f = Power\ Final$$
$$P_i = Power\ Initial$$

The power ratio is also often referred to as the power factor or the power gain factor. This terminology should be intuitive since the ratio of the final power to the initial power is the gain. The following equation manipulation demonstrates this fact.

Note : The symbol $\triangleq$ stands for the words "is defined as."

Pegasus Lectures, Inc.

$$P_f = Gain * P_i$$

dividing both sides by the initial power yields:

$$\frac{P_f}{P_i} = Gain$$

13.4 Applying the Equation for Decibels

The following examples illustrate how the equation is applied.

◊   ***Example:***   If the power is increased by a factor of 2, what is the increase in power in dB?

We are given that $\frac{P_f}{P_i} = 2$, since the problem states the power was increased by a factor of 2.

Plugging this information into the power form of the equation yields:

$$10 * log\left(\frac{P_f}{P_i}\right) = 10 * log\left(2\right) = 10 * 0.3 = 3 \ dB.$$

◊   ***Example:***   If P_f = 10 Watts, and P_i = 1 Watt, what is the increase in power in dB?

We are given that $P_f = 10 \ W$ and $P_i = 1 \ W$

Therefore $\frac{P_f}{P_i} = \frac{10 \ W}{1 \ W} = 10$

Plugging this information into the power form of the equation yields:

$$10 * log\left(\frac{P_f}{P_i}\right) = 10 * log\left(10\right) = 10 * 1 = 10 \ dB.$$

◊   ***Example:***   If the power is decreased by a factor of 100, what is the decrease in power in dB?

We are given that $\frac{P_f}{P_i} = \frac{1}{100}$, since the problem states the power was decreased by a factor of 100.

Plugging this information into the power form of the equation yields:

$$10 * log\left(\frac{P_f}{P_i}\right) = 10 * log\left(\frac{1}{100}\right) = 10 * \ -2 = \ -20 \ dB.$$

So the power was decreased by 20 dB.

It is critical that you notice that the answer format is a decrease of 20 dB and not a decrease of -20 dB. Since the question asks "for the decrease", the answer must be in the format of "the decrease is ..." Since the word decrease already implies a minus sign, you cannot include the minus sign, or you will have created a double negative. If the question had asked for the change, the answer would be -20 dB, since the word change does not imply negative or positive.

13.5 The Amplitude Form of the Decibel Equation

As mentioned earlier, measuring acoustic power is very difficult, whereas knowing the actual transmit voltage is relatively straight forward. As a result, we would like to have a way of relating the amplitude to decibels. It is important to note that decibels is always a logarithmic power ratio. To develop the "amplitude form" we will apply the relationship between power and amplitude that we have already learned earlier in this chapter, as well as a fact about logarithms learned in Chapter 1. Specifically:

1) Power is proportional to the amplitude squared.
2) The logarithm of a multiplication is the same as the sum (addition) of the two logarithms.

We will start with our equation definition of logarithms and make substitution based on the two facts above.

$$dB \triangleq 10 * \left(\log_{10} \left(\frac{P_f}{P_i} \right) \right)$$

$$\text{but } \frac{P_f}{P_i} = \left(\frac{A_f}{A_i} \right)^2$$

substituting yields:

$$dB = 10 * \left(\log_{10} \left(\frac{A_f}{A_i} \right)^2 \right) = 10 * \left(\log_{10} \left(\frac{A_f}{A_i} * \frac{A_f}{A_i} \right) \right)$$

$$dB = 10 * \left(\log_{10} \left(\frac{A_f}{A_i} \right) + \log_{10} \left(\frac{A_f}{A_i} \right) \right) = 10 * \left(2 * \log_{10} \left(\frac{A_f}{A_i} \right) \right)$$

$$dB = 20 * \left(\log_{10} \left(\frac{A_f}{A_i} \right) \right)$$

This derivation leads us to what is commonly referred to as the "amplitude form" of the decibel equation.

Amplitude form

$$dB \triangleq 20 * \log \left(\frac{A_f}{A_i} \right)$$

Where:
A_f = amplitude final
A_i = amplitude initial

Similar to the amplitude form, the ratio of the initial and final amplitude is referred to as the amplitude ratio, amplitude factor, or gain factor.

13.6 Why Two Forms and When to Use Which Form

First, we must state unequivocally that both of these forms of the decibel equation are equivalent. Twenty times the log of the amplitude ratio is equivalent to ten times the log of the power ratio. The reason why it is useful to know both forms is that we sometimes know information about power or intensity (such as Watts or Watts/m²), whereas other times we know information about the amplitude (such as Volts or any unit which is a measure of the four acoustic variables). If you are given information about a change in amplitude, you can use the amplitude form, or you can compute $[A_f /A_i]^2$ and then use the power form. Because the likelihood of making a simple math error increases with the requirement to square a ratio, most people choose to use the amplitude form which already compensates for converting amplitude into power.

The following examples illustrate how the amplitude form of the equation is applied.

◊　　**Example:**　　If the initial transmit amplitude is 0.1 Volts and the transmit amplitude is increased by a factor of 100, what is the final amplitude, and what is the change in dB?

We are given that $A_i = 0.1\ V$ and that the amplitude is increased by a factor of 100.

From this gain factor we can determine that $A_f = 0.1\ V * 100 = 10\ V$

In reality we don't need this information since the problem already gives us the

amplitude factor: $\dfrac{A_f}{A_i} = 100$

Plugging this information into the amplitude form of the equation yields:

$$20 * log\left(\frac{A_f}{A_i}\right) = 20 * log\,(100) = 20 * 2 = 40\ dB.$$

Note: That we could also have solved this problem by converting the amplitude factor into a power factor by squaring and then using the power form of the equation instead, as follows:

Since $Power \propto \left(Amplitude\right)^2$

$$\frac{P_f}{P_i} \propto \left(\frac{A_f}{A_i}\right)^2$$

So an amplitude factor of 100 is the same as a power factor of $100^2 = 10,000$

$$or\ \left(\frac{A_f}{A_i}\right) = 100 \Rightarrow \frac{P_f}{P_i} = 10,000$$

Plugging this information into the power form of the equation yields:

$$10 * log\left(\frac{P_f}{P_i}\right) = 10 * log\,(10,000) = 10 * 4 = 40\ dB$$

and we get the same answer as when we used the amplitude form.

◇ **Example:** If the acoustic pressure field is decreased by a factor of 10, in decibels, what is the change in power?

Since pressure is a measure of amplitude, we will use the amplitude form
The problem tells us that the amplitude has decreased by a factor of 10, or:

$$\frac{A_f}{A_i} = \frac{1}{10}$$

Plugging this information into the amplitude form of the equation yields:

$$20 * log\left(\frac{A_f}{A_i}\right) = 20 * log\left(\frac{1}{10}\right) = 20 * -1 = -20 \ dB.$$

Since the question asks for the change, the answer is -20 *dB*.

13.7 Exercises

Answers Pg. 443-444

1. P_f = 1,000 Watts
   P_i = 10 Watts
   What is the change in dB?

2. The input receiver signal is 1 mV
   The output receiver signal is 100 mV
   What is the gain?
   What is the gain in dB?

3. If you start with $2,500 and after five years you have $250,000, by how many dB have you increased your money? (Use amplitude form)

4. By how many dB has the signal decreased if the signal intensity decreases by a factor of 1,000 penetrating to 6 cm?

5. Fill in the table

Gain Ratio	Power Form	Amplitude Form
1/1,000	-30 dB	-60 dB
1/100	-20 dB	-40 dB
1/10	-10 dB	
1/2	-3 dB	-6 dB
1	0 dB	
2	3 dB	6 dB
10		20 dB
100	20 dB	
1,000		
10,000		80 dB
100,000		
1,000,000	60 dB	120 dB
10,000,000	70 dB	140 dB

Pegasus Lectures, Inc.

Use the table from problem 5 to answer the following questions:

6. An increase of power of a factor of 2 is equivalent to _____ dB.

7. A decrease in power of a factor of 2 is equivalent to _____ dB.

8. An increase in amplitude of a factor of 2 is equivalent to _____ dB.

9. A decrease in amplitude of a factor of 2 is equivalent to _____ dB.

10. A decrease in power of a factor of 1,000 is equivalent to _____ dB.

11. An increase in amplitude by of a factor of 100 is equivalent to _____ dB.

14. Comparing Frequency with Amplitude

14.1 Frequency and Amplitude are Disjoint
In the mathematical sense, the term "disjoint" means having no elements in common. In other words, if two topics are disjoint, the two topics are completely separate or unrelated. It is imperative for you to keep the concepts of frequency and amplitude separate in your mind. This distinction will become critical when reviewing Doppler. The propensity to intermix the concepts of frequency and amplitude leads to much confusion when performing, interpreting, or optimizing Doppler.

With respect to sound, the frequency corresponds to the pitch. In comparison, the amplitude refers to the volume, or the loudness of the sound.

> Frequency ⇒ Pitch
> Amplitude ⇒ Volume

14.2 Graphical Representation
The following two graphs demonstrate how frequency can be changed independent of amplitude and amplitude can be changed independent of frequency.

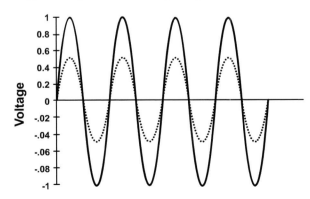

Fig. 33 **Same Frequency but Different Amplitude**

The graph of *Figure 33* depicts two waves that have the same frequency, but different amplitudes. For these two waves, the sound would have the same pitch, but the dotted wave would be softer and the solid line would be louder.

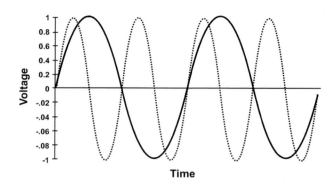

Fig. 34 **Same Amplitude but Different Frequencies**

In comparison with the previous graph, the graph in *Figure 34* depicts two waves that have the same amplitude, but different frequencies. For these two waves, the sound would be of different pitches. The dotted line represents a sound that would have a higher pitch, and the solid line represents that the sound would have a lower pitch. The loudness of the two waves would be approximately the same, presuming that the person listening has the same sensitivity to both frequency ranges.

14.3 Exercises

Answers Pg. 444-446

1.   What is the wavelength of 5 MHz ultrasound in soft tissue?

2.   What is the wavelength of 5 MHz ultrasound in bone?

3.   What is the wavelength of 10 MHz ultrasound in bone?

4.   Given a wavelength of 1 mm and a frequency of 2 MHz, what is the propagation velocity? Do you think this medium is stiffer than soft tissue, blood, bone?

5.   Stiffness is _____ related to compressibility, _____ related to elasticity, _____ related to inelasticity.
        a) inversely, inversely, proportionally
        b) inversely, inversely, inversely
        c) inversely, proportionally, proportionally
        d) proportionally, proportionally, inversely

6.   As the density increases, the propagation velocity _____ . (Make the assumption that the stiffness does not change.)

7.   If the transmit voltage is increased from 2 to 4 Volts, the frequency will _____ .

8.   Match the two columns.

A	B
infrasound	20 Hz - 20 kHz
diagnostic ultrasound	0 - 20 Hz
audible	2 MHz - 10 MHz
ultrasound	> 20 kHz

9. If the amplitude is increased by a factor of nine, the power is _____ by a factor of ____, and the intensity is also _____ by a factor of ____.

10. What happens to the intensity if the amplitude is increased by a factor of 3?

11. What happens to the intensity if the power is increased by a factor of 3?

12. What happens to the intensity if the area is increased by a factor of 2?

13. If we keep the area fixed, and if the intensity increases by a factor of 4, what change has occurred to the amplitude?

15. Conceptual Questions   Answers Pg. 447-448

1. The frequency is determined strictly by the wave _____.

2. The period of a wave is determined strictly by the wave _____.

3. The propagation velocity is determined strictly by the properties of the _____.

4. The wave source can not change the propagation _____ which is strictly determined by the properties of the _____.

5. The two properties of the medium which determine the propagation velocity are _____ (related to density) and _____ (related to compressibility and stiffness).

6. The propagation velocity _____ with increased density. (Assume no change in stiffness.)

7. As the density decreases, the propagation velocity _____. (Assume no change in stiffness.)

8. As the stiffness increases, the propagation velocity _____.

9. A stiff material is not very elastic, so stiffness and elasticity are _____ related.

10. A material which is inelastic is a stiff material, and therefore has a high _____ velocity.

11. Inelasticity and incompressibility are related to _____.

12. Elasticity and _____ are inversely related to stiffness.

13. A gas is generally more compressible than a_____ which is generally more compressible than a solid.

14. Air is more compressible than bone and has a much _____ propagation _____.

15. _____ is sound below human hearing.

16. _____ sound is sound within human hearing.

17. _____ is sound above human hearing.

18. _____ ultrasound is approximately from 2 MHz to 10 MHz.

19. All sound waves are _____ mechanical waves.

20. Human hearing is approximately _____ to _____.

21. Infrasound is below _____.

22. Ultrasound is any sound above _____.

23. _____ is the rate at which energy is transferred.

24. _____ is proportional to the (amplitude)^2.

25. If the amplitude is doubled, the power is _____.

26. If the amplitude is halved, the power is _____.

27. If the amplitude is increased by a factor of two, the power is increased by a factor of _____.

28. If the amplitude is decreased by a factor of two, the power is decreased by a factor of _____.

29. Power is measured in units of _____.

30. The _____ is defined as the concentration of energy.

31. The fundamental units for _____ is power per area.

Pegasus Lectures, Inc.

32.   If power is given in Watts and the area is given in _____, the intensity has units of Watts/cm².

33.   If the area is increased by a factor of two and the power is unchanged, the intensity is decreased by a factor of _____.

34.   If the power increases by a factor of two and the area is unchanged, the intensity _____ by a factor of _____.

35.   If the power _____ by a factor of two, and the area increases by a factor of two, the intensity does not _____.

36.   If the amplitude doubles, the power _____. If the area is not changed, the intensity also _____.

37.   Intensity is proportional to the _____ which is proportional to the _____ squared.

38.   The intensity is inversely proportional to the _____.

KEY CONCEPTS
Waves

- Waves transfer energy from one location to another location.

- Waves are generally broken into one of two classifications: mechanical waves which need a medium to propagate and electromagnetic waves which can propagate through a medium but do not have to have a medium to exist.

- Sound is a mechanical wave.

- The fact that sound is a mechanical wave indicates the physical interaction which occurs between the medium and the wave.

- Mechanical waves can propagate either in transverse or longitudinal mode.

- A transverse wave results in the particles moving perpendicular to the wave direction.

- A longitudinal wave propagates by a series of compressions and rarefactions back and forth in the same direction as the wave propagation direction. Sound is a longitudinal wave.

- As the wave propagates, interactions with the medium cause changes measurable in four quantities called the acoustic variables.
  - Pressure
  - Density
  - Temperature
  - Particle motion (distance)

- Understanding the parameters which characterize a wave is important to understand ultrasound system controls, how to improve image quality, and how to reduce risks of bioeffects.

- The frequency of the wave represents the number of compressions (or rarefactions) which occur per second (unit is Hz = 1/sec).

- The period is the reciprocal of the frequency (units is sec).

$$P = \frac{1}{f}$$

- The frequency (and hence the period) are determined strictly by the wave source.

- The propagation velocity of a wave (c) is determined by the properties of the medium, independent of the frequency used.

- The propagation velocity is determined by the square root of the bulk modulus divided by the density.

- The system presumes the propagation velocity to be 1540 m/sec (the approximate average propagation velocity, excluding bone and lung, commonly referred to as "soft tissue").

- For biological materials, a higher density usually translates into a significantly higher bulk modulus, increasing the propagation velocity.

- There are many terms which are used in place of the bulk modulus. The stiffness is proportional to the bulk modulus which is inversely related to the compressibility. Therefore, as the stiffness increases, the compressibility decreases and the propagation velocity increases. The inverse also holds true. As the stiffness decreases, the compressibility increases and the propagation velocity decreases.

Pegasus Lectures, Inc.

- The wavelength is a critical parameter which is determined both by the frequency (determined by the source) and the propagation velocity (determined by the medium).

- You must know the wavelength equation

$$\lambda = \frac{c}{f}.$$

- On some credentialing exams you may be asked to solve the wavelength equation in terms of given numbers.

- On a drawing, the period and the wavelength appear to be the same parameter. Be careful to pay attention to whether the horizontal axis represents time or distance.

- The amplitude of a wave is defined as the maximum variation of a variable from its mean

$$Amplitude = max - mean = mean - min = \frac{max - min}{2}$$

- The units for the four acoustic variables and voltage are all measures of amplitude.

- Power is proportional to the amplitude squared. This non-linear relationship expresses the fact that small increases in amplitude result in significant increases in power (if the amplitude is tripled, the power increases by a factor of 9)

$$Power \propto \left(Amplitude\right)^2$$

- Intensity is defined as the power divided by the area

$$Intensity = \frac{Power}{Area}$$

- Since the intensity is proportional to the power and the power is proportional to the amplitude squared, increasing the amplitude (voltage) by a factor of 3 increases the intensity by a factor of 9.

- The intensity is an important parameter since it gives a better indication of the signal strength (and the risk of bioeffects) than just the power or the amplitude.

- The amplitude and the frequency are measures of independent parameters (amplitude and frequency are disjoint). In terms of sound, amplitude is a measure of loudness whereas frequency is a measure of pitch.

- Sound is subdivided into classifications based on the human hearing range (audible range).

- Sound below 20 Hz is referred to as infrasound.

- Sound above 20 kHz is referred to as ultrasound.

- Diagnostic ultrasound is a further subdivision of ultrasound which specifies the approximate useful range for conventional, non-invasive ultrasound (typically stated as 2-12 MHz although frequencies higher and lower are sometimes used.)

- The top of the diagnostic frequency range is restricted by penetration.

- The lower range of the diagnostic frequency range is restricted by resolution.

- Since the dynamic range of signals returning from the body is extraordinarily large, non-linear compression in the form of logarithms is used.

Chapter 2

- Decibels is a definition based on logarithms and are defined as the logarithmic power ratio:

$$\left(dB \triangleq 10 * \log \frac{P_f}{P_i} \right)$$

- The amplitude form of decibels is applied when the changing parameters are given as measures of amplitude instead of power (voltage or any of the units for the acoustic variables). The amplitude form is:

$$\left(dB \triangleq 20 * \log \frac{A_f}{A_i} \right)$$

- You should know that a factor of 2 in power is equivalent to 3 dB: since $10 * log(2) = 10 * 0.3 = 3$ dB.

- You should know that a factor of 2 in amplitude is the same as a factor of 4 in power (since power is proportional to amplitude squared) which is equivalent to 6 dB since $20 * log(2) = 20 * 0.3 = 6$ dB.

Note: See Appendix F: Physical Units and Appendix G: Equations for additional review.

CHAPTER 3

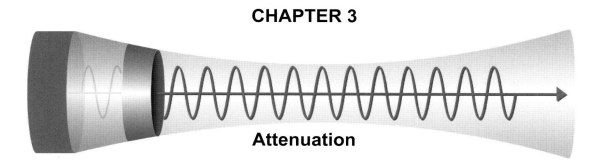

Attenuation

Introduction

In Level 1, we will develop the rudimentary physics which forms the foundation for understanding the changes which occur to the wave because of the physical interaction with the medium. In Level 2, we will directly relate the various aspects of attenuation with specific patient situations. As always, the foundation for conceptual understanding is built in Level 1, and the application is developed and explored in Level 2.

1. Attenuation

Attenuation can be defined as a decrease in wave amplitude (or intensity) due to the mechanical wave interaction with the medium. The word attenuation already implies a decrease, so when referring to attenuation, a negative sign is not used. Stating that a signal has been attenuated by 10 dB is the same as stating the signal has been reduced or decreased by 10 dB, or changed by -10 dB. It is incorrect to state that the signal was attenuated by -10 dB, since this sentence now has a double negative.

A comprehensive understanding of the mechanisms for attenuation is crucial for understanding diagnostic ultrasound. The mechanisms for attenuation are precisely what makes ultrasound work and not work. Without understanding attenuation effects, it is impossible to understand how and why the controls of an ultrasound system work (Chapter 6), the sources of artifacts (Chapter 8), the advanced topics of harmonic imaging, contrast imaging (Chapter 10), and future ultrasound developments.

We will divide the topic of attenuation into three subtopics, each subtopic corresponding to a physical or mechanical interaction with the medium. Specifically, we will subdivide attenuation into the categories of:

- Absorption
- Reflection
- Refraction

2. Absorption

Absorption is a conversion of energy from the sound wave into heat within the medium. The fact that energy is lost to heat within the tissue should be intuitive from our description of how a mechanical wave propagates in Chapter 2. As the wave encounters the molecules (particles) of the medium, some of the energy is transferred. This transfer of energy is responsible for the particle displacement which results in compression and rarefaction. As with moving any physical entity, energy is required. How much of the wave energy is lost to heat through this interaction is dependent on the molecular interactions within the medium and the frequency of moving (compressing) the medium.

2.1 Absorption and Viscosity

The molecular interaction is sometimes referred to as the viscosity of the medium. A high viscosity medium implies that the molecular attraction within the medium is high, requiring greater energy to move the molecules within the medium. (Viscosity is formally discussed in Chapters 12 and 13.) Therefore, higher viscosity mediums result in greater energy losses to heat through absorption than lower viscosity mediums.

2.2 Absorption and Frequency Dependence

If the frequency of the wave is increased, the amount of energy lost to heat increases. This fact should be intuitive since an increased frequency implies that the molecules are being "moved" more frequently. The simple demonstration of this mechanical interaction is rubbing your hands together. If you rub your hands together a few times per second, not much heat is generated. If instead you rub your hands together many times per second (higher frequency) significantly more heat will be produced. Therefore, higher frequency waves lose energy faster to heat through absorption than lower frequency waves.

3. Reflection

Reflection is formally defined as the phenomenon of causing a propagating wave to change direction such that some of the wave energy does not continue to propagate forward. More simply stated, reflection implies a change in energy propagation direction such that some of the energy returns in the general direction of the source.

Reflection is the foundation for diagnostic ultrasound. Unlike x-ray, which is based on transmitted energy, diagnostic ultrasound is based on receiving and processing the reflected energy. There are different types of reflection. Understanding the various types of reflection forms the foundation for understanding how to best utilize the imaging capabilities of ultrasound while simultaneously minimizing the number of mistakes leading to possible misdiagnoses.

The concept of reflection is certainly not new to any of us. Every one of us sees examples of reflection every day. Some examples include the reflection from looking in a mirror, seeing the reflection of car headlights off street signs, seeing the sunlight shimmering off a river or pond, and even hearing echoes from buildings or mountains. In fact, nearly everything we see is based on reflection of some sort. The easiest way to understand the aspect of reflection which is important to diagnostic ultrasound is to relate the concepts to every day occurrences with which we are already familiar. We will begin by considering how the different types of reflection occur based on the geometry of the interaction.

3.1 Geometric Aspects of Reflection

3.1.1 Defining Terms

The Angle of Incidence

Before discussing the types of reflection, we must define a system which standardizes an understanding of the wave direction relative to the reflecting structure. With respect to reflection, the angle formed between the wavefront and the interface of the reflecting structure is called the incident angle (angle of incidence).

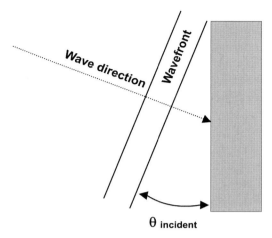

Fig. 1   **Measuring the Incident Angle**

Note: As defined, the incident angle is not the same as the angle formed between the wave propagation direction and the interface of the reflecting structure. In fact, these two angles are complements (add together to equal 90 degrees.) To make this point clear, we will need to discuss the difference between the wavefront and the wave direction.

Wavefront Versus Wave Direction

As the name suggests, the wavefront is the front surface of a wave. In contrast, in an undisturbed region of the wave, the wave direction is always perpendicular to the wavefront. The fact that the wave propagation direction is perpendicular to the wavefront is pretty intuitive if you consider your experience at the beach. If you are standing on shore, the wave direction is coming into shore, but the wavefront is perpendicular to the wave direction, and parallel to the shoreline.

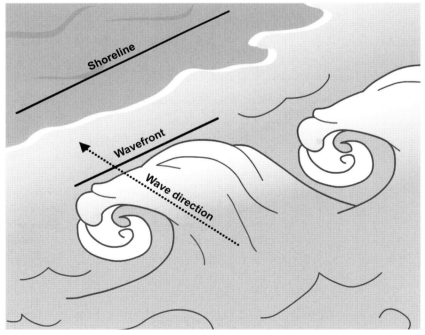

Fig. 2   **Wave Direction and Wavefront**

How to Define The Incident Angle Referenced to the Wave Direction
Since the wavefront and the wave direction are perpendicular (90 degrees apart), the incident angle can also be measured as the angle formed between the line perpendicular to the reflecting structure (called the normal line) and the wave direction. *Figure 3* demonstrates why both approaches to measuring the incident angle are equivalent. (If you recall similar triangles from geometry, the following figure demonstrates why these two approaches are equivalent.)

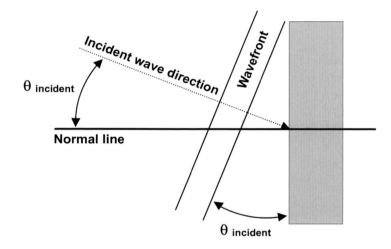

Fig. 3 **The Incident Angle**

Normal Incidence
The term "normal incidence" implies that the wavefront is parallel to the reflecting structure, or that the wave direction is parallel to the normal line. In other words, with normal incidence, the angle formed between the wave direction and the normal line is zero degrees. Normal incidence is illustrated in *Figure 4*.

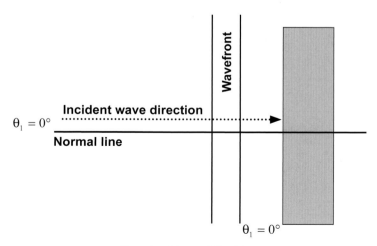

Fig. 4 **Normal Incidence**

Figure 5 is intended to clarify how the incident angle is specified when using a transducer.

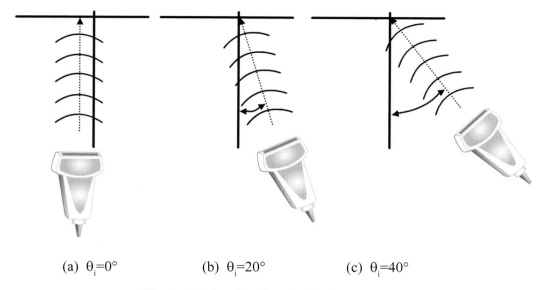

(a) $\theta_i = 0°$ (b) $\theta_i = 20°$ (c) $\theta_i = 40°$

Fig. 5   **Various Incident Angles**

View Animation and Image Library CD

The Angle of Reflection

The angle of reflection is measured using the same method as the angle of incidence, except using the reflected wavefront instead of the incident wavefront. Just as there are two equivalent ways of specifying the incident angle, there are two equivalent ways of specifying the reflected angle. For specular reflection, the angle of incidence is always equal to the angle of reflection. This fact is well known by anyone who has ever played billiards (pool) or racquetball. Of course in both of these examples, the presumption is made that the reflecting surface is smooth and that there is no spin involved, imparting angular momentum which would affect direction.

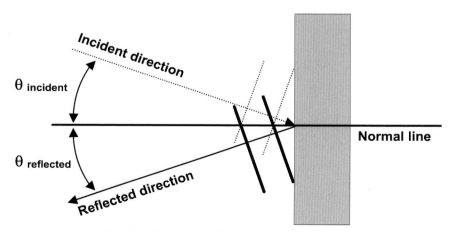

Fig. 6   **The Angle of Reflection**

The Angle of Transmission

As we will learn, at an interface or boundary between two different mediums, it is common to have a percentage of the wave energy reflect and a percentage of the wave energy that continues propagating through the second medium, referred to as the transmission percentage. Like the incident angle and the reflected angle, the transmission angle is also measured with respect to the angle formed by the wavefront and the reflecting surface. Of course, for the transmission angle, the angle is measured between the wavefront of the transmission wave and the reflecting surface. As with the incident angle and the reflected angle, this approach is equivalent to making the angular measurement between the transmitted wave direction and the line normal to the structure. *Figure 7* depicts all three angles in one diagram.

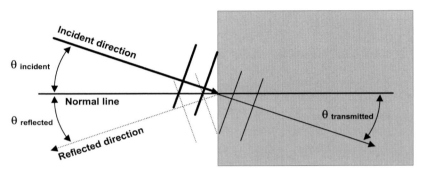

Fig. 7　**Angle of Transmission**

3.1.2 Specular Reflection

The word specular refers to a "mirror-like" reflection. Specular reflection occurs from a surface which is large and smooth relative to the wavelength of the wave. Some common examples are light from a mirror, reflections on the calm, smooth surface of a pond, and reflections from polished metal surfaces. For specular reflection, the angle of incidence always equals the angle of reflection. Therefore, the incident angle can dramatically affect where the reflection will appear. This angle dependence is one of the most critical parameters to understand regarding specular reflection.

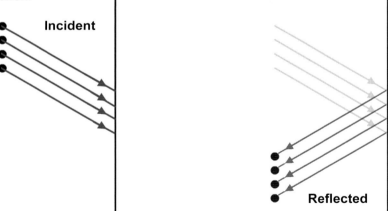

Fig. 8　**Specular Reflection**

View Animation and Image Library CD

3.1.3 (Back) Scattering

In contrast with specular reflection, scattering occurs when the surface of the reflecting surface is rough with respect to the wavelength. The resulting reflection is redirected in many different directions, hence the name "scattering". An example of scattering is the reflection of light from a shower glass door or the diffuse light that reflects back from a textured metal surface. Unlike specular reflection, scattering has little angular dependence.

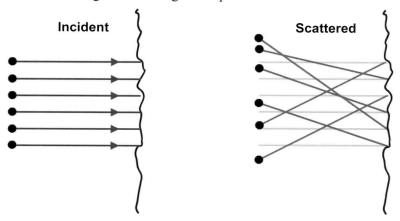

Fig. 9   **Back Scattering**

   **View Animation and Image Library CD**

3.1.4 Rayleigh Scattering

Rayleigh scattering occurs when the reflecting structures are very small with respect to the wavelength. Since the wavelength depends on the frequency, Rayleigh scattering is also frequency dependent. As the frequency of the wave increases, the wavelength decreases, making the structure look effectively larger. As a result, Rayleigh scattering increases with increasing frequency. Some common examples of Rayleigh scattering are light off the air molecules in the atmosphere and sound reflecting from red blood cells (RBCs).

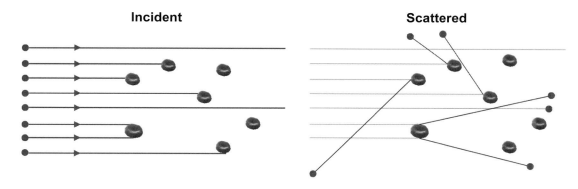

Fig. 10   **Rayleigh Scattering**

3.2 Acoustic Aspects of Reflection

If we return to our definition of a sound wave as a transfer of energy through mechanical interaction, we will discover the foundation for understanding reflection based on the acoustic parameters of the mediums. In the description of the wave propagation, recall that energy transferred as molecules were imparted with energy which caused a compression. In this description, there was no mention made of varying particle sizes or varying density in the undisturbed medium. Therefore, there was a tacit assumption that all of the particles were similar in size and the density uniform. The question is, what would happen if this assumption were not true?

3.2.1 Momentum Analogy

Imagine that you are playing marbles. Consider the difference when you roll a small marble at a very large marble (an aggie), versus rolling a small marble at another small marble. We will assume that you are a very good shot and can hit the target marble head on.

When the two marbles are of similar size, there is a significant transfer of energy from the rolled marble into the stationary marble. The result is that most of the momentum will be transferred to the small stationary marble and it will begin to roll. In comparison, when the small marble collides with the much larger marble, the large marble barely moves, but the small marble strongly reflects.

3.2.2 Defining the Acoustic Impedance

In physics, the momentum is determined by multiplying the mass of an object by its velocity, or:

$$momentum = m \times v$$

For molecules of a medium being mechanically displaced through wave propagation, we will replace the velocity of the marble with the velocity of the wave, c. Instead of referring to the mass of the marble, we will refer to the density of the molecules, ρ. Now the "momentum" transfer for a sound wave propagating through a medium will be related to the density times the propagation velocity. This term is given the name "acoustic impedance" denoted by the letter Z. Therefore, the acoustic impedance of a material is defined as:

$$Z = \rho \times c$$

The units for the acoustic impedance can be simply determined by multiplying the units for density (mass per volume) with the units for the propagation velocity (distance per time).

$$\text{units for } Z = \frac{kg}{m^3} * \frac{m}{sec} = \frac{kg}{m^2 sec}$$

This unit has been given the name of Rayls, or

$$1 \frac{kg}{m^2 sec} = 1 \ Rayl.$$

In the upcoming sections, we will see how the change in acoustic impedance from medium to medium or within a medium will affect the amount of reflection that occurs.

3.2.3 Impedance Mismatch Analogy

Now let's change our analogy so that we are rolling 100 marbles towards a paper wall. When the marbles are rolling through the air, there is no reflection. Since the air is relatively homogenous (constant throughout), there is no change in impedance and hence, no reflection. However, when the marbles encounter the paper wall, a transfer of momentum can occur. Imagine that the marbles are rolled hard enough such that only 27 of the 100 reflected back from the paper wall. If 27 are reflected back, 73 rolled right through the paper. In other words, there is a conservation of energy. All of the marbles either reflect back or transmit through. The reason for the reflection is clear, the paper wall represents a difference (mismatch) in impedance relative to the air.

Now repeat the process rolling 100 marbles but replace the paper wall with a cardboard wall. When the marbles encounter the cardboard wall, more will reflect back and fewer will transmit through. Since the cardboard represents a greater impedance mismatch, there will be more reflection and less transmission (similar to our momentum analogy). If the cardboard wall is replaced by a concrete wall, you can safely imagine that all of the marbles will reflect and none will transmit through the wall. In other words, as the impedance mismatch increases, the amount of reflection increases.

3.2.4 Conservation of Energy

From the impedance mismatch analogy, we saw that the reflected number of marbles plus the transmitted number of marbles equals the incident number of marbles. At an interface between two different mediums, the momentum was conserved and all of the energy was either reflected or transmitted. This analogy is actually a bit simplified because it ignores any energy lost to heat during the collision. In other words, if we assume that there is no energy lost to absorption, at an infinitesimal boundary between two mediums, the reflected energy plus the transmitted energy will equal the energy that arrived at that boundary. Written mathematically:

$$\text{Reflection \% + Transmission \% = 100\%.}$$

Therefore, making the presumption that there is no energy conversion to heat, calculating the reflection percentage also yields the transmission percentage simply by subtracting from 100% of the energy at that interface.

3.2.5 Reflection Equation

From our analogy, we can start to build an equation which will determine the percentage of reflection that will occur at an interface between two different mediums. First, we know that the amount of reflection increases with an increase in acoustic impedance mismatch. In other words, if the acoustic impedance of medium 1 is significantly different than the acoustic impedance of medium 2, there will be a large reflection.

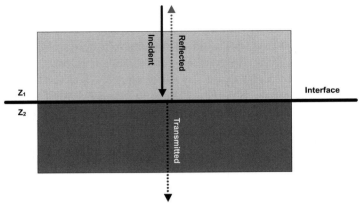

Fig. 11 **Reflection and Transmission**

Mathematically, a difference is represented by the operation of subtraction. Therefore, the reflection will depend on the difference in impedances or:

$$Reflected \propto \left(Z_2 - Z_1\right).$$

We would like to have a reference for our calculation of the reflected energy. The most common approach to giving a mathematical reference is to divide by a total to convert into a percentage. Therefore, by dividing by the total impedance, we will now have a percentage of reflection, or:

$$\% \, Reflected \propto \frac{\left(Z_2 - Z_1\right)}{\left(Z_2 + Z_1\right)}.$$

The last step is to determine the percentage of power and energy that is reflected. Since the acoustic impedance is a measure of amplitude, to convert an amplitude to power, the amplitude expression must be squared. Squaring the amplitude expression now yields the expression for percentage reflected energy, or:

$$\% \, Reflected = \frac{I_{reflected}}{I_{total}} = \left[\frac{Z_2 - Z_1}{Z_2 + Z_1}\right]^2.$$

As with our analogy, this equation presumes that the angle between the wavefront and the interface is 0 degrees (incident angle of 0 degrees which is the same as saying that the wave direction is perpendicular to the interface). There is a more complex form of the equation which accounts for oblique incidence discussed in Level 3. For now, this simplified form will be sufficient and will be useful in helping you intuitively realize how reflection and transmission occur.

3.2.6 Transmission Equation

We have already stated that presuming no absorption, the reflected energy plus the transmitted energy equals all of the energy at an interface. The simplest way to calculate the transmission percentage is to calculate the reflection percentage and subtract from 100% (or in decimal form to subtract from 1).

$$\% \, Transmitted = \frac{I_{transmitted}}{I_{total}} = 1 - \left[\frac{Z_2 - Z_1}{Z_2 + Z_1}\right]^2$$

Pegasus Lectures, Inc.

3.2.7 Applying the Concept of Acoustic Impedance Mismatch

The equations just derived show how the acoustic impedance mismatch is used to determine what percentage of the incident wave will be transmitted and what percentage will be reflected at an acoustic interface. When there is a large difference between the acoustic impedances of the two interfacing materials, there will be a large reflection and, correspondingly, a small transmission. When there is no acoustic impedance mismatch at a boundary, there will be no reflection and 100% transmission at that boundary. These two situations are illustrated in the following examples.

◊ **Example:** *What happens if* $Z_2 = Z_1$ *(no impedance mismatch)?*

$$Z_2 = Z_1 \Rightarrow \left[\frac{Z_2 - Z_1}{Z_2 + Z_1}\right]^2 = \left[\frac{0}{2Z}\right]^2 = 0 \Rightarrow \{\text{No Reflection}\}$$

In other words, if there is no acoustic impedance mismatch there will be no reflection, or, equivalently, 100% transmission.

◊ **Example:** *What happens if* Z_2 *is much greater than* Z_1 *,* $(Z_2 >> Z_1)$ *?*

$$(Z_2 >> Z_1) \Rightarrow \left[\frac{Z_2 - Z_1}{Z_2 + Z_1}\right]^2 \approx \left[\frac{Z_2}{Z_2}\right]^2 = 1 \Rightarrow \{100\% \text{ Reflection}\}$$

If Z_2 is significantly greater than Z_1, $Z_2 - Z_1$ is effectively equal to Z_2. For example $1000 - 1$ is almost equal to 1000. Similarly, $Z_2 + Z_1$ is also almost equal to Z_2.

4. Refraction

4.1 Refraction Defined

Up to this point, we have concentrated on the reflected energy. Presumably, any transmitted wave at an interface between two media would continue traveling in the same direction as before traversing the interface. This presumption is incorrect. Refraction is effectively the bending of the wave at an interface of two media. Refraction occurs due to a change in propagation velocity when the wave is incident at an angle other than normal (0 degrees). The phenomenon of refraction is most commonly exhibited by placing a spoon or pencil into a glass of water in bright sunlight. Since light travels at different velocities in the water, glass, and air, there is a bending of the light rays, making the spoon appear bent in the water.

4.2 Visualizing Refraction

As depicted in the *Figure 12*, assume that the propagation speed in medium 2 is higher than in medium 1. The resulting transmitted beam will bend to the right. The reason for this bending is shown by following the wavefront over time. While the entire wavefront is within medium 1, (from time t_1 through t_4), the propagation direction remains unaffected. Between times t_4 and t_5, the left edge of the wavefront travels through the interface and begins traveling at the faster velocity of medium 2. Note that during this time period, the right portion of the wavefront is still in medium 1, and is still traveling at the slower velocity, hence traveling a shorter distance. The difference in distances traveled during this time period is indicated by the varying length arrows.

By connecting the tips of these arrows, the new wavefront at time t_5 is visualized. You should note that this wavefront is now bent. Between times t_5 and t_6, the right edge of the waveform also transitions from the slower speed to the higher speed, but still travels a shorter distance than the left, which has spent the entire time period at the higher propagation velocity of medium 2. Between times t_6 and t_7, the entire wavefront is in the faster medium 2, and hence, the entire wavefront travels a uniform distance. Recall from earlier in this chapter (Section 3.1) that the wave direction is always perpendicular to the wavefront. By drawing the line perpendicular to the new wavefront at any time after time t_5, the new wave direction is depicted and refraction is apparent. In essence, the refraction is a distortion of the wavefront caused by one side of a wavefront traveling at a faster rate than the other side of the wavefront.

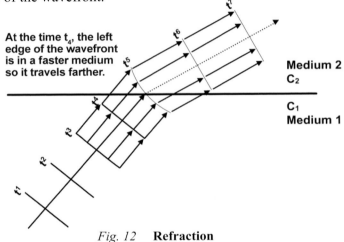

At the time t_4, the left edge of the wavefront is in a faster medium so it travels farther.

Medium 2
C_2

C_1
Medium 1

Fig. 12 **Refraction**

View Animation and Image Library CD

In this example, notice that the incident angle was oblique (other than 0 degrees) and that there was a change in propagation velocities between the two interfacing mediums. We will now consider what happens when either one of these two conditions does not hold.

4.3 Oblique Incidence but No Change in Propagation Velocities

Imagine in the last example if the propagation speeds were equal in both mediums, or $c_1 = c_2$. As depicted in *Figure 13*, even though the left edge of the wavefront arrived at the interface between the two mediums earlier than the right edge, since there was no change in propagation velocity, the left edge would continue to travel at the same rate as the right edge of the wavefront. Since the entire wavefront is traveling at the same velocity, there is no disparity in distance traveled which would distort the wavefront. As a result, there is no refraction. Therefore, for refraction to exist, there must be a change in propagation velocities between the two interfacing mediums. Clearly, the greater the difference in propagation velocities, the greater the degree of refraction that can occur.

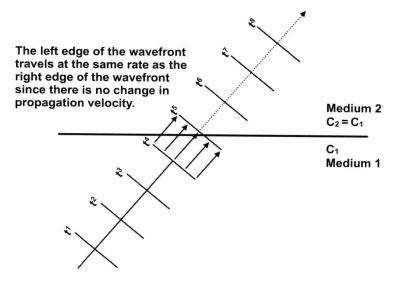

The left edge of the wavefront travels at the same rate as the right edge of the wavefront since there is no change in propagation velocity.

Medium 2
$C_2 = C_1$

C_1
Medium 1

Fig. 13   **No Refraction if No Change in Propagation Velocity**

4.4 Normal Incidence (Incident angle = 0 degrees)

Imagine now if a wave has normal incidence to an interface between two mediums, and that the propagation velocities are significantly different. Will there be any refraction?

Before we illustrate this example, we will again review what it means to have a normal beam. Since there are so many different ways of expressing this concept, this is usually a point of confusion for many students.

As expressed earlier in this chapter, the angle of incidence, the angle of reflection, and the angle of transmission can be measured two different ways. In general, since the wave direction is easily depicted as a ray (an arrow tipped line), the preferred method for measuring the angle is between the wave direction relative to the normal (the line which is perpendicular to the interface). In other words, when a sound beam direction of travel is perpendicular to an interface, (90°), the incident angle is 0°. If the direction of travel is 30° to the interface, then the angle of incidence is 90° - 30° = 60°. These two examples are depicted in *Figure 14* and *Figure 15*.

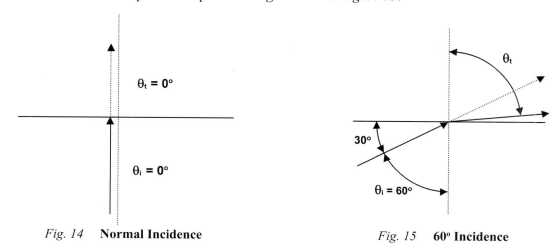

$\theta_t = 0°$

$\theta_i = 0°$

θ_t

30°

$\theta_i = 60°$

Fig. 14   **Normal Incidence**   *Fig. 15*   **60° Incidence**

The key is to pay particular attention to the wording. All of the following statements are equivalent

- Normal incidence
- Beam perpendicular to the interface
- Beam orthogonal to the interface
- Beam at 90 degrees to the interface
- 0 degree incident angle
- Wavefront parallel to the interface

We are now ready to determine the outcome of a beam at normal incidence with an interface with varying propagation velocities.

For this example, from the *Figure 16*, it is clear that the propagation velocity in medium 2 is higher than the propagation velocity in medium 1. This fact is demonstrated by the wavefronts being drawn farther apart in time in medium 2 than in medium 1.

Note: As the wavefront approaches the interface, since the wavefront is parallel to the interface, the entire wavefront reaches the interface at the same time. The result is that the entire wavefront accelerates at the same time. As a result, there is no distortion of the wavefront, and because the wave is allowed to travel faster, there has been no redirection of the wave. In other words, when there is normal incidence, there is no refraction.

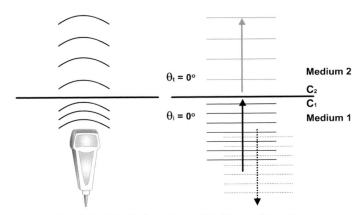

Fig. 16   **No Refraction with Normal Incidence**

4.5 Snell's Law

4.5.1 The Equation
Not surprisingly, there is a mathematical expression which predicts when refraction will occur, and to what degree. The rule which predicts the amount of refraction is called Snell's law. From our discussions above, it should be evident that Snell's law will involve the propagation velocity in the incident medium and the propagation velocity in the transmitted medium (the medium into which the wave propagates as it crosses the interface). Also, it should not be surprising that Snell's law will also involve the incident angle. Snell's law relates the ratio of the propagation velocities with the ratio of the sines of the incident and transmitted angles, or:

$$\text{Snell's law: } \frac{c_i}{c_t} = \frac{sin(\theta_i)}{sin(\theta_t)}.$$

Snell's law can be written in many different forms by simple mathematical manipulation as discussed in Chapter 1. For example, all of the following forms express Snell's law:

$$c_i \bullet sin\left(\theta_t\right) = c_t \bullet sin\left(\theta_i\right)$$

$$c_i = c_t \bullet \frac{sin\left(\theta_i\right)}{sin\left(\theta_t\right)}$$

$$\frac{c_i}{sin\left(\theta_i\right)} = \frac{c_t}{sin\left(\theta_t\right)}$$

Figure 17 puts all of the pieces discussed to this point together, illustrating the terms referenced in Snell's law.

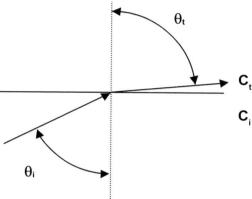

Fig. 17   **Depiction of Variables in Snell's Law**

Note: Snell's Law determines the presence and amount of refraction; it does not tell what percentage of the incident beam energy is transmitted and what percentage of the beam energy is reflected. The amount of reflection and transmission is determined by the acoustic impedance mismatch.

4.5.2 Determining Degrees of Refraction from the Transmission Angle

Another common point of confusion is determining when there is refraction from the application of Snell's law. Quite simply, refraction exists when the transmitted angle does <u>not</u> equal the incident angle, or $\theta_i \neq \theta_t$. (The greater the difference between the incident and transmitted angle, the greater the amount of refraction.) Consider the following two diagrams.

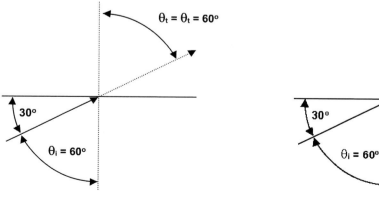

Fig. 18   **No Refraction**   Fig. 19   **20° of Refraction**

In the first example, *Figure 18*, the transmitted angle is equal to the incident angle. For these two angles to be equal, the wave direction cannot have changed as the wave crossed the interface, and hence, there is no refraction. In the second example, *Figure 19*, the transmitted angle is larger than the incident angle by 20 degrees. In other words, the wave direction has been changed by 20 degrees. Clearly, the greater the difference between the incident angle and the transmitted angle, the greater the amount of refraction.

It is unfortunate that sometimes the transmitted angle is also referred to as the refraction angle. This nomenclature is poor since a transmitted angle may exist when there is no refraction. As illustrated, in *Figure 18*, the transmitted angle is 60 degrees. Referring to this angle as the refraction angle is very confusing since, in this case, there is no refraction. Within this text, we will always refer to the angle on the transmitted side as the "transmitted angle" and avoid the confusion associated with naming that angle the "refraction angle".

4.6 The Critical Angle

We have already seen that there can be no refraction if the incident angle is 0 degrees, or if there is no change in propagation velocity across an interface. Clearly, as the change in propagation velocity increases, or as the beam gets farther away from normal incidence, the amount of refraction will increase. It is possible to get so much refraction that none of the incident beam will transmit across the interface, causing total internal reflection. The incident angle at which total internal reflection occurs is called the critical angle.

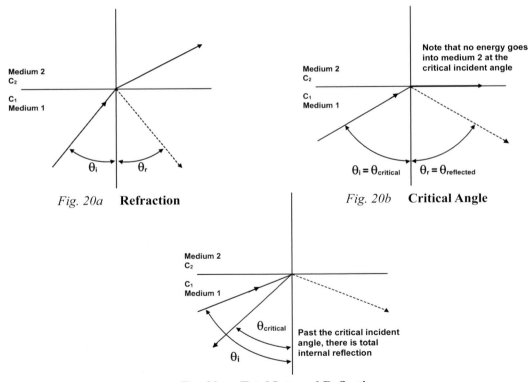

Fig. 20a   **Refraction**

Fig. 20b   **Critical Angle**

Fig. 20c   **Total Internal Reflection**

Notice that in *Figure 20a*, the incident angle is smaller than the critical angle, so there is still some transmission, albeit refracted. In *Figure 20b*, the incident angle exactly equals the critical angle, resulting in the refracted beam traveling along the interface between the two media. In *Figure 20c*, the incident angle is larger than the critical angle resulting in total internal reflection.

5. Conceptual Questions   Answers Pg. 449-450

1. _____ means a diminishing or decrease.

2. Attenuation is the result of three wave interactions with the medium: _____, _____, and _____.

3. In soft tissue, _____ is the dominant factor creating attenuation.

4. _____ is the conversion of energy from sound waves into heat within the medium.

5. Absorption increases with increasing _____.

6. The word _____ refers to the "bending" of a ray or beam at an interface between two different media.

7. Refraction is governed by _____ law.

8. _____ law for refraction depends on the ratio of the propagation velocities of two different media at an interface and the incident angle.

9. The term _____ in reference to angles means the same as zero degree incidence.

10. For _____ incidence there can be no _____.

11. For normal incidence, the amount of reflection is determined by the acoustic _____ mismatch.

12. The acoustic impedance has units of _____.

13. The acoustic impedance equals the _____ times the _____ _____.

14. Density has units of kg/m^3 and the propagation velocity has units of m/sec. So 1 Rayl equals _____.

15. A large impedance mismatch will result in a high percentage of _____ or, equivalently, a _____ percentage of transmission.

16. No _____ mismatch will result in no reflection or, equivalently, 100% _____.

17. The amount of refraction is given by _____ law, whereas the amount of _____ is given by an equation based on the acoustic impedance mismatch.

18. The acoustic impedance of air is _____ than the acoustic impedance of tissue.

19. _____ reflection occurs from surfaces which are large and smooth with respect to the wavelength.

20. A mirror gives a good example of _____ reflection.

21. _____ occurs from surfaces which are small or rough with respect to the _____.

22. _____ _____ refers to the frequency dependency of scattering. Rayleigh scattering of light through the atmosphere causes the sky to appear blue.

6. Ultrasound Terminology

6.1 Echogenicity

Echogenicity refers to the strength and/or type of the signal reflection. There are at least five terms which are used to refer to the strength of the echo.

Anechoic:
No echogenicity
(no or almost no reflected signal)

Example: fluids, cysts, lipids and/or intraplaque hemorrhage

Fig. 21a **Anechoic mass (cyst) in the liver**

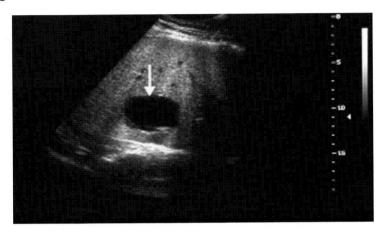

Hypoechoic:
Low echogenicity
(low level reflected signals)

Example: fatty plaque, some masses

Fig. 21b **A small (5-6 mm) hypoechoic mass in the liver compatible with metastatic disease**

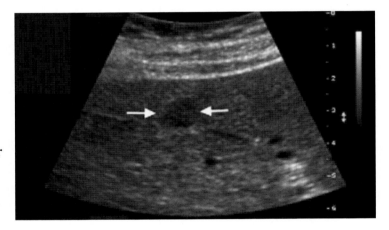

Hyperechoic:
High echogenicity
(moderate to high reflected signals)

Example: fibrous plaque, any specular reflectors

Fig. 21c **Transverse view through a normal liver with a hyperechoic or echogenic area in the liver which is from the ligamentum teres**

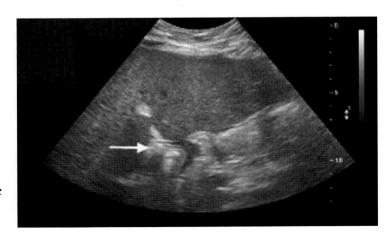

Pegasus Lectures, Inc.

Calcified:
Strongly echogenic usually with acoustic shadowing

Fig. 21d **Calcified Plaque with Acoustic Shadowing at the Origin of the Internal Carotid Artery**

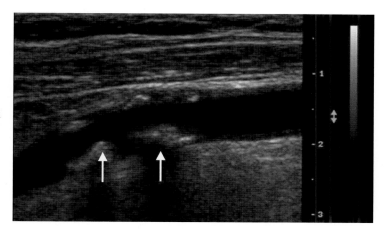

Complex:
Mixed echogenicity with or without acoustic shadowing

Fig. 21e **Complicated Plaque with Multiple Levels of Echoes at the Origin of the Internal Carotid Artery**

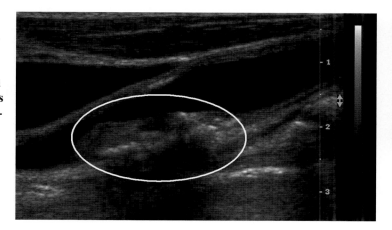

6.2 Uniformity

There are two terms which are used to refer to how uniform the signal is. Homogenous, or homogeneity, implies that the signal is relatively uniform. Heterogeneous, or heterogeneity, implies that there is variation within the signal. These terms can be applied to any aspect of the image including the characteristic appearance of tissue, thrombus, plaque, etc. These terms become very important when referring to plaques since heterogeneous plaques tend to be less stable and have a greater risk of hemorrhage and creating embolic events.

It is also important to realize that the terms for "uniformity" refer to the appearance of the image and not the actual characteristic of the tissue itself. If a tissue were truly homogenous, it would appear black since there would be no reflection based on the absence of an acoustic impedance mismatch (like fluids). When a structure appears homogenous in an image, it really implies that the variation within the medium is uniform, not that the medium itself is purely uniform.

View Animation and Image Library CD

6.3 Plaque Surface Characteristics

a) Smooth: Continuous intimal surface, tends to be less symptomatic and more stable

b) Irregular: Discontinuous intimal surface, tends to be more symptomatic and less stable (more likely to embolize)

7. Attenuation Rates

7.1 Table of Attenuation Rates

As a result of scattering, refraction, and absorption, the intensity of the ultrasound beam decreases as it travels through the medium. Since scattering and absorption increase with frequency, the amount of attenuation is frequency dependent as well as depth and medium dependent.

Soft tissue attenuation rate:	0.5 dB/(cm-MHz)
Muscle attenuation rate:	1.0 dB/(cm-MHz)
Blood attenuation rate:	0.125 dB/(cm-MHz)

Table 1: **Attenuation Rates**

Notice how the values in the table are exact multiples of each other. These values have been simplified so as to be easier to remember and apply. A more complete and precise table exists in Level 3.

Note: The denominator is comprised of two different units, cm and MHz. Be sure not to confuse the dash in the denominator with subtraction. Look carefully at the examples below to make sure that you understand this notation.

7.2 Calculating Approximate Attenuation

Perhaps the biggest cause of error in calculating the attenuation is not paying close enough attention to whether the problem is asking for a roundtrip attenuation, or a one-way attenuation. The following examples will illustrate how the difference in wording indicates one-way versus roundtrip measurement.

◊ **Example:** In soft tissue, what is the attenuation of a 5 MHz ultrasound beam at a depth of 10 cm?

$$\left(\frac{0.5 \text{ dB}}{(cm\text{-}MHz)} \right) \times \left(10 \text{ cm} \right) \times \left(5 \text{ MHz} \right) = 25 \text{ dB attenuation.}$$

Note: The wording expresses "at a depth of 10 cm" and does not imply roundtrip. As a result, the total distance traveled is 10 cm, not 20 cm.

◊ **Example:** In soft tissue, what is the attenuation of a 5 MHz ultrasound beam imaging to a depth of 10cm?

$$\left(\frac{0.5\ \text{dB}}{(cm \cdot MHz)}\right) \times (20\ cm) \times (5\ MHz) = 50\ \text{dB attenuation.}$$

Note: In contrast with the first example, the second example implies a round-trip calculation. To image a structure at a depth of 10 cm implies that the beam must travel 10 cm to the structure and reflect back another 10 cm. The total distance traveled is 20 cm.

7.3 Interpreting Calculated Attenuation

In the last example, we calculated an attenuation of 50 dB. Recall that decibels are a logarithmic power ratio. As a review of logarithms, we will translate the answer of 50 dB back into an intensity (which is directly related to power) ratio.

$$-50\ \text{dB} = 10\ \log\left(\frac{I_f}{I_i}\right)$$

$$-\frac{50}{10} = \log\left(\frac{I_f}{I_i}\right)$$

$$10^{(-5)} = \frac{I_f}{I_i}$$

$$\frac{1}{100,000} = \frac{I_f}{I_i}$$

In other words, the beam intensity for imaging a 10 cm depth is 1/100,000 the original beam intensity. Recall that in this problem we assumed no muscle, only "soft tissue," a relatively unlikely scenario. The attenuation rate in muscle is greater than the attenuation rate in soft tissue. Since it is unlikely that there would be no muscle imaging to a depth of 10 cm, the attenuation of 50 dB calculated is likely lower than the attenuation in reality.

Given the result of this calculation, it should be evident why you are not likely to use a 5 MHz transducer imaging at a 10 cm depth. Since the attenuation is frequency dependent, using a higher frequency would result in even more attenuation. This example illustrates the first half of the classic trade off in ultrasound between attenuation and resolution.

Note: The word attenuation means a decrease and implies a negative sign.

8. Absorption in the Body

In Level 1 we discussed how absorption is the conversion of wave energy into heat. There are two critical points to be made about absorption which will be discussed in 8.1 and 8.2.

8.1 In Soft Tissue, Absorption is the Dominant Factor Creating Attenuation

Rephrased, this statement means that within "soft tissue", more of the energy is lost to heating the tissue than is redirected through reflection or refraction. This fact is important for two reasons: first, absorption reduces the amount of the energy that there is to reflect, reducing penetration and signal strength; second, since the energy being absorbed causes tissue heating, there is a potential risk of thermal tissue damage, or thermal bioeffects.

8.2 Absorption Increases Exponentially with Increasing Frequency

This point is critical since it tells you something about the rate at which the energy is absorbed. Recall from the math section that an exponential relationship means that small changes in one variable cause much larger changes in the related variable. In this case, a slight increase in the transmit frequency, or operating frequency, will cause significantly more absorption. This fact should be well known to you, since there is always significantly less penetration using a higher frequency transducer than a lower frequency transducer while imaging (assuming conventional imaging techniques). Also, the fact that the rate of attenuation is exponential with increasing frequency will help determine the processing steps and control adjustments necessary on the imaging system. Therefore, this concept will be important for understanding system operations discussed in Chapter 6.

8.3 Fluids and Absorption

Fluids tend to absorb less sound energy than soft tissue. Recall from Level 1 that the energy loss to heat is related to the density and the viscosity of the medium. In general, fluids have lower densities and lower viscosities than tissues. Water has a very low absorption rate.

This fact is important since:

1. Fetal imaging involves scanning through amniotic fluid which is primarily water.
2. Pelvic scanning usually involves scanning through a full bladder. Scanning through a fluid filled cystic structure changes the attenuation rate relative to nearby tissue (producing what is generally referred to as enhancement artifact).
4. Sound attenuation in a fluid is lower than in tissue, so when scanning through a fluid-filled region, the thermal index models may underestimate the maximum temperature rise (discussed in Chapter 9).
5. Imaging of fluid-filled phantoms for Doppler do not necessarily accurately mimic the behavior of true in vivo scanning (discussed in Chapter 11).
6. Whales can communicate very long distances in water; as much as 600 to 1,000 miles. (Maybe this will not be on any exam, but it is still neat to know.)

9. Reflection in the Body Based on Geometric Conditions

9.1 Specular Reflection

In Level 1 we discussed three distinct types of reflection which can occur at an interface or boundary. Specular reflection is the strongest reflective mode, but is highly angle dependent. Therefore, a distinction must be made between the strength of the reflection and the strength of the reflection received back to the transducer. For specular reflection, if the reflected angle returns the signal back in the receiving path of the ultrasound transducer, then specular reflection will yield the strongest signals. In contrast, for a pure specular reflector, if the reflection angle directs the reflected signal away from the receive path of the transducer, then no signal will be registered.

Notice that we referred to a "pure" specular reflector. A pure specular reflector results in only specular reflection and virtually no scattering at all. In practical terms, most structures in the body are not pure specular reflectors, generating some scattering as well. In essence, you can think of reflection as a spectrum of effects. There are clearly some structures which are very strong specular reflectors, there are certainly some tissues which behave generally as a source for scattering, and some structures which behave primarily as Rayleigh scatterers.

9.1.1 Examples of Specular Reflectors

Some examples of relatively strong specular reflectors are:

- The diaphragm
- Boundaries between organs
- Vessel walls
- Heart walls
- Valve leaflets
- Calcifications
- Fascial sheathing
- The surface of bones and tendons
- The surface of a fluid-filled or air-filled cavity
- Prosthetic valves
- Biopsy needles and catheters
- Pacemakers and pacemaker wires
- Some prosthetic implants

Fig. 22a **Specular Reflection from the Humeral Head in the Shoulder**

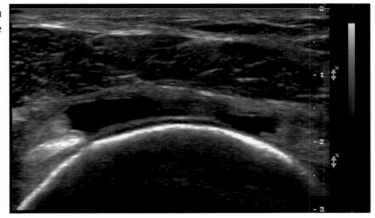

Fig. 22b **Specular Reflection from the Anterior leaflet of the Mitral Valve and Aortic Valve Cusp**

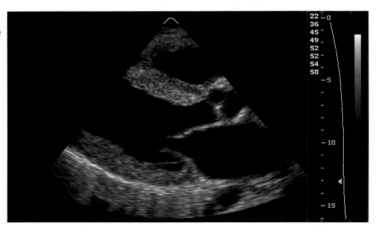

Fig. 22c **Specular Reflection from a Prosthetic Mitral Valve**

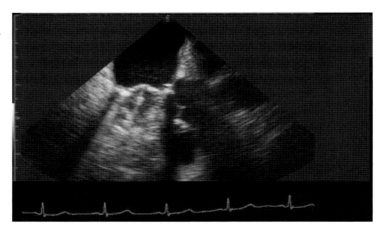

Fig. 22d **Fetal neck: Specular Reflections from Spiny Processes and the Cranial Bone**

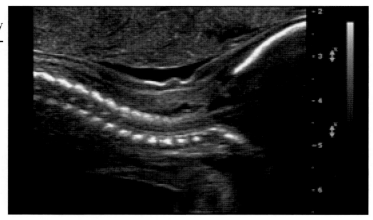

9.1.2 Specular Reflection the Principal Source of Imaging Artifacts

Although the formal discussion of artifacts is in Chapter 8, for now, it is valuable to develop the relationship between the mechanism of specular reflection and the concept of artifactual data. As you will learn, artifacts will sometimes lead to a conclusion that disease is present when it is not, or that disease is absent when it really is present. Either way, a wrong conclusion is reached which certainly does not help the patient. From understanding the physics of the mechanisms which cause the artifacts, these mistakes can often be avoided.

The primary mechanism for generating imaging artifacts is specular reflection. Note that this statement is not the same as stating that specular reflection is the only source for imaging artifacts. There most certainly are other mechanisms besides specular reflection as the source of imaging artifacts. However, the preponderance of artifacts is the result of beam interaction with a structure that is large and smooth with respect to the wavelength, or specular reflection. It cannot be overstated that the direction of specular reflection depends heavily on the angle of incidence. Therefore, the first and most important point for understanding imaging artifacts is assessing the incident angle with respect to the specular reflecting structures.

9.1.3 Identifying Specular Reflection Based Artifacts (Step-by-Step)

Step 1:

When imaging, or viewing an ultrasound image, the first step should always be to identify the structures which potentially could generate specular reflections, principally in the relative near-field. In general, the relative near-field refers to structures that are at 5 cm deep or shallower. This does not mean that specular reflectors deeper than 5 cm cannot cause artifacts; it is just that the increased path length to deeper structures results in attenuation and timing effects which tend to reduce the severity of these effects. Whenever specular reflectors are present in the relative near field, you can be pretty certain that some imaging artifacts will be present.

Step 2:

Once specular reflectors have been identified, the second step is to determine the angle of incidence formed between the wave direction (ultrasound beam) and the surface of the specular reflectors. This step requires that you understand how ultrasound images are created using different transducer types and imaging formats. Viewing the exact same structures, the image appearance and even presence of specular reflection based artifacts will vary significantly depending on the imaging format being used (unsteered linear, steered linear, curved linear, or sector).

Step 3:

The third step is then to assess where the specular reflection will travel and the propensity for this energy to produce an artifact. To successfully complete this step, you must become familiar with the primary mechanisms which can cause specular related artifactual images and structures. Fortunately, based on the physics, there are really only two mechanisms, specifically a redirection of the beam from the presumed straight path, and a reverberation. Both of these mechanisms are formally discussed in Chapter 8. As a note, although there are only a few mechanisms, unfortunately, the names for these artifacts has generally been based in the appearance of the artifacts in the image, and not based on the mechanism of creation. As a result, there are many names for artifacts based on how they appear, all which have the same mechanism of creation. As if recognizing and minimizing artifacts is not challenging enough, the problem is confounded by a myriad of names such as ring down artifact, comet tail artifact, mirroring artifact, multi-path artifact, etc. (discussed in Chapter 8, Artifacts).

Step 4:

Given that there is a likely source and mechanism of artifact in an image, the next step should be to vary the incident angle. In general, structures that are real should maintain the same relative location within the image no matter the angle. When artifacts based on specular reflection exist, a change in angle usually causes a change in either appearance or relative location of structures. It is important to realize that changing the angle may introduce new artifacts. Therefore, repeating the steps listed above is necessary each time the angle is changed. This change in angle can be achieved by changing the steering (for transducers with steering capability – see Chapter 5), rocking the transducer (both heel-to-toe and elevationally), and using a different imaging window.

This methodical process should become routine for every imaging or interpretation session. Without a methodical, physics based approach as just introduced, artifacts are often unrecognized. The result can be an inaccurate or even completely incorrect diagnoses. The goal is to reduce these errors by reducing the very complex situation of imaging to manageable, somewhat controllable, understood steps.

Note: It is strongly suggested that you reread Section 9.1.3 as you begin studying Chapter 8 on artifacts.

9.2 Scattering in the Body

9.2.1 Speckle and "Tissue Texture"

In part, the appearance of tissue texture in an ultrasound image is created by scattering. As discussed in Level 1, scattering occurs when the surface characteristics of the tissue are "rough" with respect to the wavelength. In other words, when the variation in the tissue texture is larger than the wavelength, the wave energy is scattered. In essence, each region of tissue acts as its own transmitter, scattering signals in many different directions. Since the distance from each point in the tissue to different locations on the transducer face is different, there are small time delays between the receiving of these reflections. When these signals are added together, there is some partial constructive and destructive interference, resulting in larger and smaller signals. The result is the appearance of a "speckle" pattern, giving the impression of tissue texture.

With increasing frequency, the wavelength decreases. As the wavelength decreases, the different distances from each point in the tissue to the transducer face becomes a larger percentage of the shorter wavelength. As a result, the waves go from constructive interference to destructive interference over a smaller region. The result is a finer speckle pattern, as is generally perceived when using higher frequency transducers. *Figures 23a* and *23b* demonstrate the difference in speckle pattern when imaging thyroid tissue.

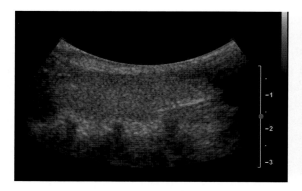
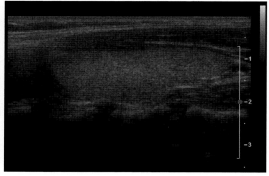

Fig. 23a **Coarse Speckle Pattern (loss of definition between muscle and gland)**

Fig. 23b **Fine Speckle Pattern (neck muscles visible anterior to thyroid)**

9.2.2 Examples of Scattering in the Body

Whereas the boundaries between organs tend to be primarily specular reflectors, the tissues themselves are generally scatterers. Heart muscle, skeletal muscle, liver parenchyma, and kidney, are all good examples of tissues that primarily cause scattering.

9.3 Rayleigh Scattering

9.3.1 Wavelength Relative to Red Blood Cells (RBCs)

The diameter of a red blood cell is typically 6 to 8 μm. From Chapter 2, we learned that the wavelength for diagnostic ultrasound at 5 MHz is about 308 μm. At 10 MHz, the wavelength decreases to 154 μm. Even at this very high imaging frequency, the wavelength is still much, much larger than the size of a red blood cell. Since Rayleigh scattering occurs when the reflectors are very small with respect to the wavelength, reflection from blood is predominantly Rayleigh.

9.3.2 Some Consequences of Rayleigh Scattering

Excluding pure specular reflection at an angle which results in no energy reflected back to the transducer, Rayleigh scattering is clearly the weakest reflective mechanism for imaging. As we will learn in the upcoming sections, the acoustic impedance of the RBCs is relatively close to the acoustic impedance of the plasma, further exacerbating this weak reflection. As a result, for conventional imaging frequencies, the reflection from blood is a much weaker signal than the reflection from tissue. The result is that blood pools generally appear dark in an ultrasound image. Whereas there are conditions where blood visualization occurs (see spontaneous contrast in Chapter 7), it is not the norm.

Since Rayleigh scattering is a weak reflective mode, for Doppler, it is absolutely critical that all precautions are taken to maximize signal strength. In essence, this fact requires that lower frequencies should be used for almost all Doppler imaging. The only exceptions to this rule are when the imaging is relatively superficial. As discussed previously, as the frequency increases, the wavelength decreases, making the red blood cells "appear" larger, thereby increasing the amount of scattering. In fact, Rayleigh scattering predicts that the amount of scattering increases as the fourth power of the frequency. For superficial imaging, this relationship between frequency and increased scattering implies that using a higher frequency will produce a stronger Doppler signal. However, penetrating through more tissue for deeper imaging, the increased attenuation more than dominates the increased scattering, resulting in weaker signals. As a result, for deeper Doppler imaging, if the frequency used is too high, there may be inadequate signal strength to accurately detect the blood flow.

9.4 Reflection in the Body Based on Acoustic Aspects

9.4.1 The Acoustic Impedance Mismatch

In Level 1 we determined that the percentage of reflection (for normal incidence) is determined by the equation:

$$\% \ Reflected = \frac{I_{reflected}}{I_{total}} = \left[\frac{Z_2 - Z_1}{Z_2 + Z_1} \right]^2 .$$

Of course the reality is that the beam is not always normally incident to all structures. In Level 3, the equation which predicts percentage reflection for non-normal incidence is given. For intuitive understanding (and for board level questions), knowing the equation only for normal incidence is acceptable. At varying angles, the percentage reflection decreases. Therefore the equation for normal incidence gives an upper band on the percentage reflection.

9.4.2 The Acoustic Impedance

Before we begin applying the reflected energy equation, we should review what determines the acoustic impedance of a material. The acoustic impedance is calculated as $Z = \rho \times c$. Recalling that more dense materials generally have a higher bulk modulus (lower compressibility), we would expect dense materials to also have a higher propagation velocity. As a result, more dense materials generally have much higher acoustic impedances because both the density and the propagation velocity are increased.

Consider the difference in acoustic impedance between a ceramic material and tissue. The density and propagation velocity of a stiff crystal will both be significantly higher than the density and propagation velocity of tissue. Therefore, the acoustic impedance of the crystal will be much greater than the acoustic impedance of the tissue.

In Level 3, a table of acoustic impedances is listed for general knowledge and for further developing intuitive reasoning.

9.4.3 Examples

◊ **Example 1:** Given that the acoustic impedance of a PZT crystal is 38 MRayls, and the acoustic impedance of tissue is approximately 2 MRayls, how much reflection will occur at the interface of a crystal put directly on this tissue?

Fig. 24 **Acoustic Impedance Mismatch between PZT and Tissue**

The reflection at the interface between the crystal and the tissue is calculated by plugging the impedance values into the reflection percentage equation developed in Section 3.2.5. Ideally, there would be 100% transmission into the patient and no reflection at the surface.

$$\% \ Reflected = \left[\frac{38 \ \text{MRayls} - 2 \ \text{MRayls}}{38 \ \text{MRayls} + 2 \ \text{MRayls}} \right]^2 = \left[\frac{36}{40} \right]^2 = \left[\frac{4 \times 9}{4 \times 10} \right]^2 = \left[\frac{9}{10} \right]^2 = 0.81$$

Note: Since the expression is squared, it does not matter which medium is considered to be medium 1 and which is considered to be medium 2.

So at the surface, 81% of the energy is reflected right back into the transducer. This is the same as stating that only 19% of the energy is transmitted into the patient, a far cry from the desired 100%. If this seems bad, the situation is actually worse than it already appears. As the sound propagates into the body, most of the sound will be absorbed, and only small fractions of the non-absorbed remaining percentage (from the 19%) will reflect back. On return, the small fraction then encounters the same acoustic impedance mismatch, this time going from the low impedance of the tissue to the higher impedance of the crystal. The result is 81% of that very small percentage will be reflected right back into the body and only 19% will be received by the crystal.

$$\text{Roundtrip} = 0.19 \times 0.19 = 0.036 \text{ or } 3.6\%$$

Effectively only 3.6% of the signal that is not absorbed and which reflects back from the very small mismatches within the tissues is received, which is essentially 0. This fact serves as the motivation for designing transducers with a material that is affixed to the front of the crystal called a matching layer.

◊ ***Example 2:*** As just demonstrated, since the acoustic impedance mismatch between a crystal material and tissue is so great, there is very poor transmission into and out of the patient. By adding an intermediate material called a matching layer, the effective mismatch can be reduced to improve efficiency in both directions. Imagine that a matching layer with an acoustic impedance of 10 MRayls is placed between the crystal and the patient. What is the net effect?

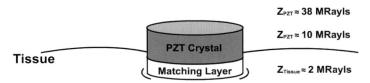

Fig. 25 **Impedance Matching**

To solve this problem we will have to perform two calculations. The first calculation will be to determine the percentage of energy which is transmitted into the matching layer. The second calculation will determine the percentage transferred from the matching layer to the patient.

$$\% \ Reflected = \left[\frac{38 \text{ MRayls} - 10 \text{ MRayls}}{38 \text{ MRayls} + 10 \text{ MRayls}} \right]^2 = \left[\frac{28}{48} \right]^2 = \left[\frac{4 \times 7}{4 \times 12} \right]^2 = \left[\frac{7}{12} \right]^2 = 0.34$$

So 100% - 34% = 66% of the energy is transferred into the matching layer. We now need to calculate the transmission efficiency into the patient.

$$\% \ Reflected = \left[\frac{38 \text{ MRayls} - 2 \text{ MRayls}}{38 \text{ MRayls} + 2 \text{ MRayls}} \right]^2 = \left[\frac{8}{12} \right]^2 = \left[\frac{4 \times 2}{4 \times 3} \right]^2 = \left[\frac{2}{3} \right]^2 = 0.44$$

So 56% of the energy that penetrates into the matching layer is transmitted into the patient. Since only 66% of the total transmitted energy made it into the matching layer, we must multiply the two percentages to get the overall efficiency of transfer.

$$\text{Overall one way percentage} = 0.66 \times 0.56 = 0.37 \text{ or } 37\%$$

Again, since on return, the signal encounters the same mismatch, we must square this percentage or:

$$\text{roundtrip percentage} = 0.37 \times 0.37 = 0.14 \text{ or } 14\%$$

Although 14% is not wonderful, it is almost 4 times greater than the overall transmission efficiency without a matching layer (3.6% as calculated in the previous example).

◊ **Example 3:**   In the last two examples there is an implicit assumption that is not true. Although there is no mention made, the assumption must be that there is no air trapped between the surface of the transducer and the surface of the skin. For this example, given that air has an acoustic impedance of approximately 0.0004 MRayls, let's remove the artificial assumption and see what happens.

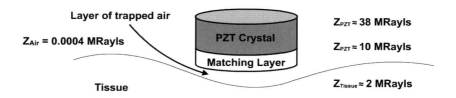

Fig. 26   **High Impedance Mismatch with Air**

To fully solve the problem, we would need to perform the calculation three times, one for each interface. However, since the mismatch between the matching layer and the air is so enormous, we can pretty quickly answer this question practically by stating that there will be virtually 100% reflection at the air to matching layer interface, resulting in no transmission. For completeness sake, we will perform the calculation anyway.

Note that the first calculation was already performed in Example 2. So we already know that 66% of the transmitted energy is transferred to the matching layer. Now let's calculate the percentage transferred from the matching layer into the air boundary.

$$\% \, Reflected = \left[\frac{10 \text{ MRayls} - 0.0004 \text{ MRayls}}{10 \text{ MRayls} + 0.0004 \text{ MRayls}}\right]^2 = \left[\frac{9.9996}{10.0004}\right]^2 = 0.9998 \text{ or } 99.98\%$$

100% - 99.98% = 0.02% of the energy is transferred from the matching layer to the air. We now need to calculate the transmission efficiency into the patient from the air.

$$\% \, Reflected = \left[\frac{2 \text{ MRayls} - 0.0004 \text{ MRayls}}{2 \text{ MRayls} + 0.0004 \text{ MRayls}}\right]^2 = \left[\frac{1.9996}{2.0004}\right]^2 = 0.9992 \text{ or } 99.92\%$$

So 0.08% of the energy that penetrates into the air is transmitted into the patient. Since only 66% of the total transmitted energy made it into the matching layer, and only 0.02% made it from the matching layer into the air, and then only 0.08% of that made it into the patient, we must multiply the three percentages to get the overall efficiency of transfer.

Overall one way percentage = $0.66 \times 0.0002 \times 0.0008 = 0.0000001$ or 0.00001%

Again, since on return, the signal encounters the same mismatch, we must square this percentage or:

Roundtrip percentage = $0.0000001 \times 0.0000001$ = Essentially 0%.

This example clearly demonstrates the need for using gel when imaging. The role of gel is to eliminate any air that can be trapped at the interface, causing an enormous acoustic impedance mismatch that is virtually insurmountable for imaging.

Note: The the low acoustic impedance of air could be easily anticipated by considering the equation which predicts acoustic impedance. The density of air is extremely low. The propagation velocity in air, relative to stiffer materials like tissue or the matching layer, is also extremely low. The result is that the acoustic impedance of air is extremely low.

◊ **Example 4:** Imagine that there is a large mass in a kidney with an acoustic impedance of 1.64 MRayls. Presuming that the acoustic impedance of the surrounding kidney tissue is 1.62 MRayls, calculate the percentage reflection from normal incidence to the mass.

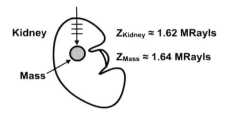

Kidney $Z_{Kidney} \approx 1.62$ **MRayls**

$Z_{Mass} \approx 1.64$ **MRayls**

Mass

Fig. 27 **Small Impedance Mismatch**

This time we want to know the reflected percentage change at the interface between the kidney and the mass. Plugging in the values for the mass and the kidney yields:

$$\% \; Reflected = \left[\frac{1.64 \; \text{MRayls} - 1.62 \; \text{MRayls}}{1.64 \; \text{MRayls} + 1.62 \; \text{MRayls}} \right]^2 = \left[\frac{0.02}{3.26} \right]^2 = 0.0038 \; \text{or} \; 0.38\%$$

Since this is a very small percentage reflection, there is a chance that this mass will not be visualized, regardless of the size of the mass. This exercise demonstrates a very important lesson about ultrasound in specific and testing in general, "just because you do not visualize something, doesn't mean that there isn't anything there."

◊ **Example 5:** For the following image of the vertebral artery, what percent of the beam that reaches the vertebral spinous process bone is transmitted deeper than the spinous process given that the acoustic impedance of the bone is approximately 6.7 MRayls, and the surrounding tissue has an acoustic impedance of approximately 1.7 MRayls (assuming no absorption within the bone)?

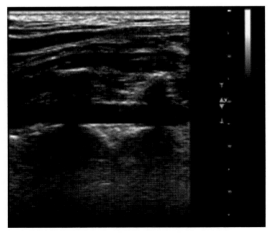

Fig. 28 **Shadowing from Bone**

This time we want to know the transmission percentage after two interfaces, the anterior and posterior aspect of the bone to tissue interfaces. Since the mismatch is the same on either side, we will solve the equation once and then apply the results a second time. Plugging in the values for the bone and the tissue yields:

$$\% \ Reflected = \left[\frac{6.7 \ \mathrm{MRayls} - 1.7 \ \mathrm{MRayls}}{6.7 \ \mathrm{MRayls} + 1.7 \ \mathrm{MRayls}} \right]^2 = \left[\frac{5}{8.4} \right]^2 = 0.35 \ \mathrm{or} \ 0.35\%$$

So the transmission past the anterior aspect of the bone is approximately 65%. After the posterior aspect, 35% of the remaining energy will again reflect back leaving:

Transmission percentage deeper than bone = $0.65 \times 0.65 = 0.42$ or 42%.

Excluding the absorption within the bone, a total of 58% of the energy that reached the anterior aspect of the vertebral artery has reflected back from either the anterior or posterior interface with the tissue. If you then consider the fact that absorption in bone is approximately five to fifteen times greater than the attention in tissue, you should now have a good appreciation why a shadow exists deeper than most bony structures.

9.4.4 Considering Tissue as an Infinite Series of Small Mismatches

We can consider the body as being comprised of an infinite number of reflecting boundary surfaces, or small acoustic impedance mismatches. The most obvious boundaries are the transitions from one organ to another, such as blood vessel wall to lumen, or heart wall to chamber, kidney to liver, etc. However, we can also consider every organ as comprised of infinitesimally thin layers or boundaries, each of which will have various types of reflection. The type of reflection which occurs at each of these boundaries will clearly impact the amount of energy reflected back to the transducer. Additionally, the small acoustic impedance mismatches at each of these boundaries will determine what percentage of the incident energy will be reflected.

The strength of the signal clearly depends on how much of the wave energy is reflected back to and received by the transducer: the stronger the backscatter, the stronger the signal. However, there is a limited amount of energy within the wave. If there is too much reflection at any one boundary, or at multiple boundaries collectively, then there will not be enough energy to visualize any of the deeper boundaries. In reality, we are therefore relying on there being enough of an acoustic impedance mismatch to produce a strong enough reflection so as to be visualized, but not so much reflection such that deeper tissue is in the "shadow" of the stronger reflecting tissue. As we will learn in later sections, when there is an excessive amount of attenuation for a more superficial structure, the artifact called shadowing is visualized, where structures below the strongly attenuated structured are either poorly visualized, or not visualized at all.

9.4.5 Water-Path Scanners

For "water path scanners" an acoustic standoff or water standoff is used between the transducer crystal(s) and the patient. This approach is generally used when it is desirable to image broad areas, especially with superficial structures. Standoffs are also advantageous for allowing better angles to superficial specular structures since very little energy is lost within the standoff. The one disadvantage is the acoustic impedance mismatch at the surface of the pad.

9.4.6 Important Points About Scattering, Specular Reflections, and Rayleigh Scattering

1. A truly homogenous medium would produce no echoes (anechoic) since there would be no acoustic impedance mismatch. Fluids tend to be relatively homogenous and hence, anechoic (no echoes).

2. Tissues are never "truly homogenous" and, hence, produce varying degrees of echogenicity. Since the interface between various organs tends to be "specular" in nature, in general, the best B-mode (2-D) images are produced when the angle of incidence is normal to the surface of the organs (vessels) being imaged.

3. Most tissue in the body is "rough" with respect to the wavelength of diagnostic ultrasound, producing scattering. It is the scattering which gives the apparent tissue texture to ultrasound.

4. Specular reflectors are most often the cause of imaging artifacts. Some examples of very strong specular reflectors are bones, the diaphragm, and gas bubbles.

5. Specular reflections from large, smooth surfaces are very angle dependent and may not be received back to the transducer if the angle of incidence is not normal (beam direction perpendicular to the structure's smooth surface). As a result, small variations in the incident angle can cause significant changes in the display intensity, as well as any associated artifacts with the specular reflector. This fact is critical for minimizing the presence of specular reflection based image artifacts.

6. A good example of a Rayleigh scatterer is blood. The red blood cells (RBCs) are very small relative to the wavelength used in diagnostic ultrasound.

7. Rayleigh scattering is a very weak reflection mechanism. Additionally, the acoustic impedance of the RBCs is relatively close to the acoustic impedance of the plasma. As a result, the echoes from the blood pool are very weak. This fact creates some extra difficulty when performing spectral and color Doppler.

8. Fresh thrombus is not always identifiable using ultrasound. The reflected signal energy from a fresh thrombus is usually very low, since a fresh thrombus is comprised of aggregated red blood cells. Recall that Rayleigh scattering occurs from structures which are small relative to the wavelength.

9. As frequency increases, the wavelength decreases, making the surfaces within the body appear rougher; as a result, the amount of scattering increases with increasing frequency. In addition, absorption increases with increasing frequency. As a result, since more of the ultrasound energy is scattered and absorbed at high frequency, penetration decreases (less energy is transmitted).

10. The range of reflected signal amplitudes (signal dynamic range) can vary widely from specular reflectors to Rayleigh scatterers. As a result, compression is necessary to accommodate the much smaller dynamic range of the human eye. This compression has the potential to "hide" small variations in signal which may be critical. Extreme care must be taken to guarantee that no signals have been "compressed out". This will become a motivating factor for understanding compression and system controls.

10. Refraction in the Body

10.1 Effects of Refraction

As expressed in Level 1, refraction is a change in beam direction caused by a distortion of the wavefront. This distortion of the wavefront occurs when a wave traverses an interface between mediums of varying propagation speeds at an angle such that the wavefront is not parallel to the interface (normal incidence). The effects of refraction in imaging are numerous. The principal effects are:

- Edge shadowing
- Displacement of a structure in the image laterally
- Artifactual second image (actual structure exists in correct position and artifactual replica exists laterally displaced from actual structure)
- Loss of signal intensity from dispersion of beam
- Degradation in lateral resolution

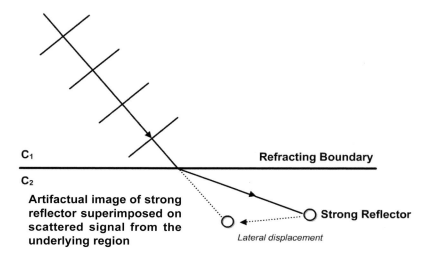

Fig. 29   **Lateral Displacement Caused by Refraction**

Ultrasound always presumes that the reflections returning to the transducer came from the steered direction. If a transmitted beam is pointing straight ahead, then the reflections are presumed to come from structures straight ahead. If the beam is angled at thirty degrees, then the reflections are presumed to come from structures along the path of 30 degrees. In *Figure 29*, notice that since the beam direction was refracted, the echoes that return are not from the presumed direction, but from an angularly displaced path. When the reflected signal encounters the interface, the beam is again refracted and returned to the transducer. Since the transducer presumes that the data emanated from the original transmitted direction, the reflection is drawn laterally displaced from its true source.

You should also note that in this case, the propagation velocity in medium 2 is faster than the propagation velocity in medium 1. This fact can be determined by analyzing the direction in which the beam was bent. *Figure 30* illustrates this point.

176

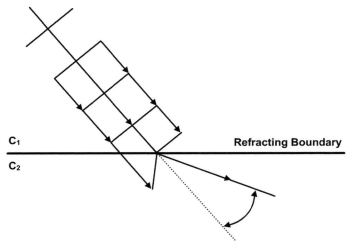

Fig. 30 **Determining Refraction Direction**

Notice that the "page left" edge of the wavefront encounters the interface before the "page right" edge of the wavefront. If the propagation velocity in medium 2 is higher than in medium 1, the left edge travels farther than the right. When the resulting points of the wavefront are connected, the new wave direction is as shown. Therefore, the propagation velocity in medium 2, for this case, is higher than the propagation velocity for medium 1.

This change in velocity is important to recognize since the depth a structure is displayed depends on the flight time of the ultrasound. Recall that ultrasound always presumes a propagation velocity of 1540 m/sec. Therefore, if a higher velocity medium is encountered, the flight time is decreased. Interestingly, in this case, since the beam was bent, the flight path is longer but the propagation velocity is faster. The longer flight path would increase the time, but the higher velocity works to decrease the time. Since these two errors work in opposite directions, the resulting structure is displaced almost purely laterally. If the beam was bent, but the propagation velocity were not increased, the increased path length would result in the artifact being drawn deeper as well as being laterally displaced. This fact is demonstrated in *Figure 31* and *Figure 32*.

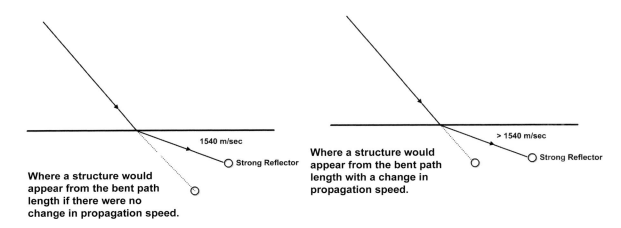

Fig. 31 **Lateral and Depth Displacement**   *Fig. 32* **Lateral Displacement**

Chapter 3

Notice that in the hypothetical situation of *Figure 31*, since the flight path from the bent beam is longer than if the structure were on the presumed axis of the beam, and since the propagation velocity remained the same, the overall time for the echo to return is increased. A longer flight time implies a deeper structure. Therefore, the drawn structure is displayed too deep because of the increased time, and laterally displaced because of the bent beam. In *Figure 32*, although the flight path is longer, the velocity increased. The increased time of the flight path offsets the decreased time of the increased velocity. Therefore, the structure is drawn at the same depth, but laterally displaced because of the bent beam.

10.2 The Critical Angle and Refractive Shadowing

With refraction artifact, there is a lateral displacement as a result of the beam refraction. Another artifact associated with refraction is acoustic shadowing (sometimes referred to as edge shadowing or refractive edge shadowing). As the name suggests, a "shadow" is a dark region in the ultrasound image. We have already discussed the fact that greater than normal reflection can result in shadowing. When a structure reflects more than normal there is less energy to insonify deeper structures below. Since we have already learned the mechanisms that cause refraction, we can now consider what refraction situations would result in shadowing.

Consider *Figure 33* in which a beam is incident at an angle far from 0 degrees (non-normal incidence). Because there is a change in propagation velocity at the interface, the beam will be refracted as shown. In many cases, the critical angle is achieved, at which all of the energy of the wave is internally reflected, and none transmitted into the interfacing medium. Since most or all of the energy is directed away from the original axis of the beam, there is very little, if any, energy to insonify the deeper region along the original beam axis. The result is either weak reflection or no reflection from this region. For ultrasound, when there is a very weak signal or no signal present, the image appears close to black or black. Hence, regions of shadowing occur in the image.

Refractive shadowing is very common whenever viewing vessels, cystic structures, gas bubbles, prosthetic devices, and bones.

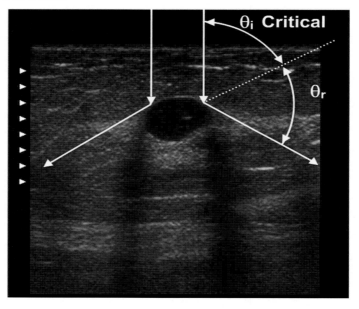

Fig. 33   **Refractive Shadowing and the Critical Angle**

Pegasus Lectures, Inc.

10.3 Applying Snell's Law

In Level 1 we learned that Snell's law predicts the presence of refraction and the degree of refraction. From the equation, we know that a greater disparity in propagation velocities will increase the degree of refraction. From the equation, we also know that a larger incident angle will also increase the degree of refraction that occurs. The following examples of the application of Snell's law should further demonstrate the concepts which have been discussed to this point.

◊ *Example 1:* **Applying Snell's Law with Normal Incidence**

The fact that no refraction occurs with normal incidence can easily be shown by applying Snell's law as in the following example.

How much refraction occurs for normal incidence ($\theta_i = 0°$)?

$$\text{Snell's law:} \quad \frac{c_i}{c_t} = \frac{sin(\theta_i)}{sin(\theta_t)}$$

Rewrite the equation in terms of the known variable.

Multiply both sides by $sin(\theta_t)$: $\frac{c_i}{c_t} \times sin(\theta_t) = sin(\theta_i)$.

Since the $sin(\theta_i) = sin(0^0) = 0$,

$$\frac{c_i}{c_t} \times sin(\theta_t) = 0.$$

And since it is not physically possible for the propagation velocity to equal 0,

$$sin(\theta_t) = 0$$
$$\text{and } (\theta_t) = 0^0.$$

Since the transmit angle, $\theta_{tt,}$ equals the incident angle, θ_{ti}, the beam has not changed direction, and hence, there is no refraction.

◊ *Example 2:* **Applying Snell's Law with Equal Propagation Velocities**

The fact that no refraction can occur if the propagation velocities are equal at an interface (regardless of the incident angle) can also easily be demonstrated using Snell's Law.

$$\text{Snell's law:} \quad \frac{c_i}{c_t} = \frac{sin(\theta_i)}{sin(\theta_t)}$$

If $c_i = c_t$, then $\frac{c_i}{c_t} = 1$

Therefore: $\frac{sin(\theta_i)}{sin(\theta_t)} = 1.$

Multiplying both sides by the $sin(\theta_t)$ yields:

$$sin(\theta_i) = sin(\theta_t),$$
$$\text{therefore, } \theta_i = \theta_t.$$

As already discussed, if the incident angle equals the transmitted angle, there has been no bending of the beam, and hence, no refraction.

◊   **Example 3:   Applying Snell's Law and the Critical Angle**

At the critical angle, all of the beam travels along the surface of the interface, implying a transmitted angle of 90 degrees. Therefore, if Snell's law predicts a transmitted angle of 90 degrees, the critical angle has been reached. For this example we will calculate the critical angle between a tissue to bone interface. We will assume that the propagation velocity in tissue is the soft tissue value of 1540 m/sec. For bone we will presume the approximate average of 4080 m/sec.

The last step of this problem requires finding the inverse sine of an angle. From the unit circle you learned in Chapter 1, you may not get the exact angle, but you can get close enough.

$$\text{Snell's law: } \frac{c_i}{c_t} = \frac{sin(\theta_i)}{sin(\theta_t)}$$

We would like the incident angle by itself, so we will multiply both sides by $sin(\theta_t)$,

$$\frac{c_i}{c_t} \times sin(\theta_t) = sin(\theta_i)$$

Plugging in the values yields:

$$\frac{1540\frac{m}{sec}}{4080\frac{m}{sec}} \times sin(90°) = sin(\theta_i)$$

$$\frac{154}{408} \times 1 = sin(\theta_i)$$

$$0.37 = sin(\theta_i) \Rightarrow \theta_i = 22°$$

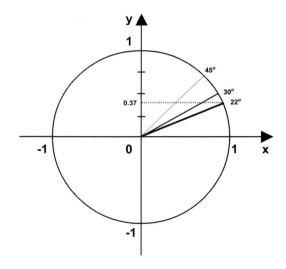

Unit Circle

Fig. 34   **Estimating the Angle with a Sine of 0.37**

Imagine how disconcerting total internal reflection can be. If the angle between the ultrasound beam direction and a structure in the body is far enough away from perpendicular, no ultrasound energy or little ultrasound energy travels distal to that interface. We have already learned that this can result in structures being drawn in incorrect locations or acoustic shadowing in the ultrasound image. This is one of the principal reasons that 2-D, or B-Mode imaging, is best performed with the incident beam perpendicular to the structure. This same artifact can also cause spectral and color Doppler signals to drop out. As always, you must assess the angle between specular reflectors and the incident beam to determine the likelihood and type of artifact which can exist.

Note: The critical angle has been reached when the calculated transmitted angle is 90°.

10.4 Important Points about Refraction

1. The incident angle is measured relative to the (normal) line perpendicular to the interface.

2. There is no refraction if the ultrasound beam has normal incidence (the beam direction is perpendicular, orthogonal, or 90° degrees) to the interface between two media.

3. A perpendicular beam implies that the incident angle is 0°.

4. There is no refraction if there is no change in propagation velocity across the interface of two media.

5. As the difference in propagation speeds increases, and as the angle gets further away from normal incidence, the amount of refraction increases.

6. There is an angle of incidence at which there is no transmission and 100% internal reflection. This angle is called the critical angle.

7. At the critical angle, the transmission angle is 90°.

8. Refraction is considered an artifact which can cause objects to be drawn at the wrong location (primarily laterally displaced) or not even drawn at all.

9. Refraction can cause loss of signal strength, and cause acoustic shadows in a 2D image.

10. Refraction can also cause a loss of Doppler signal strength, and at the critical angle, can even make the Doppler spectrum or color Doppler disappear.

Chapter 3

11. Exercises   Answers Pg. 450-451

1. What are the three mechanical wave interactions with the medium which constitute attenuation?

    _____

    _____

    _____

2. Absorption is the conversion of energy from an acoustic wave to _____ .

3. Absorption (increases / decreases) with increasing frequency.

4. Of the three interactions which constitute attenuation, which is the dominant factor in soft tissue?

5. What law tells at what angle an incident beam will be transmitted?

6. Write the law for question # 5 and define each term.

7. Normal incidence implies that the incident beam direction is _____ to the media interface.

    a) parallel
    b) perpendicular
    c) obtuse
    d) oblique

8. Normal incidence is really just a special case governed by _____ law. For normal incidence, θ_i = _____ . Since $\sin(\theta_i) = 0$, $\sin(\theta_t) = 0$, implying $\theta_t = 0$ and there is no _____ .

9. If you are given the intensity of a normal incident beam, what would you need to know to calculate the intensity of the transmitted beam at the interface of two media?

10. The acoustic impedance is given by the equation Z = _____ .

11. The unit for acoustic impedance is the _____ .

12. The percentage of a normal incident beam reflected and transmitted at the interface of two media is given by:

13. Percentage transmitted + percentage reflected must equal _____ .

14. For specular reflection, the incident angle is equal to the _____ .

    a) the normal angle
    b) the refraction angle
    c) the reflected angle
    d) the transmitted angle

15.   If the wavelength is small with respect to the structure size and the surface is smooth _____ reflection should occur.

16.   If the surface is rough and the wavelength is large with respect to the structure size _____ reflection should occur.

17.   _____ scattering indicates that the amount of scattering changes with wavelength.

18.   For _____ tissue the attenuation rate is approximately 0.5 dB/(cm-MHz).

19.   For muscle, the attenuation rate is approximately _____.

20.   At a depth of 5 cm, in muscle, what would the attenuation be for a 7.5 MHz beam?

21.   Imaging to a depth of 5 cm, in muscle, what would the attenuation be for a 7.5 MHz beam?

12. Review of Attenuation

1.   Attenuation is dependent on both the characteristics of the wave and the characteristics of the medium.

2.   Attenuation represents a transfer of energy (a change in any of the acoustic variables) through absorption (conversion of sound to heat) and scattering represented by reflection and refraction.

3.   Absorption is the conversion of wave energy into heat and is the dominant form of attenuation in soft tissue.

4.   Attenuation through absorption increases exponentially with higher operating frequencies. Attenuation in soft tissue is approximately 0.5 dB/(cm-MHz) and in muscle is approximately 1 dB/(cm-MHz).

5.   The amount of energy reflected is determined by the acoustic impedance mismatch, the incident angle, and the type of reflection.

6.   Ignoring absorption, the sum of the transmitted energy and reflected energy equals the incident energy (energy is conserved).

7.   We consider three categorizations of reflection: specular, scattering, and Rayleigh scattering.

8.   Specular reflection is dependent on "smoothness" and size of the reflector relative to the wavelength. Specular reflection is highly angle dependent.

9.   Scattering occurs from surfaces which are "rough" relative to the wavelength.

10.   Rayleigh scattering occurs when the reflectors are small relative to the wavelength. Rayleigh scattering is a very weak reflective mechanism.

11.   The acoustic impedance (with units of Rayls) equals the density times the velocity.

12. The percentage of reflection and transmission at a normal interface can be determined by the equations:

$$Z = \rho \times c.$$

$$reflection\ \% = \left[\frac{Z_2 - Z_1}{Z_2 + Z_1} \right]^2 \bullet 100\%$$

$$transmission\ \% = \left[1 - \left[\frac{Z_2 - Z_1}{Z_2 + Z_1} \right]^2 \right] \bullet 100\%$$

13. There is a very undesirable tradeoff between improving resolution and decreasing penetration due to increased attenuation at higher frequency imaging. Harmonic imaging (discussed in Chapter 10) is an attempt to minimize this tradeoff.

14. Refraction is determined by Snell's Law: $c_t (\sin \theta_i) = c_i (\sin \theta_t)$.

13. Table of Acoustic Values

The following table lists the density, propagation velocity, acoustic impedance, and absorption rates for various materials. You should note that the attenuation rate is specified at a frequency of 1 MHz. For the simplified material of Level 2, the attenuation rates were rounded off, and specified as being a simple linear relationship between increase in frequency and increase in logarithmic attenuation. In reality, the frequency relationship is considerably more complex and is highly dependent on the properties of the material. Some materials demonstrate relationships as low as the square root of the frequency, whereas others demonstrate relationships proportional to the square of the frequency. The treatment of these frequency dependencies is not included here.

Material	Density (ρ) $\dfrac{kg}{m^3}$	Velocity (c) $\dfrac{m}{sec}$	Impedance (z) $MRayls = \dfrac{1\times10^6 \ kg}{m^2 \times sec}$	Absorption (a) $\dfrac{dB}{cm}$ (@1 MHz)
Air	1.2	330	0.0004	12
Castor oil	950	1500	1.4	0.95
Water	1,000	1484	1.52	0.0022
Fat	920	1450 - 1480	1.35	[0.63]
Brain	1030	1510 - 1560	1.55 - 1.66	[0.75]
Kidney	1040	1560	1.62	-
Lung	400	500 - 650	0.26	[40]
Liver	1060	1570	1.64 - 1.68	[1.2]
Spleen	1060	1570	1.65 - 1.67	-
Muscle	1070	1560 - 1580	1.65 - 1.74	[0.96 - 1.4]
Blood	1060	1560 - 1580	1.62	[0.15]
Bone	1380-1810	4080	3.75 - 7.38	[14.2 - 25.2]
Aluminum	2700	6400	17	0.18
Brass	8500	4490	38	0.020
Mercury	13,600	1450	20	0.00048
Stainless Steel	7840	5790 m/sec	45	0.4

Table 2: **Acoustic Parameters**

Note: The gray area of the table represents the values used in determing the approximate average of "soft tissue."

The principal source for this table was <u>Medical Imaging Signal and Systems</u> by Prince and Links, Prentice Hall 2006.

14. Reflection and Transmission Percentage for Non-normal Incidence

The equation developed for determining the percentage reflection was based on the assumption that the incident angle was 0 degrees. The general equation is given by:

$$\% \, Reflected = \frac{I_{reflected}}{I_{incident}} = \left[\frac{Z_2 \cos(\theta_1) - Z_1 \cos(\theta_2)}{Z_2 \cos(\theta_1) + Z_1 \cos(\theta_2)}\right]^2$$

The transmitted percentage can then be generated by subtracting the fractional reflection from 1, or:

$$\% \, Transmitted = 1 - \left[\frac{Z_2 \cos(\theta_1) - Z_1 \cos(\theta_2)}{Z_2 \cos(\theta_1) + Z_1 \cos(\theta_2)}\right]^2$$

$$\% \, Transmitted = \frac{\left(Z_2 \cos(\theta_1) + Z_1 \cos(\theta_2)\right)^2}{\left(Z_2 \cos(\theta_1) + Z_1 \cos(\theta_2)\right)^2} - \frac{\left(Z_2 \cos(\theta_1) - Z_1 \cos(\theta_2)\right)^2}{\left(Z_2 \cos(\theta_1) + Z_1 \cos(\theta_2)\right)^2}$$

By expanding both expressions and subtracting this expression simplifies to:

$$\% \, Transmitted = \frac{4 Z_1 Z_2 \left(\cos(\theta_1)\right)\left(\cos(\theta_2)\right)}{\left(Z_2 \cos(\theta_1) + Z_1 \cos(\theta_2)\right)^2} .$$

Note: The simplification can be made easier if you remember the rule about differences of squares from algebra.

From these general equations, the specific equations for normal incidence are easily generated by plugging in a value of 0 degrees for the incident and transmitted angles. Recall that the cosine of 0 degrees is 1.

$$\% \, Reflected = \left[\frac{Z_2 \cos(0^0) - Z_1 \cos(0^0)}{Z_2 \cos(0^0) + Z_1 \cos(0^0)}\right]^2 = \left[\frac{Z_2 \times 1 - Z_1 \times 1}{Z_2 \times 1 + Z_1 \times 1}\right]^2 = \left[\frac{Z_2 - Z_1}{Z_2 + Z_1}\right]^2$$

To calculate the transmission percentage, instead of introducing another equation, we used the conservation theorem to subtract the reflection percentage from 100%. This approach works fine, but for the purists who enjoy equations, the general form of the transmission equation above can also be simplified by plugging in for the cosine of 0 degrees yielding:

$$\% \, Transmitted = \frac{4 Z_1 Z_2}{\left(Z_2 + Z_1\right)^2} .$$

15. Matching Layer

Let us return to our matching layer example of Level 2. What is the ideal acoustic impedance for the matching layer given the impedance of the crystal at 38 MRayls, and the acoustic impedance of the tissue at 2 MRayls?

Pegasus Lectures, Inc.

The following table shows the effective percent transmission for matching layers of acoustic impedances ranging from 37 MRayls to 3 MRayls, assuming a crystal impedance of 38 MRayls and a tissue impredance of 2 MRayls.

Matching Layer Impedance (Z) (MRayls)	Transmission % One way	Transmission % Round trip
37	19.46%	3.79%
36	19.93%	3.97%
35	20.42%	4.17%
34	20.92%	4.38%
33	21.44%	4.60%
32	21.98%	4.83%
31	22.54%	5.08%
30	23.11%	5.34%
29	23.71%	5.62%
28	24.32%	5.91%
27	24.95%	6.22%
26	25.60%	6.55%
25	26.27%	6.90%
24	26.95%	7.27%
23	27.66%	7.65%
22	28.38%	8.06%
21	29.12%	8.48%
20	29.87%	8.92%
19	30.64%	9.39%
18	31.41%	9.86%
17	32.18%	10.36%
16	32.95%	10.86%
15	33.70%	11.36%
14	34.43%	11.85%
13	35.12%	12.33%
12	35.74%	12.77%
11	36.26%	13.15%
10	36.65%	13.43%
9	**36.85%**	**13.58%**
8	36.78%	13.53%
7	36.33%	13.20%
6	35.33%	12.48%
5	33.55%	11.26%
4	30.64%	9.39%
3	26.04%	6.78%

Table 3:   **Matching Layer Example: Assuming Match for 38 MRayls to 2 MRayls**

From *Figure 36*, we see that the highest efficiency is achieved when the matching layer has an impedance greater than 8 and a little less than 9 MRayls. This solution can be calculated by taking the geometric mean of the impedances to be matched. In this example:

$$\text{Best Matching Impedence} = \sqrt{Z_{crystal} * Z_{tissue}}$$
$$= \sqrt{76 \ MRayls^2}$$
$$= 8.7 \ MRayls$$

16. Two Matching Layers

The optimal impedance for dual matching layer design can be calculated by solving this set of simultaneous equations as follows:

$$Z_{ML1} = \sqrt{Z_{crystal} * Z_{ML2}}$$
$$Z_{ML2} = \sqrt{Z_{tissue} * Z_{ML1}}$$

Starting with the ideal impedance for matching layer 1, square both sides to get:

$$\left(Z_{ML1}\right)^2 = Z_{crystal} * Z_{ML2}$$
$$Z_{ML2} = \frac{\left(Z_{ML1}\right)^2}{Z_{crystal}}$$

By substitution:
$$\frac{\left(Z_{ML1}\right)^2}{Z_{crystal}} = \sqrt{Z_{tissue} * Z_{ML1}}$$

Square both sides to get:
$$\frac{\left(Z_{ML1}\right)^4}{\left(Z_{crystal}\right)^2} = Z_{tissue} * Z_{ML1}$$

Simplifying yields:
$$\left(Z_{ML1}\right)^3 = Z_{tissue} * \left(Z_{crystal}\right)^2$$

Pegasus Lectures, Inc.

$$Z_{ML1} = (Z_{tissue})^{\frac{1}{3}} \bullet (Z_{crystal})^{\frac{2}{3}}$$

To solve for the ideal impedance of the second matching layer we begin with substitution:

$$Z_{ML1} = \sqrt{Z_{crystal} \bullet Z_{ML2}} = (Z_{tissue})^{\frac{1}{3}} \bullet (Z_{crystal})^{\frac{2}{3}}$$

Square both sides to yields:

$$Z_{crystal} \bullet Z_{ML2} = (Z_{tissue})^{\frac{2}{3}} \bullet (Z_{crystal})^{\frac{4}{3}}$$

$$Z_{ML2} = \frac{(Z_{tissue})^{\frac{2}{3}} \bullet (Z_{crystal})^{\frac{4}{3}}}{Z_{crystal}}$$

$$Z_{ML2} = (Z_{tissue})^{\frac{2}{3}} \bullet (Z_{crystal})^{\frac{1}{3}}$$

For the example given:

$$Z_{ML1} = (Z_{tissue})^{\frac{1}{3}} \bullet (Z_{crystal})^{\frac{2}{3}} = (2 \text{ MRayls})^{\frac{1}{3}} \bullet (38 \text{ MRayls})^{\frac{2}{3}} = 14.24 \text{ MRayls}$$

$$Z_{ML2} = (Z_{tissue})^{\frac{2}{3}} \bullet (Z_{crystal})^{\frac{1}{3}} = (2 \text{ MRayls})^{\frac{2}{3}} \bullet (38 \text{ MRayls})^{\frac{1}{3}} = 5.34 \text{ MRayls}$$

Lets's now calculate the efficiency using two "ideal" matching layers and compare with the efficiency of using one "ideal" matching layer.

$$\text{Reflection}_{ML1}\% = \left[\frac{Z_2 - Z_1}{Z_2 + Z_1}\right]^2 = \left[\frac{38 - 14.24}{38 + 14.24}\right]^2 = 0.21$$

So the transmission percentage is 79%

$$\text{Reflection}_{ML2}\% = \left[\frac{Z_2 - Z_1}{Z_2 + Z_1}\right]^2 = \left[\frac{14.24 - 5.34}{14.24 + 5.34}\right]^2 = 0.21$$

So the transmission percentage is 79%

$$\text{Reflection}_{tissue}\% = \left[\frac{Z_2 - Z_1}{Z_2 + Z_1}\right]^2 = \left[\frac{5.34 - 2}{5.34 + 2}\right]^2 = 0.21$$

One way, the overall transmission percentage is: 0.79 x 0.79 x 0.79 = 0.49

So the roundtrip efficiency is given by (0.49)² = 0.24, or 24%

Compared with the highest efficiency achievable with a one matching layer design, the overall efficiency (roundtrip) almost doubled.

17. Determining the Maximum Imaging Depth from the Dynamic Range

In general, the maximum imaging depth for an ultrasound system is determined by the overall sensitivity of the system. When the reflected signal is commensurate with the level of the thermal noise of the system, there is very little that can be done to adequately detect the signal. There are some adaptive techniques which rely on the coherence of the signal and the random nature of the noise to adaptively improve the signal detection. For these techniques, the goal is to identify noise from signal and then remove the noise through statistical or masking techniques.

These techniques aside, a general rule of thumb is the maximum attenuation which can be adequately detected is between 65 and 80 dB. Whereas there might be situations where more dynamic range can be supported (depending on the imaging situation, the efficiency of the transducer, noise floor of the system, and intensity limiting models to restrict the likelihood of bioeffects), 80 dB of attenuation is usually significant enough to warrant changing the imaging approach.

The calculation can be easily made to determine the maximum imaging depth for a specific transducer frequency, if we presume 80 dB maximum input dynamic range and an attenuation rate of approximately $\dfrac{1\ dB}{cm \times MHz}$, one way. (Of course, the result will vary from reality if our assumptions about attenuation or system dynamic range are incorrect.) For a 5 MHz transducer, the calculation is:

$$80\ dB = \frac{1\ dB}{cm \times MHz} \times \left(2 \times \text{Maximum Imaging depth } (cm)\right) \times 5\ MHz$$

$$\frac{80\ dB}{10\ dB} = 8\,(cm) = \text{Maximum Imaging depth } (cm).$$

Not surprisingly, since we are starting with the assumption that the attenuation in decibels is linear with increasing frequency, we would get a maximum imaging depth of 4 cm at 10 MHz. Note that stating that the rate of attenuation with increasing frequency changing linearly with decibels is not the same as stating that attenuation varies linearly with frequency. This point should be obvious if you consider the fact that decibels is already a non-linear measurement.

Attenuation

- Attenuation implies a decrease in signal strength and occurs through absorption, reflection, and refraction.

- Absorption is the conversion of energy into heat within the medium.

- Absorption is the dominant form of attenuation in "soft tissue."

- Absorption increases exponentially with increasing frequency.

- Fluids tend to absorb energy much less than tissue.

- Bones absorb at a significantly higher rate than the "soft tissues."

- The type of reflection that occurs at an interface depends on the wavelength relative to the surface geometry.

- If the surface is large, smooth, and flat with respect to the wavelength, specular reflection occurs (mirror-like reflection).

- If the surface is rough with respect to the wavelength, scattering occurs.

- If the reflecting structures are small relative to the wavelength (such as occurs with red blood cells) Rayleigh scattering occurs.

- Specular reflection is highly angle dependent and also the primary cause of most imaging artifacts.

- Rayleigh scattering is a very weak reflection mechanism.

- The amount of scattering increases with increasing frequency. Since the wavelength decreases as the frequency increases, the surface appears "rougher" increasing scattering.

- Although scattering increases with increasing frequency, absorption increases even faster with increasing frequency. This is the reason you should use lower frequencies for Doppler unless imaging very superficial blood flow.

- The amount of reflection that occurs at an interface is determined by the acoustic impedance mismatch across the interface.

- The acoustic impedance of a material is given by the density times the propagation velocity:

$$Z = \rho \times c.$$

- Higher acoustic impedance mismatches produce greater reflection.

- You should know the equation for percentage energy reflection based on acoustic impedance mismatch:

$$\text{Reflection } \% = \left[\frac{Z_2 - Z_1}{Z_2 + Z_1} \right]^2.$$

- The amount of transmission is simply calculated as 100% minus the reflected percentage.

$$\text{Transmission } \% = 100\% - \text{Reflection } \%$$

- Because of the large acoustic impedance mismatch between the relatively low impedance of tissue and the relatively high impedance of a crystal, a matching layer is used to improve efficiency.

- The matching layer (or layers) has an intermediate impedance between the impedance of the tissue and the crystal.

- Refraction refers to the bending of a beam that occurs at an interface when there is a change in propagation velocity between the two interfacing media and the beam is incident at an angle other than normal.

- Snell's law predicts the amount of refraction that will occur:

$$\frac{C_i}{C_t} = \frac{sin(\theta_i)}{sin(\theta_t)}$$

- As the propagation velocities differ by increasing amounts, and as the incident angle is further from normal, the refraction increases, ultimately achieving a critical angle at which total internal reflection occurs.

- Attenuation rates give approximate rates at which a signal power decreases per depth and frequency of operation.

- The attenuation rate for soft tissue (one-way) is approximated to be 0.5 dB per cm and per MHz of the transmit frequency.

$$\text{Soft tissue attenuation} \approx \frac{0.5 \text{ dB}}{\text{cm} * \text{MHz}}$$

- The attenuation rate for muscle (one-way) is approximated to be 1 dB per cm and per MHz of the transmit frequency.

$$\text{Muscle attenuation} \approx \frac{1 \text{ dB}}{\text{cm} * \text{MHz}}$$

Note: Notationally there are many ways of expressing the depth and frequency dependence of the attenuation rate. You should have noticed that many different formats have been used throughout the book to make you familiar with the various notations.

$$\left(\frac{dB}{cm - MHz} = \frac{dB}{cm * MHz} = \frac{dB}{cm \times MHz} \right)$$

Note: See Appendix F: Physical Units and Appendix G: Equations for additional review.

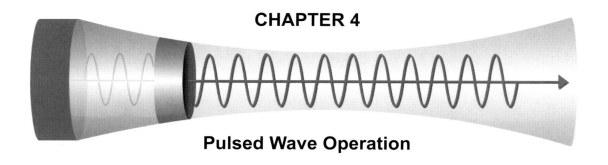

CHAPTER 4

Pulsed Wave Operation

Introduction

In our discussion of waves, there was no discussion of turning the wave on and off. In order to keep the wave concepts separate from the timing logistic of the wave, the timing issues were intentionally omitted. As we will learn in this chapter, there is a major benefit associated with not leaving the wave transmitting continuously, but rather pulsing it on and off repetitiously. Not surprisingly, when the wave is pulsed on and off for operation, we refer to the technique as pulsed wave operation. In contrast, if we leave the transmitter on continuously, we refer to the technique as continuous wave. In ultrasound, most techniques are pulsed. Still, there are times when continuous wave operation is used. Of course, there must be a drawback to PW as well as an advantage, otherwise continuous wave would cease to be used. The details of how long the wave transmitter will be allowed to transmit and how long the wave transmitter will be turned off, the benefits and the trade-offs will serve as the basis for this chapter.

1. Motivation for Using Pulsed Wave (PW)

In continuous wave, the transmit is continuous and the receive is continuous, simultaneously. To simultaneously transmit and receive, we must have two transducers, one to transmit and one to receive. To avoid having to hold two separate transducers, a single transducer is "divided" into two halves; one half to continuously transmit and the other half to continuously receive. As a result of the continuous receive, echoes are received from all depths simultaneously, rendering it impossible to tell from where the echoes originated. This lack of range specificity, referred to as range ambiguity, is the greatest limitation of continuous wave operation.

1.1 Range Ambiguity and Continuous Wave (CW)

To demonstrate the problem of range ambiguity, consider *Figure 1*. In this example a continuous sound source transmits a signal towards some mountains in the distance. In time, the sound waves reach the first mountain and start to produce echoes. Meanwhile, since the sound source continues to produce wavefronts, new wavefronts continue to arrive producing more echoes. In time, the second mountain is also reached. The reflections from mountain 2 are also continuous. As time passes, the continuous stream of echoes from mountain 2 intermixes with the continuous stream of echoes from mountain 1. This process continues such that the reflection from mountain 3 also intermixes with the echoes from mountain 1 and mountain 2. As a result, there is a reflection, but there is no way of distinguishing the origin of the intermixed reflections. In other words, there is no range specificity.

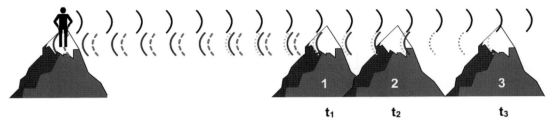

Fig. 1 **Echoes Return from all Mountains Intermixed using a Continuous Wave (CW)**

View Animation and Image Library CD

1.2 Range Specificity and Very Short Pulse

Imagine if instead of continuously transmitting and receiving, the transmitter were repeatedly pulsed on and then off as in *Figure 2*.

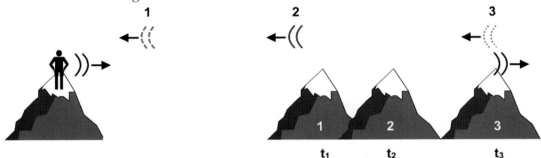

Fig. 2 **Echoes are Separated in Time using a Pulsed Wave (PW)**

Notice now that the echoes from each of the three mountains are separated in time. Obviously, the first returning echo comes from mountain number 1. The second echo returns from mountain number 2, and the third derives from mountain 3. Because each of these echoes are separated in time, it is now possible to distinguish, or "resolve" each of the mountains. Additionally, by knowing the propagation speed of sound, the distance can also be calculated by measuring the time until the echoes return. Of course, since the time of travel (flight) is a based on a roundtrip, a factor of 2 must be built into the calculation of the distance from the observer to the mountains.

View Animation and Image Library CD

1.3 Range Specificity and Longer Pulse Pulsed Wave (PW)

In the first example, using continuous wave there was no range resolution. In the short pulsed mode of the second example, there was very good resolution. What would happen if in the pulse mode the pulses lasted for a longer period of time as demonstrated in *Figure 3*? Would the resolution be as good?

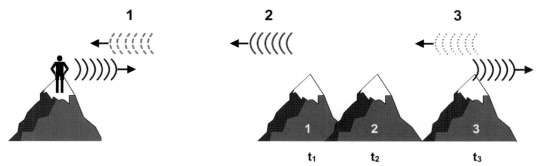

Fig. 3   **Longer Pulse but Still Three Distinct Echoes**

Notice that because the pulse is now longer, the echoes from each of the mountains are also longer. As a result, the echoes from each of the three mountains are less distinct. In essence, there is less separation in time between each of the returning echoes from each of the mountains.

However, in *Figure 3*, there are clearly three distinct echoes, and hence, all three mountain peaks have been resolved. So in this case, the resolution was still adequate to determine the number of mountains and location of each. What would happen if the pulse became just a little bit longer in time?

1.4 Range Ambiguity and a Longer Pulse
In *Figure 4*, the transmitted pulse has become even longer. As a result, the echoes from each mountain have also become longer.

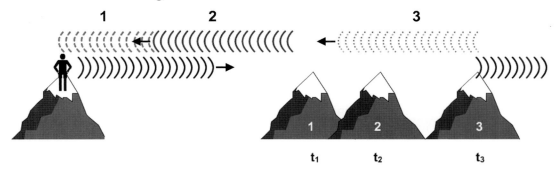

Fig. 4   **Loss of Range Resolution for Mountains 1 and 2**

Notice how there is no longer a separation in time between the echoes from the first and second mountain. Since the echoes are no longer distinct, the two mountains will be detected as only one big mountain. There is no longer adequate range resolution to resolve these two structures. You should also notice that although the echoes from mountain 2 and mountain 3 are very close together, they are still distinct. As a result, the third mountain is resolved relative to the first two mountains. The question should now be, "why could mountain 3 be distinguished from mountain 2 but not mountain 1 from mountain 2?" The answer is quite simple, it is easier to resolve (distinguish between) structures that are farther apart than closer together. Since the distance separating mountain 2 from mountain 3 is greater than the distance separating mountain 1 from mountain 2, it is easier to resolve the third mountain from the second mountain than it is to resolve the second mountain from the first.

   **View Animation and Image Library CD**

2. Pulsed Wave Definitions

We have just seen that range resolution is the motivation for creating a pulsed wave modality (PW). With the exception of continuous wave Doppler, diagnostic ultrasound is performed in the pulsed mode. Given that the wave will now be turned on and off, there are additional time related parameters needed to specify the pulse timing. Additionally, since the pulsed wave will occupy physical space in the medium, there will be some new distance related parameters needed to specify the physical length of the pulse. Therefore, the next few sections are devoted to defining these time and length based parameters for pulsed wave operation.

2.1 Time Related Pulsed Wave Definitions

2.1.1 Pulse Duration (PD)
As the name suggests, the Pulse Duration is the amount of time for which a transmit pulse lasts. Note that the use of the word duration is very helpful since it indicates time. *Figure 5* depicts the parameter referred to as the pulse duration.

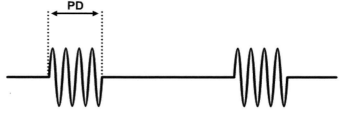

Fig. 5   **Pulse Duration**

2.1.2 Pulse Repetition Period (PRP)
Again, if you pay attention to the naming convention, it will be significantly easier not to confuse this term with other similar sounding terms. As the name suggests, the pulse repetition period (PRP) refers to the time until a transmit pulse is repeated. *Figure 6* depicts the parameter referred to as the pulse repetition period.

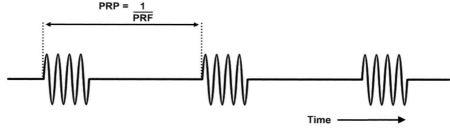

Fig. 6   **Pulse Repetition Period**

In Chapters 1 and 2, we learned the fundamental reciprocal relationship between time and frequency. Therefore, the reciprocal of the pulse repetition period is called the pulse repetition frequency (PRF), as depicted in *Figure 6*. These relationships are expressed below.

Pulse Repetition Period: time from the start of one pulse to the start of the next pulse.

$$\left(PRP = \frac{1}{PRF} \right)$$

Pulse Repetition Frequency: number of pulses that occur per time.

$$\left(PRF = \frac{1}{PRP} \right)$$

2.1.3 Duty Factor (Duty Cycle)

Referring to *Figures* 5 and 6, it should be clear that the pulse refers to the transmission of energy as a wave. Therefore, the pulse duration indicates the duration of time work is being performed by the source. As you will see in later sections, it will be beneficial to develop an expression for the percentage of time that work is actually being performed. To make this point clear, we will use an analogy.

Let's say that you work 2 days of the week. Your pulse duration (the time you work) is 2 days. The pulse repetition period (the time until you repeat the work process), is 7 days, or 1 week.

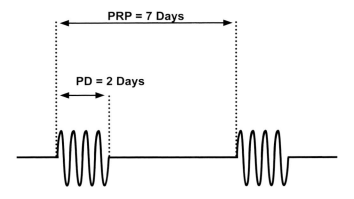

Fig. 7   **Work Week Duty Factor Example**

Therefore, to calculate your duty factor (the percentage of time you work), you would simply divide the 2 days by the 7 days, or:

$$Duty\ Cycle = \frac{2\ Days}{7\ Days} = 0.29 \ \ or \ \ 29\%.$$

From this analogy, it should be relatively clear that for PW operation, the duty cycle equals the time the source is transmitting energy divided by the time until the process is repeated or:

$$Duty\ Factor = \frac{PD}{PRP}.$$

Clearly, the largest duty factor is 1 (or 100%). When the duty factor is 1, it implies that the source is always transmitting which is the definition of continuous wave. Therefore, for a pulse wave, the duty factor must always be less than 1.

Since the duty factor is proportional to the pulse duration, anything which increases the pulse duration also increases the duty factor (presuming no change to the pulse repetition period). In *Figure 8*, notice that the second transmitting scheme has a longer pulse duration than the first transmitting scheme related to the increased number of cycles in the pulse. The result is a higher duty factor.

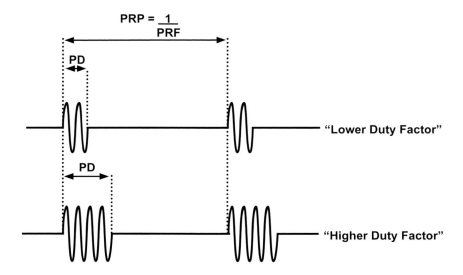

Fig. 8 **Longer Pulse Duration Increases the Duty Factor**

The duty factor is also inversely related to the pulse repetition period (PRP). Therefore, by increasing the PRP, the duty factor decreases (presuming a constant pulse duration). Notice in *Figure 9* that both transmitting schemes have the same pulse duration, but that the second scheme has a shorter PRP. A shorter PRP, for a fixed PD results in an increase in the duty factor.

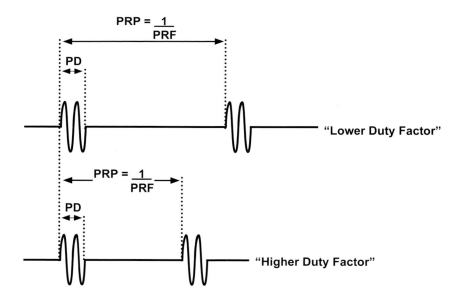

Fig. 9 **Shorter Pulse Repetition Period Increases the Duty Factor**

The following is a numerical example to illustrate how the duty factor is calculated:

◊ **Example:**
Calculate the duty factor if the pulse duration is 2 msec and the pulse repetition period is 10 msec.

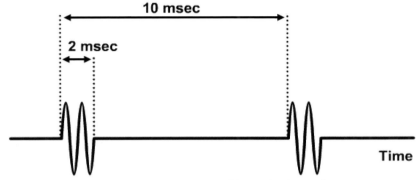

Fig. 10   **Duty Factor: Numeric Example**

$$Pulse\ Duration\ (PD) = 2\ msec$$

$$Pulse\ Repetition\ Period\ (PRP) = 10\ msec$$

$$Duty\ Factor = \frac{PD}{PRP} = \frac{2\ msec}{10\ msec} \bullet 100\% = 20\%$$

2.2 Distance Related Pulsed Wave Definitions

2.2.1 Spatial Pulse Length (SPL)

From our analogies, we have already referred to what is known as the "pulse length." *Figure 11* displays the pulse length in a more conventional drawing method without mountains and reflections present. Unfortunately, the word "length" is sometimes used in reference to time (duration is a more accurate word for time). Therefore, to make certain that there is no ambiguity in the terminology, the word "spatial" is often added as a modifier for the term pulse length. Since "spatial" indicates physical dimension, the term "spatial pulse length" leaves no possible confusion with a temporal measurement.

This naming convention is especially important since, pictorially, the spatial pulse length appears to be the same as the pulse duration. As warned in Chapter 2, you must pay careful attention to the parameter being measured. Although on a still image the two parameters look similar, the pulse duration (PD) is a measure of time and the spatial pulse length (SPL) is a measure of distance.

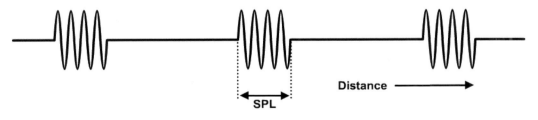

Fig. 11   **The Spatial Pulse Length**

2.2.2 The Spatial Pulse Length and Range Resolution

From the previous range specificity examples in Section 1.2-1.4, it is clear that as the spatial pulse length increases, the range resolution degrades. In the limit, as the pulse length becomes infinite as in continuous wave (CW), there is no range resolution. By further analyzing the situations described above we can determine the equation which specifies the ability to resolve two structures separated in depth (range resolution).

In the pulsed range specificity examples you should have noticed that the separation between the echoes was always twice the distance between the two mountains. To make certain that you understand why the factor of two exists, we will use *Figure 12*. At time 1, the transmit pulse has reached mountain number 1, and an echo is produced. During the time required for the transmit pulse to travel to the second mountain, time 2, the echo from the first mountain has been traveling in the opposite direction. Since the speed of sound is the same in both directions, the reflected pulse from the first mountain has traveled the same distance back to the source (a distance of x) as the transmitted sound has traveled away from the source (a distance of x). Therefore, the separation between the first echo and the second echo is x + x, or 2x.

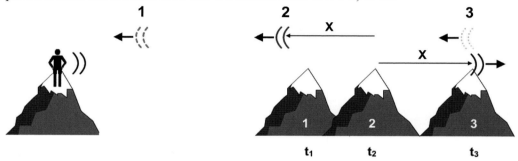

Fig. 12   **Range Resolution and the Spatial Pulse Length**

The factor of 2 increase in separation distance is often referred to as the roundtrip effect, since the sound has to travel to a structure and then back from the structure in a reflective mode. In terms of resolution, if there is no separation between the echoes from two distinct objects, then only one object is detected. Since the separation between echoes is twice the distance between the structures, the resolution equals half of the pulse length. If the pulse length is greater than twice the separation distance between two structures, the echo from the first and second structures will connect into one long echo. Therefore, the equation which specifies the range resolution is:

$$Range\ resolution = \frac{spatial\ pulse\ length}{2}.$$

View Animation and Image Library CD

2.2.3 Other Names for Range Resolution

There are three other names commonly used to refer to range resolution:

- Depth resolution
- Axial resolution
- Longitudinal resolution

In this textbook we will interchange between the names so as to build familiarity and comfort with the various nomenclatures.

3. Relating Wave Parameters and Pulsed Wave (PW) Parameters

3.1 The Difference Between a Wave Parameter and a PW Parameter

A principal source of confusion in ultrasound is the distinction between wave parameters and pulsed wave parameters. As just described, the pulse wave parameters are associated with the fact that the wave is pulsed on and off. In contrast, the wave parameters (as defined in Chapter 2) are the specific characteristics of the wave itself. When using waves in a pulsed wave mode, both sets of parameters are applied. Within the pulse, the wave parameters such as operating frequency, period, wavelength, propagation velocity, and amplitude apply. The pulsed wave parameters define the duration of the pulse, how often the pulse is repeated, and the spatial length the pulse occupies in the medium. Sections 3.2 and 3.3 will help you to make these distinctions as well as develop the mathematical relationships which link these parameters.

3.2 Time Related Wave Parameters and a PW Parameters

3.2.1 Pulse Duration (PD) and Period (P)

The frequency of a wave (often referred to as the operating frequency) expresses how many compressions and rarefactions occur per time. The reciprocal of the frequency, the period, is the time between one compression and the next occurring compression (or between successive rarefactions). The frequency (and period) is therefore determined by the vibrational rate of the crystal. In contrast, the pulse duration is the entire time the crystal is vibrating, creating the wave. *Figure 13* shows the relationship between the period and the pulse duration.

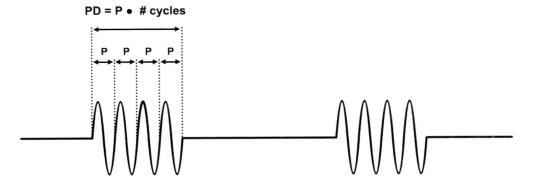

PD = P • # cycles

Fig. 13   **Calculating the Pulse Duration**

From *Figure 13*, it is clear that the pulse duration is related to the period of the wave and the number of cycles in a pulse. In *Figure 14*, there are four cycles in the pulse. As a result, the pulse duration equals the time for one cycle (the period) multiplied by the number of cycles in the pulse (in this case four). In general form, the PD can be determined by:

$$Pulse\ Duration = Period\ \times\ \#cycles.$$

◊ **Example:**

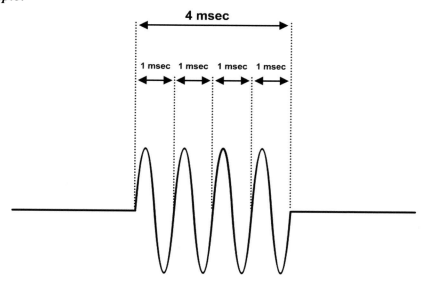

Fig. 14   **Pulse Duration: Numerical Example**

In *Figure 14,* there are 4 cycles per pulse and the period is 1 msec, so the pulse duration is:

PD = 4 x 1 msec = 4 msec.

3.2.2 PRP (and PRF) and Propagation Velocity and Imaging Depth

As specified, the pulse repetition period is the time between transmitting pulses. In practical terms, what determines how often a transmit will be repeated is the time it will take for the sound wave to travel the required roundtrip distance. This time to travel the required roundtrip distance is, as expressed by the distance equation learned in Chapter 1, affected by the imaging depth and the propagation velocity. In general situations, the PRP is therefore a function of the propagation velocity and the imaging depth. However, in ultrasound we presume a fixed propagation velocity, which effectively leaves the imaging depth as the only parameter that affects the PRP, and hence, the PRF.

3.2.3 Duty Factor and Wave Parameters

From a first glance, it would be easy to assume that since the duty factor is the relationship of the transmit time (PD) to the pulse repetition time (PRP), that the duty factor is purely determined by the pulsed wave parameters, and is not impacted by the wave parameters. This assumption is incorrect since it neglects the fact that the pulse duration is related to the period and the period is a wave parameter. Consider *Figure 15*:

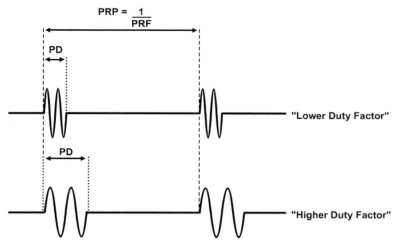

Fig. 15 **Effect of Period on Duty Factor**

Notice that both of these transmitting schemes have two cycles per pulse and the same PRP; however, since the period is longer in the second scheme, the pulse duration is longer. Since the duty factor is proportional to the pulse duration, a longer pulse duration results in a higher duty factor.

3.3 Distance Related Pulsed Wave Definitions

3.3.1 Spatial Pulse Length and Wavelength
Both wavelength and spatial pulse length are measures of distance. However, as the name suggests, the wavelength is a wave parameter and the spatial pulse length is a pulse wave parameter. Just as there is a relationship between the period and the pulse duration, there is an analogous relationship between the wavelength and the spatial pulse length. The wavelength is the physical distance from one compression to the next compression within a medium. In contrast, the spatial pulse length is the entire physical distance the pulse occupies in the medium at a given instant. *Figure 16* depicts this relationship.

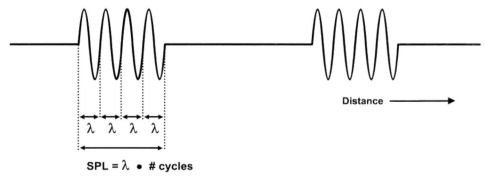

Fig. 16 **Determining the SPL**

From *Figure 16* it is clear that the equation relating the wavelength and the spatial pulse length is:

$$Spatial\ pulse\ length = \lambda \times \#cycles.$$

Note that the spatial pulse length depends on the wavelength, and that the wavelength depends on the propagation velocity and the operating frequency, as expressed by the wavelength equation. Therefore, changes in either the propagation velocity or the operating frequency will result in a change in spatial pulse length, presuming no changes to the number of cycles in the pulse.

$$\text{Recall}: \lambda = \frac{c}{f}$$

$$\text{Since } SPL \propto \lambda$$

$$SPL \propto c \text{ and } SPL \propto \frac{1}{f}.$$

3.3.2 Axial Resolution

The axial resolution was shown to equal the spatial pulse length divided by 2. Since the spatial pulse length depends on the wavelength, which in turn depends on the propagation velocity and the frequency of operation, the axial resolution must also depend on the propagation velocity and the frequency of operation. As the frequency increases, the wavelength decreases, decreasing the spatial pulse length, yielding better resolution. Similarly, if the propagation velocity decreases, the wavelength decreases, decreasing the spatial pulse length, thereby improving the axial resolution. Remember, for resolution smaller numbers are always better.

4. The Foundational Drawing for Pulsed Wave

The saying is that a picture is worth a thousand words. In the case of keeping straight and understanding pulsed wave operation, this adage is an understatement. *Figure 17* combines the parameters we have just learned into one figure. You will also note that for convenience sake, all parameters related to time will be drawn above the baseline and all parameters related to distance will be drawn below the baseline.

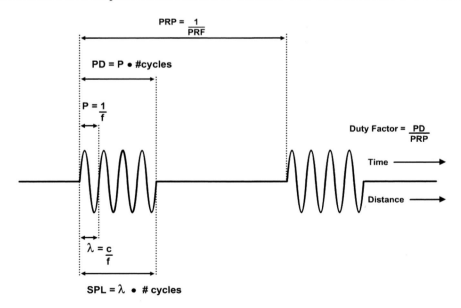

Fig. 17 **Foundational Drawing for PW Operation**

In Level 2, there will be additions to this figure with specific explanations of how each of these parameters affects diagnostic ultrasound. For now, it is suggested that you make certain you can draw this figure with the book closed.

Pegasus Lectures, Inc.

5. Pulsed Wave and the Need to Understand Timing

Whenever you think about pulsed wave operation, you should be thinking about timing. Pulsed operation is defined by parameters that specify the timing of when to turn on and off the transmitted wave. The timing aspects are very important for two major reasons:

1. Effect on temporal resolution (including aliasing) and
2. Effect on risk of bioeffects.

Recall that the motivation for creating a pulsed wave modality was to overcome the fundamental limitation of no range specificity with continuous wave operation. Of course, with the benefits there must come some trade-offs. The fundamental trade-off is a potential degradation in temporal resolution. Temporal resolution is the ability to detect (resolve) changes in time. In other words, by pulsing the wave on and off, the timing has been affected, potentially restricting the ability to detect quickly changing events.

Another related outcome of changing the timing is the change in energy distribution into the patient. By turning the transmit signal on and off, very different heating situations are created than when the transmit is left on continuously. As a result, the amplitude of the signal will be significantly varied depending on the pulsing situation. In general, short pulses will be allowed very large amplitudes whereas long pulses will be forced to use smaller amplitudes. The high amplitude short pulses will have a different risk of bioeffects than the lower amplitude long pulses. Therefore, from the standpoint of analyzing bioeffects, the timing parameters of pulsed wave will become very important.

6. Definitions for Pulse Wave Related Imaging Parameters

As with any discipline, half of the battle is developing fluency in the language and terminology. Since there are so many terms that can potentially be used to refer to similar concepts, we will define the terms necessary to facilitate understanding the application of pulsed wave techniques.

1. **Pulsed wave**
   Any modality which turns the transmitter on and off periodically so as to reduce range ambiguity. Note that pulsed wave refers not only to PW Doppler, but also color Doppler, 2-D imaging, 3-D imaging, and M-mode.

2. **Acoustic line**
   A single sound beam transmitted in a specific direction and the associated echoes. Although the word "line" is used, a more appropriate description is a beam since the word "line" implies one dimension, whereas a sound beam clearly has three dimensions.

3. **Receive line**
   The returning echoes registered by the system from a single direction over the time between the transmit event and the time until the next transmit occurs as dictated by the imaging depth.

4. **Display line**

A display line (or image line) is the data displayed on the screen that corresponds to a single direction within the patient. For "simple" ultrasound imaging applications, there is a one-to-one correspondence between transmitting and receiving a single beam and the displayed data in the image. For more complex modes, there may be multiple acoustic lines to form one display line, or multiple display lines from one acoustic line.

5. **Line**

The general term used to refer to a beam, either transmitted, received, or displayed.

6. **An image**

An image is the picture generated by sequentially transmitting many acoustic lines in various directions and then reconstructing the "time sequentially" received data. Other terms often used are a frame, a scan, or a scan region.

7. **Frame time**

The time required to transmit multiple beams until the desired region of the patient is scanned (also referred to as the scan time, the acoustic scan time, or the acoustic frame time).

8. **Frame rate**

The reciprocal of the frame time. A better name for this parameter is the frame frequency, since this name shows the reciprocal nature with respect to the frame time.

9. **Sampling rate**

The frequency at which signals are detected or "viewed". As discussed in Chapter 1, the sampling rate indicates the maximum frequency detectable without aliasing as governed by the Nyquist Criterion. As with the frame rate, a more intuitive name is the sampling frequency.

7. Scanned and Non-Scanned Modalities

In order to assess both the temporal resolution and the risk of bioeffects associated with various modalities, we will need to classify ultrasound scanning techniques into one of two categories: "scanned modalities" and "non-scanned modalities." By grouping scanning modalities into one of these two categories, we will reduce the effort required to remember the relationships between each mode and these two very important topics.

7.1 Scanned Modalities

A scanned modality implies that over time, wave energy is transmitted in a controlled pattern in different directions, insonifying a two or three-dimensional region. The three common ultrasound modalities that represent a scanned modality are 2-D imaging (B-mode), color flow imaging, and the newer modality of 3-D imaging. *Figure 18* demonstrates how a 2-D sector image is generated over time by transmitting multiple beams distributed over both time and space.

At time 1, the first beam is transmitted, generating the left-most region of the image. At time 2, the second beam is moved over just slightly, creating the next region in the image. Over time, the entire region of interest is scanned, generating a two-dimensional image. When the end of the frame area is reached, the process is repeated starting with line 1 again.

Pegasus Lectures, Inc.

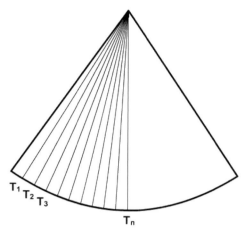

Fig. 18   **Scanned Modalities**

View Animation and Image Library CD

7.2 Non-scanned Modalities

In contrast to a scanned modality, non-scanned modalities transmit in the same direction repeatedly over time. The most commonly used ultrasound modalities which are non-scanned are CW Doppler, PW Doppler, M-mode, and the almost extinct early mode of ultrasound called A-mode. Note that a non-scanned modality results in multiple transmits over time, just as a scanned modality uses multiple transmits over time. The distinction is where the energy is transmitted. For the non-scanned modality, each successive transmit is in the same direction as the previous transmit.

Figure 19 demonstrates the non-scanned modality of PW Doppler. A Doppler line is transmitted at time 1, time 2, time 3, and repeatedly in the same direction until the PW is turned off.

Chapter 4

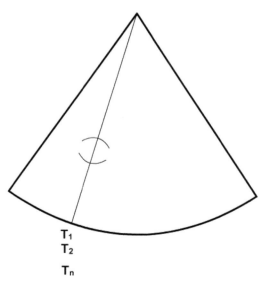

Fig. 19   **Non-scanned Modalities**

8. Relating PW Parameters to Ultrasound

We have thus far defined the PW parameters in the general sense, without giving specific references to application in ultrasound. To fully appreciate the significance of these parameters, we must make the association between the practical application in ultrasound and the theoretical descriptions.

8.1 The Pulse Duration

Not all pulses are the same. For diagnostic ultrasound, the pulse duration varies significantly with the imaging modality being employed. To achieve the specific requirements for each application, the transmit pulses must vary wildly. As a result, a pulse in 2-D will look very different than a pulse for color Doppler, which will vary with respect to a pulse in PW Doppler.

We have already learned that the pulse duration is the product of the period and the number of cycles in the pulse. The period (reciprocal of the operating frequency) is determined by the user relative to the imaging situation. When scanning to a shallow depth on an easy to image patient, a higher frequency can be chosen. When scanning to deeper depths, or when scanning a difficult to image patient, a lower frequency must be chosen. But the pulse duration is also determined by the number of cycles in the pulse. You will notice that there is no control on the ultrasound system called "number of cycles in the pulse." So how is the number of cycles controlled?

To some extent, the number of cycles in a pulse is a function of the modality you choose. For reasons that will be discussed throughout the upcoming sections, in 2-D imaging, a very short pulse duration is generally desired. As a result, when 2-D imaging is activated, the system attempts to produce pulses with as few cycles as possible. In comparison, pulsed Doppler generally requires a longer pulse. Therefore, when PW Doppler is activated, the system naturally produces pulses with more cycles. This fact is illustrated in *Figure 20*.

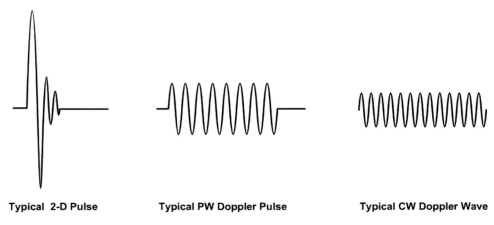

| Typical 2-D Pulse | Typical PW Doppler Pulse | Typical CW Doppler Wave |

Fig. 20   **Pulse Characteristics for Various Modes**

Notice how the 2-D pulse only has a few cycles but a very large amplitude, the pulsed wave Doppler pulse has many cycles and a much smaller amplitude, and CW Doppler is continuous with an even lower amplitude. As you will learn in the Doppler chapter, in PW there is a control which allows the user to determine the number of cycles desired in the pulse, although the label is not "the number of cycles in the pulse." Of course, in the limit, when you activate CW Doppler, the transmit is continuous and you have chosen to transmit with a virtually infinite pulse duration.

8.2 The Pulse Repetition Period and the PRF

8.2.1 Dependence on the Imaging Depth

In Sections 3 and 4, we learned that the PRP is related to both the propagation velocity and the distance of travel. Since for ultrasound machines a propagation velocity of 1540 m/sec is always assumed, the maximum achievable PRP is therefore dependent only on the imaging depth. If the imaging depth is increased, then the time to and from the imaging depth desired is increased, increasing the PRP. Because of the reciprocal relationship between time and frequency, the PRF is simply the reciprocal of the PRP. Therefore, the principle determinant of the maximum achievable PRF is the imaging depth.

In practical terms for ultrasound, the PRP is really the same as the time required to acquire a single "line" of data. The sequence of events is as follows:

Time 1: a pulse is transmitted
Time 2: transmit pulse arrives at maximum imaging depth
Time 3: echo from maximum imaging depth is received back at the transducer
Time 4: another pulse is transmitted, repeating the process, creating another line of data

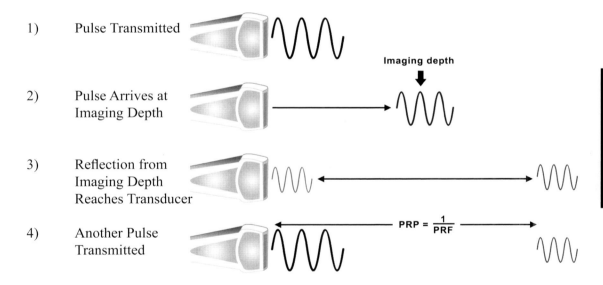

Fig. 21   **Imaging Depth and PRP**

View Animation and Image Library CD

Given that the PRP and PRF are determined by the depth, we can now calculate actual PRP and PRF values. In Chapter 1, we learned that imaging 1 cm required 13 μsec presuming a propagation velocity of 1540 m/sec. (Recall that imaging 1 cm requires a travel of 2 cm which by the distance equation takes 13 μsec.) Therefore, to calculate the line time (the PRP), we must multiply the imaging depth by 13 μsec, or:

$$acoustic\ line\ time\ (PRP) = \frac{13\ \mu sec}{cm} \times imaging\ depth\ (cm).$$

8.2.2 Sample Calculations
With this general equation, we are now ready to calculate some real world values.

◊ **Example 1:**   What is the minimum PRP if the imaging depth is 8 cm?

$$acoustic\ line\ time\ (PRP) = \frac{13\ \mu sec}{cm} \times 8\ (cm) = 104\ \mu sec = 0.1\ msec.$$

◊ **Example 2:**   *What is the maximum PRF if the imaging depth is 8 cm?*

$$acoustic\ line\ time\ (PRP) = \frac{13\ \mu sec}{cm} \times 8\ (cm) = 104\ \mu sec = 0.1\ msec.$$

$$PRF = \frac{1}{PRP} = \frac{1}{0.1\ msec} = 10\ kHz$$

◊ **Example 3:**   What is the maximum PRF if you need to image to a depth of 10 cm?

Our approach to calculating a PRF is, of course, to first calculate the PRP. Once we know the PRP, the PRF will be obtained by simply taking the reciprocal of the PRP.

Let's imagine for a moment that to solve this problem, you have forgotten that every 1 cm of imaging depth requires 13 μsec. We will therefore need to use the distance equation to determine the line imaging time (PRP). First, because of the roundtrip effect, imaging to a depth of 10 cm is the same as the sound traveling a distance of 20 cm. Second, we know the speed of sound in soft tissue is 1540 m/sec. By the distance equation we can determine the time necessary for an ultrasound pulse to travel 20 cm roundtrip.

$$distance = rate \times time$$
rewriting for time by dividing both sides by the rate yields:

$$time = \frac{distance}{rate}$$

plugging in the values for distance and rate yields:

$$time = \frac{20\ cm}{1540\ \frac{m}{sec}} = \frac{0.2\ m}{1540\ \frac{m}{sec}} = \frac{0.2\ sec}{1540} \approx 130\ \mu sec = 0.13\ msec.$$

Pegasus Lectures, Inc.

So the minimum amount of time between firing a pulse and firing the next pulse, for an imaging depth of 10 cm is 130 μsec, or 0.13 msec.

Note: Either form of the answer is acceptable. Recall from Chapter 1 that there are an infinite numbers of ways of writing each number.

To determine the PRF, we take the reciprocal of the PRP, or:

$$PRP = 0.13 \ msec$$

$$PRF = \frac{1}{(PRP)} = \frac{1}{(0.13 \ msec)} = 7.69 \ kHz.$$

8.2.3 The Use of the Words Maximum and Minimum

In the problems just solved, you will notice that the pulse repetition periods calculated were referred to as the minimum PRP, and the pulse repetition frequencies calculated were referred to as the maximum PRF. The minimum was used with respect to the PRP since we calculated the absolute minimum time that could be used between transmitted pulses for the desired imaging depth. In other words, for an 8 cm imaging depth, there is no choice but to wait at least 104 msec until the next transmit occurs, but there is no rule that specifies that we cannot wait longer than that and just not use the data. As you will learn in later chapters, there are times where the minimum PRP is not used for a given depth. The two common situations where the minimum PRP is not used is in pulsed wave Doppler so as to achieve lower Doppler scales, and with superficial imaging to reduce the amount of artifact caused by range ambiguity. Both of these topics will be discussed in detail in their respective chapters.

Not surprisingly, the reciprocal of a minimum time is a maximum frequency. Hence, the reciprocal of the minimum PRP yields the maximum PRF.

8.3 The Spatial Pulse Length

8.3.1 Frequency and Pulse Length

For 2-D imaging, one of the most important indications of image quality is the detail resolution. From the experiments with a sound source on a mountain, we ascertained that the longitudinal resolution (axial, range, or depth) is equal to the spatial pulse length divided by 2, or:

$$Axial \ resolution = \frac{spatial \ pulse \ length}{2} = \frac{\lambda \bullet \# cycles}{2},$$

and

$$\lambda = \frac{c}{f}.$$

From the equation, it is clear that better resolution (a smaller number) can be achieved by either a shorter wavelength and/or a fewer cycles in the pulse. Since we have no control over the propagation velocity, the one way to achieve a shorter wavelength is to increase the transmit frequency. Of course, you can only adjust the frequency in as much that there is still adequate penetration.

Since increasing the frequency to achieve a shorter wavelength is not always an option, we need to assess the other option: reducing the number of cycles in the pulse.

8.3.2 Cycles and Pulse Length
For 2-D imaging, the reality is that you do not have any control over the number of cycles in the pulse. Since the system is designed to optimize resolution in modalities where resolution matters most, activating 2-D automatically results in the fewest possible cycles for a given transducer and system. In other words, by design, the system will automatically give you the best axial resolution possible for the transducer and imaging system chosen.

8.3.3 Backing (Damping) Material
Since resolution is so important in 2-D imaging, the transducer is driven with a very short pulse. However, as anyone knows who has ever rung a bell or listened to a tuning fork, a single impulse can produce a very long ring time (many cycles). Therefore, since a single electrical impulse stimulating a transducer to ring naturally produces many cycles in the generated acoustic pulse, the axial resolution will naturally be poor.

To overcome this problem, transducers are designed with a special block of material called either a backing or damping material. The purpose of the damping material is to decrease the natural resonance of the crystal so that fewer cycles are produced. By decreasing the number of cycles in the pulse, both the pulse duration and the spatial pulse length are decreased. *Figure 22* demonstrates the difference between an undamped and damped crystal when driven with a single impulse.

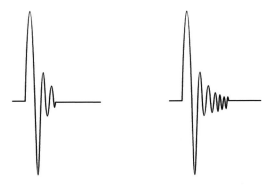

Damped response to impulse   **Undamped response to impulse**

Fig. 22   **Damping and Ringdown**

8.4 Using the PRP (Line Time) to Calculate the Frame Time (and Frame Rate)

8.4.1 Temporal Resolution and Non-Scanned Modalities
For non-scanned modalities, the ability to accurately detect changes with time is simply related to the PRF. After every transmit period there is a listening period. Therefore, the frequency of the transmitting pulses (the PRF) is the same as the frequency of listening (or sampling). Since the PRF indicates how frequently you are receiving data, the PRF dictates the fastest changing signal detectable. So for all pulsed non-scanned modalities (PW Doppler, M-mode, and A-mode) the time resolution is strictly related to the PRF, and hence the PRP.

8.4.2 Temporal Resolution and Scanned Modalities

For scanned modalities, there is another timing restriction besides the line time (PRP). In comparison with non-scanned modalities which re-transmit an acoustic line in the same location, a scanned modality "spends" time looking over a scan region before returning back to the same location. Therefore, the time between successively looking in the same location is not determined just by the line time, but is also determined by the number of lines transmitted in the entire frame.

Consider *Figure 23*. Let's assume that the imaging depth is set to 8 cm, and let's further presume that there are 200 lines in a single frame. How much time elapses between successive transmits in the same location of the frame? In other words, what is the time to produce a frame such that an individual line is repeated?

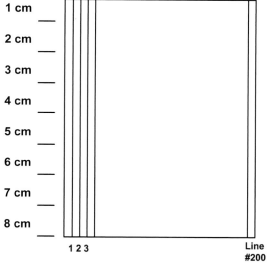

1 2 3   Line #200

Fig. 23   **Calculating the Frame Time**

From our earlier Example 2, we calculated the PRP to be 104 μsec for an imaging depth of 8 cm. All 200 lines of the frame must be transmitted until the initial line in the same location will be repeated. Therefore, the total time is:

$$time\ to\ complete\ all\ lines = \frac{104\ \mu sec}{1\ lines} \bullet \frac{200\ lines}{frame} \approx \frac{20,000\ \mu sec}{frame} = \frac{20\ msec}{frame}.$$

8.4.3 Frame Time and Frame Rate

In the above example, the time to produce a frame (the frame time) is 20 msec. As always there is a well known relationship between a time based measurement and a frequency based measurement. The reciprocal of the frame time is called the frame rate. The term "frame rate" is an alternative way of saying the "frame frequency". This nomenclature is often confusing because the word rate is also often used to refer to the speed with which something travels as well as a frequency. Unfortunately, the term frame rate seems to have become ubiquitous, even though the term frame frequency is more illustrative and accurate. Whenever you see the term frame rate, replace the word "rate" in your mind with the word "frequency." Regardless of the terminology, the frame rate is simply the reciprocal of the frame time, or:

$$Frame\ rate\ (frequency) = \frac{1}{Frame\ time}.$$

For the above example, the frame rate is:

$$Frame\ rate\ (frequency) = \frac{1}{frame\ time} = \frac{1}{20\ msec} = 0.05\ kHz = 50\ Hz$$

8.4.4 Frame Time (Frame Rate) Equation

So from this example, we see that calculating a frame time is mathematically quite simple:

$$Frame\ time = \frac{Time}{Line} * \frac{\#Lines}{Frame}.$$

This equation is just a mathematical way of stating common sense. Imagine if you have to perform a repetitious job of mowing your square lawn. If it takes 3 minutes to make one pass with the lawn mower and it takes 30 passes to cover the entire lawn, then it will take 30 * 3 minutes or 90 minutes to mow your whole lawn. In other words, the total time equals the time to perform the job once (time/line) multiplied by the total number of times the job has to be performed (lines/frame).

Recalling that the line time (PRP) is calculated as:

$$\frac{Time}{Line} = \frac{13\ \mu sec}{cm} * Imaging\ depth\ (cm)$$

This equation can be written in another form which builds in the calculation of the line time as:

$$Frame\ time = \frac{13\ \mu sec}{cm} * \frac{Imaging\ depth\ (cm)}{Line} * \frac{\#Lines}{Frame}.$$

8.4.5 Frame Rate Examples

◊ **Example 1:**
The depth is set to 10 cm and there are 128 lines per frame. What is the maximum frame rate?

$$Frame\ time = \frac{13\ \mu sec}{cm} * \frac{10\ cm}{Line} * \frac{128\ Lines}{Frame} = 16.64\ msec$$

$$Frame\ rate = \frac{1}{Frame\ time} = \frac{1}{16.64\ msec} = 60.1\ Hz$$

◊ **Example 2:** The depth is set to 8 cm and there are 100 lines per frame. What is the maximum frame rate?

$$Frame\ time = \frac{13\ \mu sec}{cm} * \frac{8\ cm}{line} * \frac{100\ Lines}{frame} = 10,400\ \mu sec = 10.4\ msec$$

$$Frame\ rate = \frac{1}{Frame\ time} = \frac{1}{10.4\ msec} \approx 0.1\ kHz = 100\ Hz$$

◊ **Example 3:** What would happen to the frame time and the frame rate if you doubled the number of image lines in the above example?

Doubling the number of image lines doubles the frame time since the frame time is proportional to the number of lines.

Doubling the number of image lines halves the frame rate since the frame rate is inversely proportional to the frame time.

8.5 Comparing Temporal Resolution for Scanned and Non-Scanned Modalities

From our examples of Section 8.4.5, it should be obvious that the frame rate is always much slower than the PRF. For this example, the PRF is 10 kHz and the frame rate is 50 Hz. This fact is common sense since the PRF is related to the time to transmit a single line whereas the frame rate is related to the time to transmit an entire scan or (frame) of lines. As a result, non-scanned modalities whose temporal resolution is governed by the PRF have far better temporal resolution than scanned modalities whose temporal resolution is governed by the frame rate.

9. Color Doppler, Frame Rate, and Temporal Resolution

9.1 General

Color Doppler is perhaps the most challenging of the pulsed wave modalities to fathom. The reason is color Doppler has some of the characteristics of spectral Doppler, and some of the characteristics of 2-D imaging. As a result, both techniques must be understood to fully understand color Doppler.

For understanding color theory, the starting point is the Doppler equation. Therefore color theory will be developed in Chapter 7 after the development of the Doppler equation. For understanding the temporal aspects of color Doppler, the starting point is the basic premise that color Doppler gives an estimate of the mean velocity taken in conjunction with the pulse wave parameters we have learned throughout this chapter.

9.2 Creating a Color Scan

Unlike conventional 2-D, color Doppler does not transmit only one acoustic line in a given direction and then move over and transmit another acoustic line to create a scan. Unlike spectral Doppler, which produces no scan, color Doppler does not transmit acoustic lines only in the same direction, producing no scan. Instead, color is a hybrid of the two techniques. In order to register a mean Doppler shift, color must transmit multiple acoustic lines in the same direction. These multiple acoustic lines are generally referred to as a "color packet" or "color ensemble". The packet size can vary (generally between 4 and 12 inclusively). From this ensemble of lines, a mean velocity can be estimated for each depth along the line. Once an estimate has been produced to create a single display line, the packet is then reproduced in a neighboring region, producing a mean estimate at that location. This process is repeated until the desired region is scanned. Once the desired region is scanned, the process is repeated, producing a second frame of color, etc.

Figure 24 demonstrates the generation of one color display line from a packet of transmitted acoustic lines. At time 1, the first acoustic line is transmitted and then received. At time 2, another transmit pulse is created, transmitted in the same direction as the acoustic line at time 1. This process is repeated until the entire packet is complete. As drawn in *Figure 24*, the packet size (ensemble length) is 5. From these 5 acoustic lines, the mean velocity is estimated at each depth location along the line, and one display line is generated.

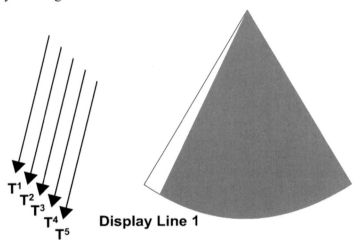

Display Line 1

Fig. 24   **A Packet Size of 5 to Create One Color Display Line**

View Animation and Image Library CD

9.3 Calculating the Color and Overall Frame Rate
In essence, within a packet, color Doppler is a non-scanned modality. To produce the color image, a collection of color packets are scanned across the patient. In other words, the acoustic lines which constitute a packet are non-scanned, but then to produce a frame, the packets are scanned. Consider how much more time is required to produce a color scan than to produce a standard 2-D image. Every display line of a color image requires an entire packet of color lines. Therefore, to calculate the frame time, you must multiply the number of display lines by the packet size, or:

$$color\ frame\ time = \frac{time}{packet\ line} * \frac{\#\ packet\ lines}{display\ line} * \frac{\#\ display\ lines}{frame}.$$

Logistically, color Doppler images are never displayed without a 2-D reference image. Therefore, the overall frame time is the sum of the 2-D frame time and the color frame time.

The following example illustrates these concepts.

◊ **Example** Presume an imaging depth of 8 cm. Using a color packet size of 9, if there are 100 display lines in an image, what is the frame rate?

We will first calculate the 2-D frame time:

$$2\text{-}D \ frame \ time = \frac{13 \ \mu sec}{cm} * \frac{8 \ cm}{line} * \frac{100 \ lines}{frame} = \frac{10.4 \ msec}{frame}$$

Note: This is the same problem as Example 2 in Section 8.4.5.

Now we will calculate the color frame time:

$$color \ frame \ time = \frac{104 \ \mu sec}{packet \ line} \bullet \frac{9 \ packet \ lines}{display \ line} * \frac{100 \ display \ lines}{frame} \approx \frac{90,000 \ \mu sec}{frame} = \frac{90 \ msec}{frame}.$$

Note: We could have also arrived at this result by just multiplying the 2-D frame time by 9. This should make sense since there are 900 acoustic lines in the color frame and only 100 acoustic lines in the 2-D frame.

The overall frame time is the sum of the color and 2-D frame times, or:

$$color \ frame \ time = \frac{90 \ msec}{frame} + \frac{10 \ msec}{frame} = \frac{100 \ msec}{frame},$$

and the overall frame rate is:

$$overall \ frame \ rate = \frac{1}{frame \ time} = \frac{1}{100 \ msec} = 0.01 \ kHz = 10 \ Hz.$$

9.4 Color and Poor Temporal Resolution

From this example, we see that the frame rate dropped from 100 Hz with just 2-D imaging to 10 Hz with color imaging. This result should make sense since every display line represents a packet of acoustic lines, each of which requires time to travel. As a result, color Doppler is considered to have the worst temporal resolution of the ultrasound modes.

Note: The poor temporal resolution of color Doppler is an important concept to understand.

Chapter 4

9.5 Choosing a Packet Size, the Trade-Off

In the early days of color Doppler imaging, most systems presented the user with a relatively accessible control which allowed for direct control of the color packet size. With time, the advent of soft keys, better preset designs, and significantly more imaging functions (with the need for even more controls), the control for the packet size became buried in a sub-menu, and sometimes even bundled in with other color controls. As a result, it has become significantly more challenging, on most systems, to identify the color packet control. To find this control, the user now has three options: consult the user manual, ask the clinical specialist from the manufacturer of the equipment, or "dig around" in the software menus.

Even before making the decision to change the color packet size, the question must be asked if the trade-off is desirable. Choosing a larger packet size produces smoother color, with less color noise, and improved sensitivity to weak signals, but obviously sacrifices temporal resolution. Conversely, decreasing the color packet size increases the frame rate, but potentially decreases color smoothness and color sensitivity.

Note: This trade-off is also a very important concept to understand.

10. Optimizing Frame Rate and Temporal Resolution

When good temporal resolution is critical, there are a series of steps which can be taken to increase the frame rate. As we have already seen many times, improving one aspect of an ultrasound image almost always creates a trade-off in a different aspect. For temporal resolution, improvement almost always comes at the expense of detail resolution, a much smaller scan region, or both. Of course not all types of imaging require fast frame rates, and therefore do not warrant any degradation in detail resolution. Quite simply the criterion for deciding is the faster the changes that need to be detected, the more the frame rate matters. Therefore, imaging a liver or pancreas requires very little temporal resolution, whereas imaging a shunted flow or a pediatric heart generally requires optimal temporal resolution. The following list outlines the steps which can be taken to increase frame rate, thereby potentially improving the temporal resolution.

1. Narrow color box size (color sector)
2. Decrease color box depth
3. Activate parallel processing
4. Decrease color packet size
5. Decrease color line density
6. Narrow 2-D image size (2-D sector)
7. Decrease 2-D depth

11. Typical Values and Ranges for Wave, PW and Frame Parameters

	Parameter	Determined by:	Value (range)	Specific Mode
Wave	Operating frequency (f)	source	2 MHz – 10 MHz	All
	Period (P)	source	0.5 μsec – 0.1 μsec	All
	Wavelength (λ)	$\lambda = \dfrac{c}{f}$	154 μm - 770 μm (in soft tissue)	All
	Propagation velocity (c)	medium	337 m/sec – 4080 m/sec	All
Pulse Wave	Pulse Duration (PD)	$PD = P \times (\# cycles)$	0.2 μsec - 1.0 μsec	2-D
			0.4 μsec - 16 μsec	PW Doppler
	Pulse Repetition Period (PRP)	13 $\mu sec \times$ depth	13 μsec - 260 μsec	All
	Pulse Repetition Frequency (PRF)	$\dfrac{1}{PRP}$	77 kHz – 3.85 kHz	All
	Duty Factor	$\dfrac{PD}{PRP}$	< 1%	2-D
			1% - 10% (varies significantly)	PW Doppler
			100%	CW
	SPL	$SPL = \lambda \times (\# cycles)$	300 μm - 1540 μm (in soft tissue)	2-D
			600 μm - 2.5 cm	PW Doppler
Frames	Frame Time	$= \dfrac{time}{line} \bullet \dfrac{\# lines}{frame}$	5 msec – 100 msec	2-D
		$= \dfrac{time}{line} \bullet \dfrac{total \ \# lines}{frame}$	10 msec – 600 msec	Color
	Frame Rate	$\dfrac{1}{frame \ time}$	200 Hz – 10 Hz	2-D
			100 Hz – 8 Hz	Color

Table 1: **Ultrasound Related Parameter Table: Typical Values and Ranges**

12. The Foundational Drawing for Pulse Wave Revisited

We are now ready to update the pulsed wave diagram we began in Level 1. The ability to draw *Figure 25* from memory is critical to demonstrate knowledge of pulsed wave operation. Furthermore, the ability to draw *Figure 25* for any of the credentialing exams is invaluable.

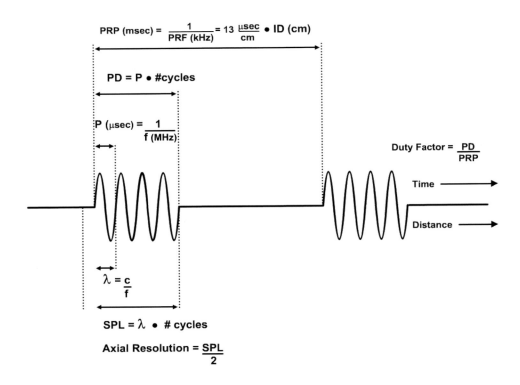

Fig. 25 **Pulsed Wave Timing Diagram**

Figure 25 will be addressed again when discussing bioeffects. Clearly, the timing issues and duty factor will have direct consequence on the likelihood of artifacts. Therefore, there will be future additions to this already information laden diagram.

13. Exercises   Answers Pg. 452-455

1.   In bone, what is the roundtrip acoustic transit time to a target 2.04 cm deep?

2.   How far can ultrasound travel through soft tissue in

   a) 1 second?
   b) 2 seconds?
   c) 10 seconds?

3.   To what depth can ultrasound travel through air (presuming roundtrip flight) in:

   a) 1 second?
   b) 2 seconds?
   c) 10 seconds?

4.   What is the minimum PRP and maximum PRF to image in soft tissue at a depth of 5 cm?

5.   What is the maximum frame rate if it takes 0.1 msec to transmit a single line with 100 lines per frame?

6.   For color Doppler, the same line is transmitted multiple times to improve signal to noise. A packet is defined as the number of times a specific line is transmitted. At a depth of 10 cm in soft tissue, with a packet size of 10 and 100 packets per frame, what is the maximum frame rate?

7.   If a pulse contains 8 cycles and the period is 0.2 µsec. What is the pulse duration?

8.   If a pulse contains 8 cycles and the frequency is 1 MHz. What is the pulse duration?

9.   If the PD is 10 msec and the frequency is 1 kHz, how many cycles are in the pulse?

10.   If system A has 4 cycles/pulse and is operating at 5 MHz and system B has 4 cycles/pulse and is operating at 10 MHz, which system has a shorter pulse duration?

11.   If two systems are operating at the same frequency and the same number of cycles per pulse, then the pulse durations

   a) are equal
   b) are unequal
   c) cannot be determined.

12.   If the PD = 2 msec and the PRP = 5 msec, what is the duty cycle?

13.   If the duty cycle is 0.6% and the PRP is 10 msec, what is the PD?

14.   If the duty cycle is 0.6% and the PRF is 0.1 kHz, what is the PD?

15.   A duty factor of 100% has a special name, what is that special name?

14. Bandwidth

14.1 Bandwidth Defined
In the recent years, there has been considerable talk about bandwidth in just about every arena of life. We hear about cell phone bandwidth, cable television bandwidth, digital satellite bandwidth, internet bandwidth, etc. There is also considerable talk about bandwidth in ultrasound.

Specifically, bandwidth is defined as the useful range of frequencies over which anything can operate. There are many different types of bandwidth. There is transducer bandwidth, transmit bandwidth, receive bandwidth, system receiver bandwidth, display bandwidth, etc. In general, you must specify the bandwidth to which you are referring.

14.2 Pictorial Representation of Bandwidth
Figure 26 represents a graph of a transducer bandwidth. Notice that the horizontal axis represents increasing frequency and the vertical axis represents the response sensitivity or signal amplitude. For this graph, the sensitivity is specified in decibels.

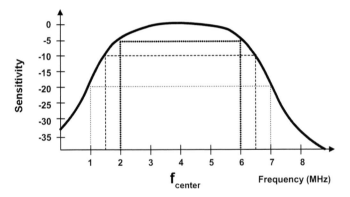

Fig. 26   **Bandwidth**

From this graph, we see that at frequencies below 2 MHz there is relatively little sensitivity. Similarly, at frequencies above 6 MHz there is little sensitivity. But how sensitive is sensitive enough? To discuss bandwidth accurately, the attenuation points must be specified as demonstrated below.

The 6 dB bandwidth point is the range of frequencies that exist between the two corner frequencies at which the signal sensitivity is decreased by 6 dB. For the above example, the signal has decreased by 6 dB at 6 MHz and at 2 MHz. The 6 dB corner frequencies are 6 MHz and 2 MHz. Since there is a range of 4 MHz between these two corner frequencies, we would say that the 6 dB bandwidth is 4 MHz, or:

$$\text{-6 dB bandwidth} = (6 - 2) \text{ MHz} = 4 \text{ MHz.}$$

Similarly, the 10 dB bandwidth point is the range of frequencies that exists between the two corner frequencies at which the signal sensitivity is decreased by 10 dB. For the above example, the signal has decreased by 10 dB at 6.4 MHz and at 1.6 MHz. The 10 dB corner frequencies are 6.4 MHz and 1.6 MHz. Since there is a range of 4.8 MHz between these two corner frequencies, we would say that the 10 dB bandwidth is 4.8 MHz, or:

$$\text{-10 dB bandwidth} = (6.4 - 1.6) \text{ MHz} = 4.8 \text{ MHz.}$$

For engineering purposes, we will generally specify at least two or three different bandwidth points, so as to more accurately characterize the response of the system we are measuring. For completeness, see if you can derive the 20 dB bandwidth and corner frequencies from the graph in *Figure 26*.

$$\text{-20 dB bandwidth} = (7 - 1) \text{ MHz } = 6 \text{ MHz}$$

14.3 Bandwidth Calculation

From the above example, we see that the bandwidth is defined as the maximum corner frequency minus the minimum corner frequency for a specified attenuation rate, or:

$$\text{bandwidth (BW)} = \text{maximum frequency - minimum frequency.}$$

14.4 Fractional Bandwidth

For transducers, a much more commonly used metric is the fractional bandwidth. As the name suggests, the fractional bandwidth is determined by dividing the bandwidth by the operating frequency.

$$\text{fractional bandwidth } (FBW) = \frac{\text{bandwidth}}{\text{operating frequency}}$$

Consider *Figure 26* assuming that the operating frequency is the same as the center frequency, f_c, the 6 dB fractional bandwidth would be (4 MHz / 4 MHz) or 100%. Note that the 4 MHz in the numerator represents a range of frequencies, while the 4 MHz in the denominator represents a single frequency in the center of the band. Transducers are considered to be broadband when they have more than approximately an 80% fractional bandwidth. The bandwidth in the figure would represent a broadband design.

14.5 Quality Factor

The quality factor gives the exact same information as the fractional bandwidth and is the reciprocal of the fractional bandwidth

$$\text{quality factor (QF)} = \frac{1}{\text{fractional bandwidth}} = \frac{\text{operating frequency}}{\text{bandwidth}}.$$

There has been an implicit assumption that broader bandwidth is better. Although, in general, wider bandwidth is better, there are cases when more bandwidth has no real advantage. Let us consider when wide (or broad) bandwidth and high fractional bandwidth are useful.

14.6 The Value of Greater Bandwidth

14.6.1 Flexibility

First, a wide bandwidth transducer offers flexibility, since it can be operated at different frequencies. The user is allowed to choose an operating frequency within the band that is best suited for the modality and the specific patient. This ability to run at different frequencies is often called "frequency agility" or "multi-Hertz." Additionally, this flexibility allows for the B-mode image to be created at a higher frequency while simultaneously performing color and spectral Doppler at lower frequencies.

This is critical since the reflection from the blood can be very weak due to Rayleigh scattering (discussed in Chapter 3). The increased attenuation at the higher frequencies further weakens these signals, the signal potentially non-diagnostic. The following diagram represents a broad-band transducer which can be used as a multi-Hertz transducer. For less required penetration but better resolution, the higher frequency band is used. For greater penetration, the user switches to a lower operating frequency, utilizing the lower range of the overall bandwidth. Of course there is a degradation in resolution.

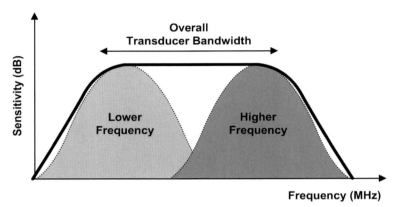

Fig. 27   **Multi-Hertz Operation**

Note that using the entire bandwidth at the same time, without any advanced techniques, is not desirable. For easy to image patients, the poorer resolution data from the low frequency data will arrive simultaneously with the better resolution higher frequency data, degrading the best possible image quality. By using just the higher frequency bandwidth, the longer wavelength reflections will be absent and hence, there will be better resolution. For difficult to image patients, where penetration is critical, using the full bandwidth is again not ideal. In order to minimize the risks of bioeffects, we are only allowed to transmit so much energy into the patient. Any energy that is being transmitted at the higher frequency reduces the amount of energy that can be transmitted at the lower frequency range. As a result, if we transmit over the entire bandwidth, we are not allowed to transmit with as much power at the lower frequency, which yields the most penetration. Therefore, for penetration, it is better to transmit using the lower frequency range and not be restricted by the transmitting of energy in a range that will not penetrate well.

14.6.2 Dynamic Frequency Tuning (Sliding Receive Filters)

Second, broad bandwidth is useful for a technique called "dynamic frequency tuning" or "sliding receive filters." If a high frequency is used, a high resolution image is achieved in the near field. If a low frequency is used the resolution is worse, but there may be significantly more penetration. Dynamic frequency tuning attempts to optimize both resolution and penetration. The concept behind "dynamic frequency tuning" is to transmit over the whole bandwidth and then change, or "slide" the receive frequency from higher to lower with increasing depth. In this way, the echoes from the near field are very high resolution while there is still some lower frequency energy from the deeper depths. The greater the bandwidth, the greater the range over which the filters can slide, or be "dynamically tuned."

The diagram in *Figure 29* represents the use of dynamic frequency tuning. The echoes that return from the shallowest depths still have a fair amount of high frequency energy. So as to preserve the high frequency resolution, only the high frequency band is received, ignoring the echoes from lower frequencies. In the figure, the high frequency band is designated as BW_1. As the signals return from deeper depths, later in time, the high frequency attenuates faster than the lower frequency energy. Therefore, there would be inadequate penetration at the higher frequency band. Instead, the filters in the receivers shift to receive a lower frequency band, designated as BW_2. The same process is repeated for signals arriving later and later. The net result is good resolution in the near field and relatively good penetration in the far field. In this diagram, the image was broken into four bands. In reality, the system slides the receive filters continuously, not in four discrete steps, so there are no major discontinuities as in the figure drawn.

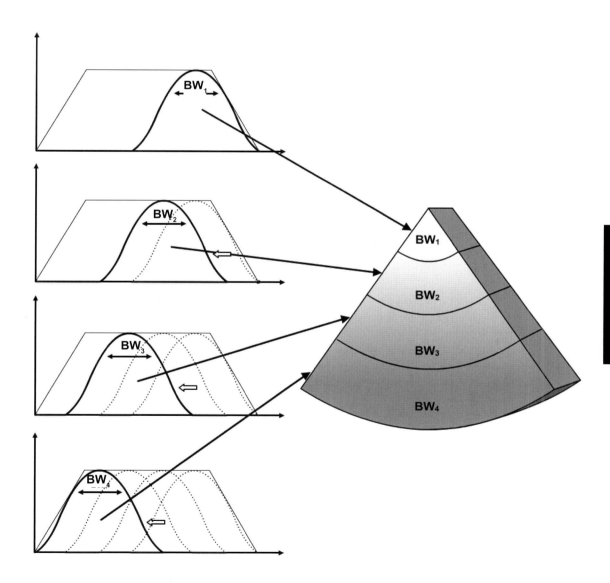

Fig. 29   **Dynamic Frequency Tuning**

14.6.3 Harmonic Imaging

Third, broad bandwidth is useful for harmonic imaging. As will be discussed in Chapter 10, in second harmonic imaging, the transmit is performed at the fundamental frequency and the receive is performed at twice the fundamental frequency. This can obviously only be achieved if the transducer has enough bandwidth to operate proficiently at both of those frequencies.

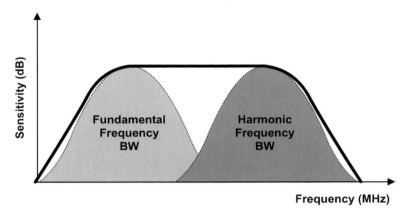

Fig. 29   **Use of Bandwidth for Harmonic Imaging**

14.6.4 Frequency Fusion (Frequency Compounding)

Fourth, broad bandwidth is useful to allow for many different types of parallel processing techniques. These techniques typically involve transmitting over a broad range of frequencies and then receiving and processing the beam at two or more different narrower frequency bands. The different frequency bands are each processed to produce images which are then fused together. This technique can therefore result in better overall image quality.

14.6.5 CW Doppler and Bandwidth

Is there ever a time when more bandwidth is not helpful? The answer is yes. As you will see in section 16, CW Doppler requires very little bandwidth. Therefore, if given a choice (as in *Figure 30*) between a narrower bandwidth and more sensitivity (A), or a broader bandwidth and less sensitivity (B), the more sensitive transducer A would be much better for Doppler. Also, which of the two transducer designs would you believe would be better when penetration is needed? Although transducer A has less bandwidth, at low frequencies there is significantly better penetration. Since high frequency energy does not help with penetration, transducer A is clearly better in this case as well.

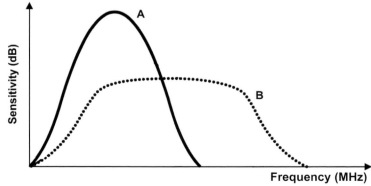

Fig. 30   **More Bandwidth is Not Always Better**

Pegasus Lectures, Inc.

15. Pulse Duration (Width) vs. Bandwidth

15.1 The Reciprocal Relationship
We have already learned that time and frequency have a reciprocal relationship. A long time corresponds to a low frequency and a short time corresponds to a high frequency.

If the impulse response of a transducer is short (short pulse duration), the transducer will have a wide bandwidth: $\left(\dfrac{1}{small\ number} = big\ number \right)$. If the impulse response of the transducer is long, the transducer will have a narrow bandwidth: $\left(\dfrac{1}{big\ number} = small\ number \right)$. The following figure demonstrates the reciprocal relationship between the pulse duration and the bandwidth of a transducer.

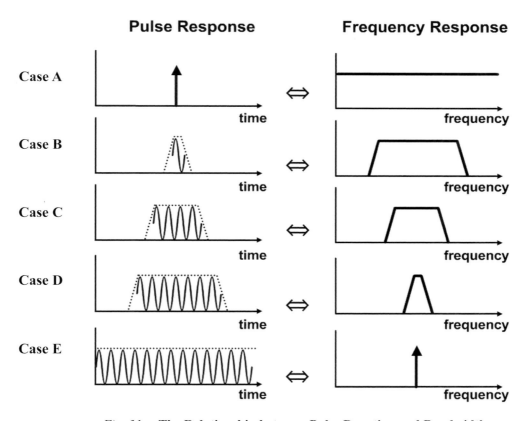

Fig. 31   **The Relationship between Pulse Duration and Bandwidth**

Referring to the various scenarios depicted, you should see demonstrated the inverse relationship between the time and frequency domain. In Case A, the time response is infinitesimally short, creating an infinitely wide bandwidth. Although an infinitesimally short ring time is not possible, it is very instructive to show the inverse relationship with bandwidth. Earlier in this chapter (Section 8.3.3) we discussed the use of a backing material to decrease the number of cycles in a pulse so as to decrease the spatial pulse length, improving axial resolution. We now see that there is another advantage of the use of a backing material. By decreasing the number of cycles in the pulse, the pulse duration is also shortened, increasing the bandwidth.

The term "pulse width" is sometimes used in place of the term "pulse duration." This naming choice is less desirable since the meaning is less discernible from just the name itself. In this sense, the word "width" is referring to how wide a pulse looks when pictured as a drawing over time. This definition is slightly more intuitive for engineers and physicists who are used to measuring time parameters on an oscilloscope, but much less intuitive for sonographers. My suggestion is to use the term pulse duration, but be familiar with the term pulse width in case you are asked by someone a little less sensitive to inconsistencies in terminology.

15.2 The Meaning of the Operating Frequency and Bandwidth Relationship
Notice in Case B of *Figure 31,* that if the transducer is only allowed to ring for a single full cycle there is extremely broad bandwidth. This demonstrates another very important point: a transducer is always operating at a range of frequencies centered around the operating, or "center" frequency, and never just at one frequency. In other words, when we say that we are using an operating frequency of 4 MHz, we are really saying that the center of the bandwidth is 4 MHz, and that we are using a range of frequencies centered around 4 MHz. If resolution is critical, as it is in B-mode imaging, then the bandwidth is generally quite wide. If resolution isn't as critical, as in CW Doppler, then the bandwidth can be quite narrow.

15.3 Bandwidth Required for Doppler
Notice in Case D of *Figure 31* that if the transducer rings for a long time, as it does with a large sample volume in PW Doppler and in continuous wave, then there is very little bandwidth. In essence, the widest bandwidth is necessary for B-mode imaging, followed by color Doppler, spectral PW Doppler, and then CW spectral Doppler.

16. Conceptual Questions   Answers Pg. 455-457

1.   The frequency and the _____ are reciprocals.

2.   The pulse repetition frequency and the _____ repetition _____ are reciprocals.

3.   The _____, like the period, has units of _____.

4.   The _____, like the _____, has units of one over time, which has the name

       _____.

5.   The _____ is the time between pulses repeating.

6.   The _____ is the frequency at which the pulses repeat.

7.   The deeper the imaging depth, the lower the _____, or the more time it takes before repeating a pulse.

8.   The frame _____ depends on how much time it takes to shoot one line, and the number of _____ within the frame.

9. If one line takes 0.1 msec, and there are 120 lines in one frame, the frame time is _____.

10. The pulse duration has units of _____.

11. If a pulse has 4 cycles and each cycle lasts 1 msec, the _____ _____ equals _____.

12. If a pulse has _____ and each cycle lasts 2 msec, then the pulse duration equals 12 msec.

13. The time for a cycle to repeat itself is called the _____.

14. The _____ _____ equals the number of cycles multiplied by the time for one cycle to occur and is called the period.

15. The _____ _____ is the percentage of time the pulse is on divided by the total time between repeating pulses.

16. The time a pulse is "on" is called the _____ duration.

17. The "total time" between repeating pulses is called the _____ _____ _____.

18. Since the duty cycle is the "on time" divided by the _____, the _____ cycle equals the pulse _____ divided by the pulse repetition period.

19. The duty cycle is also called the duty _____.

20. The _____ _____ can never be greater than 1 or 100%.

21. A duty factor of _____ means the "pulse" is always on.

22. A duty factor of _____ means there is no pulse.

23. A duty factor of _____ means the pulse duration equals one half the pulse repetition period.

24. A duty factor of 50% means the pulse _____ equals one half the pulse _____ _____.

25. If the duty cycle is .33 and the PRP is 1 msec, then the pulse duration is _____.

26. If the duty cycle is .33 and the pulse duration is .66 seconds, then the PRP is _____.

27. The spatial pulse length has units of _____ whereas the pulse duration has units of _____.

28. The _____ _____ _____ equals the number of cycles multiplied by the wavelength (λ).

29.   The _____ _____ equals the number of cycles multiplied by the period.

30.   You should notice a similarity between the _____ _____ _____ and the pulse duration. The spatial pulse length has units of distance and is therefore related to the wavelength, which also has units of distance. The _____ _____ has units of time and is therefore related to the _____ which also has units of time.

31.   The operating frequency is the same as the transmit _____ .

32.   The _____ is defined as the maximum frequency minus the minimum frequency over which a transducer or system has sensitivity.

33.   The _____ bandwidth is defined as the bandwidth divided by the operating frequency.

34.   The quality factor is the inverse of the _____ bandwidth.

35.   Since the fractional bandwidth equals the bandwidth divided by the operating frequency, and since the quality factor is the inverse of the fractional bandwidth, the quality factor equals the operating frequency divided by the _____ .

36.   A shorter pulse duration leads to a wider _____ .

37.   An infinitely short pulse duration theoretically creates _____ bandwidth.

38.   _____ spectral Doppler requires the least bandwidth.

39.   Transmitting at 2 MHz implies that the center frequency of the bandwidth being used is _____ .

40.   A _____ _____ is used to shorten the ring down of a transducer.

41.   Shortening the ring down of a transducer also shortens the _____ _____ _____ , improving the range resolution.

42.   The motivation for using a pulsed mode instead of a continuous mode is because CW has no _____ resolution.

Pulsed Wave Operation

- Continuous waves have no ability to resolve structures separated in depth.

- Pulsing is a technique which yields the ability to resolve structures separated in depth.

- For resolution, smaller numbers are better.

- The shorter the pulse, the better the depth resolution, depth resolution is also referred to as longitudinal, axial, radial, or range resolution.

- The longitudinal resolution equals the spatial pulse length divided by 2.

$$\text{Axial Resolution} = \frac{SPL}{2}$$

- The factor of 2 derives from the fact that the roundtrip effect is helping to separate the echoes from objects at varying depths.

- Because of the desire to use pulsed wave to achieve some axial resolution, many parameters which describe the pulse must be defined.

  o The time the pulse lasts is called the pulse duration (PD).

  o The pulse duration is determined by the period multiplied by the number of cycles in the pulse.

$$PD - P \bullet \# cycles$$

  o The time between transmit events (from the start of one pulse until the pulse is repeated) is called the pulse repetition period (PRP).

  o The PRP is determined primarily by the imaging depth and is equal to the imaging depth (in centimeters) multiplied by 13 μsec per cm.

$$PRP = ID(cm) \times \frac{13\,\mu sec}{cm}$$

  o The pulse repetition frequency is simply the reciprocal of the PRP.

$$PRF = \frac{1}{PRP}$$

  o Typically PRF values are in the kHz range.

- The ratio of the PD to the PRP is referred to as the duty factor. The highest value the duty factor can reach is 1 or 100% which indicate CW.

$$DF = \frac{PD}{PRP}$$

- The duty factor is an indicator for the risk of thermal bioeffects.

- The physical length the pulse occupies in the medium is called the spatial pulse length (SPL).

- The SPL is equal to the wavelength multiplied by the number of cycles in the pulse.

$$SPL = \lambda \bullet \# \ cycles$$

- A backing or damping material is used to shorten the number of cycles in a pulse from a transducer.

- By reducing the number of cycles in the pulse, the pulse duration is decreased which results in an increase in the bandwidth.

- By reducing the number of cycles in the pulse, the spatial pulse length is decreased which results in improved axial resolution.

- A scanned modality implies that, over time, the acoustic beams are transmitted in different directions.

- A non-scanned modality implies that, over time, the acoustic beam is repeatedly transmitted in the same direction.

- Non-scanned modalities present greater thermal risks than scanned modalities.

- The frame time is the product of the time to produce an individual acoustic line and the number of lines in the frame.

$$\text{Frame time} = \text{PRP} \times \frac{\#\ \text{lines}}{\text{frame}}$$

- The frame time (better termed the frame frequency) is simply the reciprocal of the frame time.

$$\text{Frame rate} = \frac{1}{\text{frame time}}$$

- Higher frame rates result in better temporal resolution.

- Color Doppler generally has the worst temporal resolution since each display line of color is comprised of an entire "packet" or "ensemble" of acoustic lines.

- The bandwidth is defined as the range of frequencies over which a device can operate.

- The fractional bandwidth is defined as the bandwidth divided by the center frequency or the operating frequency.

$$FBW = \frac{BW}{FC}$$

- The quality factor is the reciprocal of the fractional bandwidth.

$$QF = \frac{1}{FBW}$$

- Broadband transducers can be used for many techniques such as harmonic imaging, dynamic frequency tuning, and frequency fusion (compounding).

- A short impulse response (pulse duration) implies a broad bandwidth. A long pulse duration implies a narrow bandwidth.

- CW Doppler requires very little bandwidth, whereas 2D imaging requires significant bandwidth.

Note: See Appendix F: Physical Units and Appendix G: Equations for additional review.

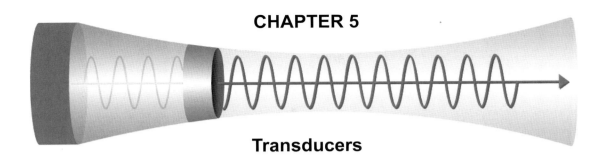

CHAPTER 5

Transducers

Introduction

In Chapter 2 we discussed waves and the parameters that define a sound wave useful for diagnostic testing. In Chapter 3, we discussed the interaction that occurs between the mechanical wave of sound and the medium, responsible for ultimately returning the signal back for interpretation. In Chapter 4, we discussed various timing schemes so as to achieve the desired axial resolution. You will note that there was no discussion specific to the device responsible for producing these waves which interact with the patient to produce time variant signals for processing and interpretation. The approach not to discuss this topic is very deliberate. It is very difficult to discuss the specifics of a complex device before you understand the requirements for the device. Since we now know some of the parameters that are desirable for a wave, we are now ready to discuss these devices called transducers.

The subject of "transducers" is very broad. Since there are many different types of transducers and many different applications for transducers, we will start by discussing the basic principles and general theory in Level 1. Level 1 is designed to teach the rudimentary principles without encumbering the reader with specifics about transducer application in clinical ultrasound. Once the general aspects are understood, Level 2 will discuss specific transducer designs, advantages and disadvantages of various technologies, and applications. Level 2 will be structured in a unique manner, following the technology development path from the early days through the most advanced present day designs. The hope is that by splitting the material into two distinct sections (the theory in Level 1, and the application in Level 2), we will significantly reduce the amount of confusion which arises from the many permutations and interactions between the types of transducers, the application of various transducer types, the benefits and limitations to each design, and the desired features and technology driving the future.

The importance of learning about transducers needs to be stressed. Aspects of the transmitted wave directly affect the quality of the scan, what modalities can be performed, and the risk of bioeffects. Since the transducer and transducer design directly affect the beam, it is logical that understanding transducer theory and function will be critical to performing a good clinical diagnostic ultrasound test on a patient.

1. Transducer Basics

1.1 Transducers Defined
A transducer is any device which converts energy from one form to another. Using the meaning of the prefix in the definition, a transducer is a device which converts energy across the device from one form to another form. There are many forms of transducers in the world. Do not make the mistake of defining the word too narrowly to only mean "ultrasound" transducers.

1.2 Examples of Transducers

◊ **Examples:**   microphones

stereo speakers

temperature sensors (thermocouples, thermistors)

light bulbs

lasers

eyes

ears

nerves

1.3 Ultrasound Transducers and Bi-directionality

To be specific, an ultrasound transducer utilizes the properties of piezoelectric materials to convert electropotential energy (voltage) into mechanical vibration (sound or pressure) as well as convert mechanical vibrations back into electrical energy. This fact implies that the same transducer can potentially be used to both send out a signal into the patient (transmit) and receive a signal from the patient (receive), in juxtaposition to a system where a separate device is required for each. You will note that not all of the examples of transducers given above can operate bi-directionally. Light bulbs don't convert photons back into electrical energy and ears certainly do not convert electrical impulses from the brain back to sound waves that emanate from the ear. The fact that an ultrasound transducer can work bi-directionally (exhibits reciprocity) is a fortuitous benefit.

2. Ultrasound Transducers and the Piezoelectric Effect

2.1 The Piezoelectric Effect

The piezoelectric effect is a phenomenon by which a mechanical deformation results when an electric field (voltage) is applied to certain crystal materials, or a varying electrical signal is produced when the crystal structure is mechanically deformed.

Simply put, when you drive a crystal with a voltage, it resonates mechanically at some characteristic frequency. When you vibrate the crystal mechanically at some characteristic frequency, a voltage is produced. The following illustration depicts the basic conversion back and forth (bi-directionally) between electrical energy and acoustic energy.

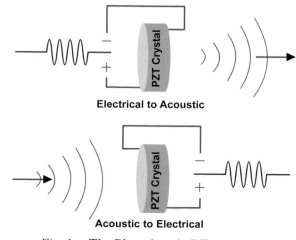

Fig. 1   **The Piezoelectric Effect**

2.2 The Piezoelectric Mechanism

A simplified description is provided here in Level 1, but in Level 3 of this chapter, there is a formal discussion of the piezoelectric effect. (Hopefully, you will be intrigued enough by the interesting aspects of piezoelectricity to venture into Level 3 for the more complete description.)

All atoms and molecules of a material are bound together with electrical binding forces. This fact is well known since it is the foundation of nuclear energy. For crystals which exhibit the piezoelectric effect, the molecules are dipolar. As the name suggests, molecules that are dipolar have two poles, one pole which is positive and the other which is negative.

If electrodes (electrical contacts) are placed across the crystal with a voltage potential applied, the poles of the molecules will shift to align with the polarity of the electrodes. Remembering that "opposites attract" (like magnetic poles) the negative poles rotate toward the positive electrodes and the positive poles align with the negative electrodes.

For *Figure 2a* , since the negative electrode is placed on the left side, the positive poles rotate to the left. When this rotation occurs, the molecules are now slightly farther apart, causing an expansion of the crystal. If instead, as demonstrated by *Figure 2b*, the polarity of the voltage is reversed, the molecules will rotate to the right, resulting in a closer spacing of the molecules, causing the crystal to contract. If the voltage potential is then eliminated, the molecules will then shift back to their normal alignment and spacing, "shrinking" back to the original dimension *Figure 2c*. Therefore, by varying the electrical field, a mechanical "distortion" of the crystal occurs.

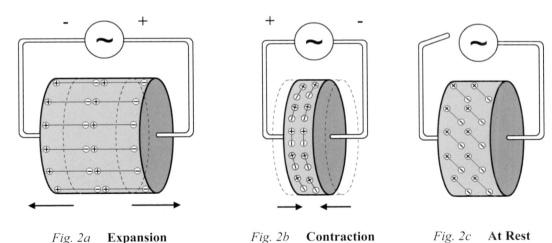

Fig. 2a   **Expansion**   Fig. 2b   **Contraction**   Fig. 2c   **At Rest**

The result is that a varying electrical field produces a physical change in the dimension of the crystal. If the crystal is then placed against a medium, the physical vibration can be coupled into that neighboring medium. As discussed earlier, how much of that vibration is transferred depends on the acoustic impedance mismatch between the crystal and the medium.

An analogy for this phenomenon is applying a force to two blocks connected by a spring. If a force is applied on the two blocks in opposite directions, the spring will be stretched and the blocks will be farther apart than the resting condition. By releasing the force on the objects, the two objects will recoil towards each other, but because of momentum, the objects will actually get closer together than the original separation distance. As a result, the two blocks will start traveling away from each other, oscillating until finally coming to rest at the same separation distance as the resting condition.

How far these objects are separated, and how long the oscillation occurs depends on the force applied, the mass of the blocks, and the properties of the interconnecting spring. Just as the mechanical resonance is related to the parameters of the spring, the resonance of the crystal is related to the parameters of the crystal. Clearly, a single impulse will cause the crystal to ring at a resonant frequency.

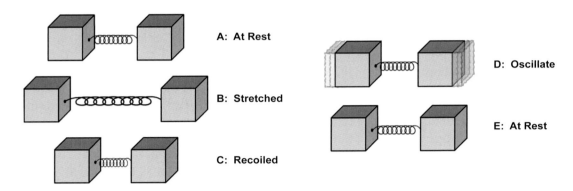

Fig. 3   **Block Analogy of Crystal Oscillation**

From both our analogy and our description of the piezoelectric effect, we can imagine that applying a stronger electrical field will produce a greater mechanical distortion. In essence, the amplitude of the acoustic energy is related to the amplitude of the electrical signal driving the crystal. To produce a higher amplitude acoustic signal (pressure field), a higher voltage is applied to the crystal.

2.3 Natural Piezoelectric Materials

The most notable naturally occurring piezoelectric material is quartz (SiO_2). The original work done with piezoelectric properties by Pierre and Jacque Curie in the latter 1880's was using quartz. Quartz is commonly used today for its piezoelectric properties. Confirmation of this fact is as simple as looking at the advertising for most battery operated watches. The battery is the source of the electrical energy, and the quartz acts as a very well calibrated vibrational source for measuring time. Quartz is also commonly used as a clock system for many electronic circuits. Part of the reason quartz is used so frequently in electronic circuits is because of its very reliable and controllable behavior. Quartz is regularly controlled to be consistent to better than 1 part in 10^8. Also, quartz as a natural piezoelectric material has a relatively high efficiency of conversion referred to as the coupling coefficient (in thickness or piston mode). The coupling coefficient is a measure of efficiency of conversion between electrical and mechanical signals. There are other naturally occurring materials such tourmaline, topaz, sugar cane, Rochelle salts (sodium potassium tartrate tetrahydrate), and even bone, but when is the last time you heard someone marketing their watch as Rochelle salt or bone activated?

2.4 Manufactured Piezoelectric Materials

There are many materials which can be manufactured that can exhibit the piezoelectric effect. Some examples are barium titanate, lead zirconate titanate, barium lead zirconate, lead metaniobate, and polyvinylidene fluoride (PVDF). Now that you saw a partial laundry list of would be contenders, the material most commonly chosen for ultrasound transducers has been lead zirconate titanate (PZT). PZT became the material of choice for medical applications because of:
   • High coupling coefficient (efficiency)
   • High frequency of natural resonance
   • Very good repeatable characteristics for stable designs

One issue with the use of PZT as the crystal material in medical applications is its relatively high impedance. Generally, the impedance of PZT ranges from around 30 to 40 MRayls, depending on the type of PZT used. Since the impedance of tissue is so much lower, this high impedance results in a significant acoustic impedance mismatch with the patient. As we learned in Chapter 3, a large acoustic impedance mismatch results in poor transmission. This large mismatch becomes the motivation for the use of a matching layer. Although other materials such as PVDF have much lower impedances, around 4 MRayls for PVDF, the coupling coefficient is much lower, resulting in inadequate sensitivity. You will note that although quartz has a relatively high coupling coefficient as a naturally piezoelectric material, its coupling coefficient is about one tenth that of PZT. As a result, quartz is never used as the piezoelectric material for ultrasound transducers which need extraordinary sensitivity. Newer transducers are now making use of a combination of materials called composites to address some of these issues. Composite materials are discussed in Level 2 of this chapter.

2.5 Poling

In our example above, we started with the assumption that all of the poles of the molecules were nicely aligned, with the positive poles pointing in one direction and the negative poles pointing in the other. The efficiency of piezoelectric materials can be improved through a process called "poling." The process of poling involves taking the crystal material and placing it in an oven of extremely high temperatures. The increased temperature, allows the molecules to "slide" more freely, such that the molecules can move to align themselves when a large electrical field is introduced. As a result, the molecules adopt a well behaved pattern where the positive poles align in one direction and the negative poles align in the other direction. In other words, each molecular dipole is now aligned in a specific orientation which enhances the physical distortion that occurs with an applied varying electric field. When the material is removed from the large electrical field and heat, the molecules remain in the new orientation.

2.6 Curie Point

As mentioned, Pierre and Jacque Curie worked with quartz in the latter part of the 1800's. As a result, the temperature at which a material will lose its poling and hence, efficiency as a piezoelectric material, is called the Curie temperature. The Curie temperature for PZT is approximately 300° Celsius. The probability of mistakenly heating a material close to or beyond its Curie point is extremely low (300° Celsius is 572° Fahrenheit). However, as you will learn later throughout this chapter, the process of transducer construction utilizes materials such as epoxies, which will break down well before the Curie point, causing delamination and overall destruction to your transducer. For this reason, you should make certain not to autoclave any transducer, unless you desire a very expensive paperweight.

3. Frequency of Operation and Crystal Dimension

3.1 Pulse Wave

As stated in the introduction to this chapter, one of the reasons for waiting to cover the topic of transducers until this point was so that the most important parameters for ultrasound application would be recognizable. One of the fundamental wave parameters discussed was the operating frequency. In Chapter 2, we stated that the operating frequency is determined by the source. It is now time to discuss that source. For pulse wave operation, the frequency of operation depends primarily on the thickness of the piezoelectric material and the propagation velocity within the piezoelectric material. The following illustration demonstrates how a pulsed electrical signal is converted into a pulsed acoustic signal. In case A, the crystal is thicker, resulting in a longer time for the crystal to fully expand and contract. In the expansion state, the transducer compresses the neighboring medium. Therefore, a slow compression rate implies a longer period and hence, a lower frequency. In case B, the crystal is half as thick as in case A. As a result, the crystal can expand and contract twice as fast.

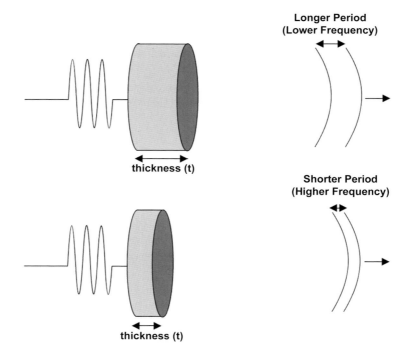

Fig. 4   **Relationship Between Crystal Thickness and PW Operating Frequency**

    View Animation and Image Library CD

So for pulsed operation:

$$f_0 \propto \frac{1}{thickness}$$

Now imagine that there are two crystals identical in thickness but one crystal has a higher propagation velocity than the other crystal. The higher propagation velocity implies that the material can expand and contract faster, reducing the time between compression (the period). Since the frequency is the reciprocal of the period, a shorter period implies a higher operating frequency. Therefore, the operating frequency is proportional to the propagation velocity, or:

$$f_0 \, (MHz) \propto Propagation \ Speed \ in \ Crystal \ \left(C_{crystal}\right)$$

So the equation for the operating frequency in PW must express a proportional relationship with the propagation velocity in the crystal, and an inverse relationship with the thickness of the crystal. Before we write the equation, we must consider one more aspect of the physical situation. When the crystal expands, it expands in two different directions. Only half of the motion is in the direction of the coupled medium. Therefore, there is a constant factor of 2 in the denominator to account for this expansion. The equation is therefore:

$$f_0 (MHz) = \frac{Propagation\ Speed\ (mm/\mu sec)}{2 \bullet (thickness)(mm)}.$$

You will notice that the units for each of the variables has been fixed to a specific format. By forcing the units to be in millimeters per microsecond and millimeters, the frequency will have the units of MHz. Although you do not have to force the units as suggested here, it does make calculations a little bit easier and more readily solved in your head.

3.2 Continuous Wave

In contrast with pulse wave operation, in continuous mode the ultrasound frequency is determined by the frequency of the transmit signal or, equivalently, the drive voltage frequency of the pulser. For continuous wave, although the crystal has a natural resonant frequency, the constant driving of the crystal by the drive voltage overrides the natural response. The result is that the frequency of the transducer will match the frequency of the transmit voltage.

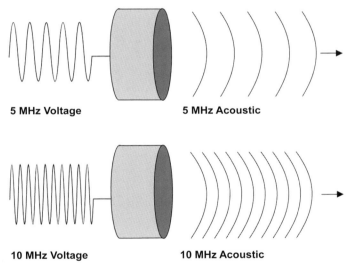

5 MHz Voltage   **5 MHz Acoustic**

10 MHz Voltage   **10 MHz Acoustic**

Fig. 5   **CW Operating Frequency**

So for continuous operation:

$$f_o = Transducer\ Frequency = Drive\ Voltage\ Frequency.$$

Note that although the frequency of operation is determined by the frequency of the drive voltage, for sensitivity reasons, we would never choose to run a transducer outside its natural bandwidth. If a transducer naturally resonates with a 4 MHz bandwidth centered around 6 MHZ, we would run it in CW as high as 8 MHz and as low as 4 MHz, but not usually above or below that range since the transducer would be very inefficient.

4. Impulse Response of a Transducer

In Chapter 4, when discussing bandwidth, we learned that, like a bell, when a transducer is driven with a single impulse, a resonance occurs, and more than a single cycle of mechanical vibration is produced. The response of a crystal to a single, short duration pulse is called the crystal's impulse response. When the crystal has a long impulse response, there are many cycles in the pulse which leads to a long spatial pulse length and degraded axial resolution. With a short impulse response, there are fewer cycles in the pulse and improved axial resolution. Ideally, we would have perfect control of the pulse parameters to make it as short as desired when resolution is critical.

Figure 6 demonstrates some actual pulse responses for two different transducer designs.

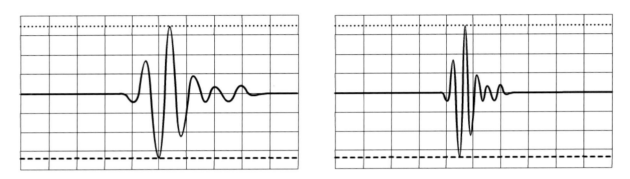

Fig. 6   **Pulse Response For a 2MHz and a 4MHz Crystal**

You will notice that both of these transducers produce more than one cycle when driven with a single transmit pulse (impulse). You will also notice that the pulse actually grows in amplitude and then decays over time. In the first case, the period is 0.5 µsec, so the operating frequency is close to 2 MHz. In the second case the period is approximately 0.25 µsec, so the operating frequency is close to 4 MHz.

5. Beam Characteristics with a Simple, Single Disc Transducer

5.1 Simple, Single, Disc Transducers
Now that we understand the basic principles, theory, and components of a transducer, we can assess the "beam characteristics" produced by a simple transducer. The simple single disc shaped transducer was the first transducer produced and used in ultrasound. Transducers with this simple design are still in use today. Whereas many transducer designs are now much more complex using multiple, rectangular elements, all of the concepts learned here are instructive in developing the foundation to base our understanding of the more complex designs.

5.1.1 Physical Dimensions of the Crystal
First, we must identify the physical dimensions of the crystal. For the simple, round crystal there are clearly two important geometric parameters, the diameter (D), and the thickness (t). We will learn that the diameter plays a major role in determining the beamwidth, while the thickness plays a role in determining the transducer operating frequency. You must make certain to not confuse these two parameters, each affects very different aspects of the sound beam.

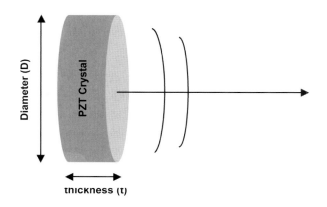

Fig. 7 **Single Disc Crystal Dimensions**

5.1.2 The Beamshape

The dimensions of the beam, or beam shape, is basically the region in the patient through which the sound wave propagates. As a result, you will notice that quite frequently, with respect to ultrasound waves traveling, you will see the word "beam" used interchangeably with the idea of a traveling wave over time. For example:

"As the wave travels through the body, there is more attenuation at deeper depths."
or
"As the beam travels through the body, there is greater attenuation at deeper depths."

Both of these sentences express the same idea, using different terminology. To be precise, the beam is the path the wave travels, whereas the wave is the energy which is traveling.

CW and Beamshape

With continuous wave, the beam is continuous and the beam shape can be visualized all at one time like a beam of light from a flashlight (See *Figure 8*). The "beam" begins as the width of the transducer converges to a narrower region and then diverges. As long as the flashlight is left on, the beam retains this consistent shape.

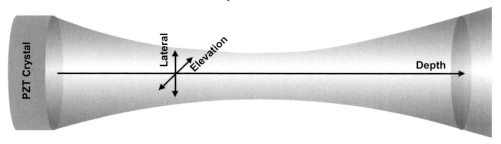

Fig. 8 **Beamshape**

 **View Animation and Image Library CD**

PW and Beamshape

It is generally easier to understand the dimensions of a continuous wave beam than dimensions of a pulsed wave beam. Unlike CW, the beam shape is not "present" all the time in pulsed wave. For pulsed wave, the beamshape represents the general shape that is created as the pulse travels over time. The "beam" emanates from the transducer face as the width of the transducer (T_1 in *Figure 9*). If you were to take a "snapshot" a short period of time later (T_2), the wave pulse will obviously have traveled to a deeper depth, and the beam will physically cover a slightly narrower area (converging). A little later in time (T_3), the wave would again have traveled deeper, and the beam would continue to converge until it reaches the minimum width. Later still in time (T_4), the beam will start to diverge, and continue to diverge over time (T_N).

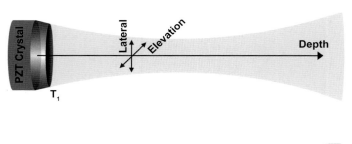

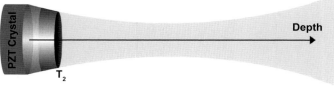

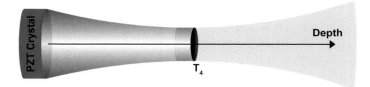

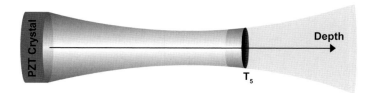

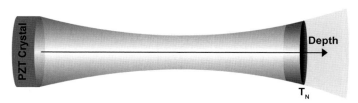

Fig. 9   **Beamshape Swept Over Time in PW**

View Animation and Image Library CD

Pegasus Lectures, Inc.

5.2 The Beam Parameters

5.2.1 Depth (axial, longitudinal, radial, range)

The direction of a beam away from the transducer is referred to as the axis of the beam, the depth direction, the longitudinal direction, or the radial direction. Regardless of the terminology used, this dimension is the direction in which the wave is propagating (continuous wave or pulsed wave). As a longitudinal wave, the depth represents the direction in which the compression and rarefaction propagate. For pulsed wave, the depth represents the direction in which the pulse length is measured.

5.2.2 Beamwidth: Lateral (azimuthal, side-by-side, transverse, angular)

For a round crystal, the beamwidth is symmetric in both planes. As we will see for non-symmetric crystals, the beamwidth will be different in the two different planes, giving rise to another dimensional definition called elevation. For now, since both dimensions are equal, we will refer to the beamwidth as the lateral dimension. Unfortunately, just as there are many different terms referring to the depth of the beam, there are many terms which refer to the lateral dimension of the beam, such as: azimuthal, side-by-side, transverse, and angular. Fortunately, the term most commonly used is "lateral".

5.3 The Natural Focus

As we have seen from the beamwidth pictures, *Figure 8* and *Figure 9*, the beam converges at a specific depth and then diverges from this specific depth. The depth at which the beam reaches its narrowest beamwidth is called the "natural focus." The region shallower than the natural focus is referred to as the near field, near zone, or the Fresnel zone. The region deeper than the natural focus is referred to as the far field, the far zone, or the Fraunhofer zone.

These simple disc transducers are often referred to as "unfocused," since nothing has been added to affect the "natural focus" of the transducer. Be careful not to confuse the concept of an "unfocused transducer" with the absence of a natural focus. A focused transducer is a transducer in which a technique has been employed to either move or allow the focus to be moved to a depth other than the natural focus. Even the beam pattern for an "unfocused" transducer naturally converges and then diverges from the point referred to here as the natural focus.

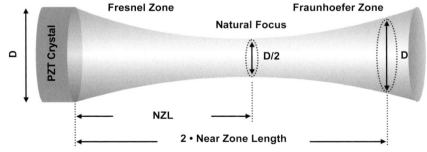

Fig. 10   **Basic Beam Characteristics**

For the unfocused transducer, notice that the beamwidth is approximately ½ the crystal diameter at the focus. Also notice the symmetry of the beam. At twice the focal depth, the beam returns to approximately the same diameter as the crystal diameter. As the depth increases the beam continues to diverge.

Beamwidth = D/2 at the focus   *Beamwidth = D at 2 * focal length*

Chapter 5

Note: The beam profiles drawn are extremely simplified from reality. In reality, the beams are not neatly defined by distinct boundaries within which wave energy exists, and outside of which no energy exists. Furthermore, the near-field of the beam is extremely complex, with rapidly varying pressures. Therefore, these simplified drawings are to serve as a tool to help explain general principles, and not as absolute truths. In Level 2, a more realistic beam profile is given.

5.4. Varying the depth of the Natural Focus

There are two parameters which principally affect the depth of the natural focus, the operating frequency and the diameter of the crystal. Somewhat counter-intuitively, a higher frequency produces a deeper focus for a fixed crystal diameter. A larger diameter crystal, for a fixed operating frequency also increases the depth of the natural focus. The equation which determines how the focal depth changes with changes to these two parameters is developed in Level 2 of this chapter. The following diagram depicts how a larger crystal produces a deeper focus (for the same operating frequency).

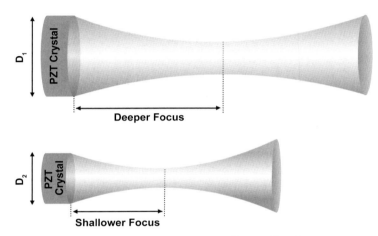

Fig. 11 **A Larger Diameter Results in A Depper Focus (for the same operating frequency)**

6. Limitations of the Simple Crystal

Let's consider what some of the problems and limitations would be if we tried to use the simple crystal just described as a transducer on a patient.

First, if this transducer were to be used directly on a patient with no other modifications, it would not function at all. The acoustic impedance of a crystal such as PZT is extremely high relative to tissue. Recall from Chapter 3, a large acoustic impedance mismatch results in a large reflection and very little transmission. When the large reflection occurs at the transducer/patient interface, there is little energy coupled into and out of the patient. The result would be virtually no penetration. Clearly, the transducer design must be modified to ameliorate this situation.

Second, as demonstrated in Section 4, the impulse response of a simple crystal may have many cycles, leading to a long spatial pulse length and poor axial resolution. Without some modification, the simple crystal we have discussed will clearly have suboptimal axial resolution.

Third, we have just learned that the focus of the simple transducer is determined by the operating frequency and by the crystal diameter. What if the natural focus is not at the desired depth? With the current design there is no way to affect the focus. There are at least two major reasons why having a "fixed" focus can be detrimental. As we will learn later in this chapter, the lateral and elevation resolution are determined by the beamwidth; the wider the beamwidth, the worse the resolution. Since the beam reaches a minimum width at the focus, the best lateral resolution occurs at the lateral focus. Similarly, the best elevation resolution occurs at the elevation focus. The second reason is related to the beam intensity. As we learned in Chapter 3, the beam intensity is inversely proportional to the beamwidth. As the beamwidth increases, the intensity decreases. If the beam intensity decreases, there is less reflected signal power. Eventually the signals will be too weak to be detected. As a result, a deeper focus allows for better penetration. Clearly, the ability to control focus is desirable for improved imaging.

Fourth, the simple transducer described is only capable of imaging straight ahead. In essence, there is no way of visualizing anything which is not directly under the transducer face. With this design, the only way a region of the body can be scanned is to physically move the transducer over the region of interest. This limitation makes it very difficult to interpret complex geometries and disease states. Clearly, it is highly desirable to have a mechanism which allows our beam to be "steered" in different directions so that a scan can be created.

The next three sections discuss methodologies to address the issues of impedance mismatch, poor impulse response, and a less than optimal way to fix the focus at one set depth shallower than the natural focus. As will be discovered in Level 2, the desire to have a variable focus and the ability to steer to create an image will together drive the evolution of transducer technology.

7. Minimizing the Acoustic Impedance Mismatch

7.1 High Impedance Piezoceramics

Recall that the acoustic impedance of a material is given by the equation $Z = \rho * c$. For any piezoceramic crystal both the density and the propagation velocity will be very high, hence, the acoustic impedance will be extremely high. In comparison, tissue has a much lower density and a significantly lower propagation velocity. As a result, the impedance of tissue is significantly lower. For example, the acoustic impedance of most forms of PZT is approximately 35 MRayls, while the acoustic impedance of tissue is typically less than 2 MRayls. Since the amount of reflection is proportional to this mismatch, we clearly need to find another manner in which to couple the energy from the crystal into the patient.

7.2 Matching Layer

A matching layer is used to minimize the acoustic impedance mismatch between the high impedance of the transducer crystal and the low impedance of the tissue. In essence, the matching layer is a thin layer of material attached to the front crystal of the transducer. The material is chosen such that it has an acoustic impedance lower than that of the crystal, and higher than that of the tissue. As the sound propagates from the crystal to the matching layer, there is more transmission than if the interface had been directly to tissue. Then, as the sound propagates from the matching layer to the tissue, there is still more transmission because of the closer impedance match. Note that this technique also helps minimize the reflection back into the body of the returning echoes.

Many transducer designs now use multiple matching layers. Obviously each successive matching layer (in the direction from the crystal towards the patient) has a lower impedance so as to better match the crystal impedance to the tissue impedance.

7.3 Quarter Wavelength Thickness

Since both interfaces of the matching layer represent relatively large acoustic impedance mismatches, a significant percentage of reflection can occur. Additionally, a fair amount of this energy will ping back and forth between the surfaces creating multiple echoes (reverberation artifact). If these reverberations are not somehow cancelled, the image will be full of bright white reverberation artifacts. Therefore, unless a method to overcome this problem is found by improving the acoustic coupling, we have introduced a new problem, perhaps just as insidious.

By controlling the thickness of the matching layer, this reverberation problem can be significantly reduced. The ideal thickness for a conventional matching layer scheme is quarter wavelength. In other words, the matching layer should have the thickness of a quarter of the wavelength at the operating frequency. The reason for this thickness is based on the idea of constructive and destructive interference.

Since a full wavelength is 360 degrees, a quarter wavelength represents 90 degrees. If the thickness of the matching layer is quarter wavelength, the wave at the far surface of the matching layer (the patient side) will be 90 degrees out of phase with the wave at the first surface (interface between the crystal and matching layer). On its return path back from the far interface, the wave is delayed another 90 degrees. Therefore, when the matching layer thickness is quarter wavelength, the reflection which occurs from the patient side of the matching layer is out of phase by half a wavelength with the reflection which occurs at the interface between the crystal and the matching layer. As we learned in Chapter 1, waves which are out of phase by half a wavelength (180 degrees) add destructively and cancel. This is the ideal situation since we clearly want any reflection from the surfaces of the matching layer to cancel out. This destructive interference is illustrated in *Figure 12*.

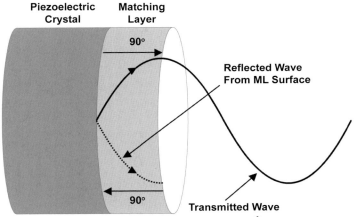

Fig. 12 **Cancellation of Wave Reflection for $\frac{\lambda}{4}$ Matching Layer**

7.4 Composites with Lower Acoustic Impedances

Many of the composite materials are now designed to have much lower acoustic impedances than PZT, improving the acoustic coupling factor. As discussed earlier, other piezoeclectric materials that had lower impedances than PZT and hence, better matched to tissue, also had much lower efficiency. As a result, even though these materials had less of an acoustic impedance mismatch with tissue, they were just not sensitive enough to be used. The use of polymers with much lower impedances in composite designs reduces the severity of the mismatch between the crystal and the patient. This does not mean that matching layers are still not needed, it means that since smaller steps exist, better matching can be produced.

8. Axial Resolution and Backing Material

8.1 Axial Resolution

Axial resolution is defined as the ability to distinguish between two structures in the axial (longitudinal, radial, depth, or range) dimension. Recall that Chapter 4 began with a discussion on "range" resolution. In fact, the reason for creating a pulsed wave modality was to overcome the inability to resolve structures in depth in the continuous mode. If you recall, we demonstrated that a shorter spatial pulse length resulted in better resolution. We will now review those results with the intention of relating the pulse requirement with transducer design and construction.

Consider what happens when a pulse train encounters two objects separated in depth by a distance of "x". To distinguish the two separate objects, the reflected echoes from the first and second objects must be distinct in time and must not connect. For the echoes to connect, the echo from the second object would have to return while the pulse train was still insonifying the first object. This can only happen if the pulse train length, (SPL) is twice as long as the separation between the two objects. In other words, the roundtrip effect helps to separate the echoes between objects, hence, the axial resolution is half the spatial pulse length. (Remember that a smaller number is always better for resolution since a smaller number implies the ability to resolve structures which are closer together.)

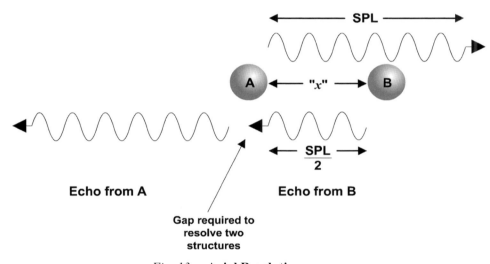

Fig. 13   **Axial Resolution**

The axial resolution is determined by the spatial pulse length:

$$Axial\ Resolution = \frac{Spatial\ Pulse\ Length}{2}.$$

8.2 Backing Material

In Chapter 4 we learned that the spatial pulse length is determined by the number of cycles within the pulse and the wavelength. We know that the wavelength is inversely proportional to the operating frequency. As a result, using a higher operating frequency results in better axial resolution. Sometimes increasing the frequency to achieve better axial resolution is not an option based on the required imaging depth (the size of the patient).

The other method of shortening the spatial pulse length so as to improve the axial resolution is to decrease the number of cycles within the pulse. A backing material is used to shorten the ring time of a transducer, thereby decreasing the number of cycles within the pulse. Fewer cycles within the pulse decreases the spatial pulse length. Also recall that fewer cycles within a pulse decreases the pulse duration and thereby increases the bandwidth.

The backing material shortens the ring time by absorbing some of the ring energy. The backing material generally is made from a powdered tungsten mixed into an epoxy resin. By changing the composition and thickness of the backing material, various degrees of damping can be achieved. A higher damping leads to a shorter pulse, improving the axial resolution. However, since some of the energy is absorbed into the backing material, the efficiency of the transducer decreases. As a result, the quality factor of the transducer is said to decrease. Recall that the quality factor is the reciprocal of the fractional bandwidth as defined in Chapter 4.

9. Lateral Resolution

9.1 Equation
Lateral resolution is defined as the ability to resolve two structures in the lateral dimension (side by side, angular, transverse, or azimuthal).

Consider what happens if a beam is wide enough so that two side-by-side structures are insonified simultaneously. The echoes from both objects add together and there is no way of distinguishing between the two objects, as shown in the figure below. In contrast, if the beam is narrower than the separation between the two objects, there is no way both objects could ever reflect from the same beam, and therefore no way that the two objects could ever mistakenly appear as one structure.

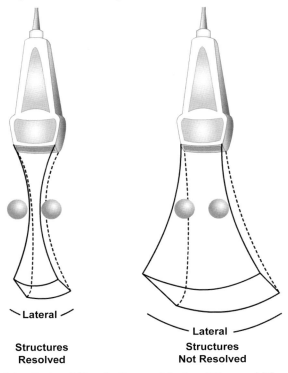

> Lateral
> **Structures Resolved**

> Lateral
> **Structures Not Resolved**

Fig. 14   **Lateral Resolution and Lateral Beamwidth**

Pegasus Lectures, Inc.

From these observations, it is evident that the best lateral resolution occurs with narrower beams and that the lateral resolution is defined by the beamwidth.

Lateral resolution = Lateral beamwidth

9.2 Changing the Focus

For many applications the natural focus of a transducer is inadequate or suboptimal. Besides changing the physical size of a crystal to affect the beam diameter, four different focusing schemes have been developed and utilized, such as:

1) lenses
2) curved elements
3) electronic focusing
4) mirrors

Of these four techniques, only three are actually frequently employed. The use of an acoustic mirror, although possible, has not been a popular technique employed in ultrasound, therefore, we will constrain ourselves to discussing the three remaining techniques. Of these three techniques, electronic focusing can only be achieved when there is more than one transducer crystal, referred to as an array.

Therefore, electronic focusing will be discussed when we cover the topic of array transducers in Level 2 of this chapter. This leaves two techniques to consider for a simple transducer, a lens and curving the surface of the crystal itself. In reality, both of these techniques function in the same manner, with the only difference being that one approach requires the addition of another material while the other approach is created from the lens material itself.

9.2.1 Lenses

The idea of an acoustic lens is quite simple. Just as occurs with optics and light waves, the sound waves can be caused to converge more quickly than would occur naturally, producing a shallower focus. Of course, if the beam focuses at a shallower depth, the beam also begins to diverge at a shallower depth. Lenses have been used extensively for ultrasound transducers for many years, and are still frequently used. However, newer crystal materials, and newer styles of transducers are reducing the need for lenses. The ability to eliminate lenses is desirable since lenses result in another acoustic impedance mismatch between the matching layer and the patient and are generally very absorptive. The result is a decrease in efficiency and potential surface heating of the transducer.

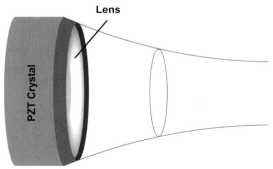

Fig. 15 **Use of Lenses for Focusing**

9.2.2 Curved Surface

Piezoelectric material generally tends to be very brittle. As such, generating a curved surface to behave like a lens is extremely challenging, and up until recently, was less commonly employed than attaching an acoustic lens. More recently, with the advent of more flexible composite materials, the curved approach is becoming more widely utilized. Using a curved crystal surface to act as the lens eliminates the additional acoustic impedance mismatch and the extra source of absorption that the lens introduces.

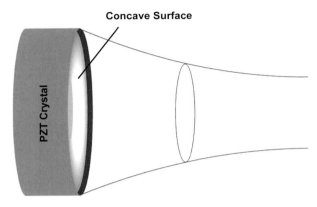

Fig. 16   **Use of Curved Surface for Focusing**

9.2.3 Diffraction Limiting

Another important point is that all of the focusing techniques can only affect the beamwidth in the near field relative to the natural focus. Beyond the near field, the beam is diffraction limited, and there is no way in which to get the waves to constructively and destructively interfere so as to create a narrower beam. If a deeper focus is required, the only practical solution is to use a larger transducer diameter.

10. Simple Block Diagram Model of a Transducer

In the preceding sections, we have learned many requirements for a transducer. The following block diagram model is a valuable didactic tool. You should be able to explain the functionality of each of the components with this model.

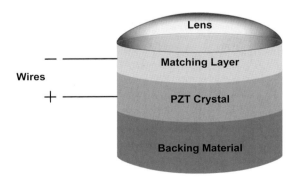

Fig. 17   **Simple Transducer Block Diagram**

Piezoelectric crystals:	Convert electropotential (voltage) into acoustic waves and acoustic waves back into voltage
Backing material:	Shortens spatial pulse length improving longitudinal resolution
Matching layer:	Minimizes the acoustic impedance mismatch from crystal to tissue and tissue back to crystal
Wires:	Transmit - delivers voltage to crystal Receive - delivers echo voltage to system receivers
Lens:	Helps to focus beam in elevation plane

11. Exercises   Answers Pg. 458

1.   A transducer is *anything* which converts one form of _____ to another.

   a) wave
   b) sound
   c) vibration
   d) energy

2.   Ultrasound transducers convert voltage (electropotential energy) to _____ energy and _____ energy to _____.

   a) acoustic, thermal, acoustic
   b) acoustic, acoustic, voltage
   c) current, current, thermal
   d) current, current, voltage

True or False

3.   _____ All transducers use the piezoelectric effect.

4.   _____ All ultrasound transducers use the piezoelectric effect.

5.   _____ PZT is a piezoelectric material.

6.   _____ PZT stands for lead zirconate titanate.

7.   _____ Some materials can be made piezoelectric through a process called poling.

8.   _____ The Curie point is the temperature at which a material loses its Piezoelectric properties and is approximately 300° for PZT.

12. Beam Dimensions Revisited

In Level 1, the basic principles of transducers were taught, including beam dimensions from a simple single crystal. In Level 2, we will begin by taking a more mathematical and analytical approach to assessing the resulting beam from the single, round crystal transducer.

12.1 Depth of Focus (Focal depth) and Equation

12.1.1 Equation
The distance from the surface of the transducer to the natural focus is called the "focal depth" or the "Near Zone Length" (NZL).

The Near Zone length is given by the equation:

$$NZL = \frac{D^2}{4\lambda}$$

In general, students learn the above equation in a slightly modified form. The reason for modifying this equation is that through a substitution and an assumption about the medium, the equation can be rewritten in a form that can be calculated in your head. We will transform this equation as follows:

Recall: $f * \lambda = c \Rightarrow \lambda = \dfrac{c}{f}$

Substituting yields: $NZL = \dfrac{D^2}{4\left(\dfrac{c}{f}\right)} = \dfrac{D^2 f}{4c}$

If we assume c = 1540 m/sec then: $NZL = \dfrac{D^2 f}{4c} = \dfrac{D^2 f}{4 \times 1540 \dfrac{m}{sec}} = \dfrac{D^2 f}{6160 \dfrac{m}{sec}} = \dfrac{D^2 f}{6000 \dfrac{m}{sec}}$

Now if we force the units for the frequency to be in MHz and the units for the crystal diameter to be in mm, we will be able to ignore the units in the numerator since a milli squared is the reciprocal of a mega, or: $\left(10^{-3}\right)^2 \times 10^6 = 1$.

This allows us to rewrite the equation as $NZL \approx \dfrac{D^2\,(mm) \bullet f_0\,(MHz)}{6000\ m}$.

Now if we multiply both sides by 10^{-3}, or milli we get: $NZL\,(mm) \approx \dfrac{D^2\,(mm) \bullet f_0\,(MHz)}{6}$.

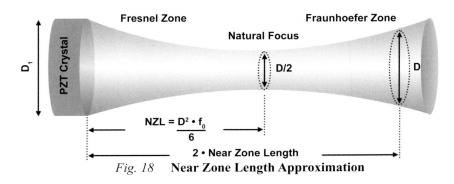

Fig. 18   **Near Zone Length Approximation**

12.1.2 Using the Modified Equation

Perhaps the best way to illustrate how to apply the modified equation is through example.

◊ **_Example:_**   At what depth would the natural focus be for a 3 MHz transducer with a diameter of 1 cm?

The first step is to convert the diameter from cm to mm, since the modified form requires the diameter to be written as mm. In Chapter 1, we learned how to convert between units. Since mm is a smaller unit than cm, the number in front of mm must be larger than 1. Between mm and cm there is one decimal shift. Therefore, we must move the decimal point 1 place to make the number larger or, 1 cm = 10 mm.

Since the operating frequency is already in MHz, no conversion is necessary.

Plugging these numbers into the equation yields:

$$NZL\,(mm) \approx \frac{D^2 f}{6} = \frac{10^2 \times 3}{6} = 50\ mm = 5.0\ cm.$$

Notice that once the diameter and frequency are converted to the appropriate form, the units can be ignored. You should also note that this problem could be solved by using the unmodified equation as follows:

$$NZL = \frac{D^2}{4\lambda} = \frac{D^2}{\left(4\dfrac{c}{f}\right)} = \frac{D^2 f}{4 \times 1540\dfrac{m}{sec}} = \frac{\left(1\ cm\right)^2 \times 3\ MHz}{6160\dfrac{m}{sec}} = \frac{0.0001\ m^2 \times 3\ MHz}{6160\dfrac{m}{sec}}$$

$$= 0.0487\ m = 48.7\ mm = 4.87\ cm.$$

This example demonstrates how the modified form of the equation simplifies the calculation. Because this modified form assumed a propagation velocity of 1540 m/sec, it can only be appropriately applied in soft tissue.

12.1.3 Effect of Aperture on NZL

From the equation $NZL\,(mm) \approx \dfrac{D^2\,(mm) \bullet f_0\,(MHz)}{6}$ we know that the NZL is proportional to the square of the diameter, or $NZL \propto D^2$. As demonstrated in the example below, if the diameter of one crystal is twice the diameter of the second crystal, the corresponding near zone length will be four times greater. In other words, by increasing the diameter by a factor of 2, the depth of the natural focus increases by a factor of 4.

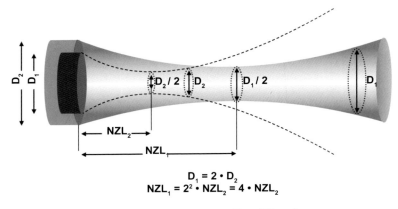

$$D_1 = 2 \cdot D_2$$
$$NZL_1 = 2^2 \cdot NZL_2 = 4 \cdot NZL_2$$

Fig. 19 **Effect of Diameter on Focal Depth**

When you compare the two different beams from the two different crystals from *Figure 19*, you should notice that the smaller crystal achieves a much narrower beam at shallower depths. You should also notice that the larger crystal achieves not only a significantly deeper focus, but also a narrower beam at relatively deeper depths. As we will learn in the upcoming sections, small diameter crystals are good for superficial imaging, and large diameter crystals are better for deeper imaging.

12.1.4 Effect of Frequency on NZL

From the equation of $NZL(mm) \approx \dfrac{D^2(mm) \bullet f_0(MHz)}{6}$ we know that the NZL is proportional

to the operating frequency, or $NZL \propto f_0$. If the operating frequency of the second crystal is twice the operating frequency of first crystal, the corresponding near zone length will be two times greater. In other words, by increasing the operating frequency by a factor of 2, the depth of the natural focus increases by a factor of 2.

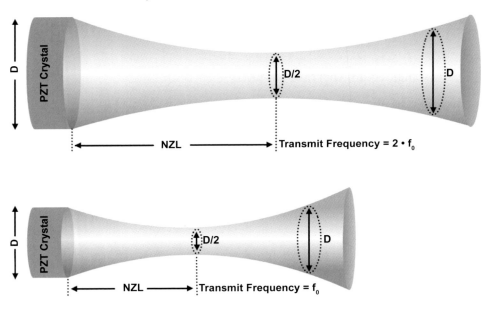

Fig. 20 **Effect of Frequency on Focal Depth**

Pegasus Lectures, Inc.

Note: Although a deeper focal depth results from using a higher operating frequency, this use of higher frequency also results in increased attenuation. To improve penetration, attenuation through absorption must be minimized. Therefore, because of the increased attenuation, transducers are generally designed with lower operating frequencies, and larger diameters instead.

12.2 Depth of Field (focal region)

The depth of field , also referred to as the focal region, refers to the general region above and below the focus where the beam is approximately the same width. For beams that converge and diverge quickly, there is a very short (or shallow) depth of field. For beams that converge and diverge slowly, there is a very broad (or deep) depth of field. *Figure 21* demonstrates the difference between a shallow and broad depth of field.

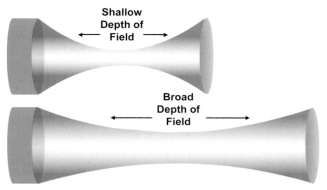

Fig. 21   **Shallow and Broad Depth of Field**

Just as shorter pulse lengths produce better axial resolution, narrower beams produce better lateral resolution. When the depth of field is shallow, there is a very small range over which the intensity and lateral resolution remain relatively constant. When the depth of field is broad, there is a much longer region over which the lateral resolution and the intensity (ignoring attenuation affects) remain relatively constant. The concept of depth of field is often compared with taking pictures with a camera. If a close-up picture is taken, the camera aperture will be set very small, yielding a very shallow focus with a very short depth of field. The result is a very "narrow beam" which produces extremely high resolution for objects at, or very near to the focal depth. However, since the beam converges and diverges very quickly, any objects that are shallower or deeper than the focus tend to be blurred. Think about a picture you have seen of a bee in a field of flowers, or a close-up of an individual in a crowd of people. In comparison, if the focus is set much deeper, the detail resolution is certainly lost, but objects at many different depths are now in focus.

This same concept applies in ultrasound. If there is a very shallow depth of field, only a very short depth range will have very good lateral resolution.

12.3 True Beam Shapes

More than once, we have made reference to the fact that the beam profiles are highly simplified. The following beam profile is illustrative of the complexity of a true beam.

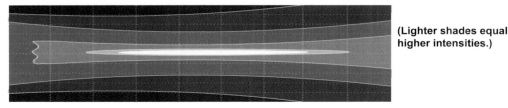

(Lighter shades equal higher intensities.)

12.4 Changing Intensity from Beam Convergence and Divergence

Recall in Chapter 2 that the beam intensity was defined as the power divided by the beam area. In the most simplistic world, from this definition, the highest intensity of the beam would always exist at the focus. This should make sense since the focus is the region of the beam where the area is the narrowest. Since the intensity is inversely related to the beam area, a smaller area results in a higher intensity.

In reality, this analysis is overly simple and most frequently incorrect. There are two reasons why this analysis is not correct:

- This analysis incorrectly presumes that there is no change in power with depth (ignores attenuation affects).
- This analysis relies on the overly simple beam models that we have drawn in order to make discussion of beams easier and the topic less threatening.

A better analysis would take both of these facts into account leading to the conclusion that the highest intensity must be either at focus or shallower than the focus, and usually shallower than the focus. We know that realistically there will always be attenuation when the beam is propagating through the body. Therefore, the power is not constant at each depth, but rather decreasing with depth. Therefore, the two parameters that determine the intensity are working in opposite directions in the near field. From an area standpoint, the intensity is increasing as the beam is converging. From a power standpoint, the intensity is decreasing as the depth is increasing. Which of these two parameters dominate depends on the rate of convergence in comparison with the rate of attenuation.

Also, we cannot ignore the fact that the beam is not such a simple, symmetric, well-defined shape with constant behavior everywhere within, especially in the near field. In the near field, there are all sorts of beam intensity variations as constructive and destructive interferences occur.

Why This Point Matters:

If you are asked where the highest intensity occurs on a board exam, you must assume the over-simplified approach and answer "at the focus". However, clinically, you should realize that this is incorrect. The reason why this fact matters is twofold:

1. *Frequently sonographers make the mistake of not moving the focus deeper for difficult to image patients, leading to poor signal-to-noise and decreased clinical value.*

   Unlike the near field, in the far field, both the beam dimension and the power are working to change the intensity in the same direction. In the farfield, the beam is continuously diverging, decreasing the beam intensity. Also, as the depth increases, there is more attenuation, again making the beam less intense. The result is clear, in the far field, the beam intensity drops precipitously. Therefore, when the focus is left too shallow, significant signal is lost. This fact is often overlooked by many sonographers.

2. *There are times when putting the focus a little deeper than the actual region of interest will improve signal strength in the region of interest.*

There are two reasons why this approach might increase sensitivity a little bit. First, the highest intensity is almost always a little shallower than the focus. Second, when you place the focus deeper, the system is often allowed to increase the maximum allowed transmit power. This increase is allowed since the beam is presumed to be not as focused at the shallower depths, which is most likely where the power restriction occurs. This technique still may not result in beautiful images for the more "difficult-to-image" patients but might make the difference between a diagnostic and non-diagnostic scan.

13. Transducer Evolution Overview

In the early days of ultrasound, a single disc shaped crystal transducer was used. These simple transducers could essentially be used in one of two ways, either to register Doppler shifts and produce corresponding audio, or to record changes in reflectivity and present a modality called A-Mode. These simple transducers could only look straight ahead, and could only view a different region of the body by being manually angled. In essence, this was a one-dimensional scanning technique. Over time came the desire to have the ability to look at more than one region "simultaneously", or at two-dimensional data. The first step in the process was to create a modality called static B-scan. Although not exactly a "real-time" process, the static B-scan allowed for the building up of an image over time by manually "sliding" the transducer across the patient. The depth aspect was produced with the one-dimensional technique, and the lateral dimension of the imaging was created through the manual motion of the transducer across the patient. Relative to modern imaging, this process is extremely crude, but relative to blind imaging, this was the beginning of a revolution in medicine.

From the limits of static B-scans, came the motivation to create an "automated" system that could generate images without the sonographer physically dragging the transducer to create the second dimension of data. Mechanical transducers were produced, in which the simple crystal was now attached to the head of a motor. By wobbling the motor at various angles, an angular region of the body could now be swept over time.

As with all mechanical systems, there were many issues and limitations. Because of the many limitations, there was a desire to create a system which would not require moving parts to create a two-dimensional scan. This desire led to the creation of array transducers using a technique called phasing. An entire family of phased array transducers has been created so as to meet the specific requirements of different types of scanning. Because these arrays have multiple elements in one dimension, these transducers are referred to as 1-D arrays. For all of the unbelievable flexibility and power of 1-D arrays, there are still a few fundamental drawbacks. Specifically, 1-D arrays cannot change the focus in the elevation direction (the direction orthogonal to the lateral direction), and 1-D arrays cannot automatically acquire data in the third dimension to create three-dimensional scans.

Around the early to middle part of the nineties, the first 1.5 D array was created. This transducer had three elements in the elevation direction. In comparison with the lateral dimension which generally has 64 or more elements, three elements will certainly not give the same degree of flexibility. Therefore, even though there was more than one element in the elevation direction, it was termed a 1.5-D array. The multiple elements in the elevation direction could be turned on all together, making an effectively larger "diameter" transducer in elevation, or only the center element turned on, creating a smaller "diameter" transducer. Recalling from the equation learned earlier in this chapter, the focal depth is proportional to the square of the diameter. Therefore, this new style transducer allowed for two different focal depths in elevation.

Of course the story does not end with 1.5-D arrays. The desire to have a completely variable focus in elevation is certainly compelling, but by itself did not motivate the giant leap from 1.5-D technology to 2-D array technology. Instead, the desire to have a non-manual, non-mechanical approach to creating three-dimensional imaging drove the technology. A 2-D array has multiple elements in both the lateral and elevation direction, allowing for both steering and focusing virtually anywhere in a three-dimensional volume below the transducer.

We will now use this technological evolutionary path as the outline for discussing the operation, utility, strengths, and weaknesses of the various transducers from each generation. As we arrive at the limits of a technology, we will use those limits to contextualize the desire for a new technology that can overcome those constraints. Therefore, as with the advancement of technology, the limitations at each stage will become the driving factor for discussing and understanding each successive generation.

In anticipation of the technology which produces 2-D imaging, we will begin by reviewing the dimensions of a 2-D image, and then start the evolutionary progression beginning with the blind pencil probe.

14. Imaging Dimensions

Before learning about the transducers which produce two-dimensional images, we must first define the dimensions which make up a two-dimensional scan. Fortunately, the terminology is consistent with the terms we have learned for the dimensions of a beam.

Even though the image is two-dimensional, there are really three-dimensions in the scan. The three corresponding imaging planes are axial, lateral, and elevation as pictured below. The elevation plane is, in general, the forgotten plane since there is no direct visualization of this plane in 2-D imaging. With the advent of 3-D imaging, the elevation plane is beginning to receive more consideration. Many imaging mistakes are made because people neglect the elevation plane.

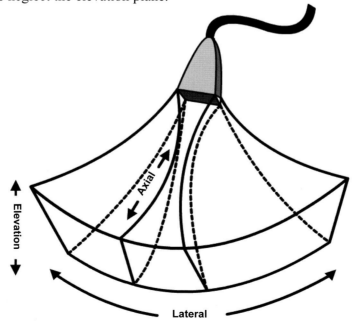

Fig. 22   **Scan Dimensions**

Both the axial and lateral planes have many different names which are used interchangeably. You must recognize all of these different appellations.

Lateral:
- azimuthal
- side-by-side
- transverse
- angular

Axial:
- radial
- depth
- longitudinal
- range

15. The Pedof (Blind, Doppler Only Transducer)

These simple round transducers are still in use, most often referred to as a pedof, a pencil, or a blind Doppler probe.

Single Element, Blind, Pedof, Pencil, or (Doppler Only Transducer)

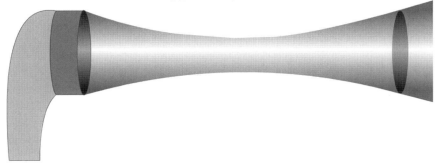

Fig. 23   **Pencil Probe Beam**

Description:
Generally used for Doppler
Single crystal (sometimes split into two halves for CW Doppler)
Transducer angled to flow by clinician (manual steering)
Beam is symmetric in elevation and lateral
Usually designed to have a broad depth of field
Usually very narrow band since used for Doppler only

Disadvantages:
Does not create an image
Manual steering
Fixed focus for transmit
Fixed focus for receive

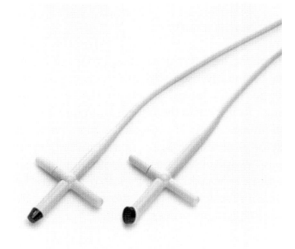

Advantages:
Usually extremely sensitive in Doppler since designed specifically for Doppler
Relatively inexpensive to make
Relatively inexpensive electronics necessary (single channel system)
Small footprint allowing for insonation in smaller areas such as between ribs and suprasternal notch

Discussion
In the past few years, one of the biggest benefits most often overlooked was the superior sensitivity of these transducers for performing Doppler. Since the bandwidth requirements for Doppler are very low in comparison to the requirements for 2-D imaging, these transducers can generally be peaked for sensitivity in a very small frequency range (a high Quality Factor.) The result has been superior sensitivity in the narrow band of operation. Unfortunately, fewer and fewer people routinely use the Pedof probes since there is no associated image and requires more expertise. Whether or not these transducer designs persist as more sensitive depends on whether or not ultrasound manufacturers roll the new generation of more sensitive piezocomposite materials, new matching layer technologies, and new production processes into these transducers. If so, then these transducers will most probably continue to be the most sensitive probes for Doppler. If not, then the newer technology used for imaging transducers will eventually surpass the performance of the existing pencil probes.

Major Limitation Leading To A New Technology
If ever there was an obvious issue to tackle, this one is it. Since these transducers cannot produce an image, there is a desire to find a means by which to scan two-dimensional space. As mentioned in the previous section on transducer evolution, the first approach was to manually drag the transducer in the lateral dimension, called a static B-scan. For cardiac imaging, a static B-scan is not very practical because of the presence of ribs which cause shadowing. Although more practical for vascular and abdominal scanning, the quality of a B-scan is very limited. This leads to the desire to have an automated approach to creating a linear scan. The resulting technology was called a linear switched array. For the cardiac world, the new approach had to accommodate both the need to acquire a scan automatically and the difficulty of gaining access in the presence of ribs.

In order to understand a linear switched array, we will need to first discuss the idea of linear sequencing as a scanning technique.

16. Sequencing

Sequencing refers to exciting groups of elements in a specific pattern to linearly scan a region. Sequencing is commonly used with large linear and curved linear arrays. Since the geometry of these transducers is large (in the lateral direction), the lateral dimension of the scan can be accomplished without beam steering. Referring to the images of Figure 24, notice how the first beam is created by exciting the first group of elements at time T_1. Once the echo has returned from the depth of interest (determined by the depth knob setting), a second beam is transmitted, at time T_2, by exciting a second grouping of elements, creating a laterally displaced beam. Continuing in this manner, groups of elements are fired in a linear sequence creating a scan region. The width of this scan region is determined by the user by setting the scan or "image" size on the screen. Once the end of the scan or frame is reached (T_N), the first group of elements is again excited and the process repeated.

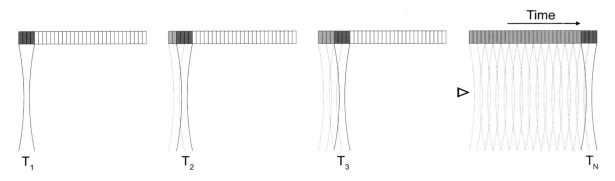

Fig. 24   **Sequencing**

View Animation and Image Library CD

17. Linear Switched Array

As the name suggests, a linear switched array is a group of elements which can be turned either on or off through electronic switches. These transducers were physically large and consisted of many elements (generally 200 elements or more). These transducers did not have any steering capability, therefore, the image shape was always rectangular. The large lateral dimension of the transducer was to provide a large field of view. For linear switched arrays, the image was built up over time using the sequencing process just described.

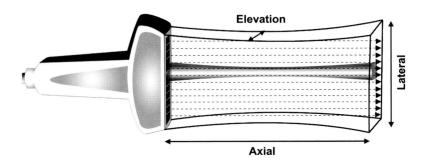

Fig. 25   **Linear Switched Array**

Chapter 5

Description:
Used for vascular 2-D imaging, Doppler, and color Doppler (Linear Switched Array obsolete now)
Creates a rectangular image
Multiple rectangular crystals arranged linearly
Elements fired in a specific sequence to create image
Beam is not necessarily symmetric in elevation and lateral planes

Disadvantages:

Fixed transmit focus

Fixed receive focus

No image steering capabilities (must look straight ahead)

More expensive to make than single element mechanical transducers

More expensive electronics necessary (potentially one channel for each element)

Advantages: (relative to single element mechanicals)

Allows for creation of a wide linear image in near field (good for vascular)

Discussion

Most linear transducers produced now are phased linear and not switched linear arrays. Even the smaller, less expensive systems nowadays have circuitry to perform phasing and electronic focusing. Therefore, there is no real motivation or cost benefit to producing transducers that can only be sequenced. Even if the steering through phasing is never used for conventional imaging, as with modern curved linear transducers, the phasing can be used to steer the Doppler appropriately. However, since the sequencing mechanism discussed is routinely used for curved linear and phased linear arrays, it is useful to have reviewed this transducer type.

Major Limitation Leading to a New Technology

Switched linear transducers had no steering capability. As a result, when viewing a diving vessel, other than manually rocking the transducer, there was no ability to change the angle to better capture the specular component of the reflection. The lack of steering is also problematic since most imaging artifacts are based on specular reflections which are very angle dependent. Furthermore, the ability to achieve good color filling and accurate Doppler measurements requires control over Doppler angles. For these reasons, there is a technology drive to create an ability to steer the ultrasound beam in directions other than straight ahead. This will lead to the phased array concept and a whole family of transducers within this family.

18. Mechanically Steered

For the cardiac branch of imaging, we were left with two specific requirements, the ability to create a scan in an automated fashion, and to somehow image in the presence of ribs. The first approach which met both of these requirements is a mechanical sector transducer.

When a transducer is referred to as "mechanical" the term applies to how the beam is steered to create the image. As depicted in Figure 26, a mechanical image is produced by actuating the motor to point the transducer crystal in different directions over time. At Time 1, the crystal is pointed to the farthest left of the image. Once the appropriate acoustic line time has expired (based on the imaging depth), the crystal is pointed in another direction and a second transmit pulse is produced (Time 2). When the signal has been received from the imaging depth, the process is repeated until the entire scan region, as specified by the user, is scanned. When the entire frame is produced (Time N), the motor returns the crystal to pointing in the first direction and the entire process is repeated.

Fig. 26 **Mechanical Steering**

View Animation and Image Library CD

The sector name is given because of the image shape produced. A sector is a wedge of a circle. The sector shape was produced specifically to deal with the issues of limited access because of the presence of ribs. Since bone represents an extremely large acoustic impedance mismatch, a source of specular reflection, significant absorption, attempting to view the heart through ribs results in large acoustic shadows. To overcome this issue, a small transducer footprint is used and the beams are allowed to fan out with depth. This approach results in a narrow near field and a much broader far field, or a sector shape.

Conventional mechanical transducers had to have a dome over the top of the crystal. As a result, the image is similar to a sector image but with a rounded top where the dome exists. The reason for this dome is very practical and is based on the need to maintain patient contact. Since a motor wobbles a crystal back and forth, it is very difficult, and sometimes impossible, to maintain skin contact. Instead, by putting the crystal behind the dome, the dome stays in constant contact and the crystal can wobble within the dome. Of course, the presence of the dome results in a new issue, "what can fill the space in the dome around the crystal, allow the sound to propagate, and allow the crystal to be mechanically steered?"

Obviously air is a poor choice because of its extremely low acoustic impedance which would cause a catastrophic impedance mismatch. Usually, these transducers were filled with a very viscous grease, or more commonly, a viscous oil. Of course if any air got into these transducers, the large impedance mismatch resulted in acoustic shadowing in the region below the air bubble. Extracting the air bubbles with a syringe refill kit was challenging and time consuming, and usually was left to the person in the lab who became frustrated with trying to angle the transducer so that the air bubble rose to the upper corner, causing the shadow along the edge of the image instead of in the middle of the image.

Chapter 5

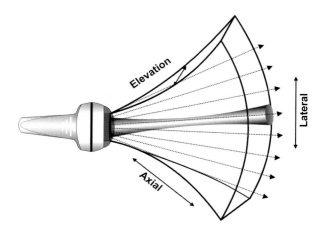

Fig. 27   **Mechanical Sector Scan**

Description:
Used for 2-D imaging, M-mode, Doppler, and color Doppler

Creates a sector image with a "curved top"

Single crystal (sometimes split into two halves for CW Doppler or a second small crystal off to the side dedicated for Doppler.)

Transducer steered by wobbling motor, rotating crystal, or mirrors

Beam is symmetric in elevation and lateral planes

Usually designed to have a broad depth of field

Usually designed to have a very deep focus

Disadvantages:
Fixed focus for transmit

Fixed focus for receive

Parts wear out (mechanical wear)

Parts break (somewhat fragile)

Motion artifacts

Limited temporal resolution

Very little imaging flexibility

Air pockets in gel causing acoustic shadowing

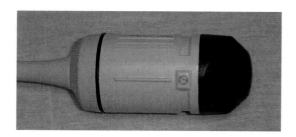

Advantages: (relative to phased arrays)
Relatively inexpensive to make

Relatively inexpensive electronics necessary (single channel system)

Discussion

There are still some mechanical transducers in use today, although fewer each passing year. Usually these transducers are designed for lower cost systems, or limited applications. Mechanical sectors were designed primarily for cardiac, where a static B-scan was not much of an option. Also, since sector images have such a limited near field, these mechanical sectors were not as useful for vascular or abdominal imaging. As a result, static B-scan and mechanical transducers coexisted for a while. The result was two slightly diverging development paths that ultimately converged to drive the desire for a new technology.

Major Limitation Leading to a New Technology

For mechanical transducers, the limitation of a fixed focus leads to a technology to provide variable focus. This technology spawns the mechanically steered annular array.

19. Mechanical Annular Array

For an annular array, the image is still produced by mechanically steering the crystal. For an annular array, the single round crystal is diced into a series of concentric rings. The concept of an annular array is quite simple, if varying the diameter of the crystal varies the focus, then let's build a transducer with a variable diameter. The diameter is simply varied by turning on and off rings. If only the center disc is turned on, then the focus is very shallow. If the next outer ring is activated, then the diameter is larger and the focus is deeper. If the fourth ring is activated, then the focus will be considerably deeper, as indicated in *Figure 28*.

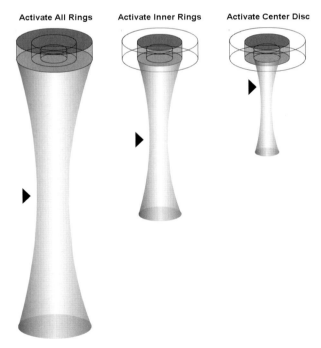

Fig. 28 **Mechanical Annular Array (varying focus)**

View Animation and Image Library CD

Chapter 5

Recall that the focus is proportional to the square of the diameter. Therefore, by having many concentric rings, the focus can be varied from very shallow to very deep.

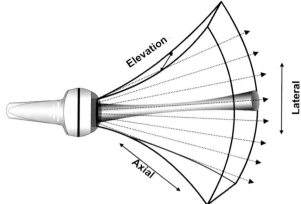

Fig. 29   **Mechanical Annular Array Scan**

Description:
Used for 2-D imaging, M-mode, Doppler, and color Doppler
Creates a sector image with a "curved top" (same shape as simple mechanical sector)
Multiple concentric "ring" elements
Transducer steered by wobbling motor, rotating crystal or mirrors
Beam is symmetric in elevation and lateral

Disadvantages:
Parts wear out (mechanical wear)
Parts break (somewhat fragile)
Motion artifacts
Limited temporal resolution
Excessive grating lobe artifacts common (grating lobes discussed in Chapter 8)
More expensive to make than single element mechanical transducers
More expensive electronics necessary (one channel for each ring element)

Advantages: (relative to single element mechanicals)
Variable focus in the lateral direction
Variable focus in the elevation direction
Variable depth of field

Discussion
In principle, annular arrays represented a large advance in technology, providing a variable focus both laterally and elevationally. In practice, these transducers did not find great favor since they were generally prone to bad grating lobe artifacts. As will be formalized in Chapter 8, grating lobes refer to the fact that wave energy does not really form one narrow beam as indicated by our over simplified beam drawings. Instead wave energy radiates in many directions producing weaker "beams" in varying directions. Because of constructive and destructive interference, the beam goes through higher and lower intensities with varying angles. All transducers have some degree of grating lobe artifact. To reduce the prevalence of grating lobe artifacts, transducers are designed with tight spacing between elements (the element spacing is referred to as the "pitch"). From a production standpoint, it is very difficult to cut small concentric rings into a disc of material. In order to accommodate the manufacturing process, the ring spacing for annular arrays was generally larger than ideal, exacerbating the grating lobes.

Grating lobes results in a lateral displacement or a lateral overlaying of data. As an example, many times people imaging with an annular array would visualize two kidneys overlapped when there was only one. As a result of this issue, annular arrays never became as "big" as expected.

One very unique feature of annular arrays is the fact that when a ring is turned on and off, both the lateral and elevation directions are affected. Until the advent of 2-D arrays in the last few years, an annular array was the only transducer capable of controlling the elevation focus. (1.5-D-arrays offered a choice in the elevation dimension, but certainly not to the same degree as multi-ring annular arrays.)

Major Limitation Leading to a New Technology

In addition to the bad grating lobes specific to annular arrays, mechanical transducers in general have many undesirable features. From the movement of the crystal, there tends to be a lateral smearing affect which degrades the lateral resolution. Additionally, in color Doppler, the motion artifact results in bright flashes of color. For the simple mechanical transducer, there is also a fixed focus. All of this is compounded by the fact that the mechanical parts tend to wear out and break, and often the dome oil would leak out and be replaced by air. The desire to create a scan with no moving parts, and the desire to have a variable focus led to the concept of phasing and phased array transducers.

Therefore, both the linear switched array path for vascular and the mechanical approach for cardiac have led to the same requirement of the ability to steer without moving parts and the ability to change the focus. Before we discuss the family of phased array transducers, we will first need to consider the technique of phasing and how it can be used to both steer and focus.

20. Electronic Steering

20.1 Understanding the Term Phase
The term "phase" is used to determine a time reference.

◊   ***Example:***   "We are in phase 3 of a 10 phase building proposal."

◊   ***Example:***   "Your hair is too long. You listen to noise and call it music. Your friends are rude, and you think you know everything." (Teenage phase)

For waves, a phase difference is the amount of time shift necessary to make two waves align. Recall that in Chapter 1 we discussed phase differences between waves and how the phase affected wave addition. When two waves were in phase, the resulting wave had a significantly higher amplitude, or constructive interference. When two waves were completely out of phase (180°), there was cancellation or destructive interference. As is more often the case, when two waves are partially out of phase, the resultant wave has an amplitude somewhere between the sum of the two individual waves.

Chapter 5

To create constructive and destructive interference, multiple waves are necessary. Each transducer element acts as an individual wave source, so a collection of elements can be brought together to create many waves simultaneously. A collection of transducer crystal elements is called an array. In simple terms, an array is really a group of small transducers (elements) which can be used in conjunction with one another to form a larger and more flexible transducer. Electronic steering refers to the fact that the steering is achieved by using small time or phase delays between the excitation pulses to each of the transducer elements within the array.

Electronic steering eliminates all of the disadvantages of mechanical steering. The fact that electronic steering requires an array leads to some further advantages such as the ability to vary the focus through changing the aperture as well as by phasing (the aperture is the active area of transducer being used), the ability to perform parallel processing, and many other advanced processing techniques. The major disadvantage of a phased array is cost. Creating a phased array transducer is considerably more complex and costly than the more simple mechanical transducers.

20.2 Electronic Steering for Transmit

To steer a beam electronically, tiny time shifted excitation pulses are applied to each element of the aperture. (The aperture is the portion or "window" of the transducer elements which is being utilized.)

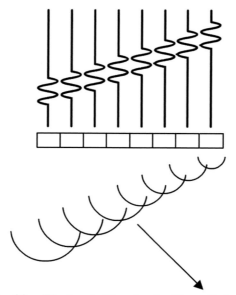

Fig. 30 **Electronic Steering by Phase Delays**

Figure 30 demonstrates the concept of applying a phased delay voltage profile to a group of elements within a transducer. The zigzagged line represents the voltage pulse for an individual transducer element. The difficulty of presenting time in a static picture again presents itself. In this case, time is represented by the "distance" between the transducer element and the voltage pulse. The farther away the zigzagged line, the later in time the pulse will arrive at the crystal. Therefore, since the pulses are not all at the same "distance" from the elements, the picture represents time differences, or "delays" between the voltages driving each of the elements.

By using Huygen's principle we can predict how each of the individual wavefronts will add to construct a beam and in what direction that beam will travel. Huygen's principle states that all points on a wavefront can be treated as point sources producing spherical secondary wavelets, whose tangential surface predicts the new position of the wavefront over time. (Note that from this principle, the laws of reflection and refraction can also be determined.) In essence, each transducer element acts as an individual transducer producing a spherical wave. Because of the time delays, each individual wave is at a different distance from the transducer face at a given moment in time. The wavefronts of each of these spherical waves begin to overlap producing more constructive interference. Eventually, with depth, the spherical waves start growing to the point where the overlap decreases more and more, resulting in less and less constructive interference. At any time, the spherical wavefronts can be connected to demonstrate the wave direction and behavior.

In the above example, notice that the new beam direction is no longer perpendicular to the transducer face. The phase delays between the excitation pulses to each of the elements result in delayed waves. The delayed wavefronts add such that the "main beam" is at an angle to the transducer face that matches the transmit phase delay profile. In essence, time delays are being used to make the transducer "appear" as if it were facing a different direction.

View Animation and Image Library CD

20.3 Electronic Steering for Receive

Just as we would like the ability to transmit a beam in a specific direction, we also would like to receive a beam from that same specific direction. In other words, if we would like the transmit signal to go in a specific direction, we would like to listen from that same direction, and not just straight ahead.

The principles that apply to delays are the same principles as apply to receive and transmit. Notice in the following figure that the path length from point "x" to element #1 is different than the path length to element #8. Therefore, if we want the signals that arrive from point "x" to all 8 elements to add up correctly as one signal, we will have to use a delay profile on the received signals from each element. In this case, since the path length is longer to element #1 than to element #8, we must delay element #8 more than element #6, which requires a greater delay than element #5, etc. Again, time is indicated as distance away from the transducer element. Since the receive pulse for element #8 is farther away than the pulse for element #6, there is a greater delay for element #8.

Receive Delays

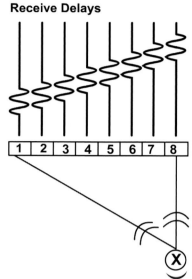

Fig. 31   **Receive Delay Profile**

20.4 Electronic Focusing for Transmit

Phase delays are also used to focus transmit and receive beams. We will start with the simple case of focusing an "unsteered" beam.

This first transmit profile is flat implying that there is no delay to the transmit pulse driving any of the elements. As a result, this "delay" profile would transmit straight ahead.

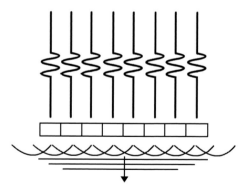

Fig. 32   **Unsteered and Unfocused Beam**

Now consider if we change the above profile to a profile that is parabolic as shown in the next figure. The end elements are driven earliest in time, so the spherical wavefronts from these two elements travel the farthest for a given period of time. The next two inner elements were driven a small time later, so the associated spherical wavefronts will be a little shallower. The element in the center of the transducer was transmitted last, and hence, the spherical wave has traveled the shortest distance. We can again use Huygen's principle to demonstrate the wave direction and behavior over time.

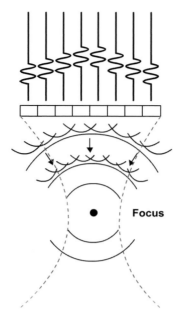

Fig. 33   **Electronic Focusing**

When the tangent to each spherical wave is connected, the beam is clearly converging to a point. If you imagine these wavefronts later in time and draw the tangent to the spherical wavefronts, as indicated by the two curved lines at the bottom of the image, it is clear that the beam is now diverging. In other words, by using small time delays (phase delays), the beam is now focusing.

To decrease the focal depth, a more "severe" phase profile can be used. For a deeper focal depth, a less severe profile can be used. If no profile is used, the result is the natural focus of the transducer and transducer lens. Recall that it is not possible to improve focusing beyond the natural transducer focus for a given transducer aperture and operating frequency. Past the focus the beam is "diffraction limited," which basically says that the beam is bending away or diverging from the center line of the beam.

 **View Animation and Image Library CD**

20.5 Electronic Focusing for Receive
Just as the same delay profile was applied on receive steering as for transmit steering, the same delay profile can be applied to focus a receive beam as for transmitting a focused beam.

20.6 Focusing and Steering Together
Not surprisingly, there will be times when we will want to both steer and focus. To both steer and focus, all that is needed is to add the delay profile from the steer to the delay profile that achieves the focus. The following figure demonstrates how a steering and a focusing profile can be added to achieve a steered and focus beam.

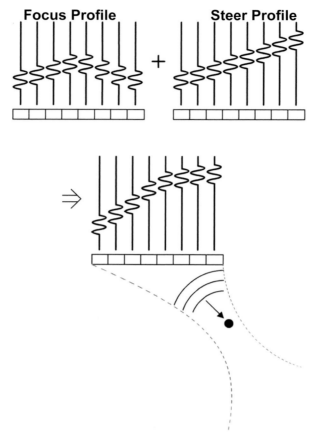

Fig. 34   **Electronic Steering and Focusing Simultaneously**

Again by using Huygen's principle, we can see that the beam is now directed at an angle from the transducer face, and the beam is converging to, and diverging from a point. As we will see with phased array transducers, steering and phasing simultaneously is very common.

 **View Animation and Image Library CD**

21. Phased Array Sector

The phased array sector transducer, like the mechanical sector, was designed with rib access in mind. These transducers typically have between 64 and 128 elements, although transducers with fewer or more elements certainly exist. The frequency range for these transducers depends on the intended application. For adult cardiac imaging, these transducers generally run as low as 2 MHz and as high as 4 MHz in conventional imaging mode. Quite frequently, the Doppler frequency will be set at or below the lowest imaging frequency, generally not going lower than about 1.8 MHz. For small adults and children, the Doppler frequency range is generally from 3.5 MHz to 5 MHz, and for pediatric imaging, the Doppler frequency range is typically from 5 MHz to about 8 MHz. Note these frequency ranges are approximate and vary from ultrasound company to ultrasound company.

Pegasus Lectures, Inc.

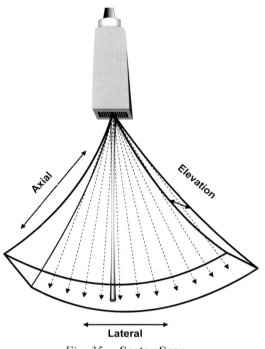

Fig. 35   **Sector Scan**

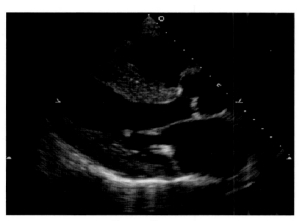

Sector Image

Description:

Used for 2-D imaging, M-mode, Doppler, and color Doppler

Creates sector image with small footprint for rib access

Multiple square or rectangular elements in a row (64 to 128 elements common)

Transducer is steered electronically by phasing in lateral dimension

Variable transmit focus by electronic phasing in lateral dimension

Continuous variable receive focus by electronic phasing in lateral dimension

Lens used to create the appropriate fixed elevation focus for intended use

Beam usually not symmetric in elevation and lateral dimensions

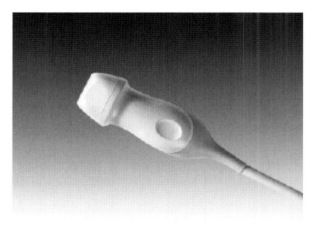

Sector Transducer

Disadvantages: (relative to mechanical)

More expensive to make than single element mechanical transducers

More expensive electronics necessary (potentially one channel for each element)

Disadvantages: (relative to 2-D arrays)

Fixed elevation focus

No steering in elevation dimension (to perform 3-D, must manually or mechanically steer in elevation)

TEE (Sector Format)

Chapter 5

Advantages: (relative to single element mechanicals)
Variable focus in the lateral dimension
Motion artifacts and problems related to mechanical parts are eliminated
Flexibility to perform parallel processing and other advanced processing techniques

Discussion
The sector image for this type of transducer is produced purely by phase delays. It is very important that you understand how the image is actually formatted so that you will understand the angle formed between the steered beam and the structures at each location in the image. This knowledge is critical to truly understanding, predicting, and controlling artifacts. Furthermore, the only way to ever truly understand direction of flow is to first understand how the image is created. This fact will become evident in Chapter 7 when flow direction is discussed. For now, we will learn how an image is created in a sector format.

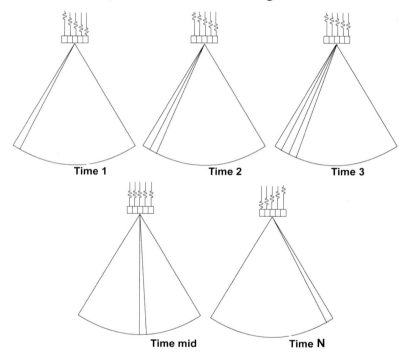

Fig. 36   **Creating a Sector Scan**

View Animation and Image Library CD

Notice that each beam is created by firing a group of elements. The waves from each of the elements propagate into the body and constructively interfere to produce a beam pattern. As we learned earlier in the chapter, by using time delays, the beams can be forced to add constructively in a direction other than straight ahead from the transducer. Referring to the diagram, notice that at Time 1, a delay profile is used to steer the beam toward the left (page left) side of the image. Since it takes time for sound to propagate into and out of the body, the system must wait 13 µsec per imaging cm until transmitting the next neighboring beam. As the echoes return in time, the receiver continuously changes the time delays so as to focus at each location along the receive line.

Pegasus Lectures, Inc.

Once the required line time has transpired, the second beam is created using a slightly more gradual delay profile. Again, the receive delay profile is continuously varied to maximize sensitivity to each specific depth and improve lateral resolution as much as possible. This process is repeated until eventually the beam required is straight ahead of the transducer. (Labeled time mid in *Figure 36*.) You should notice that since this beam does not need to be steered, the phase delay profile is flat. Past this midpoint (to the right of the midline), the phase delay profile is reversed so as to create steering in the opposite direction as the beams on the left side of the image. When the right edge of the sector is reached and the echoes received, the process repeats with the retransmission of line 1.

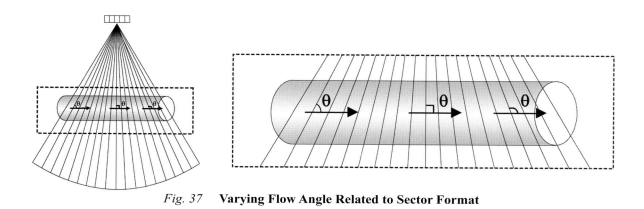

Fig. 37   **Varying Flow Angle Related to Sector Format**

Notice in *Figure 37* that although the structure drawn is straight, with no bends, kinks, or twists, the angle formed between the beam and the structure varies across the entire length of the structure. For the given figure, the only place where the beam is normal to the structure is at the very center line of the image. Of course, if the angle of the structure were diving, normal incidence would no longer occur along the midline.

Major Limitation Leading to a New Technology
Phased array transducers have been the workhorse for ultrasound for many years now. Because of the many elements and the ability to customize a design to meet the needs of a specific application such as vascular, OB, etc., there are not that many limitations that have forced a new paradigm in transducer design. Instead, iterative improvements have been made to increase sensitivity, increase bandwidth, and to allow for many new imaging and processing techniques. However, there is one major limitation to all 1-D phased array transducers, the inability to control the elevation direction by focusing or steering. The desire to control elevation so as to produce 3-D images with no moving parts becomes the motivation for 2-D arrays.

22. Linear Phased Array

Whereas sectors were designed with rib access in mind, linear transducers were produced for vascular applications where contact must be maintained with a relatively flat surface such as the neck and legs. The linear phase array is the technology that replaced the linear switched array. These transducers are physically large and usually consist of 200 to 300 elements or more. In reality, with linear phased array, the switching and sequencing aspects of a linear switched array still are utilized. The difference is that a phase array linear can also be phased to create steering and focusing when desired. As a result, we will need to consider this transducer when both steered and unsteered to fully appreciate the functionality.

Chapter 5

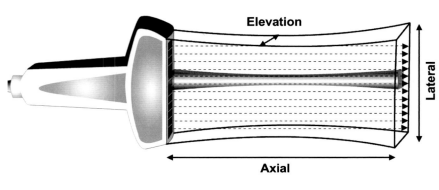

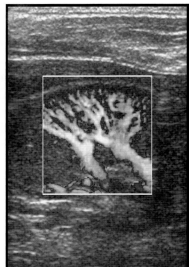

Linear Image

Fig. 38   **Linear Scan**

Description:
Used for 2-D imaging, Doppler, and color Doppler
Rectangular image created by sequencing
Parallelogram image created by phasing each group of
sequenced elements
Multiple rectangular elements in a linear array (200 to
300 elements common)
Transducer steered electronically by phasing in the
lateral dimension
Variable receive focus by electronic phasing in the
lateral dimension
Dynamic receive focus in the lateral direction
Lens used to create the appropriate fixed elevation
focus for intended use
Beam usually not symmetric in elevation and lateral
dimensions

Disadvantages: (relative to mechanical)
More expensive to make than single element mechanical transducers
More expensive electronics necessary (potentially one
channel for each element)

Disadvantages: (relative to 2-D arrays)
Fixed elevation focus
No steering in elevation direction (to perform 3-D
must manually or mechanically steer in elevation)

Advantages: (relative to single element mechanicals)
Variable focus in the lateral direction
Allows for creation of a wide linear image in the near field
Flexibility to perform parallel processing and other advance processing techniques

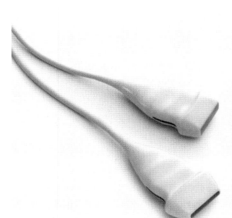

Pegasus Lectures, Inc.

Discussion

In terms of image generation, there are three different ways in which linear transducers are used. When unsteered, the image is created through sequencing, just as the switched linear array operated. When the image is steered, then a combination of phasing and sequencing is used. A third mode, called trapezoidal scanning, creates wings to the image by phasing, and produces the center part of the image through sequencing. We will start with the simplest of these three modes which is unsteered imaging.

Unsteered Imaging

Although the mechanism for an unsteered linear transducer is the same as for a switched linear transducer, we will repeat the discussion, but with more detail to serve as the foundation for discussing steered linear images.

Referring to the images below, notice how the first beam is created by exciting the first group of elements at time T_1. Notice that all of the elements in the group are excited at the same time, with no phase delay between the pulses for each element. The flat delay profile results in a beam which propagates straight ahead. Once the echo has returned from the depth of interest (determined by the depth knob setting), a second beam is transmitted, at time T_2, by exciting a second grouping of elements, creating a beam laterally displaced. Again note that all of the elements within the second group are excited at the same time, with no phase delays. Therefore, the beam is transmitted straight ahead and parallel to the first beam. Continuing in this manner, groups of elements are fired in a linear sequence creating a scan region of parallel beams. The width of this scan region is determined by the user by setting the scan or "image" size on the screen. Once the end of the scan or frame is reached (T_N), the first group of elements is again excited and the process repeated.

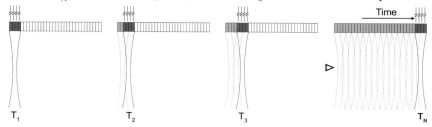

Fig. 39   **Unsteered Imaging by Sequencing**

View Animation and Image Library CD

Steered Image

A steered linear image is also produced by sequencing. However, to achieve the desired steering angle, phasing is used. Referring to the following figure, notice that when the first group of elements is activated, not all of the elements are pulsed at the same time. Instead, a phase delay results in some elements being pulsed earlier than others. As we have learned in the earlier section on phasing, this phase delay results in a constructive interference such that the main beam now travels at an angle relative to the transducer face. Once the echo has been received from the imaging depth, the next group of elements in the "sequence" is activated. Of course, it is desired that the beam created by the second group of elements be parallel to the first beam. Therefore, the same phase delay profile is applied to the second group of elements as was applied to the first. This process repeats across the entire array until the entire frame is complete, and the process repeats to produce another frame. Therefore, a steered linear image requires both sequencing and phasing to create the desired image.

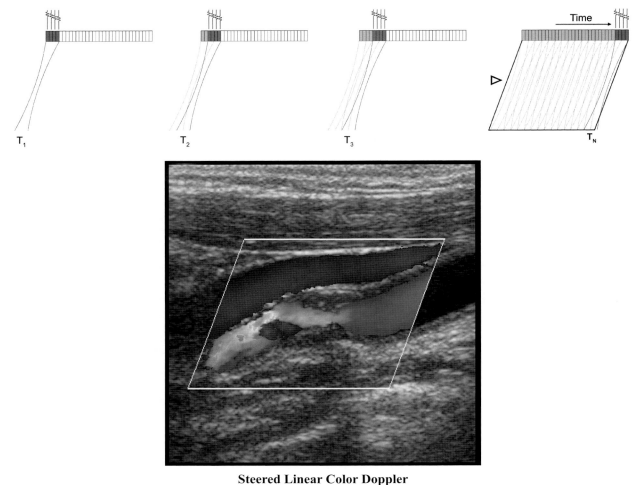

Steered Linear Color Doppler

Fig. 40 **Steered Linear Imaging**

Note that the mechanism for steering a color Doppler image with a linear phased array follows the same approach as for creating a 2-D image. Since spectral Doppler is a non-scanned modality, sequencing is obviously not necessary. However, to achieve the desired Doppler angles, phasing is certainly used.

 **View Animation and Image Library CD**

Trapezoidal Scanning

Trapezoidal scanning results in an extended field of view by creating an image that is trapezoidal in shape. (There is nothing like stating the obvious.) However, what is probably not so obvious is that trapezoidal scanning is produced by treating the linear array as if it were two different transducers. To produce the left and right "wings" of the image, a portion of the array is treated as a sector transducer. To produce the center portion of the image, the array is treated as an unsteered linear. *Figure 41* demonstrates how trapezoidal scanning is achieved.

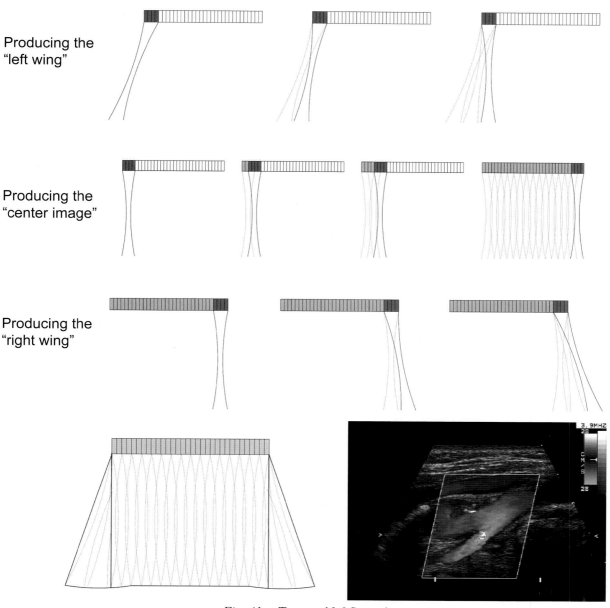

Producing the "left wing"

Producing the "center image"

Producing the "right wing"

Fig. 41 **Trapezoidal Scanning**

Note: Even when a linear phased array is not using phasing for steering, phasing is still used for focusing on transmit and dynamic (continuous) focusing on receive. Also note that no matter what the format, a linear image always has a top and bottom that are flat and parallel.

 **View Animation and Image Library CD**

Major Limitation Leading to a New Technology

Like the 1-D array sector, the main limitation is the inability to control the elevation plane for focus and 3-D imaging.

Chapter 5

23. Curved Linear Phased Array

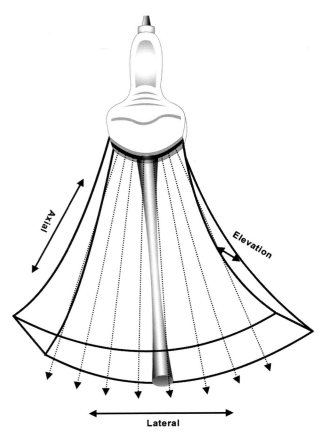

Fig. 42   **Curved Linear Scan**

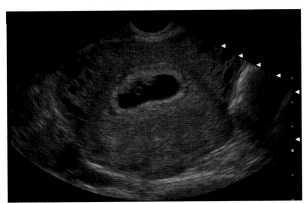

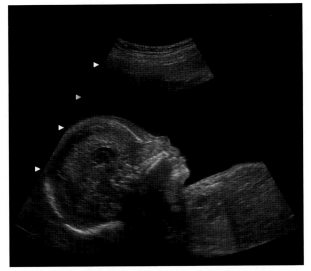

Description:

Used for 2-D imaging, Doppler, and color Doppler
Curved image created by sequencing
Multiple rectangular elements in a curved linear array
No steering necessary – geometry creates desired scan
shape
Variable receive focus by electronic phasing in lateral
dimension
Dynamic receive focus in lateral dimension
Beam usually not symmetric in elevation and lateral
dimensions

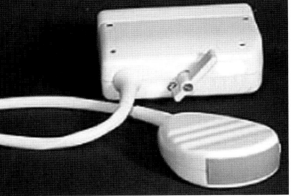

Disadvantages: (relative to mechanical)

More expensive to make than single element mechanical transducers
More expensive electronics necessary (potentially one channel for
each element)

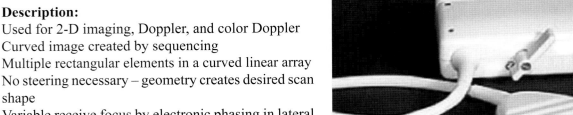

Various Curved Linear Arrays

Disadvantages: (relative to 2-D arrays)
Fixed elevation focus
No steering in elevation dimension (to perform 3-D must manually or mechanically steer in elevation)

Advantages: (relative to single element mechanicals)
Variable focus in the lateral dimension
Allows for creation of a extremely wide linear image in near field
Flexibility to perform parallel processing and other advanced processing techniques

Discussion
For conventional 2-D imaging a curved linear image is produced by sequencing only. The image shape is produced by the curvature of the front of the transducer. Larger arrays produce larger images. A more convex transducer produces a more convex image. Since sequencing has already been explained, we will only include a figure illustrative of how sequencing creates a curved linear image, without the description repeated. Many times students ask me "Then why do we call

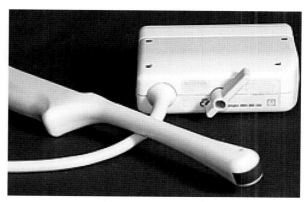

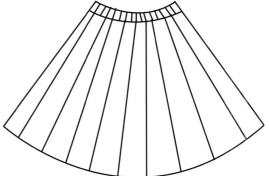

this a phased array transducer?" The answer is primarily that phase delays are used to control the transmit focus and dynamic receive focus. Also, the phasing is used to achieve appropriate angles to perform Doppler. Additionally, as we will learn in Chapter 6, techniques such as compound imaging will use steering to create curved linear images. Therefore, even though a conventional image is not produced using phasing, phasing is still used.

Major limitation leading to a new technology
Like the 1-D array sector, the main limitation is the inability to control the elevation plane for focus and 3-D imaging.

24. Multi-dimensional Arrays

24.1 1.5-D Arrays

A 1.5-D array has more than one element in the elevation direction. The following figure demonstrates the design of a 1.5-D array.

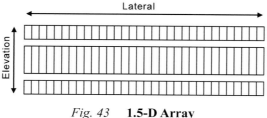

Fig. 43 **1.5-D Array**

Chapter 5

Discussion

A 1.5-D array allows for either the center row of elements to be used alone, or for the outer two groups of elements to be linked and turned on as well. If just the center aperture is used, the elevation focus is relatively shallow. If the outer group is activated as well, then the elevation focus becomes deeper.

Since any transducer format can be made as a 1.5-D array, we will not reiterate the purpose and function of sectors, linears, and curved linears again.

Major Limitation Leading to a New Technology

Although there is some control in the elevation direction, the control is very limited. The inability to create an automated 3-D image still remains. Therefore, the next generation are 2-D arrays.

24.2 2-D Arrays

Phased array transducers were developed in response to the limitations of mechanical transducers. These phased arrays are called 1-D arrays, since they possess an array of elements along a line, or in one dimension. As portrayed in the disadvantages of the phased array transducers, the 1-D transducers have a fixed elevation focus and no elevational steering capability.

In response to these limitations, 2-D transducers have been created. 2-D transducers have multiple elements in both the elevation and lateral dimensions and hence, can be electronically steered and focused in both dimensions.

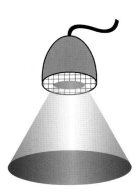

Fig. 44   **2-D Array**

Fig. 45   **This figure demonstrates a 2-D array (matrix). The arrows indicate a human hair. (Courtesy of Philips Medical Systems)**

25. Piezocomposite Materials

In the early days of ultrasound, PZT was used almost exclusively for transducer design. With the ever present desire to create transducers with greater bandwidth and improved sensitivity, more exotic approaches are now used to engineer the crystal material. A composite is generally a mixture of a polymer and piezoceramic material. One approach to create a composite material crystal is to take a block of piezoelectric material and dice it into a series of "posts". Usually the dicing cuts through about 80% of the thickness of the block. The posts are then embedded in a polymer matrix like an epoxy. Depending on the materials used, the manufacturing process, and the desired characteristics of the crystal, different ratios of polymer and piezoceramic materials will be used. To give an idea on the element spacing, for a 5 MHz transducer, the "pitch" (separation between elements) is typically about 0.1 mm. This small pitch is important to try to minimize excitation modes in directions other than the desired "piston" mode which is towards the face of the transducer, and to reduce the amount of energy that exists in the grating lobes of the beam. Once the epoxy has cured, the uncut side of the block is ground off. Electrodes are then added and the material is polarized through poling.

The result of these new composite materials has been the birth of ultra-wide bandwidth transducers. These newer transducers make performing harmonic (discussed in Chapter 10) imaging feasible. In addition to wider bandwidth, the lower impedance of the polymer provides a better match to tissue. In comparison to the impedance of PZT (35-40 MRayls), the impedance of many polymers is around 8-12 MRayls. This lower impedance implies that the addition of a matching layer (or layers) provides significantly better "matching" than with PZT crystals.

PZT Rods

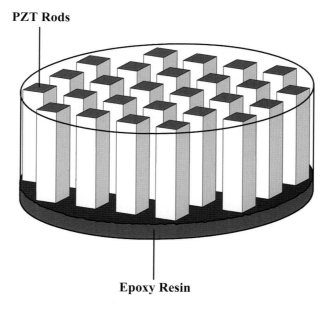

Epoxy Resin

Fig. 46 **2-D Array "Posts"**

26. Detail Resolution

Detail resolution is the collective name for the axial resolution, lateral resolution and the elevation resolution. Although the individual components have already been discussed, each is included again here so as to be put into context of a 2-D scan. The following figures will serve as a review and means by which to see all three components of detail resolution simultaneously.

26.1 Lateral Resolution
Lateral resolution is defined as the ability to resolve two structures in the lateral dimension (side-by-side, angular, transverse, or azimuthal).

Consider what happens if a beam were wide enough so that two side-by-side structures were insonified simultaneously. The echoes from both objects would add together and there would be no way of distinguishing between the two objects. In contrast, consider if the beam were narrower than the separation between the two objects. The first transmitted line would "see" the first object. The second transmitted line would see no object. The third transmitted line would see the second object. Since the echoes coming back were distinct, both objects would be drawn separately, and the two objects were adequately resolved. The criterion for lateral resolution is clearly the width of the beam, or the beamwidth.

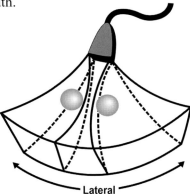

Fig. 47   **Lateral Resolution**

Lateral Resolution = Lateral Beamwidth

We have already seen that the beamwidth varies with distance from the transducer, therefore, the lateral resolution varies with depth. The best lateral resolution occurs where the beam is the narrowest laterally, or the lateral focus.

26.2 Elevation Resolution

The elevation resolution is determined by the beamwidth in the elevation plane. Just as the lateral resolution is equal to the lateral beamwidth, the elevation resolution equals the elevation beamwidth. Similarly, the elevation resolution changes with depth since the elevation beamwidth changes with depth. Finally, the elevation resolution is best where the beam is narrowest in the elevation dimension, which occurs at the elevation focus.

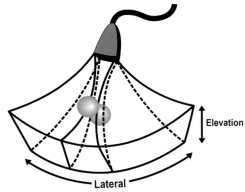

Fig. 48   **Elevation Resolution**

Elevation Resolution = Elevation Beamwidth

26.3 Axial Resolution

The axial resolution is determined by the spatial pulse length because of the roundtrip effect, the resolution is a factor of 2 better than the spatial pulse length.

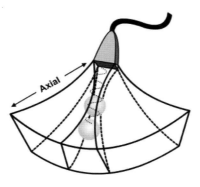

Fig. 49   **Axial Resolution**

$$\text{Axial Resolution} = \frac{SPL}{2}$$

27. Important Concepts for Transducers

Near field (Fresnel):	The area between the face of the transducer and the beam focus.
Far field (Fraunhofer):	The region past the focus.
Focus:	Where the beam reaches its minimum diameter.
Focal region (Depth of field):	Region over which the beam is most tightly focused.
Detail Resolution:	Ability to distinguish between two objects in any of the three dimensions: axial, lateral, or elevation.
Operating frequency (f_0):	The center frequency of the transmit bandwidth.
f_0 (pulsed mode):	Determined by crystal thickness and speed of sound in crystal material: $f_0 = \dfrac{c}{2 \bullet (thickness)}$.
f_0 (continuous mode):	Determined by the frequency of the drive (transmit) voltage.

For many applications the natural focus of a transducer is inadequate or suboptimal. As a result many different focusing schemes have been developed to make the focus shallower such as:

1)   Lenses
2)   Curved elements
3)   Electronic focusing
4)   Mirrors

Most 1-D array transducers actually use a combination of these techniques so that a transducer design is optimized for a specific application.

◊   ***Examples:***

- Curved linear arrays (CLA's) use a lens, curved elements, and electronic focusing.
- Phased arrays use a lens and electronic focusing.
- Mechanical transducers generally use a lens and possibly a mirror or mirrors.

As we already have discussed, there are a few very compelling reasons to want to be able to change the focus. Of the four techniques listed above, only electronic focusing allows for variable focusing. The other three techniques all result in a fixed focus. In essence, you can change the focus from the natural focus of a transducer by adding a lens to the design; however, since there is no easy way to change the lens on the transducer, the focus is now fixed by the lens.

28. Exercises `Answers Pg. 458-460`

1. _____ Blind (Doppler only) transducers have a broad depth of fie. **(T/F)**

2. _____ A phased array transducer must have multiple elements. **(T/F)**

3. _____ A mechanical system can steer and focus the beam electronically. **(T/F)**

4. _____ An annular array can be focused electronically but must be steered mechanically. **(T/F)**

5. An annular transducer has the distinct benefit of variable focus in both elevation and lateral planes. A distinct disadvantage with respect to phased transducers is that an annular transducer

   a) cannot image deeper than 10 cm
   b) is inherently less sensitive
   c) must be steered mechanically
   d) can not perform Doppler or color flow

6. Which of the following has a rectangular image?

   a) Annular
   b) Sector
   c) Linear switched array
   d) More than one of the above

7. A fundamental difference between a linear switched array and a linear phased array is that a linear switched array

   a) has a fixed focus and cannot steer.
   b) has a variable focus and can steer.
   c) has a lower maximum PRF (pulse repetition frequency).

8. Sector phased arrays principally create a sector image

   a) for rib access.
   b) to allow for more lines per scan.
   c) for cost effectiveness.
   d) to minimize the time it takes to shoot a frame.

9. The "footprint" of a transducer has two dimensions. The beamwidth is associated with the _____ dimension and the "slice thickness" is determined by the _____ dimension.

   a) axial, elevation
   b) elevation, lateral
   c) elevation, axial
   d) lateral, elevation

Chapter 5

10. Match column B to column A

	A		**B**
a)	Lens	1)	used to help focus the beam
b)	Matching layer(s)	2)	converts electrical to mechanical energy
c)	Piezoelectric material	3)	lowers acoustic impedance mismatch between the transducer and the patient
d)	Backing material	4)	delivers the drive voltage to the crystal and echo voltage to the receivers
e)	Wires	5)	used to decrease the spatial pulse length, improving axial resolution, increases transducer bandwidth, but decreases transducer sensitivity

11. Match column B to column A

	A		**B**
a)	Near field zone	1)	The ability to distinguish changes
b)	Far field zone	2)	the transmit frequency
c)	Focus	3)	where the beam reaches its minimum diameter
d)	Resolution	4)	Fresnel
e)	Operating frequency	5)	Fraunhofer

12. Which of the following does not belong?

a) Axial
b) Longitudinal
c) Depth
d) Radial
e) Azimuthal

13. Which of the following is not the same as lateral resolution?

a) Radial
b) Angular
c) Azimuthal
d) Transverse

14.   In pulsed mode, what determines the operating frequency? (Give the equation.)

15.   In continuous mode, what determines the operating frequency?

16.   The near zone length is approximately equal to $\dfrac{D^2 f}{6}$. If the frequency doubles, the NZL
        a) increases by a factor of 2.
        b) decreases by a factor of 2.
        c) increases by a factor of 4.
        d) decreases by a factor of 2.

17.   If the diameter of a transducer is increased by a factor of 2, the near zone length

        a) increases by a factor of 2.
        b) decreases by a factor of 2.
        c) increases by a factor of 4.
        d) decreases by a factor of 2.

18.   Which of the following transducers would give the shallowest focus?

        a) $D = 2$ mm, $f = 2$ MHz
        b) $D = 1$ mm, $f = 2$ MHz
        c) $D = 2$ mm, $f = 10$ MHz
        d) $D = 1$ mm, $f = 10$ MHz

19.   Which focusing technique best improves the focus in the far field?

        a) A lens
        b) Mirrors
        c) Electronic focusing
        d) Curved elements
        e) None, one can only improve focus in the near field

20.   For an unfocused transducer, what is the approximate beamwidth at the focal distance and twice
        the focal distance, given a crystal diameter of 5 mm?

        a) 5 mm, 10 mm
        b) 2.5 mm, 10 mm
        c) 5 mm, 5 mm
        d) 2.5 mm, 5 mm

21.   How thick would a crystal have to be for 2 MHz pulsed mode operation given a propagation
        velocity through the crystal of 5,000 m/sec?

22.   If the thickness of a crystal doubles, the frequency of operation for PW mode

        a) doubles.
        b) halves.
        c) quadruples.
        d) quarters.

23. Two crystals of the same thickness are used for transducers A and B. The propagation velocity on transducer A's crystal is twice that of transducer B's. Which of the following is true?

    a) A and B have the same operating frequency.
    b) A operates at twice the operating frequency as B.
    c) B operates at twice the operating frequency as A.
    d) A operates at four times the operating frequency as B.

24. Radial resolution equals _____.

25. Lateral resolution equals the _____ and therefore varies with depth since the _____ varies with depth.

29. Conceptual Questions   Answers Pg. 460-463

1. A transducer is anything which converts _____ from one form to another form.

2. An _____ transducer converts voltage into sound above human hearing and sound into a voltage.

3. An ultrasound transducer converts electropotential _____ into _____ _____ and mechanical energy into electropotential energy.

4. Ultrasound transducers use the _____ effect.

5. A commonly used material for ultrasound transducers is _____ Zirconate Titanate (PZT)

6. If a transducer is heated above its _____ temperature, it will loose its piezoelectric properties.

7. For PZT, the Curie temperature is _____.

8. When a transducer is referred to as "mechanical," it means that the _____ is performed mechanically.

9. When a transducer is referred to as "_____," it means that the steering is performed electronically.

10. A _____ is used to help focus a beam in the elevation plane.

11. The _____ plane corresponds to the beam thickness.

12. The _____ _____ is used to minimize the acoustic impedance mismatch between the PZT and tissue.

13. Without a matching layer, there would be a large _____ mismatch between the transducer and tissue causing a large _____ or equivalently small transmission.

14. The _____ _____ is used to shorten the spatial pulse length, improving longitudinal resolutions.

15. The backing material shortens the spatial pulse length by absorbing some of the pulse energy thereby _____ the transducer efficiency.

16. The near field zone is also called the _____ zone.

17. The near field is the region of the beam shallower than the _____.

18. The focus is where the beam reaches its minimum _____ and maximum _____.

19. The far field is also called the _____ zone.

20. The far field is the region of the beam _____ than the focus.

21. The focal region is also called the _____ of field and refers to the area of the beam which is most tightly _____.

22. _____ is the ability to distinguish between two objects.

23. _____ resolution is also known as axial, radial and depth resolution.

24. _____ resolution is the ability to distinguish between objects along the beam direction.

25. _____ resolution is also known as angular, azimuthal or transverse resolution.

26. _____ resolution is the ability to distinguish between structures which are side-by-side.

27. The _____ frequency is the same as the transmit frequency.

28. In _____ _____, the operating frequency is determined by the speed of sound in the crystal and the crystal thickness.

29. In pulsed mode, a thicker crystal will have a _____ operating frequency.

30. In _____ _____, the operating frequency is determined by the frequency of the drive voltage.

31. In _____ _____, a thicker crystal will not change the operating frequency.

32. The near zone length (NZL) is the distance from the face of the transducer to the beam _____.

33. Any depth shallower than the _____ is within the near zone.

34. The _____ zone _____ is proportional to the transducer diameter squared.

35. If a transducer diameter is doubled, the near zone length is _____.

36. If a transducer diameter is doubled, the focus is _____ times as deep.

37. The near zone length is proportional to the operating _____.

38. If the operating frequency is doubled, the NZL is _____.

39. The _____ is approximately one half the transducer diameter at the focus.

40. The _____ is approximately one half the transducer diameter at a distance of one near zone length.

41. The _____ occurs at a distance of one near zone length.

42. The beamwidth approximately equals the transducer _____ at a distance of two near zone lengths.

43. The beamwidth is greater than the transducer diameter at a depth greater than two _____ _____ lengths.

44. _____ can be achieved by lenses, curved elements, _____, or with mirrors.

45. A phased array transducer uses _____ focusing in the lateral dimension and a _____ for focusing in the elevation dimension.

46. The curvature of an image produced by a _____ linear transducer matches the curvature of the transducer face.

47. Mechanical transducers use lenses, and/or mirrors for focusing but cannot be focused _____.

48. Focusing can only affect the _____ _____, never the far field.

49. Beyond the Fresnel zone, the beam is said to be _____ limited.

50. In _____ mode, transmit and receive occur simultaneously, continuously.

51. For a _____ mode the operating frequency equals the drive voltage frequency.

52. In a _____ _____, transmit and receive alternate, intermittently.

53. B-mode is an example of a _____ wave mode.

54. Color flow is an example of a _____ wave mode.

55. CW Doppler is an example of a _____ wave mode.

56. In _____ _____, the operating frequency equals the propagation velocity within the crystal divided by two times the _____.

57. _____ (axial, radial, depth) resolution is the ability to distinguish between structures along the beam direction.

58. The longitudinal resolution is determined by one half the _____ _____ length.

59. _____ resolution, (angular, transverse, azimuthal) is the ability to distinguish between structures which lie side by side.

60. The lateral resolution is determined by the _____.

Chapter 5

30. The Piezoelectric Effect

30.1 Use of Piezoelectric Materials

The piezoelectric effect found its first application in the early 1900's with sonar for submarines. Since then there have been myriad applications including piezoelectric buzzers, phonograph cartridges (the stylus for records), piezoelectric igniters for gas grills and small engines, clocks for electronic circuits, reflectometers to sense defects and flaws in metal structures such as airplane wings, sensing devices to warn vehicles of objects when backing up, and of course, ultrasound.

30.2 Crystal Structures

Virtually all metals, most ceramics, and some polymers crystallize when transitioning from liquid to solid form. When people generally think about crystals, the common perception is that crystals are precious minerals with numerous, somewhat translucent, relatively clear facets. For material scientists, the term crystal implies that the atomic or molecular arrangement is regular and repeated so that no matter in what direction within the material you travel, the same arrangement (pattern) exists. This repeated pattern in all three dimensions is generally referred to as three-dimensional periodicity. The smallest repeatable pattern of molecules is called a cell. There are many different geometric organizations (cells) possible for molecules to interlink such as cubic cells, tetragonal cells, orthorhombic cells, and hexagonal cells. How the molecules "pack" to form these various cell geometries depends on the type of bonds that occur between the molecules of the particular material and the number of molecules interconnecting. The term lattice is used to refer to space arrangement of the periodicity of a crystal. Therefore, the lattice constant is the edge dimension of the cell.

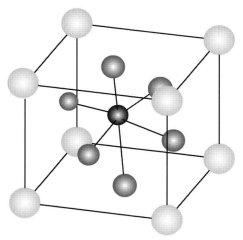

Fig. 50 **Crystal Lattice Structure**

30.3 Intermolecular Bonds

As mentioned, the cells are comprised of various arrangements of bound molecules. Unlike the bonds within the molecules, the bonds between molecules are much weaker. Specifically, intramolecular bonds which hold a molecule together are much higher energy bonds than the intermolecular bonds that hold multiple molecules together. The relatively weak intermolecular bonds allow for the molecules to have some degree of movement when acted upon by some stress.

30.4 Polarization

There are some molecules which exist in a permanent state of polarization. For these molecules, the "center of mass" for the positive and negative charges of the molecule are not coincident, thereby creating a negative pole and a positive pole. In essence, one side of the molecule possesses a greater positive charge distribution and the other side has a greater negative charge distribution, creating what is called a dipole. Unless something breaks down the bond which holds the molecule intact, the dipole is permanent.

When a group of molecules are interconnected in a cell, the cell itself can have a polarization. Similar to how a dipole exists in an individual molecule, when the center of the collection of molecular dipoles is not in the center of the cell, a cell dipole exists. Now recalling that the intermolecular bonds are relatively weak, when the temperature rises above a certain point for a given molecular material, the molecules will arrange more uniformly into more symmetric cells, reducing the polarization of the cell. Below that temperature, called the Curie point, the molecules shift slightly within the cells, increasing the distance between the positive and negative poles, referred to as the dipole distance "d". The change in the dipole distance is very small, on the order of thousandths of a nanometer. The fact that the molecular cell structure changes with temperature is the foundation for the procedure of "poling" which was briefly described in Level 1 of this chapter, and further described a little later in this section.

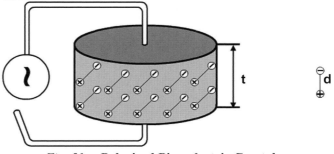

Fig. 51 **Polarized Piezoelectric Crystal**

Figure 51 depicts a crystal structure with polarized cells. Let's presume that the dipole distance in the "unperturbed state" has a length of "d". If you apply a voltage across the electrodes of the crystal, then the dipole length increases, as the positive and negative poles move towards the charged electrodes. Notice in the figure below, *Figure 52*, the negative distribution moves towards the positive electrode and the positive distribution moves toward the negative electrode. Since the dipole distance has increased, there is an expansion in the physical dimension of the crystal.

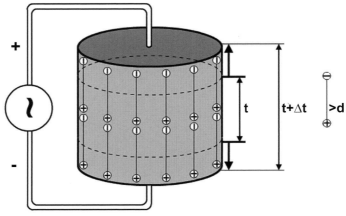

Fig. 52 **Crystal Expansion**

If you reverse the polarity of the voltage applied across the electrodes, then the poles of the molecular cells are repelled, decreasing the dipole length. This causes a contraction of the material, as indicated in *Figure 53*.

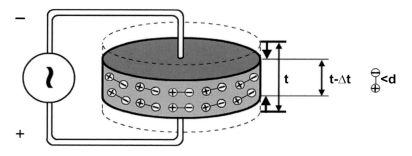

Fig. 53   **Crystal Contraction**

In the process so far described, we have seen how an applied voltage can cause a physical deformation of the crystal dimension. In a reverse manner, if you mechanically compress the material, a voltage is produced. When a stress is induced to mechanically compress the material, the dipole length is shortened. Since the positive and negative charge distributions are forced closer together, there is an increase in the repulsive forces, creating an excess of charge. By measuring the excess charge from the attached electrodes, there is now a voltage change associated with the mechanical compression. A greater applied stress results in a greater strain and a larger excess of charge, or a larger measured voltage.

In our discussion in Level 1, we described poling as a process which made materials more efficient as a piezoelectric material. In reality, many materials that are ferroelectric are made piezoelectric through poling. Ferroelectric materials shrink when an applied voltage is applied, no matter what the polarity of the voltage applied. In contrast, a piezoelectric material can be made to both expand and contract.

Through the process of poling, the molecules reposition slightly to form a more uniform polarization. When the molecules shift, the dipole distance is shortened, decreasing the crystal size. Once removed from the electric field and high temperature, the molecules remain in their new locations, in essence, leaving the crystal in a "shrunken" form. Now when a voltage is applied, it is possible to make the crystal expand from the "shrunken" state or, depending on the polarity of the voltage applied, to further shrink. In other words, by poling the material, the material has been converted from a ferroelectric material to a piezoelectric material.

New Crystal Growth Technology

Even in our more in depth treatment of poling, we have ignored some fundamental issues. From our treatment of poling, the presumption might be that all molecules align within the piezoceramic material during the process of poling resulting in a relatively homogenous transducer element. In reality, when crystals grow, there are discontinuities which develop at the molecular level referred to as grain boundaries. These grain boundaries act as imperfections such that perfect pole alignment is not achievable. At best, approximately 70% of the dipoles align, reducing the mechanical coupling coefficient (conversion coefficient from mechanical to electrical and electrical to mechanical energy). Over the last 40 years, the significant improvement in transducer performance has stemmed primarily from researching and designing new materials in conjunction with advances in matching layer technology. Very little success had been achieved relative to making more uniform crystals that would achieve higher polarization percentages.

In the early 1970's some Russian and Japanese scientists discovered a new piezocrystal with extremely uniform crystal structure. These uniform crystals could achieve significantly better polarization. However, there was considerable difficulty in growing crystals larger than a few millimeters, limiting application in the ultrasound field. In the 1990s research work led to a new technology to grow larger crystals exhibiting this improved electro-mechanical efficiency. The following figure illustrates how grain boundaries of conventional crystals lead to less efficient poling than ideal.

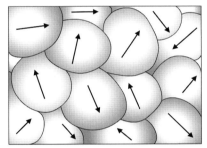

Fig. 54a **Crystal Grain Boundaries**

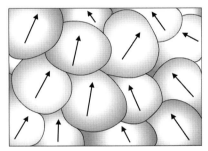

Fig. 54b **Crystal After Poling**
(Note: Imperfect Polarization)

The following figures illustrate actual crystal images under magnification. You will notice that the "conventional" PZT ceramic exhibits many grain boundaries whereas the new technology is completely uniform.

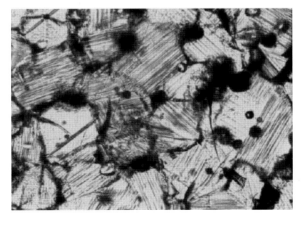

Fig. 55 **PZT Ceramic (Grain Boundaries and Imperfections Evident)**

Chapter 5

Fig. 56 **New Technology (Completely Uniform Crystal Structure)**

 **View Animation and Image Library CD**

*Crystal Growth Comparison

"To prepare conventional PZT ceramics, fine powders of the component metal oxides are mixed and then heated to form a uniform powder. The powder is mixed with an organic binder and baked into a dense polycrystalline structure. To produce PureWave crystals, the fine ceramic powder is formed using a process similar to PZT powders, however the rest of the process is unique. The powder is then melted into liquid in a platinum crucible at 1400° C using a specially designed high temperature furnace with a precisely controlled temperature profile. To nucleate the crystal from the melt at the desired orientation, a seed crystal is pulled (or drawn) away from the melting zone slowly (less than 1 mm/hour) and the crystal is grown layer by layer atomically to form a homogeneous crystal "boule" or cylinder. Boules are orientated along the desired crystallographic orientation(s) to maximize the crystal properties and then sliced into multiple wafers."

Fig. 57 **Wafer and a Crystal Boule**

The result of this new uniform crystal structure is reported to be an increase in coupling efficiency by as much as 68 to 85%. Furthermore, because of the uniform crystals structure, very wide bandwidths are achieved.

(*Excerpt and images reprinted with permission by Philips Medical Systems.)

Transducers

- A transducer is anything which converts one form of energy to another form of energy.

- An ultrasound transducer converts electropotential energy to mechanical, and mechanical energy to electropotential energy via the piezoelectric effect.

- The process of poling is used to enhance the piezoelectricity of a crystal.

- If a crystal is heated beyond the Curie temperature (300 degrees Celsius for PZT), the crystal can lose its piezoelectric properties.

- Lead zirconate titanate (PZT) historically has been the crystal material of choice for ultrasound transducers.

- Modern transducers use composite materials to achieve greater conversion efficiency with less of an acoustic impedance mismatch.

- Transducers may be single or multi-element, fixed focused or phased, mechanically or electronically steered.

- The field of view of a transducer is broken into two ranges: the near field (Fresnel) and the far field (Fraunhofer).

- The transition between the near and far field occurs at the focal depth. The focus is where the beam width is narrowest (best resolution and presumed highest beam intensity).

- Transducers can be run in continuous or pulsed mode. In continuous mode, the transmit frequency is determined by the frequency of drive voltage. In pulsed mode, the operating frequency is determined by both the propagation speed and the thickness of the element.

$$f_0\,(MHz) = \frac{\text{Propagation Speed}\,(mm/\mu sec)}{2 \bullet (thickness)(mm)}$$

- The Near zone length (NZL = distance to focus) is proportional to the diameter of the transducer squared and also proportional to the frequency of the transducer.

$$NZL\,(mm) \approx \frac{D^2\,(mm) \bullet f\,(MHz)}{6}$$

- The actual beam pattern in the Fresnel zone is extremely complex. For an unfocused transducer, a simple approximation assumes that the beam tapers from the diameter of the transducer at skin level to 1/2 the diameter at the focal distance or NZL.

- The beam diverges in the Fraunhofer zone. The beamwidth increases from approximately 1/2 the diameter of the transducer at a distance of one NZL to the diameter of the transducer at a distance twice the NZL.

- A wider transducer aperture (opening or active region) creates a narrower beamwidth in the far field. Also, the higher the frequency, the narrower the beam in the far field.

- Focusing by use of lenses, mirrors, curved elements, and electronic phasing can decrease the beamwidth, but only in the near field (Fresnel Zone). In the far field, relative to the natural focus, the beam is diffraction limited.

Chapter 5

- Generally, a longer near zone length (deeper focus) leads to greater depth of field. Larger apertures give a broader depth of field.

- The longitudinal resolution is determined by the spatial pulse length:

$$\text{Longitudinal Resolution} = \frac{\text{Spatial Pulse Length}}{2}$$

- The lateral resolution is determined by the lateral beamwidth:

$$\text{Lateral Resolution} = \text{Beamwidth}$$

As previously discussed, the beamwidth varies with depth, implying that the lateral resolution varies with depth for a given transducer.

- The elevation resolution is determined by the elevation beamwidth:

$$\text{Elevation Resolution} = \text{Elevation Beamwidth}$$

- A transducer consists of:
    - an element or multiple elements across which a voltage is applied
    - a backing material used to decrease the spatial pulse length
    - a matching layer or multiple matching layers to reduce the amount of reflection which results from a large acoustic impedance mismatch
    - an acoustic lens (or other focusing techniques) which reshapes the beam so as to provide a more optimum beam width per specific application
    - a pair of wires for each element to conduct the driving voltage and the return echo voltage from and to the system.

- A 1-D phased array has multiple elements in the lateral direction which can be turned on or off and/or phased to steer and focus laterally.

- 1-D arrays produce two-dimensional images.

- A sector phased array produces a scan in a sector format purely by phasing the elements to steer at various angles.

- The sector format was produced specifically for rib access.

- A linear phased array can be operated in a few different ways to produce a scan.
    - For non-steered 2D imaging or color imaging, sequencing is used.
    - For steered 2D imaging (some systems can steer 2D images) and steered color images, a combination of sequencing and phasing is used.

- Curved linear phased array transducers produce images purely by sequencing.

- A 2-D array has multiple elements is both the lateral and elevation direction which can be turned on or off and/or phased to steer and focus both laterally and elevationally. 2-D arrays can produce two-dimensional or three-dimensional images.

Note: See Appendix F: Physical Units and Appendix G: Equations for additional review.

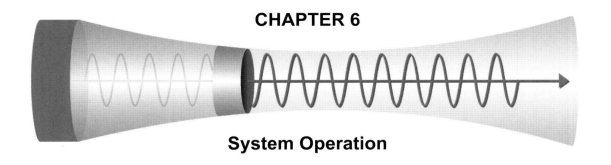

CHAPTER 6

System Operation

Introduction

In many ways this chapter is really two chapters joined by a common purpose. Level 1 focuses on the basic functions of an ultrasound machine while simultaneously concatenating all of the material in the earlier chapters into one cohesive topic. Level 2 deals with system operation from the standpoint of user interaction and higher level functions. Level 1 is designed to teach the basics of what an ultrasound system must do to make an image. Level 2 is designed to teach the basics of what the sonographer needs to do with the system and the choices faced to make an image.

One of the greatest difficulties of writing a chapter that specifically relates the physics, the system controls, the clinical advantages and disadvantages, and the theory is the lack of consistent terminology from one ultrasound provider to the next. The same basic function on system A will most likely have a very different name than the exact same technology on system B. This discrepancy in naming presents a problem since not everyone uses the same system. As much as possible, I have attempted to use generic, yet descriptive names for the system functions, only using a specific manufacturer's name when there is no other competing technology, when the name used by a specific company leads to a more "intuitive" understanding of the technique, or because the name itself has become a standard (like the use of the word Kleenex in reference to a disposable facial tissue).

1. The Basic Processes of Real-Time Imaging

There are six core functions that an ultrasound system must perform:

1. Transmit beams
2. Receive beams
3. Process the returned data
4. Perform measurements on the processed data
5. Display the processed data
6. Store the processed data

Of course each of these core functions can be further dissected into processes, and those processes again subdivided. Remembering that this is a physics book for ultrasound application and not an engineering document or physics treatise, we will spare discussion of specific electronic detail when there is no relevance in the clinical world. As such, we will not have a specific need to subdivide these processes very often within this chapter.

In the following sections, we will discuss each of these functions as an integral part of creating an image. The process of discussing the core functions will force us to integrate the material from the previous five chapters. To assist us with this task, we will start by learning related terminology and definitions, followed by a functional block diagram, relaying the links of each chapter to the current topic.

2. Important System Definitions

Many engineering terms are used to describe system performance and specifications. Many of these terms are often misused, leading to confusion and often misleading people in the ultrasound field, especially when in the market to purchase new equipment. Understanding these terms should help clarify some of the incredible functionality provided by current ultrasound systems. For continuity, many of the terms defined below will be redefined in the following sections so as to allow integration with related concepts. At the conclusion of the section you should be able to define the following terms:

- Transmit power
- Dynamic range
- Signal
- Noise and noise floor
- Signal-to-noise ratio (SNR)
- Compression
- Preprocessing
- Post processing

Note: The astute reader will note that a few of the definitions discussed below include references to Level 2 material. These references would, in an ideal world, not take place until the topic was discussed. Alas, we have found ourselves with a chicken and an egg dilemma. We cannot discuss new topics without defining the terminology, and we cannot define the terminology without discussing the technologies these terms describe. We are thus forced to break the rules of not referring to topics from a different level.

2.1 Transmit Power
There are many different names used to refer to the transmit power. Some of the names frequently used are acoustic power, output power, transmit gain, power gain, acoustic gain, output intensity, transmit voltage, and output voltage.

The transmit power knob controls the amplitude of the excitation voltage which drives the transducer crystal(s). A higher voltage corresponds to a higher amplitude mechanical oscillation of the crystal. The result is a higher amplitude sound wave. Since the power is proportional to the amplitude squared, a higher amplitude wave corresponds to a significantly higher power wave. Also, since the beam intensity is related to the power, higher power results in a more intense beam. Using a more intense beam results in stronger returning echoes. Clearly, if not enough transmit power is used, the returning echoes can be too weak and the signal inadequate.

Increasing the beam intensity also increases the risk of causing bioeffects in the patient. If the intensity were to get too high, tissue damage could result. Clearly, it is desirable to use the minimum amount of transmit power necessary to get good clinical results.

Note: Receiver gain and transmit power are completely different mechanisms. The transmit power affects the amplitude of the signal going into the patient. The receiver gain only affects the signal after it has returned from the patient. As a result, increasing the transmit power increases the risk of bioeffects. Conversely, increasing the receiver gain incurs no risk to the patient.

2.2 Dynamic Range

Dynamic range is the ratio of the maximum to the minimum of any quantity.

The term dynamic range can be applied to many different areas. To be clear, the dynamic range to which you are referring should be specified. For example:

Input dynamic range: Ratio of the maximum input signal to the minimum possible input signal

Output dynamic range: Ratio of the maximum to the minimum output signal

Display dynamic range: Ratio of the maximum to the minimum display signal

Gain dynamic range: Ratio of the maximum to the minimum applicable gain

In general, when speaking about ultrasound, if there is no specific qualifier to the term "dynamic range" the default interpretation is the input dynamic range. A formal definition for the input dynamic range of an ultrasound system is: "the range of signal amplitudes a system can receive and process without causing harmonic distortion."

2.3 Signals, Noise, and Signal-to-Noise Ratio (SNR)

2.3.1 Definitions

Signal: Any phenomenon desired to be measured
Noise: Any unwanted signals
Noise floor: The amplitude level below which no signals are visible because of the presence of noise
Signal-to-noise Ratio: The amplitude of the signal divided by the amplitude of the noise

2.3.2 What Determines a Good SNR

The signal-to-noise ratio is what specifies the signal quality, and hence, how much faith should be put in the data. A higher signal-to-noise ratio implies a better imaging situation and, excluding artifacts, more trustworthy data. Note that a strong signal by itself does not necessarily guarantee a good signal-to-noise ratio (SNR). For example, a relatively strong signal could be masked by inordinately strong noise. Therefore, even though the signal is strong, in the presence of significant noise, the ratio is still not very good. Conversely, a weak signal does not necessarily imply poor single to poor signal noise (although much more likely). If the signal is relatively weak but the noise floor is very low, then the ratio may still be relatively good. Overall, the desired situation is to have much greater signal strength than noise strength. Compare the three situations as depicted in *Figure 1*. The first example, Example A, demonstrates a very strong signal and a low noise floor, or good signal-to-noise. Example B has the same strong signal but very high noise therefore presenting poor signal-to-noise. Example B can result from very high amplitude noise in the presence of a high amplitude signal, or more commonly from high amplification of a weak signal. Example C demonstrates a low noise floor but a very weak signal, thereby again producing a poor signal-to-noise ratio.

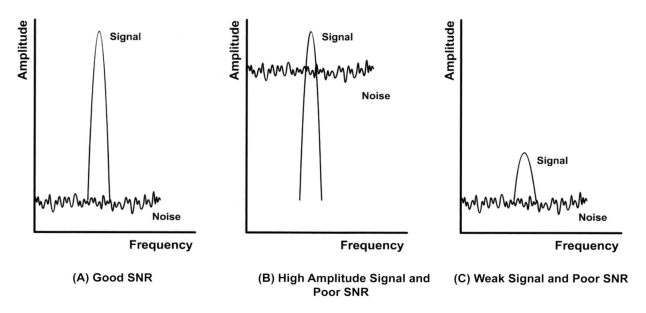

| (A) Good SNR | (B) High Amplitude Signal and Poor SNR | (C) Weak Signal and Poor SNR |

Fig. 1   **Graphical Representation of Signal-to-Noise Ratio**

2.3.3 Apparent SNR, Gain, and True SNR.

It is important to note that increasing the receiver gain does not improve the signal-to-noise ratio. Unless an electronic circuit is saturated (overgained such that some component of the signal is at the maximum circuit voltage), increasing amplification usually increases both the signal and the noise by the same amount so that the ratio stays the same. Although the true "SNR" may not change with gain, the apparent SNR might. This concept is perhaps one of the most often misunderstood concepts related to signal optimization. The confusion is derived from the fact that a certain amount of gain is necessary to make the signal bright enough so that it can be well visualized on the display within the dynamic range of both the display and the human eye. If the gain does not map the signal into this signal range, the signal will appear weak. However, this appearance is not because the signal is inadequate relative to the noise, but rather that the monitor and observer do not have the sensitivity to adequately detect the signal. By increasing the gain, both the signal and the noise are amplified the same amount, leaving the SNR unchanged. However, the signal now appears stronger giving the user the appearance of improved SNR, hence the term "apparent SNR". In other words, if the gain is too low the signal might appear weak, even if there is good signal-to-noise.

Referring to *Figure 2*, note that both examples have identical signal-to-noise ratios. However, in case A, since the signal amplitude is close to the visibility threshold of the human eye, the signal is barely perceptible. In comparison, by amplifying the signal, the peak signal is now close to the upper limit of the visibility range and appears bright white.

Pegasus Lectures, Inc.

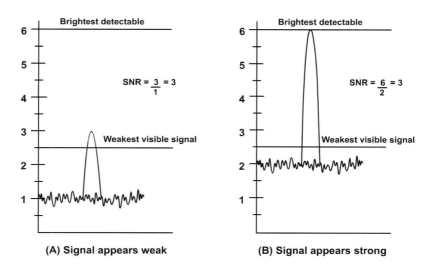

Fig. 2   **Graphical Representation of Apparent SNR**

2.3.4 Relating SNR, Noise Floor, and Apparent SNR Ultrasound Images

The images in *Figure 3* through *Figure 5* are of a transverse carotid artery with various signal-to-noise ratios and varying apparent signal-to-noise ratios. Comparisons between images are very important to grasping the concept of signal-to-noise and how to recognize adequate signal.

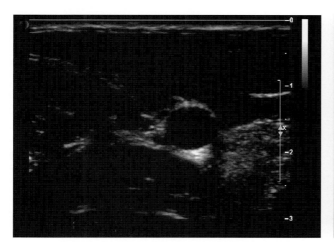

Fig. 3a   **Signal Appears Weak**

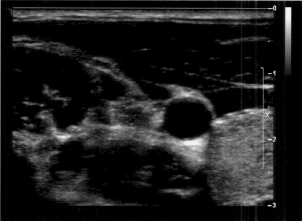

Fig. 3b   **Signal Appears Strong**

Figure 3a was created using the same transmit power as *Figure 3b* but with a lower receive gain. Therefore, *Figures 3a* and *3b* have the same signal-to-noise ratio (SNR). However, the image of *Figure 3a* has a much lower apparent SNR than *Figure 3b*. Since *Figure 3a* has a lower overall receiver gain, many of the signal intensities are mapped to values below the visual threshold. This image is analogous to the graphical representation of *Figure 2a*. In comparison, *Figure 3b* has a high enough gain so that most signals fall within the visual dynamic range. In other words, the same information is actually contained in both images, but that information is only apparent in *Figure 3b* and not *Figure 3a*. *Figure 3b* is analogous to the graphical representation of *Figure 2b*.

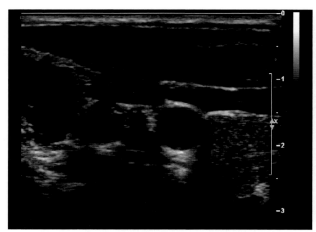

Fig. 4a   **Poor SNR (Weak Signal)**

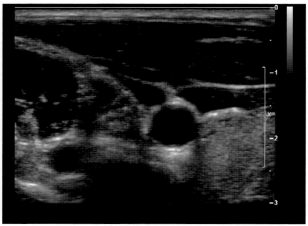

Fig. 4b   **Good SNR**

In contrast to *Figures 3a* and *3b*, *Figure 4a* was created using a much lower transmit than *Figure 4b*. As a result, only the strongest signal components of *Figure 4a* are visible in the image. Since the image was created with relatively low receiver gain, the noise floor is below the visual range so no noise is apparent in the image. Yet, the signal-to-noise ratio is clearly poor.

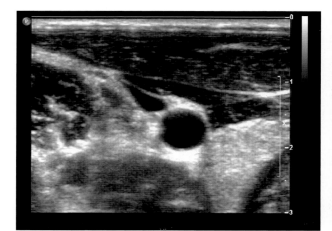

Fig. 5a   **Transmit Too High but Good SNR**

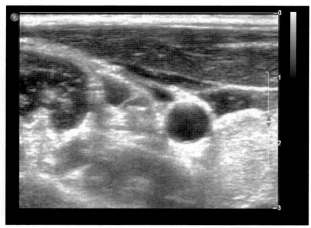

Fig. 5b   **Receive Gain Too High, SNR Good but Apparent SNR Worse**

Figure 5a has a much higher transmit power and a much lower receive gain than *Figure 5b*. As a result, *Figure 5a* has a better SNR than *Figure 5b*. Notice how the lumen of the carotid is somewhat obscured in *Figure 5b*, whereas the lumen is virtually noise free in *Figure 5a*. Throughout the entire image of *Figure 5b*, the high amplitude receive gain has mapped the noise floor into the visual range so that some of the noise obscures some signal components. In marked contrast, the lower gain of *Figure 5a* has resulted in the noise floor remaining below the visual threshold such that no noise is apparent in the image. For *Figure 5b*, since the SNR is good, reducing the receiver gain would improve the apparent SNR by forcing some of the noise below the visual threshold. Because the SNR is good, not much gain is necessary to drive the signal into the visual range. However, as the signal becomes weaker and weaker as occurs with deeper imaging, more receiver gain is necessary to drive the signal into the visual range. As depicted in *Figure 1b*, weaker signals with more receive gain results in the noise becoming apparent within the image.

2.3.5 Sources of Noise

As already stated, noise is any undesired signal. There are many sources of noise. Let us consider a few:

Electronic noise: Nothing in this world comes for free. The electronics used to amplify the tiny returning echoes add random signals (or thermal electronic noise). This added energy is created by random excitations of electrons within the electronics. The amplitude of these signals is very small; however, when you use a high receiver gain you will see this noise as random white speckle on the image or in your Doppler spectrum. In color, electronic noise shows up as random color pixels.

Clutter: Large returning echoes from structures that obliterate weaker signals. Examples include large specular reflections in imaging, valves in Doppler, etc.

Haze: There are many types of haze. Sometimes haze is created by returning echoes from sidelobes (discussed in Chapter 8). Haze may be created by poor transducer to skin contact or by beam aberration (distortion) from tissue characteristics. All cardiovascular sonographers have seen the haze associated with imaging through the lung.

Electrical interference: It is possible for transducers or ultrasound machines to receive energy emanating from other electrical devices or electromagnetic waves such as radio transmissions. This energy may be carried through the air or potentially down the power line to the system. This energy often shows up as a bright "flashlight" down the middle of an image, a "barber pole-like" flashing, or as bright white horizontal or zigzagging lines in spectral Doppler referred to as "Doppler tones".

2.3.6 Clutter One Moment May Be Signal the Next

Although clutter signals are often classified as noise, these signals are characteristically different than electronic noise, haze, and electrical interference. The fundamental difference is that "clutter" signals are related to anatomical structures and true reflections whereas the other forms are produced by sources outside the body or as an artifact. Therefore noise to one person may be signal to someone else. For example, the blood echoes during spectral Doppler are often obscured by the "clutter" signals which result from the surrounding tissue and wall motion. However, when performing tissue Doppler, the very clutter signals that were filtered out as noise are now the desired signal. This is somewhat reminiscent of the age old battle between parents and their children relative to their taste in music. Noise to one is pure harmony to the other.

2.4 Preprocessing and Post Processing

2.4.1 Conventional Definitions

The term processing refers to any conditioning of a signal in an attempt to interpret or improve the display of that signal. The terms preprocessing and post processing are specifically defined below.

Preprocessing: Signal conditioning that occurs in real time and cannot be removed from an image once acquired. Some examples are receiver gain, receive focusing, and receiver compression. All receiver functions (to be discussed later in this chapter) are preprocessing.

Post Processing: Any processing which can be changed after the data is acquired such as data compression, colorization and reject. Post processing generally is performed in the scan converter (also to be discussed later in this chapter). Post processing can be performed on frozen data as well as live imaging.

2.4.2 Changes in the Preprocessing and Post Processing Paradigm

In the last few years, designs of ultrasound systems have changed so that many functions which were once post processing techniques are now preprocessing techniques. As an example, some systems now allow for the user to go back and adjust the time gain compensation (TGC function and control will be discussed in Section 5.2.1) after the data has been frozen.

3. Basic Functions of a System (Simplified)

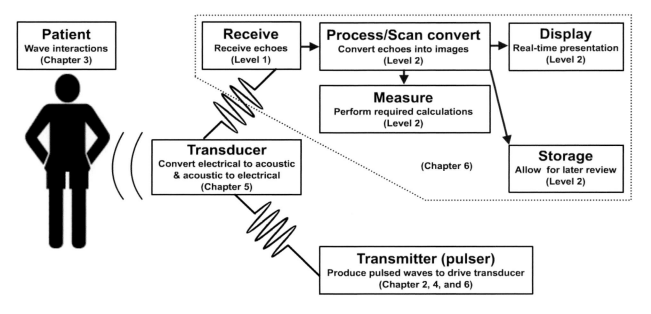

Fig. 6 **Basic Functional Block Diagram**

3.1 Putting the Pieces Together

An ultrasound system begins by creating a transmit waveform. The waveform is determined by the knobs, transducer selection, and presets that you, the user, select. The pulser then interprets all of the settings to determine the initial amplitude, frequency, and mode (2-D, CW Doppler, PW Doppler, etc.) of the excitation voltage. For phased array systems, the pulser must also account for the time or phase delays necessary to steer and focus each line. To create a 2-D image, multiple lines must be steered across physical space, potentially requiring sequencing of the transducer as well as changes in the time or phase delays.

As discussed in Chapter 5, when the transducer is driven with an electropotential waveform (voltage), the energy is converted by the piezoelectric effect into an acoustic wave. This acoustic wave is coupled into the body and is reflected, refracted, and absorbed as it travels through the body. Some of the acoustic energy is reflected back to and received by the transducer. The transducer converts this energy into an electropotential signal (voltage) which is then sent to the system receiver.

The system receiver processes the small electrical signals, detecting changes that result from interactions within the patient and conditioning the signals for conversion, measurement, and display. The conditioned and detected signals are then passed to a processing engine (usually referred to as a scan converter). The job of the scan converter is to take the streaming data and convert it into a format that can be measured, stored, and displayed. Besides the basic function of scan conversion, at this stage, there are usually many user controllable options, allowing the user to dictate how the conversion and formatting are to take place.

Once the data has been converted into a scan, the user is allowed to measure the data in various ways such as distance measurements, area measurements, volume measurements, rise times, etc. Although the user is viewing the image on the display at the time of making the measurement, the measurement is actually occurring on the data stored within the scan converter. (This is why the "measurement" function box is pictured before the "display" function in the diagram of *Figure 6*.) Both the image and the measurements are then displayed for real-time viewing, while simultaneously being sent for storage if desired.

We will now cover the functional blocks of the transmitter and receiver in more depth. Since the processing functions are more specifically related to clinical applications, the functional blocks, starting with processing, will be covered in Level 2. In Level 2, we will also further develop some specific receiver functions in terms of clinical applications.

4. Transmitter (Pulser – Transmit Beamformer)

4.1 Function

The transmitter is capable of producing a virtually infinite number of electrical waveforms to drive the various transducers used in ultrasound. Clearly, the transmitter must be able to produce continuous voltage electrical signals as well as pulsed signals. When the signals are pulsed, the transmitter must be capable of producing different operating frequencies (f_o), shorter and longer pulses (PD), and more frequent and less frequent pulses (PRF). In addition, the transmitter must be able to change the amplitude of the voltage, resulting in a change in acoustic power into the patient. When driving a phased array, the transmitter must create many excitation pulses simultaneously. In order to focus or steer, the transmitter must produce these simultaneous excitation pulses with small time delays between each pulse (phase delays are discussed in Chapter 5, Level 2). As we have already learned in the pulsed wave chapter, the timing for the transmitter is determined primarily by the depth. The phasing is determined by the desired focus and by the type of scan required. The amplitude of the transmitted signal is controlled directly by the user through the transmit power knob.

4.2 The System Control for Transmit Power
As already mentioned, there are many variations on the name used for the control of the transmit power from the transmitter. Regardless of the name, the function is the same. Increasing the output power control increases the amplitude of the voltage which drives the transducer. If the transducer is driven with a higher voltage, a higher amplitude pressure is produced. A higher pressure implies a higher acoustic power in the patient and hence, a higher intensity.

To add to the confusion is the fact that some dedicated systems do not have a user control for power. For these systems, by setting the imaging preset, the power level is determined by the system and is not changeable by the user.

4.3 Practical Concerns
There are at least two very important reasons why you should concern yourself with the role of the transmitter. First, the risk of bioeffects is most directly related to the acoustic power produced. Since the acoustic power is controlled by the transmitter, the risk of bioeffects is linked to the transmit power control. The second reason is that the signal strength is also directly related to the acoustic power. A higher acoustic output results in a stronger signal. Therefore, when imaging to greater imaging depths, turning up the acoustic power usually results in greater penetration.

5. Receiver

All receivers perform the following five operations:

1. Amplification
2. Compensation
3. Compression
4. Demodulation
5. Rejection

Of the five functions described, really only four are designed into the system. The "operation" of rejection is really a misnomer for an undesirable fact of electronics we are forced to live with. We will include rejection as a fifth operation for consistency with other books. Furthermore, we will need to address another major function of all receivers which is often neglected in most other textbooks, the process of analog to digital conversion within the receiver.

5.1 Amplification (Receiver Gain)

5.1.1 Need for Amplification
Amplification means to make bigger or to multiply. Amplification is necessary because the returning signals from the body are too small to be adequately processed within the electronics or visualized on a monitor. Amplification is partly under user control and partly under system control. Because the signals are so small, an enormous amount of amplification is necessary. Since a certain amount of gain is always necessary no matter what the imaging situation, there is a certain amount of gain which is automatically applied by the system. Since there is no way of

knowing a priori how large the signal will be returning from the patient, the user is allowed to add further amplification by changing the receiver gain knob.

5.1.2 Amplification of the RF Signal

The following diagrams demonstrate the application of gain (amplification). The first diagram *(Figure 7)* shows a low level radio frequency (RF) signal. (The signal is called an RF signal since the operating frequency is in the MHz, which is in the range of frequencies used for radios.)

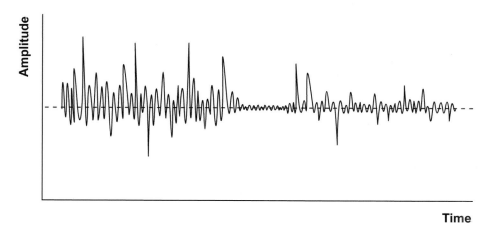

Fig. 7   **Raw RF Signal**

Figure 8 shows the same RF signal amplified. Notice how all of the characteristics of the amplified signal are the same as the un-amplified signal except for the amplitude. Amplification should preserve all other characteristics of a signal. If a signal is overamplified, distortion will occur. In terms of an ultrasound image, distortion appears as signal where no signal should be present. This distortion is usually relatively evident since overgained signals look excessively bright.

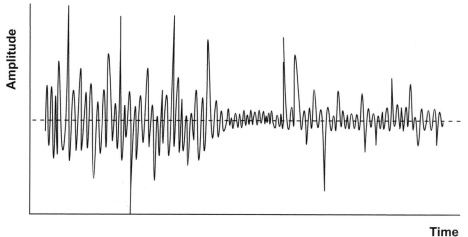

Fig. 8   **Amplified Raw RF Signal**

Chapter 6

5.1.3 The System Control

There are only a few variations on the name for the amplification control on most systems. The common names are gain, receiver gain, and amplification. Increasing the receiver gain increases the amount of amplification of the received signal and does not affect the acoustic intensity in the patient. A helpful analogy is the operation of a radio. The transmit is analogous to the radio station using a larger and more powerful antenna to broadcast and the receiver gain is like the volume knob on the radio. Imagine if the radio station increased the transmitted radio signal in the middle of a song. The larger transmitted signal would mean a larger received signal. A larger signal implies that the volume would get louder, even without you increasing the radio volume. In fact, if the transmitted signal increases too much, you may find yourself having to decrease the volume (as commonly occurs when watching TV and a commercial is aired). In contrast, turning up the receiver gain is like increasing the volume on the radio. The transmit signal is unaffected, just the amplitude of the already received signal is increased.

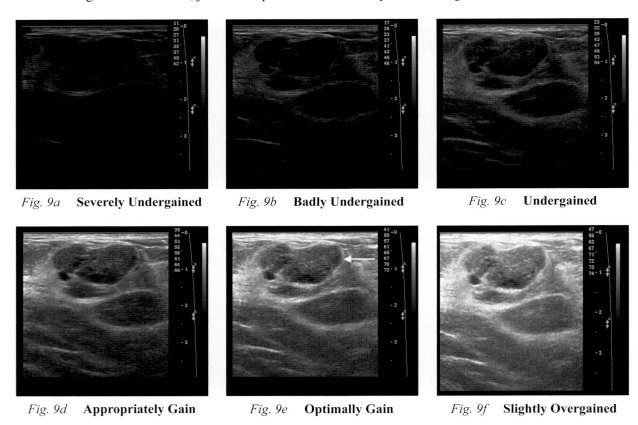

| Fig. 9a | **Severely Undergained** | Fig. 9b | **Badly Undergained** | Fig. 9c | **Undergained** |

| Fig. 9d | **Appropriately Gain** | Fig. 9e | **Optimally Gain** | Fig. 9f | **Slightly Overgained** |

View Animation and Image Library CD

The images of *Figure 9* are of a fibroadenoma of a breast (indicated by the arrow in *Figure 9e*). Each frame represents an increase in amplitude by a factor of 2 (+6 dB) from the previous frame such that the amplitude *Figure 9f* is 32 times greater (+30 dB) than the image of *Figure 9a*. Notice that in the earlier frames, the signal amplitude is so low that only the very near-field and strongest specular reflectors are visualized. As the amplitude is increased, more of the stronger breast tissue echoes are visualized. In *Figure 9d*, the receiver gain is now high enough so that the weaker signals from the mass are becoming visible. The gain of *Figure 9e* is now appropriate so that the signals from the breast tissue and the mass are visible simultaneously. The image of *Figure 9f* is overgained as evidenced by the extremely bright nearfield resulting in a loss of ability to distinguish the boundaries of the mass from the superficial breast tissue.

5.2 Compensation (Time Gain Compensation)

5.2.1 The Role of TGC

The term compensation is very descriptive. Compensation refers to the application of extra amplification (gain) to compensate for increasing attenuation with depth. Since attenuation increases with depth, compensation increases the gain with increasing depth to normalize the amplitude of the returning echoes.

On most ultrasound systems, the controls which compensate for increasing attenuation with depth are called the TGC (time gain compensation). In past days there were systems which referred to these controls as DGC (depth gain compensation) or SGC (swept gain compensation). In recent years, the term TGC has become the default name.

5.2.2 Compensation of the RF Signal

Figure 10 demonstrates the application of TGC to compensate for increasing attenuation with increasing depth. Notice that the signals from later in time (right side of the graph) are now about the same amplitude as the signals from earlier in time (left side of the graph). To fully appreciate the compensation, you should compare this graph with the uncompensated graph of *Figure 8*.

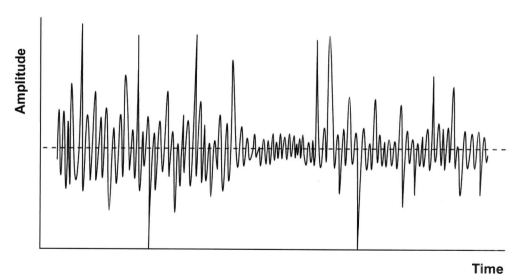

Fig. 10   **Compensated RF Signal**

5.2.3 The Relationship Between TGCs and Receiver Gain

Note that compensation is really the same as amplification, except broken into individual bands or zones over depth. Turning up the receiver gain is equivalent to sliding all of the TGC sliders (also referred to as "pots", (short for potentiometers) up at the same time. The following *Figures 11* and *12* illustrate this concept.

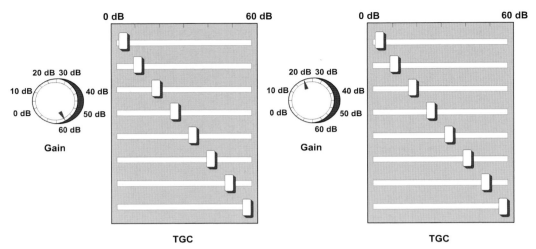

Fig. 11   **Maximum Total Gain = 120 dB**   Fig. 12   **Maximum Total Gain = 80 dB**

In *Figure 11*, the total gain for the top of the image is 60 dB from the overall gain plus 5 dB from the top TGC slider. For the bottom of the image the total gain is 60 dB from the overall gain plus 60 dB from the bottom TGC slider. For each of the depths represented by the sliders between the top and bottom, the overall gain is between the 65 dB of the top and the 120 dB of the bottom. In comparison, for *Figure 12*, the TGC profile is the same, but the overall gain is set to 20 dB. Therefore the top of the image has an overall gain of 25 dB and the bottom of the image has an overall gain of 20 dB plus 60 dB, or 80 dB.

5.2.4 Depth and TGC Zones

Most systems have 8 to 10 TGC slider controls. The imaging depth is broken into uniform depth zones, such that each slider represents a specific zone. For example, if the depth is set to 8 cm and there are 8 sliders, then each TGC represents 1 cm of depth on the image. Similarly, if the depth is set to 6 cm, then each slider

$$\text{represents} \quad \frac{6 \text{ cm}}{8 \text{ sliders}} = \frac{3}{4} \text{ cm} = 0.75 \text{ cm.}$$

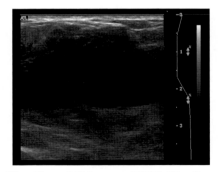
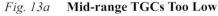
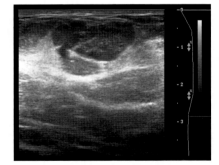

Fig. 13a   **Mid-range TGCs Too Low**   Fig. 13b   **Mid-range TGCs Too High**

These two images of *Figure 13a and 13b* of the same fibroadenoma as displayed in *Figure 9a* through *Figure 9f* demonstrate the effect of inappropriate TGC positioning. In *Figure 13a* the center TGC sliders are set too low resulting in under gaining in the depth range from slightly shallower than 1 cm to about 2.5 cm. In contrast, *Figure 13b* demonstrates the effects of over gaining the mid-region.

In Level 2, we will relate TGC profiles to clinical situations.

5.3 Compression

5.3.1 Dynamic Range

To understand the concept of compression, we must first discuss the concept of dynamic range. Dynamic range refers to the ratio of the maximum to the minimum of any quantity. Dynamic range can be used to specify the ratio of the largest to the smallest echoes from a patient, the largest to smallest signal an A/D converter can process, the largest to smallest brightness levels of a monitor, the largest to smallest signal the human eye can detect, the largest to smallest signal the human ear can hear, or even the ratio of the maximum to minimum amount in your bank account. Since dynamic range represents a ratio of two numbers, a large signal does not necessarily represent a very large dynamic range. For example, if the maximum signal is 10 Volts and the minimum signal is 2 Volts, the dynamic range is only 5 to 1. In comparison, if the maximum signal is only 1 Volt, but the minimum signal is 1 mV, then the dynamic range is 1,000 to 1.

Every one of our senses has a maximum dynamic range. For example, at the lower end of the spectrum, you may have the tactile ability to feel the weight of a grain of sand but not an individual molecule. On the upper end, it is unlikely that you are able to distinguish the difference between piles of sand dumped on you weighing 10,000 pounds versus 20,000 pounds.

The signal dynamic range (ratio of maximum to minimum echo amplitudes returning from the patient) is generally much larger than the display dynamic range (the range of signals a monitor can display). In fact, the display dynamic range generally well exceeds the visual dynamic range (the range of signals visible to the human eye at one instant in time). Therefore, although there is a big problem with the signal occupying a much larger range than what can be displayed on the monitor, there is an even bigger problem in that the monitor can display a larger dynamic range than what the eye can see.

5.3.2 Compression and Dynamic Range

Compression is the general term for any technique which maps a larger dynamic range into a smaller dynamic range. Because of the great disparity between the dynamic range of the eye and the reflected signals, compression must be performed to map the enormous signal dynamic range into the significantly smaller dynamic range of the human eye.

Figure 14 demonstrates a simple compression scheme where a range of 10:1 is mapped to a smaller range of 2:1.

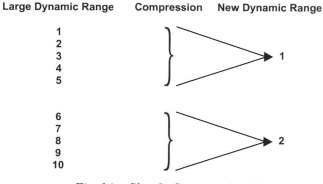

| Large Dynamic Range | Compression | New Dynamic Range |

Fig. 14   **Simple Compression Map**

Chapter 6

5.3.3 Effects of Compression and Information Loss

Notice that the process of compression depicted in *Figure 14* distorts the data such that some information is lost. In the uncompressed range, there is an obvious difference between the number 6 and the number 10. However, after applying the above compression scheme, both values would be mapped to the same value of 2. Of course there are an infinite number of compression schemes and techniques possible. Different compression schemes will have different levels of loss. The term compression is also used to refer to digital data storage such as in PACS. You will sometimes hear of lossless compression schemes for data storage. Whereas it may be possible to create lossless compression schemes for data storage, in general it is not possible to create a lossless compression scheme for compressing signal levels into brightness levels visible by the human eye.

For brightness mapping, the only time a lossless scheme would be possible is in the rare case when a signal has so few levels so as to require less dynamic range than the capability of the human eye. Therefore, compression is effectively always needed, and is an integral part of making ultrasound images that are interpretable by humans. The fact that information can be "compressed" is very important because it warns us that there is a limitation with ultrasound (and most imaging techniques). It is certainly possible that an important signal could be "compressed" out of visibility relative to the surrounding tissue or medium.

In Level 2, we will demonstrate some specific approaches to compression and further discuss the ramifications on clinical practice and practical application.

5.3.4 Compression of the RF Signal

To comprehend the effect of compression, the diagram of *Figure 15* must be compared with the uncompressed data of *Figure 8*. Notice that for *Figure 15* the lowest amplitude signals (in the middle of the graph) were little changed but that amplitude of the larger signals were reduced. As a result, the ratio of the biggest signal to the smallest signal has been reduced. For this example the compression ratio is only about a factor of two. You should also notice that another approach to compression would be to amplify the smaller signals more and the larger signals less, since this would also reduce the ratio of the largest to the smallest signal.

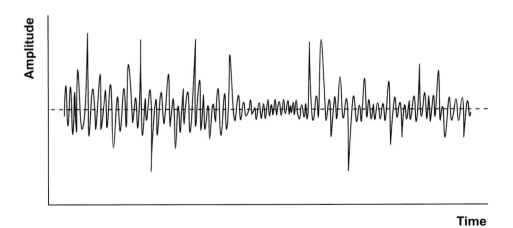

Fig. 15   **Log Compressed RF Signal**

Compression is a critical function for diagnostic ultrasound. It is important to understand that there are many different functional areas of the system which perform a degree of "compression." The receiver function of compression is not under the control of the user but is specified by the manufacturing design team. This preprocessing function should not be confused with the compression function which occurs later in the signal processing path and is controllable by the user. This later compression could be called "video compression," since it compresses the appearance of the displayed grayscale. In Level 2 of this chapter, we will further discuss the role of compression and the possible implications for diagnostic accuracy.

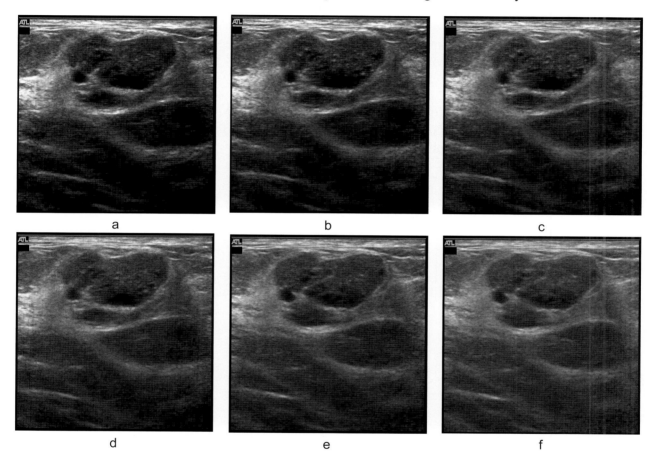

a   b   c

d   e   f

Fig. 16   **Various Compression Maps**

The vignette of *Figure 16* displays the same fibradenoma with six different compression settings. Notice that the compression in *Figure 16a* shows the most contrast, mapping the lower level signals to darker shades of grey and black. Each successive map displays less contrast by mapping the lower level signals to lighter shades of gray. In *Figure 16f*, notice that the image is considerably "softer" than *Figure 16a*, displaying the low level echoes within the mass as well as the bright white echoes from the breast ligaments and subcutaneous skin.

View Animation and Image Library CD

5.4 Demodulation

5.4.1 Modulation and Demodulation

The word "modulate" means to change or modify. Recall that sound is a mechanical wave, implying a physical interaction with the medium. As the wave propagates through the medium, the interaction causes changes (modulations) in the wave. Therefore, demodulation is the process by which the modulations of the wave are removed or detected. Hence, demodulation is often called "signal detection." For ultrasound signals, demodulation consists of two stages: rectification and "smoothing" or envelope detection. As a result, the process of demodulation is also commonly referred to as envelope detection. Rectification and smoothing effectively remove the transmit signal from the return echo, leaving just the modulation caused by the interaction with the tissue as shown in *Figure 17*.

5.4.2 Rectification

Rectification converts the negative components of a signal into positive components (changes a signal from being bipolar to unipolar). Notice how all of the signals that were below the zero baseline have been flipped to now be above the baseline.

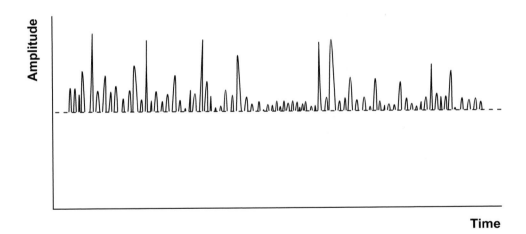

Fig. 17 **Rectification of RF Signal**

5.4.3 Envelope Detection (Smoothing)

Once rectification has occurred, the process of envelope detection basically traces the signal peaks and valleys while simultaneously applying some averaging or smoothing. The following figure illustrates the process of envelope detection.

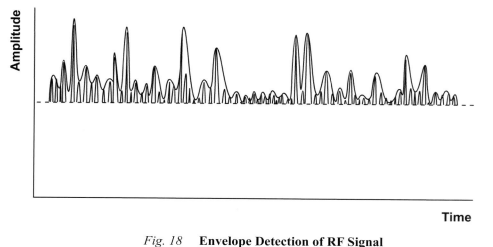

Fig. 18 **Envelope Detection of RF Signal**

5.4.4 The Detected Signal and A-mode

Figure 19 demonstrates the resultant "detected" or "demodulated" signal. The demodulated signal is the same as the early modality of A-mode. In *Figure 19*, the area of low amplitude represents low reflectivity. As was learned in Chapter 3, low reflectivity results from a low acoustic impedance mismatch, or equivalently, a relatively "homogenous" medium. The most likely medium which would produce such a low signal return is a fluid. In the figure below, this region could pertain to a fluid filled cyst, or potentially a blood pool.

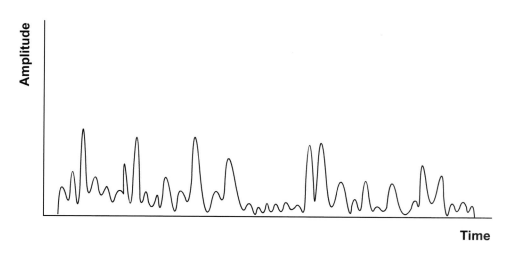

Fig. 19 **Demodulated Signal (A-mode)**

5.5 Reject

Nothing in life is perfect. Unwanted noise can be added to the signal through the body, transducer, cable, and system electronics. Generally these noise signals are smaller than the desired signals and can be suppressed. Rejection effectively sets a threshold below which signals will not be visible on display.

Figure 20 demonstrates how a reject function would work, if one actually existed in the receiver.

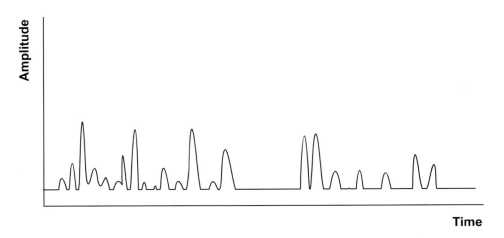

Fig. 20   **Demodulated Signal After Rejection**

In reality, this reject threshold is not actually actively set in the receiver but rather is just the limit of the sensitivity of the system. Engineers who design receivers do not actively set a reject level to limit low level signals. Instead, a level is reached below which the signals are not detected. This level is referred to by design engineers as the noise floor. Designers go through extraordinary efforts to push the noise floor of the electronics as low as possible while still preserving the required signal input dynamic range and amplification. The reason it is desireable to have the noise floor as low as possible is greater system sensitivity. The lower the noise floor, the smaller the signals that can be detected.

6. A-mode (Amplitude mode)

6.1 A-mode Display

In the early days of ultrasound, signal detection was essentially where the processing stopped. The demodulated signal was presented on a screen as a waveform with amplitude on the vertical axis and time (or depth as related through the distance equation) on the horizontal axis. This modality was called amplitude mode (a-mode), for the obvious reason that signal amplitude was displayed. In terms of the signal in A-mode, when there is a large acoustic impedance mismatch, there is a large reflection, and hence, there is a high amplitude signal. When there is a small mismatch, the reflected signal is smaller, and a lower amplitude signal is detected. Therefore, the vertical axis of the data can be referred to using many related terms such as the acoustic impedance mismatch, the signal reflectivity, the amplitude, or the signal strength.

Pegasus Lectures, Inc.

6.2 Interpreting an A-mode
The following figure demonstrates a real A-mode taken from a radial artery for a research project.

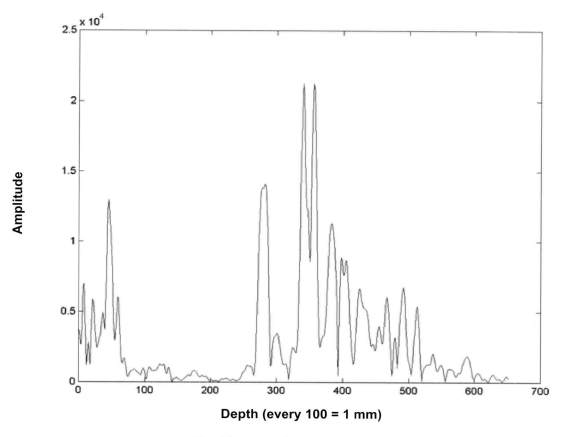

Fig. 21   **A-mode of a Radial Artery**

In the A-mode example above, note the lower amplitude reflections in the range from about 80 to about 275. This lower amplitude reflection corresponds to a relatively "homogenous" medium, in this case the blood pool within the artery. Notice the exceptionally high amplitude signals just before and after this region. These high amplitude signals represent the large acoustic impedance mismatches associated with the anterior and posterior artery walls. The large echo at about 350 corresponds to the specular reflections from tendon and fascial sheathing. Many students when first viewing this A-mode mistakenly identify this strong reflection as the reflection from bone. If this reflection were from bone, we would anticipate "shadowing" resulting in virtually no signal from deeper depths. Since this shadow is not present, we can be relatively certain that the reflector is not bone. You should also notice the increasing attenuation with increasing depth (from 400 to 650). Here we can clearly see the need for compensation.

6.3 The Use of A-mode
A-mode is rarely used as a modality with the exception of a few ophthalmic applications. Although rarely used, there is a benefit to understanding A-mode. As we will learn in Level 2, modern ultrasound images are really the compilation of many A-modes presented in grayscale. Therefore, the principles which govern A-mode govern B-mode (brightness mode also referred to as 2-D imaging).

7. Exercises Answers Pg. 464

1. Increasing the _____ gain increases the SNR.

2. Increasing the _____ gain may affect the apparent SNR, but not the true SNR.

3. The five receiver functions are:

   1) _____
   2) _____
   3) _____
   4) _____
   5) _____

4. _____ is a technique to reduce the dynamic range of a signal.

5. For deeper imaging depths _____ the operating frequency will most likely increase the SNR.

6. For a system with 10 TGC sliders, if the imaging depth is set to 20 cm, each slider represents _____.

7. What would have a greater impact on the perceived brightness of an image, increasing the overall gain by 20 dB or increasing all of the TGCs by 20 dB?

8. What is the smallest signal received if the dynamic range is 10,000 to 1 and the largest signal is 10 Volts?

8. System Block Diagram

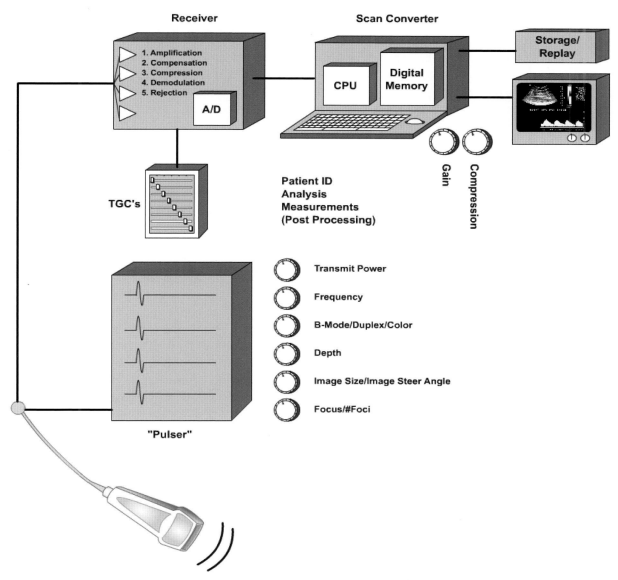

Fig. 22 **System Functional Block Diagram**

The system block diagram displays most of the major functions performed by an ultrasound system, with the exception of the phasing required for phased array operation. As described in Chapter 5, phasing is required for the transmitted and received beam. For the simplified block diagram, the "phase engine" responsible for creating the phase delay profiles operates in both the pulser and the receiver. Clearly, no attempt was made to include all of the features and all of the less fundamental processing techniques. Inclusion of every feature offered would render the block diagram complex beyond measure and virtually useless as a didactic tool. Instead, we will discuss these processing techniques one by one throughout this chapter.

Chapter 6

9. Controls that Affect Transmit and Power Distribution

9.1 Transducer Frequency and Transmit Power

Next to the pulser in the block diagram is a series of system controls. All of these controls affect the transmitted pulse and hence the power distribution in the patient, either over time, or over space. The effects of changing the transmit power are the most evident. A higher transmit power implies a higher acoustic power and hence, a higher intensity. The effects of choosing a different frequency of operation may not be quite as evident. Recall that higher frequency waves are absorbed at much greater rates than lower frequency waves. Therefore, at the very least, we would anticipate that higher frequency transducers will potentially have restrictions regarding power so as to limit thermal issues within the tissue, most specifically on the near field (shallower imaging depths).

9.2 Imaging Modalities and Image Size Transmit Power

The decision to perform a 2-D scan, versus duplex (color and 2-D) versus Doppler, or M-mode also affects power. The reason the modality affects power is related to two different aspects of the image creation: the duty factor and whether or not the modality is scanned or non-scanned. If longer pulses are desired (such as occur in color Doppler, PW Doppler, and of course, CW Doppler) the duty factor increases and the transmit power must be accordingly decreased. Since non-scanned modalities concentrate the energy in the same location from acoustic beam to acoustic beam, there is again a greater risk of thermal issues. As a result, the maximum allowed transmit power must again be decreased by the system to assure safety. Similarly, changing the image size also changes the scan region, potentially affecting the power. A smaller image size implies a more rapid scanning of the region (higher frame rate) and hence, a greater risk of thermal bioeffects. Therefore, as the scan size is decreased, the maximum transmit power may decrease. In reality, unless the image size is drastically reduced, this parameter rarely has a significant impact on the transmit power. The reason is that for a scanned modality, mechanical bioeffects are still much more likely. As you will learn in Chapter 9, the risk of mechanical bioeffects is related to the peak rarefactional pressure and not the time distribution of the signal.

9.3 Imaging Depth and Transmit Power

Changing the imaging depth changes the duty factor and hence, affects the maximum transmit power allowed. A shallower imaging depth implies a higher duty factor (a shorter line can be repeated more frequently than a longer line). A higher duty factor implies that a lower maximum transmit power is allowed.

9.4 Focus and Transmit Power

Finally, changing the focus can directly affect the acoustic power. By changing the depth of focus, the beamwidth and beam pattern can be altered significantly. Setting a shallower focus usually results in a decrease in the maximum allowed transmit power. This decrease is the consequence of having the beam come to a narrow focus at shallow depths at which not much attenuation occurs. In contrast, with a deep focus, the beam converges in the far field where the signal has already been significantly attenuated. Therefore, a deeper focus generally allows the system to increase the maximum transmit voltage without increasing risk to the patient. This fact was also discussed in Chapter 5 when reviewing the concept of focusing.

Pegasus Lectures, Inc.

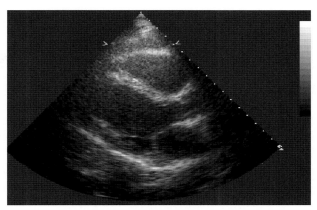

Fig. 23   **Focal Zone Positioning Too Shallow Within the Image Sector**

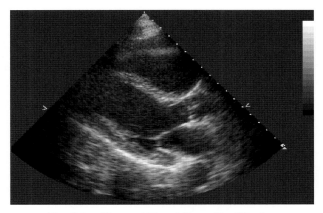

Fig. 24   **Correct Focal Zone Positioning**

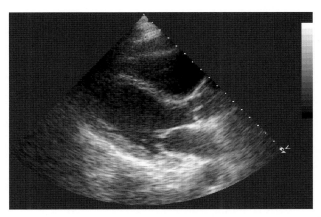

Fig. 25   **Focal Zone Positioning Too Deep Within the Image Sector**

View Animation and Image Library CD

10. TGC and Gain Revisited

10.1 Internal TGC Profiles

In Level 1, we discussed the role of amplification and the role of compensation through TGCs. Although not explicitly stated, the assumption from Level 1 is most likely that TGCs are completely under the control of the sonographer. Furthermore, from the examples given, we would presume that the dynamic range of the TGCs is generally 60 dB. This is not completely true. Because of the enormous dynamic range of signals returning from deeper depths relative to shallower depths, the amount of compensation required is generally more than 60 dB. As a result, when designing the ultrasound machine, the user is given 60 dB of TGC range and then more compensation is applied which is not under the control of the user. The amount of this internal TGC depends on the application, transducer being used, frequency, etc. It is certainly not uncommon to apply 30 dB or more of compensation before the user ever touches a TGC slider. The reason this internal TGC is applied is basically to make the TGC sliders more responsive and not overly sensitive. Imagine if a TGC slider represented 100 dB of gain instead of 60 dB as demonstrated in *Figure* 26. Even the slightest movement of the slider could result in significant changes in the brightness associated with that TGC. For the example given, in *Figure 26*, the same movement of the second slider results in 10 dB change in comparison to 17 dB change in *Figure 27*. By performing some of the required TGC before allowing user control, the user is allowed a control with less range per travel and a more easily managed control.

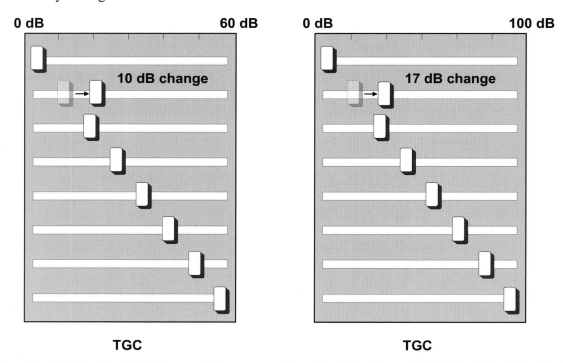

Fig. 26   **TGCs with 60 dB Dynamic Range**   Fig. 27   **More Range Would Make Too "Sensitive"**

In general, this "behind the scene" compensation does not present any significant issues since there is so much range on the TGC controls for the user to dictate. However, this fact does not always hold true for color imaging.

10.2 Internal Color TGC Profiles

In color imaging, the TGC control is entirely internal. Excluding adaptive processing which is now starting to be developed and utilized more commonly, the TGC profile for color is based on assumed attenuation. The assumed attenuation is based on the imaging depth, frequency of the transducer, and the preset which tells the system information about the region of the body being scanned. For example, the internal TGC profile for a pediatric 5 MHz cardiac transducer will most certainly be different than the internal TGC profile for a 5 MHz linear being used for vascular studies. With that said, there is absolutely no guarantee that the color TGC profile internally set is correct for all patients all of the time. Unlike 2-D, the user does not have any control which can correct for an "inappropriate" internal TGC profile. Since color data does not indicate signal strength (unlike 2-D which displays signal strength as "brightness"), when the internal TGC is incorrect for a specific patient, the problem can be masked by decreasing or increasing the overall color gain. However, there are times when the presence of color noise speckle will be apparent in only one depth region of the image while the rest of the color image is correctly gained. Conversely, one region of color may drop out when the rest of the color image appears to be correctly gained. The source of both of these problems is the internal TGC profiles. The problem is rare, but existent.

10.3 "Pre-compensated" TGC Profiles

There is also a feature on most ultrasound systems with respect to TGCs that is user selectable. This control is referred to as pre-compensated TGCs. The concept behind a pre-compensated TGC profile is that an algorithm was used to determine the best guess for the appropriate TGC profile, and the entire TGC profile is applied internally. As a result, if the TGC profile assumed is perfectly correct for the patient being imaged, the TGC profile of the sliders on the system will be perfectly flat and in the middle. If the "guessed at" profile over-compensated or under-compensated at any particular depth, then the TGC slider for that zone will be increased or decreased to "compensate" for the incorrect internal compensation. *Figure 28* demonstrates a compensated TGC profile with a patient for whom the internal profile was ideal. In comparison, *Figure 29* demonstrates a compresated TGC profile with a patient for whom the profile was a little off in zones 3,4, 7, and 8.

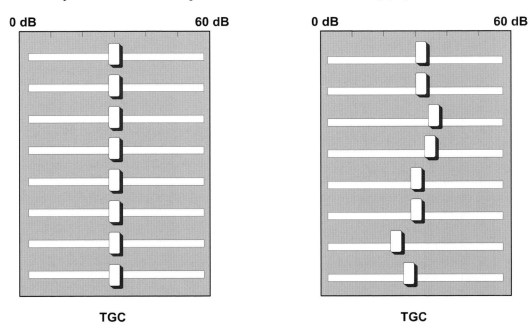

| Fig. 28 | **Starting Point Using "Pre-Compensated" TGCs** | Fig. 29 | **Adjusting "Pre-Compensated" TGCs** |

Note that unlike "uncompensated" TGC profiles, compensated TGC profiles tend to be relatively centered and may jog back and forth with depth.

10.4 TGCs and Imaging Scenarios

For completeness, we will now review TGCs for various imaging situations. For these examples we will presume conventional TGC function and not "pre-compensated" TGCs. These examples are very important for two reasons: first you should understand the operation of TGCs for proper imaging, and second because you may still be expected to know this information when taking credentialing exams.

◊ **Example:** What will the TGC profile look like if the receiver gain is set too high?

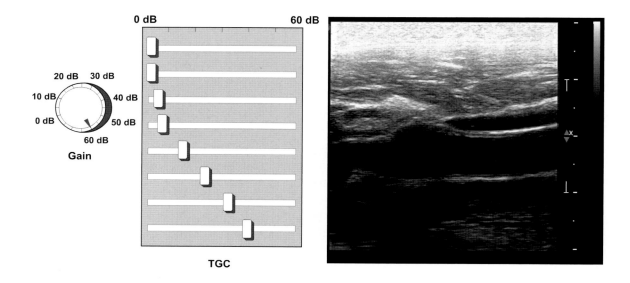

Fig. 30 **Effects of Setting Overall Gain Too High (Assuming Uncompensated TGCs)**

Notice that the near-field sliders in *Figure 30* are all set at or close to 0 dB. Remember that the amplification in each zone is the sum of the amplification from the gain knob plus the amplification from the TGC. If the receive gain is set too high, then in the near field where you need the least compensation, you would want to back down the TGC slider. The problem is that there is not enough travel on the slider and the image represented by that TGC slider will appear overgained.

View Animation and Image Library CD

◊ **Example:**   What will the TGC profile look like if the receiver gain is set too low?

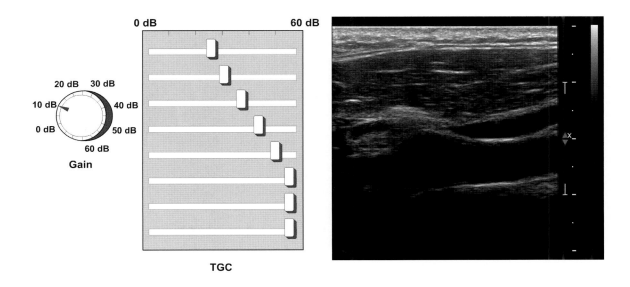

Fig. 31   **Effects of Setting Overall Gain Too Low (Assuming Uncompensated TGCs)**

In reality this question is simply the reciprocal question of the previous example. In *Figure 31*, all of the far field sliders are set to the maximum of 60 dB in an attempt to compensate for the under-amplification by the receiver gain knob. Since the TGC profile flattened out in the far field, there is still not enough gain for the region represented by the deeper sliders. The result is that the far field will be darker than appropriate.

View Animation and Image Library CD

Appropriate Use of Receiver Gain with TGCs

You should think of the overall gain control as the course adjustment and the TGCs as the fine adjustment for compensation. By starting with the TGC profile in an increasing arc from top to bottom, you can then position the overall gain so that the overall image appears close to the right amplification. Then you should go back and "tweak" the TGCs so as to optimize the gain for each depth. When the overall gain is set correctly, you should have adequate range at both the top and the bottom of the TGC sliders so that neither one is "pegged". As long as neither extreme of the TGC slider zones is pegged, using a little more receiver gain and backing down all of the TGC sliders a little, or vice versa really has no effect on the image.

Chapter 6

◊ **Example:** Which of the following two TGC profiles would represent the appropriate profile for a higher frequency transducer? (Assume you are imaging the same patient.)

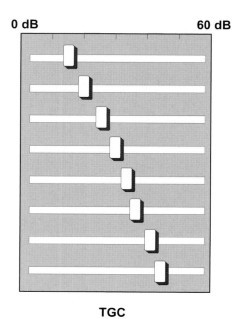

0 dB   **60 dB**

TGC

Fig. 32   **TGC Profile for Lower Frequency Transducer (same depth and patient)**

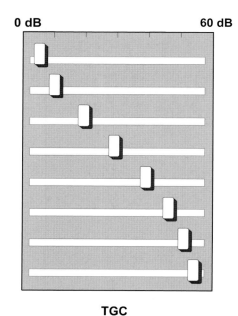

0 dB   **60 dB**

TGC

Fig. 33   **TGC Profile for Higher Frequency Transducer (same depth and patient)**

Since higher frequencies attenuate much faster than lower frequencies, for the same imaging depth, more compensation is needed. Therefore, since profile B represents a steeper sloped profile, profile B would be appropriate for the higher frequency transducer.

Note: The only way to fairly ask this question is to include the parenthetical expression "imaging the same patient" in the question. Without this phrase, the question is unanswerable because in general higher frequency transducers are used for imaging shallower imaging depths than lower frequency transducers. Therefore, a high frequency transducer TGC profile will look very similar in slope to a low frequency transducer TGC profile when operating in typical imaging situations. However, in this example, you are expected to presume that the different frequency transducers are being used on the same patient to the same imaging depth.

11. Analog to Digital Conversion

11.1 Front End and Back End of an Ultrasound System

In my experience designing ultrasound systems, terms like the "receiver" and the "scan converter" were not used as references to the major divisions of the system. Instead, seemingly more general, but also more descriptive, terms such as the "front end" and the "back end" were used. A receiver is a specific function of electronics and is not representative of all the processes which occur in the front end. Similarly, the scan converter is a specific function of the back end of the system and ignores all of the other functions required to compliment the front end functions.

The front end is the collection of electronics and functions where all of the processing takes place before the signal is sent "over the wall" to the back end for conversion into an interpretable, measurable, and storable scan.

Because the front end of the system was actually in a separate partition of the electronic box than the back end, and since the two partitions were divided by a divider wall, the expression "over the wall," was more than a figurative term. The output of the front end was actually passed from one "box" to the next "box" via digital cables and cable connectors over the box septum, or wall. As mentioned, the "receivers" are a subsystem of the front end of the system. In addition to receiving and basic signal conditioning, the front end is responsible for the beamforming (phase delaying and summation of all channels) and the conversion of the returned echoes from analog to digital format.

11.2 Role of the Beamformer

The beamformer performs two very important functions. It creates the appropriate phase delays and pulse sequencing to create the transmit beams, and it creates the appropriate phase delays and pulse sequencing to create the receive beams. In receiving, the beamformer takes the signals which return from each element of the transducer and applies the appropriate time delays, phasing, and apodization for focusing and steering before summing together all of the signals.

The term apodization refers to the limiting or restricting of which elements are active. The "active elements" are simply the elements being used at the moment. The active elements considered as a collection are often called the aperture. The aperture refers to the window through which the transducer is looking, just as the term is used for cameras.

Each active element is connected to an amplifier and processing chain. The combination of the amplifier and related processing chain is referred to as a receive channel. Most high-end systems today have 256 or 512 active receive channels. Portable systems generally have fewer channels due to space and power concerns. The benefit of more system channels is basically greater processing flexibility. Given enough channels, it is possible to treat a single system as if it were two systems imaging the same patient at the same time. Of course, the benefits of more system channels can only be realized when transducers exist with as many elements as channels. In other words, 256 channels is of little benefit when using a 32-element transducer.

11.3 Analog Received Signal and Digital Output to Back End

The signals transmitted into the body and the returning echoes from the body are analog signals (please review Chapter 1 if this term is foreign to you). Since the echoes are analog, all ultrasound signals must be received as analog signals. In all ultrasound systems designed in the last 20 years or so, these received analog signals are converted into digital signals. The process by which a signal is converted from analog to digital is not surprisingly referred to as A/D conversion (read A-to-D conversion), and was discussed in Chapter 1. Although seemingly contradictory, an "analog" system converts the signals from analog to digital format just as a digital system converts from analog to digital format. Since both analog and digital systems convert from analog to digital, it is often confusing why a distinction is made. A very simplified approach to understanding the naming distinction is that digital systems convert the signal much earlier in the receiver processing than analog systems. The distinctions between an analog and a digital system are explained in Level 3 of this chapter.

Since all ultrasound systems convert from analog to digital format, the data output from the front end of every system is in a digital format. Therefore, the processing that takes place in the back end of the ultrasound system is performed on digital data.

11.4 The Motivation for Converting from Analog to Digital
The motivation for converting the signals from analog to digital is that digital formats make the functions of grayscaling, memory storage, and post processing significantly easier and cheaper. Once a signal is converted into digital format, the signal exists in a numeric representation instead of continuous voltage levels. As an analog voltage, every processing step requires a dedicated circuit. In contrast, since digital signals are numeric, the same math engine can be used to perform multiple calculations. For ultrasound some of the desired calculations are related to grayscale mapping and compression, tissue colorization, automatic boundary detection, and spatial and time based measurements.

Because math processing functions can be used on signals no matter what the source of the signal, the same electronic math engine can be used in an ultrasound machine as in a computer, a navigation system, or an MP3 player. For many people, the term math engine is pretty foreign, but terms like CPU (Central Processing Unit) and the company specific name of an Intel Pentium are instantly recognizable. Of course, there are some math engines that are more powerful than others, offering greater processing potential, faster processing, parallel processing of data, and a greater feature set (more mathematical functions). In the world of electronics there are as many choices for processors and dedicated math processors as there are types of vehicles. As designers, the engine we choose is based on the complexity of the system, the desired functionality, and the cost allocated for more computational horsepower.

12. Scan Conversion

12.1 Paradigm Shift: From A-mode to B-mode
At the conclusion of Level 1, we discussed A-mode presentation. Relative to today's standards, A-mode seems like a primitive and crude diagnostic tool. However, this comparison isn't completely fair. The more appropriate comparison is A-mode relative to the non-invasive alternatives of the time of which there really were none other than extrasensory perception or guessing, neither of which are very reliable. Therefore, even as a one-dimensional technique, A-mode represented a giant step forward in medicine. However, it obviously did not take long for the medical field to want a two-dimensional technique. Creating a two-dimensional image presented many new challenges. In the transducer section we already discussed how 2-D scans could be created manually first, then mechanically, and finally electronically. However, even after making the changes required to the transmit signals, transducers, and the receiving electronics, there was still a major impediment; how to display two-dimensional data.

Pegasus Lectures, Inc.

For each acoustic line transmitted into the patient, the output from the system front end is a digital representation of an A-mode line. In scanned modalities, each successive acoustic line results in another A-mode line from a different region of the body. Imagine if a scan consisted of 250 lines. Can you imagine if you had to review 250 A-mode lines of data virtually simultaneously, especially when all 250 A-modes would be changing in time (from frame to frame)? Clearly what was needed was a paradigm shift. A new method of displaying data was required so that the spatial content of the data could be interpreted as well as the amplitude content of the data. This paradigm shift was the inception of B-mode (brightness mode often referred to as 2-D imaging).

12.2 Creating a B-mode From an A-mode

The conversion of A-mode to B-mode required an entirely new approach. In A-mode, the amplitude was presented simply as the height of the waveform on a graph. In brightness mode, each amplitude is mapped to a grayscale level or brightness. For conventional imaging maps, a high amplitude signal is mapped to a bright white level. Weaker signals are mapped to a gray, very weak signals are mapped to dark grays, and the absence of signal is mapped to complete black. (Inverted grayscale maps exist but are rarely used in ultrasound and almost never used with 2-D images.)

In *Figure 34a,* a single A-mode line is converted into a brightness mapped line. Notice that the horizontal axis represents depth and the vertical axis represents signal amplitude. The depth is divided into small depth increments and the amplitude assessed. Since the very shallowest signal is low amplitude, the very first pixel of the brightness mode line is dark gray. The second depth division is only a slightly higher amplitude, so the second pixel is only slightly brighter. Notice that the pixel which represents the very high amplitude signal is presented as bright white. In this manner, the entire A-mode line is converted until all of the B-mode pixels are colorized.

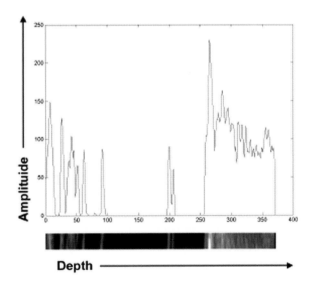
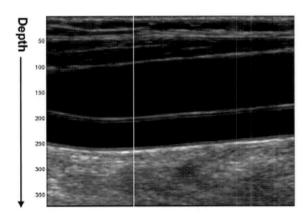

Fig. 34a **Creating B-mode from A-mode**

Figure 34a demonstrates how the vessel walls of the jugular vein and carotid artery are clearly delineated from the respective lumens in the A-mode image.

Chapter 6

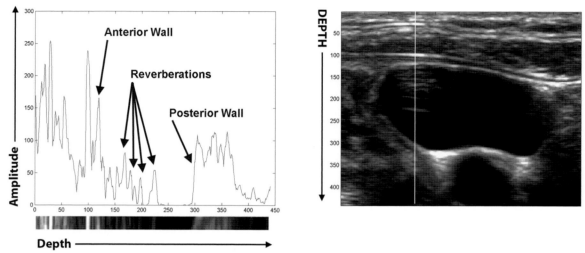

Fig. 34b **Creating B-mode from A-mode**

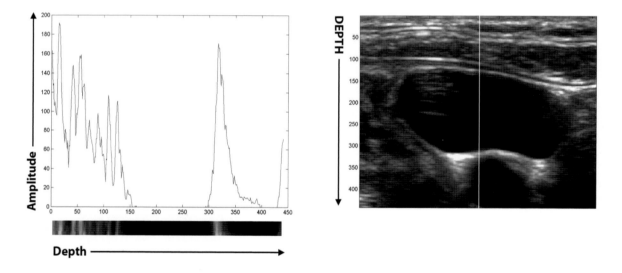

Fig. 34c **Creating B-mode from A-mode**

Figure 34b demonstrates how the reverberations within the jugular vein appear in the A-mode image (the large reflections and spikes in the region of approximately 130 to 220 on the horizontal axis of the A-mode). For comparison, notice how the A-mode is relatively free of echoes in the same region in *Figure 34c*.

12.3 The Role of the Scan Converter

There are really two core functions of the scan converter: converting the A-mode lines into B-mode lines, and then organizing the successive lines of data into a formatted image. The first role of conversion from A-mode to B-mode has just been described. The role of formatting that data can be very complex. The scan converter must keep track of which lines of data should be presented at what location on the screen. Once a frame is complete, the scan converter is sent an end of frame "flag" which warns the scan converter that the next line received is the first line of the next frame. In the simplest case, a scan converter can simply break the A-mode lines into discrete depth increments, create a pixel and display that pixel. However, there are many more complex situations which require significantly more processing. For example, consider the case of a sector scan in comparison to a linear scan.

12.4 Polar Scan Conversion and Lateral Distortion

For a linear scan, each depth increment of each A-mode line represents the same physical size in the image. In essence, the linear image is simply a uniform grid. In contrast, for a sector or curved-linear image, the near field is narrower than the far field. Since there are the same number of acoustic lines which constitute the data in the near field and in the far field, the "grid" size is not uniform from the top of the image to the bottom of the image. These comparisons are illustrated in *Figure 35*.

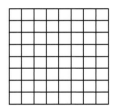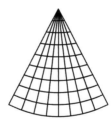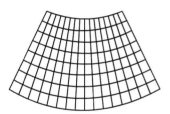

Fig. 35   **Grid Sizes for Different Imaging Formats**

For a sector, in the near field, there are many lines which essentially cover the same region of the patient. In the far field, as the beams "fan out" an individual line must cover a much wider area. Therefore, the width of the image created by the first line from shallow depths certainly cannot be the same width as the converted data from the deeper depths. As a result, the data must go through a conversion from a linear coordinate system to a polar coordinate system. In essence a polar coordinate system makes it easy to map points onto rings of a circle. Since a sector image is really a portion of a circle, a polar coordinate system is better suited than a linear system to plot data. As a result of the complex format, there is not a simple method of converting signals into uniform sized grid boxes as for a linear image. Extremely complex algorithms are required to transform the collection of lines into this format while best preserving lateral resolution and keeping the image looking uniform. Depending on the line spacing (also referred to as the line density), this polar coordinate conversion often results in a lateral distortion (banana shaped pixel effect) of the data. In the earlier days of ultrasound this scan conversion distortion was much more pronounced, especially in color Doppler imaging. Now with narrower beams, higher line densities, and improved processing this distortion has been decreased, but not completely eliminated.

12.5 Inconsistent Terminology in the Field

Scan conversion is only one of many functions that the back end of the ultrasound system must perform. In addition to scan conversion, the back end must allow for patient identification, measurements and analysis, patient reports, data storage to external devices (either attached to the system or through data I/O), input output compression mapping, myriad processing techniques, converting the signal into a video format for display, and cineloop review. Unfortunately, from some textbooks, the term scan converter has become synonymous with all of the functions of the back end of the ultrasound system. As a result, there is generally some confusion when discussing scan conversion since it implies both a specific function of the ultrasound system and an entire group of functions performed once the signal has been processed by the front end (unfortunately referred to as the receiver). The analogy is all cars have a steering wheel to steer the car, but we don't call a car a steering wheel since it gets confusing. Yes, steering is a function of the car, but it is not all the car does.

Yes, the back end of an ultrasound system scan converts, but that is not the only function that the back end performs. Historically, the term scan converter implies all of the functions of the entire back end of the system and in some circles this assumption remains.

Using the less than optimal definition of "scan converter," the scan converter is generally described as a block of digital memory with a central processing unit (CPU) and associated software. The scan converter converts the A-mode line data into B-mode lines, transforms the line data into the appropriate image format, and coordinates the data transfer for display, external storage, and internal storage for cineloop review. The digital scan converter is where all post processing occurs. Since the data are stored in the digital memory, post processing can be performed on frozen as well as live data, whereas preprocessing can only be performed on live data. Some examples of post processing are video compression, tissue colorization, edge enhancement, wall detection, measurements, and analysis. The "scan converter" also performs the secondary function of cineloop review.

Note: In the very earliest days of ultrasound there was no conversion from analog to digital format and hence, analog scan converters were used. This technique has not been used since Moses stopped scanning right about the time the Red Sea parted. If asked, analog scan converters suffer problems of performance degradation over time: inconsistent performance, image flicker, long warm up times, and fading. (Not to mention the fact they are now extinct.)

13. Preprocessing and Post Processing Revisited

13.1 Understanding the Difference

In Level 1 we defined preprocessing and post processing before discussing the role of the scan converter. With an understanding of scan conversion, it is now easier to make a clear distinction in these two terms. Any process which occurs before the scan conversion and data storage is considered a preprocessing technique. Therefore, any process that can be performed on the stored data after conversion is referred to as a post processing technique. This is precisely why post processing techniques can be performed after freezing the data where preprocessing techniques cannot be changed. Once the signals are converted into an image, there is no way to reverse and redo the non-linear processes that were performed before the image conversion occurred. What processes occur before scan conversion depends on the system design. Many systems are storing the data earlier in the processing path, allowing for more of the processes that once were considered preprocessing to now become post processing techniques. In time, as memory becomes less expensive and as storage capacity per physical size continues to increase, it is likely that systems will eventually store raw (RF) data (amplified unprocessed received echoes), making this distinction of preprocessing and post processing disappear. Virtually all of the processing techniques and tools discussed in the upcoming section are currently post processing on most ultrasound systems.

14. Compression

14.1 Compression: A Multi-Stage Process
In Level 1 we learned about the "receiver" function of compression. The compression which occurs in the system front end is not under user control. However, not all of the compression applied to the ultrasound signals occurs in the system front end. Because of the extraordinary dynamic range of the signals, and because of the relatively small dynamic range of the human eye, extraordinary compression is required. Understanding the reasons that the compression is distributed throughout the system can lead to some very important clinical results. Before we can discuss the clinical ramifications, we must first develop a better understanding of the dynamic range constraints that the compression must address.

14.2 Dynamic Range of 2-D Echoes
The dynamic range of the reflected signals from a patient is very large. For 2-D imaging, the signal range is typically 80 dB or more. For Doppler, the dynamic range is significantly greater. Remember that decibels are logarithmic, so 80 dB represents an extraordinary range. For review:

$$20 \times \log\left(\frac{A_{biggest}}{A_{smallest}}\right) = 80 \text{ dB}.$$

Dividing both sides by 20 yields:

$$\log\left(\frac{A_{biggest}}{A_{smallest}}\right) = 4.$$

(The base is 10 - recall if not expressly written, we assume a base of 10.)

$$\log_{10}\left(\frac{A_{biggest}}{A_{smallest}}\right) = 4.$$

Solving the logarithm yields:

$$\left(\frac{A_{biggest}}{A_{smallest}}\right) = \frac{10^4}{1} = 10,000:1.$$

Therefore 80 dB implies that the largest signal is 10,000 times larger than the smallest signal. If you recall the concepts of Chapter 3, you should have a good foundation for understanding why this enormous range exists. Recall that the strength of a reflection is based on the acoustic impedance mismatch. Further, you should realize that specular reflection for normal incidence, produces strong reflections back to the transducer. Additionally, the echoes from shallower depths will have experienced much less attenuation than echoes from deeper depths. The combination of these effects results in some echoes being much stronger than other echoes. As just seen, it is not uncommon for some received signals to be 10,000 times bigger than other signals.

14.3 Dynamic Range of the Human Eye

The dynamic range of the human eye is a fascinating subject. The human eye has extraordinary dynamic range, capable of seeing very bright objects such as the sun, and very faint objects such as the distant stars hundreds of thousands of light years away. To see such an enormous dynamic range, the eye adaptively controls the pupil in order to visualize a wide range of brightness levels. However, even with this tremendous adaptive control, the human eye can see fewer than 64 shades of gray, or 64 to 1 brightness levels at one instant. In other words, although the eye can see an enormous range of brightness levels, it can only distinguish between fewer than 64 shades at a specific instance.

Let's convert 64 shades into decibels so that we have a comparison with the dynamic range of the signal.

$$20 \times \log\left(\frac{64}{1}\right) = ? \text{ dB}$$

Since 64 is a power of 2, and we have memorized the log of 2,
we can solve for the log of 64 by using our rule that logarithms convert
multiplications into additions of logs or:

$$20 \times \log\left(\frac{64}{1}\right) = 20 \times \left[\log\left(2 \times 2 \times 2 \times 2 \times 2 \times 2\right)\right]$$

$$= 20 \times \left[\log(2) + \log(2) + \log(2) + \log(2) + \log(2) + \log(2)\right]$$

$$= 20 \times \left[0.3 + 0.3 + 0.3 + 0.3 + 0.3 + 0.3\right] = 20 \times 1.8 = 36 \text{ dB}$$

Therefore, the "instantaneous" dynamic range of the eye is less than 36 dB, but the signal range is generally greater than 80 dB. In the linear world, the human eye can see fewer than 64 shades of gray simultaneously whereas the signal occupies more than 10,000 levels. This enormous difference in dynamic range is precisely the reason why logarithmic compression is needed.

To demonstrate the limits of the human eye, look at the three "color bars" presented in *Figure 36*. In the top bar, it is relatively easy to distinguish all the rectangles of various brightness levels. In the middle bar, discerning each rectangle is slightly more challenging. In the last example, it is improbable that you can distinguish all 64 shaded rectangles. If you change the room lighting, you may find different results.

16 Shades

32 Shades

64 Shades

Fig. 36   **Grayscale and Visual Dynamic Range**

14.4 Why the System Allows for Compression in the Back End of the System

Some compression is always performed in the back end of the system under the control of the user. To distinguish between the compression in the front end of the system and the compression of the back end of the system under user control, we will adopt the term "video compression." The reason some compression is under user control is related to the fundamental limitation associated with compression. When data is compressed, there is generally a loss of information. It is conceivable that the very signal that needs to be detected for an accurate clinical diagnosis could be compressed out, and hence not recognized. The following example will illustrate this point. This same question was asked in Chapter 3 when dealing with contrast resolution as it relates to acoustic impedance mismatch.

Imagine that a large mass exists. If the system controls are set correctly, will it always be visualized?

The answer to this question is still "No". This answer does not mean that a user cannot incorrectly set system controls resulting in an inability to detect a mass or a thrombus. Instead, this is a statement that ultrasound has limitations based on real physics. Consider *Figure 37*. On the left side of the diagram, there is a large range of amplitudes which represents the signal dynamic range. On the other side of the diagram, there is a much smaller range representative of the instantaneous dynamic range of the human eye. Within the signal range, there are marks indicating the reflection amplitude from the mass and the reflection level from the tissue surrounding the mass. Notice that there is a distinction between these two signal amplitudes. In order to visualize the reflected signals in real time (as opposed to developing films at different grayscale levels and reviewing the information as a collection of different "exposures"), the large dynamic range must be mapped into the smaller dynamic range of the eyes. In the process of compressing the two signals, the difference between the reflection from the mass and the reflection from the surrounding tissue is reduced, potentially to the point where the distinction either no longer exists, or is no longer perceptible to the human eye. Therefore, it is quite possible that the mass will not be visualized because of the compression scheme chosen.

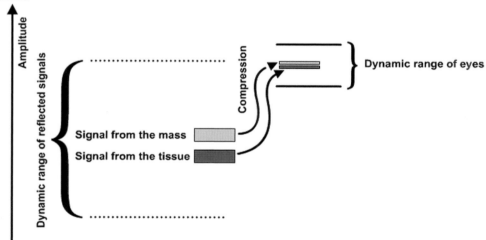

Fig. 37 **Effects of Compression**

View Animation and Image Library CD

Chapter 6

14.5 Compression Controls on the System

Since there is no way of knowing a priori when the compression will potentially expunge the very data needed, a dilemma exists. For physics based practical reasons we have no choice but to compress the data; however, this leads to the possible situation of not presenting adequate contrast resolution such that important characteristics in an image may be missed. As a result, when designing a system, the user is given many different compression mapping schemes to choose from. Each compression map still compresses the data, but does so using a different mathematical mapping. In essence, some maps may be more aggressive in compressing higher level signals leaving more dynamic range for the mid-level and low level signals. Some maps may have much more contrast, attempting to preserve a greater distinction between strong and weak signals. Recall that the function of compression must be logarithmic since the dynamic range is so large.

The following figures show the results of various compression maps on a cardiac image and a vascular image. The image on the left is an Apical 4-chamber cardiac image of a normal heart. The image on the right is a popliteal vein with a thrombus. The graph between the images represents the compression mapping used to produce the associated image. Note that the horizontal axis is the signal strength and the vertical axis is the output display intensity, ranging from 0 to 255. A value of 0 is pure black and a value of 255 is pure white.

Apical 4-Chamber	Compression Maps	Popliteal Vein Thrombus

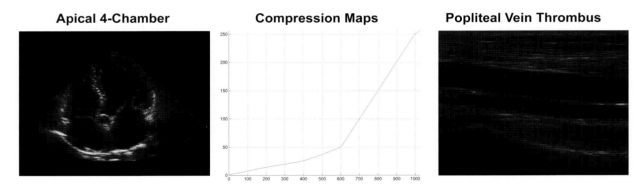

Map 1: Most dynamic range dedicated for higher-level signals. Weak signals and noise mapped out.

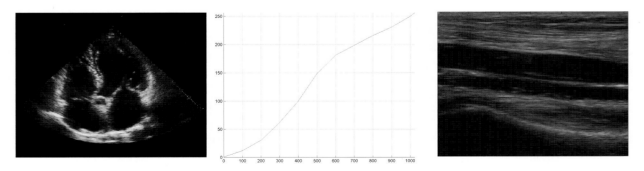

Map 2: Most dynamic range in mid-level signals. Low-level signals not very apparent.

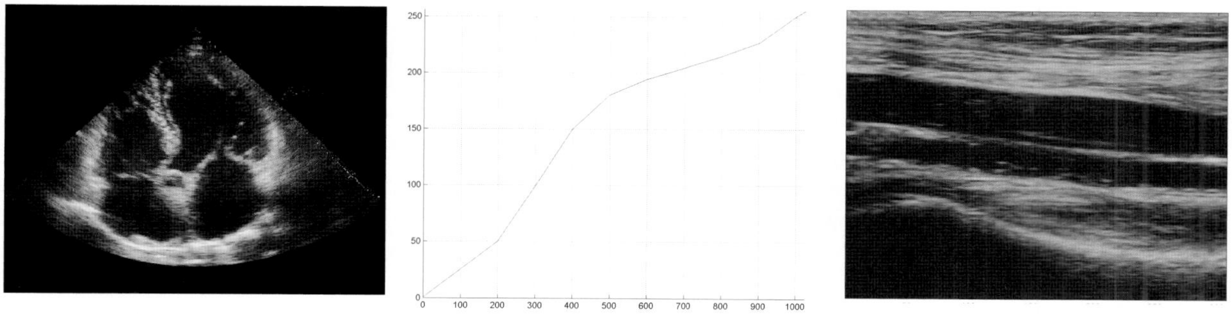

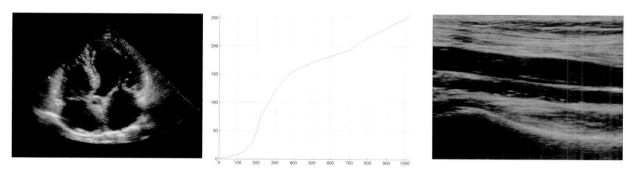

Map 3: Transition begins earlier so that weaker signals become more apparent.

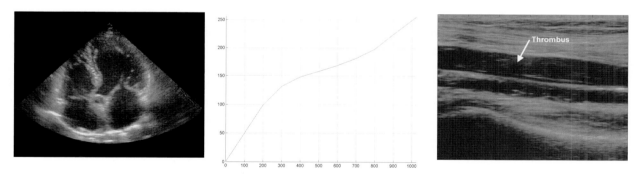

Map 4: Low-levels mapped out, rapid transition for mid-level signals.

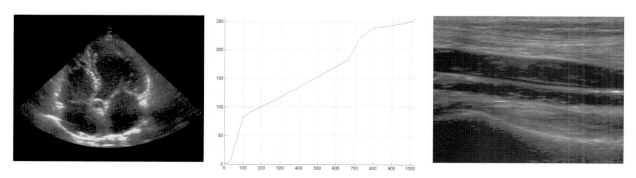

Map 5: Rapid transition to display weak level signals. Less dynamic range in mid-range.

Map 6: Extremely rapid transition to display weak level signals. Very little dynamic range in mid-range.

Chapter 6

Notice how map 5 and map 6 demonstrate the thrombus in the popliteal vein whereas the thrombus is not visualized using maps 1 through 4. However, for the cardiac image, maps 5 and 6 somewhat obscure the valves and myocardial borders. There is no perfect map for all patients and all applications.

The entire compression and grayscale mapping process is very complex since the very process of assigning grayscale levels is a non-linear compression scheme. As we will learn, a monitor is capable of producing more grayscale level signals than the eye can detect simultaneously. Also, the display brightness of the monitor is non-linear, further compounded by the fact that the eye's sensitivity to brightness is non-linear and variable with ambient light. If you are starting to get the impression that there are many variables which affect your ability to detect signals "accurately", you are catching on.

Because of the critical importance to these maps, there is usually more than one set of controls which affect the compression mapping. For example, a system may have a knob control called compression and then a family of post processing curves. Of course, every ultrasound company has their own name for these functions further exacerbating the confusion. The following list represents some of the most common names used by systems to refer to this compression mapping:

- Compression
- Dynamic range
- Grayscale
- Post processing (curves or maps)
- (Display) contrast

14.6 Using Compression Controls Correctly
The effects of compression can be very dramatic on the display and potentially can lead to misdiagnosis. Most people find a processing setting they find visually appealing and then tend not to change the compression settings very often. This approach can lead to many mistakes. Proper use of compression is to periodically vary the compression settings, especially when there is a greater likelihood of low reflective echoes such as the presence of a fresh thrombus. This changing of the controls will only add a few seconds to the scan time, but can make a significant difference to the few patients on which a mass or thrombus would have otherwise been missed.

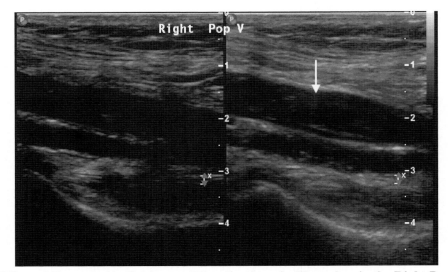

Fig. 38   **Effect of Compression Settings on Visualization of a Thrombus in the Right Popliteal Vein**

The different compression mapping between the left and right image of *Figure 38* makes the difference between detecting or missing the thrombus present in the right popliteal vein (indicated by the white arrow in the right image). The compression mapping for the right image enhances the low level echoes more than the mapping used for the left image. *Figure 39* shows the same vessel in transverse, mapped with the same two compression settings.

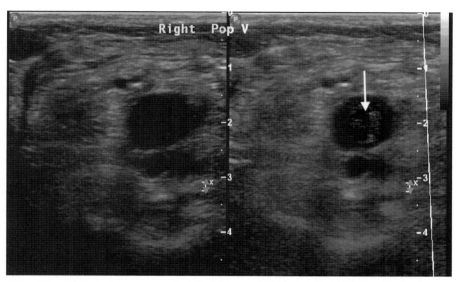

Fig. 39   **Effect of Compression Settings on Visualization of a Thrombus
(Right Popliteal Vein in Transverse View)**

Color Doppler images are included on the animation and image library CD demonstrating how the thrombus is affecting flow through the popliteal vein.

View Animation and Image Library CD

15. Tissue Colorization

As we have just learned, the dynamic range of the eye is much less than the dynamic range of the video monitor which in turn, is significantly less than the signal dynamic range. However, the dynamic range of the eye thus far has been restricted to the ability to distinguish between grayscale levels. By including color hues, the dynamic range of the eye is extended. The use of colorization maps is intended to improve visualization when significant dynamic range must be preserved. Most systems offer an assortment of maps ranging from "wheat" colors through blues, pinks, and greens. How much these maps help depends on the specific imaging situation, the compression maps chosen, and the color mapping scheme itself. For the existing mapping schemes there often does not appear too dramatic a change, although there are times when color maps makes it easier to distinguish low level signals.

View Animation and Image Library CD

16. Measurements

The measurements and analysis packages reside in the back end software. Since the data is stored in a digital format in the memory of the back end, it is possible to freeze the data, potentially scroll back in imaging time, and place calipers. What you see on the screen is just the calipers, but the process is actually a reverse mapping technique. You can think of the image as a grid as was illustrated in Section 12.4. With the placement of the calipers, the system now has a pair of coordinates (x and y or r and θ for polar coordinate systems), as well as a time coordinate. These coordinates are then referenced against the scan converted data coordinates. In this way, the specific value for the signal at that location can be identified if desired. More often, the cursor is placed in two or more locations and a geometric measurement is made. Since the system knows the physical dimensions of the image, these measurements can be converted in actual distance, area, or volume measurements.

16.1 Area Measurements
There are two different approaches to area measurements with conventional 2-D imaging. One approach is to trace the desired region and the system performs an integration to determine the area. The other approach is to indicate a radius of a presumed round structure by setting the calipers and performing an area calculation based on the area equation. Caution must be taken with both of these approaches to minimize the amount of error in the assessed area term.

16.1.1 Tracing an Area
Besides poor tracing skills, the greatest source of error in an area tracing is incorrect angle in the 2-D image. *Figure 40a* demonstrates graphically how angle can affect area measurements.

Scenario 1:　　　　　　　　　　***Scenario 2:***

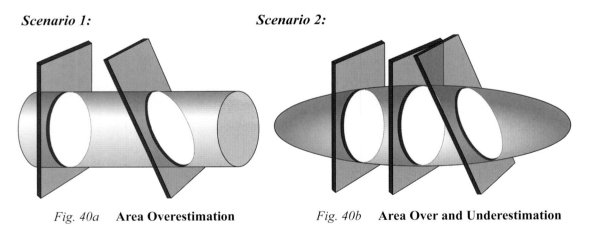

Fig. 40a　**Area Overestimation**　　　*Fig. 40b*　**Area Over and Underestimation**

For the uniform cylindrical shape such as a blood vessel, off-axis measurements usually result in an overestimation of the area as indicated by *Figure 40b*. As long as the beam intersects both the anterior and posterior wall of the vessel, underestimation from angle is not possible.

In comparison, for area measurement tracings of objects that are not uniform in cross-section such as heart chambers and diseased vessels, there are two different sources of error: location and angle. Clearly, even if the image plane is perpendicular to the structure, the cross-sectional area measured is dependent on location. For this example, there is a larger cross-sectional area in the middle of the object than at either end. The other error source is related to angle. As in the previous example, off-axis beams tend to increase the cross-sectional area.

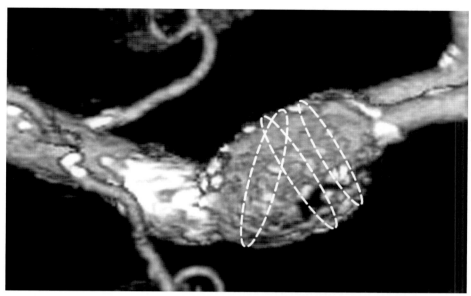

Fig. 41   **3-D Spiral CT of an Abdominal Aortic Aneurysm**
(possible measurement errors)

   **View Animation and Image Library CD**

Scenario 3:

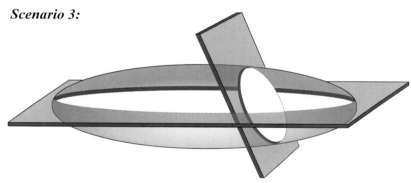

Fig. 42   **Longitudinal Plane and Area Underestimation**

Along the longitudinal axis of the nonuniform cross-sectional object, there are again two distinct sources of error: location and angle. If the imaging plane does not intersect this object in the center, then the area measurement will naturally be smaller. In this case, if the angle is incorrect, the area measurement will be smaller than reality. In the cardiac world, when this occurs when viewing a chamber, the image is said to be "foreshortened."

16.1.2 Calculated From the Radius

Just as with tracing, angle effects can be a significant source of error in area measurements calculated from a radius. Recall that area is a two-dimensional measurement whereas the radius is only a one-dimensional parameter. As we learned in Chapter 1, the area is proportional to the radius squared, or: $Area \propto r^2$. Therefore, any error in the radius measurement is squared to produce the area calculation. This source of error is depicted in *Figure 43*.

Chapter 6

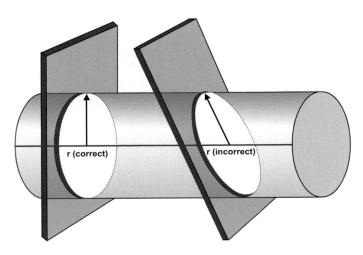

Fig. 43   **Errors in Radius Measurement are Squared for Area**

17. Video Display and Monitors

17.1 CRT

The display for most ultrasound systems is still the cathode ray tube (CRT), although this is very quickly changing with improvements in liquid crystal displays (LCD), and all sorts of new flat panel technologies including DLP (digital light processing chips) which utilize millions of tiny mirrors. With a CRT, a cathode ray tube emits electrons which are scanned across a coated screen. The screen is coated with a phosphorescent layer which "glows" when excited by electrons. By changing the electron density, regions on the screen can be made to glow more or less brightly. A short time after excitation, the phosphorescent glow begins to decay, requiring another excitation to refresh the image. For color monitors, there are actually three CRT's, one for red, one for green, and one for blue (RGB). All three beams converge on the inside of the screen to form a color image.

In general, CRTs are bulky and heavy, consuming more energy than many newer technologies and thereby producing more heat. However, CRT monitors also have held a few advantages to competing technologies which have kept them in utilization. Some of the advantages of CRT monitors are:

- Better viewing angle
- Brighter image
- More robust
- Cheaper

Of course in time, newer technologies will supercede these advantages of CRTs and replace them. It is quite likely in the next 10 years, the monitor technology will be replaced by at least two different and competing technologies. Ultrasound will benefit from the competition which currently exists for the computer monitor and high definition television market.

17.2 Monitor Formats and "Standards"

Since the performance and characteristics of the monitor used to display the data can affect perception of the data, it is important to discuss monitor formats. To begin with, we must realize that a standard monitor format in the United States is not the same as the standard format in Europe. For television, there are at least three competing standards. (Sort of makes the term "standard" an oxymoron – doesn't it?) In the U.S., the standard was set by the National Television Standards Committee (NTSC). In Europe, (outside of France) the standard is called PAL. Within France there is yet a third standard referred to as the SECAM.

17.2.1 NTSC (United States) Format

The National Television Standards Committee (NTSC) created a standard for black and white televisions that included 525 horizontal display lines and 30 frames per second. The 525 display lines are actually displayed as two interlaced fields; the odd field consisting of lines 1, 3, 5, 7, … and the even field consisting of lines 2, 4, 6, 8, … Since alternating current in the United States has 60 cycles, it was a natural choice to present each field during a single cycle of the power source. The result is that each frame required 1/60th of a second producing a total frame rate of 30 frames per second, as demonstrated below:

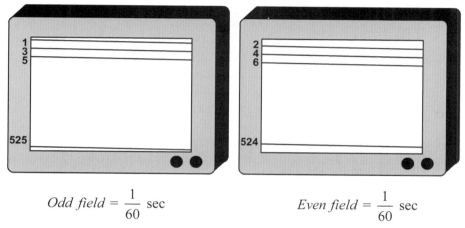

$$Odd\ field = \frac{1}{60}\ sec \qquad\qquad Even\ field = \frac{1}{60}\ sec$$

Fig. 44 **Odd Field (Interlaced Monitor)**   *Fig. 45*   **Even Field (Interlaced Monitor)**

Interlaced (odd field and even field each require 1/60 second), so the overall frame rate is therefore:

$$\frac{1}{60}\frac{sec}{odd\ field} + \frac{1}{60}\frac{sec}{even\ field} = \frac{2}{60}\frac{sec}{frame} = \frac{1}{30}\frac{sec}{frame} \Rightarrow 30\ frames\ per\ second.$$

However, with the later introduction of color, there was a new problem: how to add more data but not make all existing television sets obsolete. The solution was to add the necessary color information to each frame making the frame rate slower by about 0.1%, reducing the frame rate to 29.97 frames per second (fps). As a result, the standard United States format is 525 lines at 29.97 fps.

17.2.2 PAL

Phase alternate line is another format which is more commonly used in some places in Europe. The PAL format is higher in resolution with 625 lines, however the frame rate is slower (25 fps) since the phase for European power is based on 50 cycles per second.

17.2.3 SECAM

Sequential Couleur A'memorie (SECAM) is yet another format which uses 819 lines for the display with a frame rate of 25 fps.

17.3 Why the Monitor Frame Rate Matters

In Chapter 4 we learned how to calculate the acoustic frame rate. Since temporal resolution is directly impacted by frame rate, there was considerable discussion as to how to best optimize the acoustic frame rate. Notice that we are now making a distinction between the frame rate for the monitor and the frame rate at which we gather images (the acoustic frame rate). In some of the examples we calculated, for 2-D imaging we were able to realize frame rates of about 100 Hz. However, there is now an obvious issue. Even if we are able to generate 100 frames per second, an interlaced monitor is only capable of displaying almost 30 of these frames per second.

Consider the following situation. What happens if the acoustic frame rate is 90 Hz and the monitor is an interlaced monitor? The answer is only every third frame is displayed on the monitor and two of every three frames are just never displayed. You can imagine situations in which a short duration event takes place and is captured in only one of the 90 frames. Given that not all frames are displayed on the screen, this event may never be displayed. In other words, the limiting factor to the temporal resolution might be the monitor itself, and not the acoustic scan time.

17.4 Non-Interlaced Monitors

In recent years, formats for United States monitors have begun to change. This change is occurring for two reasons, television standards are changing to accommodate high definition broadcasts (more than 525 lines), and monitors are not required to follow the standards of televisions. One of the changes which has occurred is that non-interlaced monitors have become much more commonplace. With non-interlaced monitors there is no odd and even field to interlace. Instead, the entire field of lines is displayed at the same time, and hence produces a frame rate twice as fast as the interlaced monitors, or a frame time of 1/60th of a second.

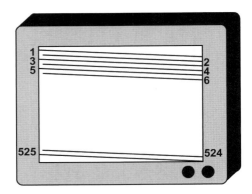

$$Entire\ field = \frac{1}{60}\ sec$$

Fig. 46   **Non-Interlaced Monitor**

A frame time of 1/60th of a second implies a frame rate of 60 Hz. In reality, it is not very likely the frame rate will ever be increased beyond this rate. The principal reason for this is the limitation of the human eye. The human eye generally cannot perceive changes faster than 60 cycles per second. Therefore, there appears to be very little motivation for achieving a higher rate that exceeds the limitation of the "interpreting device."

Note: It is hoped that you have recognized an inherent pattern in the discussions and approach. The value of learning about monitors is not related to the likelihood of you becoming an electrical engineer who designs monitors. Instead, the value is in realizing how the technology has limitations and how those limitations can affect the outcome of your clinical studies. Furthermore, there is value in understanding the limitations of human functions of vision and hearing since the limiting factor is often our inability to perceive data.

17.5 Subdividing Horizontal Lines into Pixels

The smallest division of a horizontal display line is called a pixel. Since an image already consists of horizontal lines, the pixels subdivide the screen into a grid. A high pixel density (# of pixels per inch) potentially will yield better detail resolution than a low pixel density.

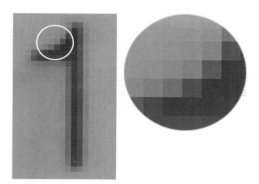 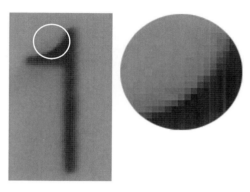

| *Fig. 47* **Larger Pixels** (Worse Resolution) | *Fig. 48* **Smaller Pixels** (Better Resolution) |

Notice that the pixel size is smaller in *Figure 48* than in *Figure 47* resulting in better resolution.

Note: For the credentialing exams it is important to note that the smallest physical division of a monitor's display is called a pixel. Do not confuse this with the smallest division of a binary number, or the smallest division of an A/D converter's output which is referred to as a bit.

17.5.1 Pixels and Brightness Levels

For conventional monitors, each pixel can be represented by multiple "layers" which can either be illuminated or left dark. Since there are two choices for each layer (light or dark), each layer is often likened to the binary counting system and the concept of a bit. You can imagine if there are eight layers and all eight layers are lit up, that pixel will appear very bright. In comparison, if the top three layers are lit up, but the bottom five are dark, that pixel will appear as a gray. Note that the brightness would be different if the bottom three layers are lit up as opposed to the top three layers. If the bottom three layers are lit, then the pixel will be a much darker shade of gray. If all eight layers are dark, then the pixel will be pure black. The following figure, *Figure 49*, demonstrates this concept.

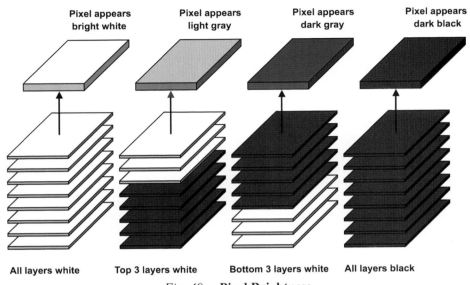

Pixel appears bright white
Pixel appears light gray
Pixel appears dark gray
Pixel appears dark black
All layers white
Top 3 layers white
Bottom 3 layers white
All layers black

Fig. 49 **Pixel Brightness**

17.6 Relating Brightness Levels to Binary

If we rename each layer with the name "bit", we can see how the binary number system now describes the total number of grayscale levels possible. Let's assume there is only one layer, or a 1 bit display. There are two choices, either light up the bit (1) or leave it dark (0). Since there are only two color levels, this type of display is called a bi-stable display. In the very early days of ultrasound, bistable displays were used. Although still periodically referred to on credentialing exams, bistable displays were also the tools of Moses, and no system today would dream of using a bi-stable monitor.

Since bi-stable displays are no longer existent, it will behoove us to consider higher bit depth displays. Imagine that a pixel is represented by two bits (two layers). The choices are shown in *Figure 50.*

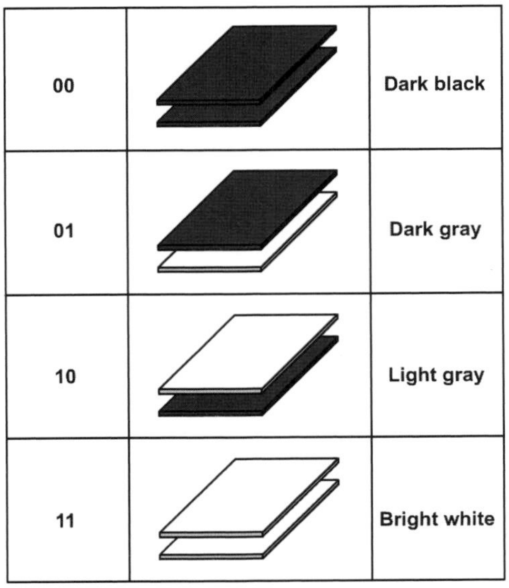

00
Dark black
01
Dark gray
10
Light gray
11
Bright white

Fig. 50 **4 Gray Levels With 2-bits**

Therefore a 2-bit display can present four varying brightness levels, or four "shades of gray". If a three-bit display existed, the number of possible gray levels would be represented by the following combinations:

000	Dark black
001	Very dark gray
010	Dark gray
011	Gray
100	Lighter gray
101	Very light gray
110	Almost white
111	Bright white

By now the pattern should be clear. The number of gray levels possible is just the number 2 raised to the power equal to the number of bits.

$$\text{gray levels} = 2^{\text{bits}}$$

$$1 \text{ bit} \Rightarrow 2^1 = 2 \text{ shades (bi-stable)}$$

$$2 \text{ bits} \Rightarrow 2^2 = 4 \text{ shades}$$

$$3 \text{ bits} \Rightarrow 2^3 = 8 \text{ shades}$$

$$4 \text{ bits} \Rightarrow 2^4 = 16 \text{ shades}$$

$$8 \text{ bits} \Rightarrow 2^8 = 256 \text{ shades}$$

Earlier in this chapter we discussed the fact that the human eye is capable of seeing fewer than 64 shades of gray. Therefore, the absolute minimum number of gray levels desired in a monitor must be at least 64, which requires 6 bits. Even though the human eye can only see 64 shades of gray simultaneously, all monitors assign at least 8 bits to grayscale and more commonly 10 bits. The question is "why?"

17.7 Brightness Levels and Ambient Light

The term ambient light refers to the background light which surrounds us. When in a sunshine filled room, the ambient light is very high. When in a room with no windows and no lights on, there is low ambient lighting. Every time a reference to the dynamic range of the eye was made, you will notice that the word "instantaneous" was used as a modifier. As mentioned earlier, the eye adjusts adaptively to the ambient lighting. In the presence of high ambient lighting, the pupil constricts, allowing the eye to discriminate between brighter shades of gray. When the ambient lighting is low, the pupil dilates, allowing the eye to detect and discriminate between low levels signals. Since there is no way of guaranteeing that the ambient light will always stay constant, the monitor must be able to produce brighter levels for when the system is used in high ambient light and lower level signals for when the system is used in lower ambient light.

The fact that the eye behaves differently with differing ambient light is important for two reasons:
1. If the monitor is not adjusted correctly for the ambient light, weak signals can be missed.
2. Data stored to external devices are not necessarily calibrated to what is appearing on the screen in high ambient light, leading to either very bright or very dark stored studies, inconsistent with what was visualized while scanning.

View Animation and Image Library CD

The first of these two points, is precisely why monitors are supposed to be calibrated for the ambient lighting condition. Calibration procedures are specific to each manufacturer but usually are very similar and entail adjusting the monitor contrast and brightness until the bottom of a calibrated color bar just fades into the background screen. This calibration should occur every time there is a change in ambient light, as well as at least every 6 months since the luminosity of a monitor tends to change over time. Since most people never read the procedure of how to calibrate a monitor, most service engineers that I have known would advise against their customers adjusting the monitor. A better solution to not touching the monitor controls is for you to learn the calibration procedure.

The second issue is always good for at least one argument in your life. Everyone at some point or another either verbally assaults someone's sense of judgment, knowledge and skill, or even parental lineage because the stored images are either very dark or very bright when reviewed. The problem generally occurs after a portable system has been taken bedside in a room that cannot be darkened or to the operating room. Since the lighting is so bright, the monitor's contrast is significantly increased. However, if you refer back to the block diagram at the beginning of Level 2 of this chapter, you will notice that digital storage occurs from data passed to the storage device from the system back end ("scan converter"). The problem is that the images displayed are being affected by the monitor settings whereas the images being stored are not. Therefore, any changes in system controls that affect signal brightness will affect the brightness of the stored data differently than the displayed data.

A simple partial solution to this problem is to create a cardboard hood with tape hinges. Whenever you need to image in a room with bright ambient light, you can reduce the direct light to the screen, decreasing the need to adjust the monitor contrast as dramatically.

18. Data Storage Devices (External)

There are two fundamental storage formats: analog storage and digital storage. The quintessential analog storage device is tape (audiotape for audio storage and VCR tape for video storage). To understand the motivation for creating a digital storage system, it is instructive to consider the limitations and drawbacks associated with analog storage.

18.1 Disadvantages of Analog Storage Devices
Analog storage devices (such as VHS VCR tape) have all of the following limitations:

- Relatively large physical size
- Worse detail resolution (only 200 horizontal lines)
- Inadequate bandwidth for accurate color fidelity (better with SVHS – but still inadequate)
- Limited frame rate of 30 frames per second (for standard US format)
- Relatively unstable (video quality degrades over time and can be either degraded or even completely erased by magnetic fields such as occur near audio speakers or MRI machines)
- Difficult and time consuming to copy
- Degradation in video quality each time copied
- Poor video quality if heads of player are dirty
- Mechanical mechanisms of rollers can wear out causing "jerky" review

18.2 VHS and SVHS (VCR)

A VCR is designed to follow the 29.97 frames per second frame rate of the standard monitor but with fewer horizontal display lines. A VHS tape is only capable of producing 200 horizontal lines. The difficulty resides in storing more information on a narrow piece of tape. An SVHS tape increases the number of lines to 400, still below the standard 525 lines for non-high definition monitors. As a result, the video stored to a VCR is a reduced set from the video which is displayed on a standard US monitor.

18.3 Disadvantages of Digital Storage Devices

With the desire to create small, portable, and fast computers, and given the desire to overcome the myriad issues associated with analog storage, digital storage was created. Examples of digital media include CDs, DVDs, Magneto Optical Disks, and computer hard drives, Of course the introduction of digital storage has some clear advantages relative to analog storage, but also has some very clear disadvantages.

18.3.1 Digital Storage Advantages

- Smaller physical size.
- No copy to copy loss (as long as the date is not converted to another format).
- Stable over time. The quality of the data does not change over time (unless transferred into a different format).
- Storage devices are less fragile (with no mechanical parts).
- Rapid advancements in technology are driving prices down rapidly while simultaneously improving both speed and memory size.

18.3.2 Digital Storage Disadvantages

- Video requires inordinate amounts of digital memory to store at the same quality as analog storage.
- Fast processor speeds are needed to be able to store digital data without loss of fidelity.
- Fast processor speeds are needed to be able to buffer video data for display without long start-up delays and without "jerky" discontinuous review.
- Fast bus speeds are necessary to transfer to the data from the storage device to the processor for display.
- Fast processor speeds are needed to encode and decode compressed video formats.
- Most digital formats do not store the separate audio track, so there is no audio with Doppler.

Level 3 covers some specific issues relating to analog and digital data storage, transfer, and data compression schemes.

19. Data Storage (Internal)

19.1 Cine (Cineloop) Review

When the scan converter is processing each line and formatting for display, the processed, formatted data is temporarily stored in a large bank of digital memory. (Recall that the data in the system back end is always in a digital format regardless of whether the system is an analog or digital system.)

The data for each individual scan converted line is stored until the block of memory is full. When full, the oldest data in the memory is written over first so that the most recent data is always resident. This memory, in conjunction with the ability to review the data in this memory, are referred to as cineloop review. When reviewing cineloop, once all of the stored data is displayed, the video loops back to the beginning, starting over with the oldest data, hence the name cineloop review.

19.2 Purposes for Cine Review
There are many purposes for cine review:
1. It allows the user to review complicated images in slow time.
2. It allows the user to compare frames and changes with time.
3. It allows the user to go back and find the best image for measurement purposes.
4. It provides a non-real-time approach to overcoming the limited frame rate of the monitor.

In Sections 17.2 - 17.4, the frame rate of monitors was discussed. For non-interlaced monitors the frame rate is 60 Hz and for interlaced monitors the frame rate is 30 Hz. In the situations where the acoustic frame rate is higher than the monitor frame rate, some frames cannot be displayed. The cineloop generally stores all frames such that in review, frames that were not viewed in real time can be viewed in "slow time." In other words, cineloop review provides a non-real-time solution to a temporal resolution limit imposed by the monitor. Of course, if the acoustic frame rate is lower than the monitor, then there are no "unviewed" frames stored in the cineloop memory.

19.3 The Recording Length of a Cine Memory
How much imaging time can a cineloop hold? This question is always challenging to answer. The memory size is determined by the hardware design. However, how many seconds or minutes of video can be stored is determined by both the memory size and the data rate. The data rate is dependent on the frame rate. For a slow frame rate, the memory can hold a longer time record. For a faster frame rate, the memory can store a shorter time record. Hypothetically, let's say that a system can hold 1,000 frames of data. If the frame rate is 10 Hz, then the memory can hold 100 seconds worth of data. If on the other hand the frame rate is 100 Hz, then the memory can only store 10 seconds worth of data.

20. Zoom (Res Mode, Magnification)

20.1 Acoustic Versus Non-acoustic
The function of zooming data, sometimes referred to as res mode (for resolution) or magnification can be performed by two fundamentally different techniques. One approach is a non-acoustic approach. The non-acoustic zoom allows the user to place a "zoom" box over the area of interest to be displayed larger on the screen and then essentially stretches the data to the new display size. The term non-acoustic is used since no new sound beams were used to generate the larger displayed image. The other approach is an acoustic approach. With an acoustic zoom, the user again is allowed to place a zoom box over the region of interest, but instead of just stretching the data, the system changes the transmit beam profile so as to potentially improve the resolution of the image. The term acoustic therefore refers to the fact that new acoustic beams were transmitted to achieve the larger display. We will discuss each of these approaches in more depth.

20.2 Non-acoustic Zoom (Read Zoom)

A non-acoustic zoom can be applied either for frozen data or in real time, hence, a non-acoustic zoom is a post processing technique. Many texts have referred to this type of zoom as a "read zoom," implying that the data is "read" from the memory after scan conversion. Fundamentally, the resolution of a non-acoustically zoomed image does not change. Whatever resolution exists in the image before zooming is the same resolution that exists after zooming. Despite this fact, there are still benefits to a non-acoustic zoom. When there are small structures which need to be measured or visualized, by zooming the structure and surrounding region, it becomes easier to place calipers and make potentially more accurate measurements. If the resolution is poor, then the zoomed image will appear very fuzzy and no advantage will be perceived. On the other hand, if the image has good resolution, by displaying larger, more detail may be perceived and appreciated. It is precisely for this reason that the term "perceived resolution" is frequently used. Perceived resolution implies that the true resolution really hasn't changed, but our perception of the resolution has changed. *Figures 51* and *52* depict non-acoustic zooms.

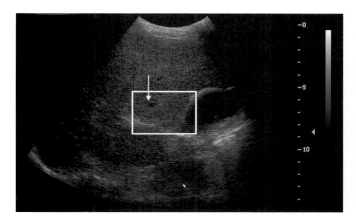

Fig. 51a   **A Small Liver Lesion of 1mm.**

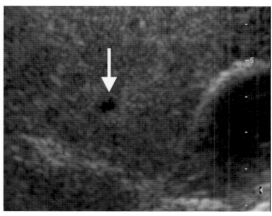

Fig. 51b   **(Non-Acoustic) Magnification of the Liver Lesion**

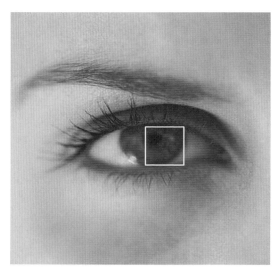

Fig. 52a   **An Eye**

Fig. 52b   **(Non-Acoustic) Magnified Zoom Region**

Chapter 6

20.3 Acoustic Zoom (Write Zoom)

An acoustic zoom cannot be applied to frozen data. Once the image is generated, it is not possible to change the transmitted or receive beam profiles so as to change the resolution of the image. Acoustic zooming is commonly referred to by most texts as a "write zoom" or "write magnification", implying that new data is written to the memory post scan conversion. When an acoustic zoom is employed, the system decides how best to transmit and receive the beams in the region of interest so as to provide optimal resolution. The following diagram illustrates how an acoustic zoom works.

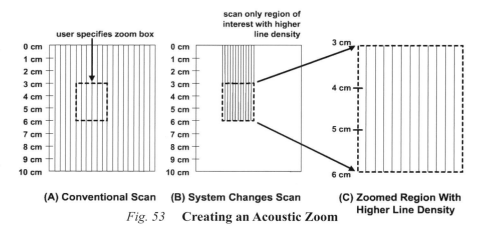

Fig. 53   **Creating an Acoustic Zoom**

Figure 53 demonstrates how a conventional linear image is created. The dotted lines represent individual beams which comprise the frame. When the user places a zoom box within the reference image, the system recalculates how best to transmit and receive the beams so as to provide optimal detail resolution. As shown in *Figure 53*, only the lines within the desired zoom region need to be transmitted. Also, since the maximum depth of interest within the zoom region is 6 cm, the line time is shortened from 130 µsec to 78 µsec. To achieve better lateral resolution, the line density is increased, with narrower transmitted beams. An increase in line density increases the frame time. In this case, the decrease in frame time associated with the smaller scan region and decreased depth will more than compensate for the increase in frame time associated with the higher line density. As a result, the frame rate (the reciprocal of the frame time) will increase. *Figure 54b* demonstrates how the new smaller scan region is displayed in a larger format.

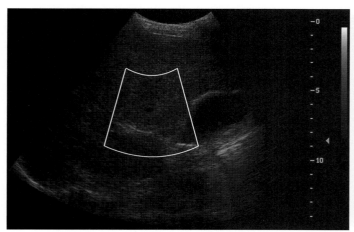

Fig. 54a   **Non-Acoustic (Read) Zoom**

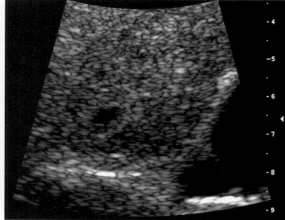

Fig. 54b   **Acoustic (Write) Zoom**

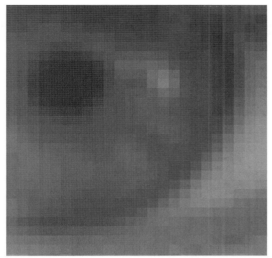

| Fig. 55a | **Non-Acoustic (Read) Zoom** | Fig. 55b | **Acoustic (Write) Zoom** |

Notice the difference in resolution between the non-acoustic images of *Figures 54a* and *55a* and the acoustic images of *Figures 54b* and *55b*. In the past years, greater differences existed between acoustic and non-acoustic zooms for ultrasound images. With technology advances, the quality of the non-acoustic zoom is now only slightly inferior, generally, to the quality of an acoustic zoom.

21. Transmit and Focus Related Alternatives to Conventional B-mode Imaging

Up to this point, we have discussed conventional imaging techniques in which a single acoustic line is transmitted for each displayed line. We have briefly made mention of other techniques in which there is not a one-to-one correlation between the acoustic lines transmitted and the lines displayed. The most obvious imaging technique which does not follow the one-to-one paradigm is color Doppler which will be developed and thoroughly discussed in Chapter 7. With respect to 2-D imaging, we will discuss two of the many techniques which differ from the conventional 2-D imaging approach. There is not a one-to-one correspondence between acoustic lines and the display lines when using multiple transmit foci or when using parallel processing.

21.1 Multiple Transmit Foci

21.1.1 Improved Lateral Resolution
Better lateral resolution than what can be achieved with conventional imaging is often required. We learned in Chapter 5 that the lateral resolution equals the beamwidth, and that the best resolution occurs where the beam reaches its minimum dimension, called the focus. For conventional, single pulse transmission, it is only possible to have one focus per acoustic line (transmit). It is however, possible to build a display line as the composite of multiple transmits, each with a different focus.

Chapter 6

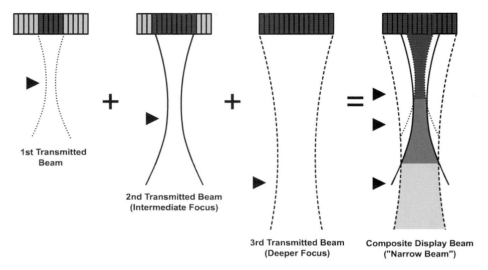

1st Transmitted
Beam

2nd Transmitted Beam
(Intermediate Focus)

3rd Transmitted Beam
(Deeper Focus)

Composite Display Beam
("Narrow Beam")

Fig. 56 **Multiple Transmit Foci**

View Animation and Image Library CD

Referring to *Figure 56*, imagine if the system transmitted and received one line with a very shallow focus, but then did not display the received data as the display line. Instead, the system now transmits and receives a second line with a deeper focus in the same direction as the first line with the shallower focus. Again, the received data is not displayed. The system then transmits and receives a third line with an even deeper focus. The system now has three received lines of data, one short line with a shallow focus, one intermediate line with an intermediate focus, and one deep line with a deep focus. The narrowest portions of each of these three receive beams are then spliced together to form one effectively "narrow" display line. The display line is the composite of multiple acoustic lines. The result is superior lateral resolution as demonstrated by the resulting beam in *Figure* 56.

21.1.2 Degraded Temporal Resolution

By now you have learned that all benefits come at the expense of trade-offs. The improved lateral resolution by transmitting multiple transmit foci is achieved at the expense of a longer time to create an individual display line, and hence, a longer time to produce an acoustic frame. Since the frame time is the reciprocal of the frame rate (frequency), a longer frame time implies a lower frame rate and a potential degradation in temporal resolution. Therefore, the use of multiple foci is generally restricted to applications in which temporal resolution is not as critical as improved lateral resolution. For example, breast and liver imaging commonly use as many as eight foci, whereas adult echo generally restricts the maximum foci to two, and pediatric echo rarely, if ever, uses more than one focus.

Clearly, the more transmit foci used, the longer the time to produce a line, and the greater the effect on the temporal resolution. Additionally, deeper multiple foci impact the temporal resolution more than shallower multiple foci. Although the display line time is affected by the number of foci, you cannot simply multiply the standard line time by the number of foci to determine the multiple foci line time; this approach will overestimate the line time, and hence, will overestimate the frame time. The reason for this overestimation is illustrated in the *Figure 57*.

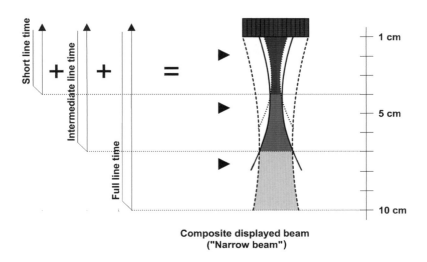

Fig. 57   **Temporal Resolution and Multiple Foci**

With an imaging depth set at 10 cm, with three transmit foci as displayed in *Figure 56*, the time to produce the composite line is clearly not the same as transmitting three 10 cm lines. Since only the very shallowest portion of the first line is being used, there is no sense in receiving signals from the full imaging depth. In this case, the line time is based on receiving signals from the maximum depth of 4 cm. For the second transmit, only the mid-range data is to be used. Again there is no sense in receiving signals from depths that will not be used. In this case, signals are received to the maximum depth of 7 cm before the third line is transmitted. Since the deepest portion of line three is used in the composite line, the entire line time is used.

For completeness, we will perform the calculation to show the difference in line times.

$$Composite\ time = \underbrace{\frac{13\ \mu sec}{cm} \times 4\ cm}_{1st\ Line} + \underbrace{\frac{13\ \mu sec}{cm} \times 7\ cm}_{2nd\ Line} + \underbrace{\frac{13\ \mu sec}{cm} \times 10\ cm}_{3rd\ Line}$$

The single line time for a 10 cm line is 130 μsec. In comparison, this composite from three foci requires 273 μsec, significantly more time than a single line, but not nearly three times as much. As more foci are added, more lines are required, and the composite line time increases. Also, as each of the foci are placed lower in the image, the associated transmit line becomes longer, increasing the composite time.

Figure 58 is an image of a cyst phantom with tissue mimicking material. Notice that there are nine transmit foci used, producing very good lateral resolution in the midfield. Notice that the resolution in the near field is good, but is not as good as the resolution in the focal region. The improved lateral resolution in the midfield is evident by comparing the "cystic" structures in this region with those of the near field. You should also notice that the resolution degrades past the focus until the cysts are barely identifiable.

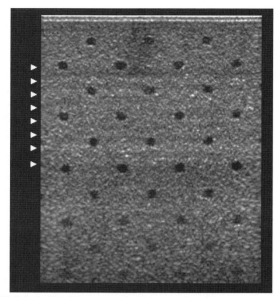

Fig. 58   **Multiple Foci Image of a Phantom Displaying "Banding" Noise**

21.1.3 Banding Noise

Referring to the same cyst phantom image, notice that within the focal region there is some banding which is caused by imperfect fusing of the multiple transmitted lines (brighter echoes stretched laterally across the image). This problem is common with multiple foci. The source of this artifact is related to the change in system parameters that occurs when changing focus. Specifically, setting a deeper focus may increase the number of elements used in the aperture to increase the focal depth and may change the maximum transmit power allowed based on the beam intensity. Changes in either of these parameters will affect the uniformity of the returning echo. Whenever there is a discontinuity in the received echo, there will be a discontinuity in the displayed image.

21.1.4 Dynamic (Continuous) Receive Focus

Although conventional imaging can only create a single transmit focus per acoustic line, an infinite number of receive foci are possible. To understand this fact, you must consider the fundamental difference between transmitting a line and receiving a line for 2-D imaging. Transmitting is an active, momentary function, whereas receiving is a passive more continuous function.

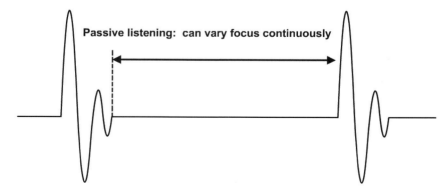

Fig. 59   **Continuous Focusing Occurs During Passive Listening Time**

During the pulse duration, the system actively dictates the parameters of the wave which propagate into the patient, including the focal depth. Once the wave starts traveling within the medium, the system no longer has any control of the wave characteristics. In essence, a process is started in motion, and whatever happens, happens. In comparison, the receiver is turned on as soon as the transmitting ends, and generally remains on until the next transmit event occurs. During the receive time, the system is free to change any receive parameters desired. As a result, it is possible for a system to dynamically change the receive focus based on the depth of the signal returning. For the earliest arriving signals (signals from the shallowest depths), a very shallow receive focus is set. As the signals arrive later in time, the delay profile is changed so that the focus is at the depth of the signal. In this way, the receive beam is as "narrow" as possible, improving the lateral resolution.

Figure 60 demonstrates how dynamic receive focusing is performed. Notice that there are two mechanisms which can be used in conjunction to affect the receive focus. The technique of apodization (changing the active window of the transducer) changes the affective focus as well as changes the delay profile. At time 1, notice that the effective aperture is very small and the delay profile is very steep. Recall that a small aperture produces a very shallow focus. Also recall that a steep delay profile also results in a shallow focus. At time 2, the aperture is larger and the delay profile is less severe. At time 3, the aperture is even larger and the delay profile is very shallow. Finally, at time 4, the full aperture of the transducer is being used for receive and the delay profile is essentially flat, hence focusing at the natural focus of the transducer.

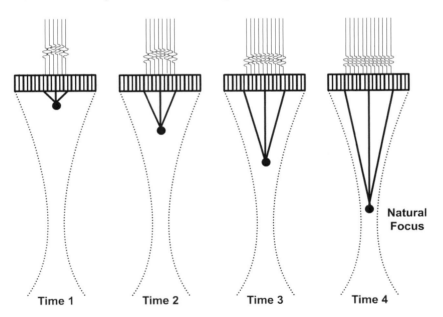

Fig. 60   **Continuous Variable Receive Focusing**

In our demonstration of dynamic focus in *Figure 60*, there are four discrete receive focii displayed. In reality, the system can continuously vary the aperture and delays so as to achieve a nearly continuous receive focus. The only trade-off to running continuous receive focusing is that more computing power and processing speed is required. In recent years, improvements in technology have made this increase in "horsepower" inconsequential such that dynamic receive focusing is performed on almost all systems, all of the time.

Chapter 6

21.2 Parallel Processing

21.2.1 History of Parallel Processing
Between 1990 and 1991, the first parallel processing system was released. I have intimate knowledge of that system since I had the privilege of designing the dual color channel hardware, gain control circuitry, and then the onerous task of balancing the two receive channels within a fraction of a decibel. That system only performed parallel processing for color Doppler. When the system was released, the user was allowed to turn the feature on or off. As the technique was perfected, and as users became used to the feature, parallel processing was defaulted to "on" and the control taken away. Some systems today are now performing parallel processing with 2-D imaging as well as color Doppler and even quad parallel processing in color Doppler.

21.3 Multiple Receive Beams Per Transmitted Beam
As the name suggests, parallel processing implies that there are two "processes" being performed simultaneously. In reality, there are thousands of processes running simultaneously, but with respect to the name, the processes really refers to the formation of two simultaneous receive beams. To create two beams simultaneously requires the ability to run the system as if there are two independent systems running in parallel. In other words, there is not a one-to-one correlation between the acoustic beams and the display beams. In complete contrast to multiple-foci which degrades temporal resolution, parallel processing improves temporal resolution.

21.4 How Parallel Processing Works
In order to receive two simultaneous beams, the transmit beam must also be modified. As illustrated in *Figure 61*, the transmit beam is produced slightly wider than normal. When receiving the data, the transducer is divided into two parallel groups of receiver channels and associated elements. One group of channels is dedicated to receiving, processing and beamforming one beam, while the other group simultaneously processes and forms the second beam. These two simultaneous receive beams must then be sent to the back end for scan conversion and display. A second transmit is then steered in the next required direction of the scan and the process repeated. As a result of parallel processing, twice as many receive beams are generated in the time required to transmit the same number of acoustic beams. Therefore, standard parallel processing potentially doubles the imaging frame rate.

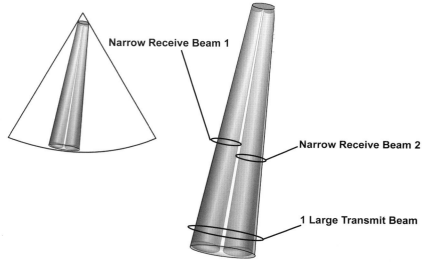

Narrow Receive Beam 1

Narrow Receive Beam 2

1 Large Transmit Beam

Fig. 61   **Multiple Receive Beams Per Transmitted Beam (Parallel Processing)**

22. Averaging Based Techniques

22.1 Adding Signals

In a perfect world, there would be no noise present in any image, and averaging techniques would have no benefits and no purpose. However, since noise is an omnipresent reality, averaging concepts are applied in many different techniques in ultrasound.

22.1.1 Improvement in SNR

The fundamental improvement which results from averaging is an improvement in the signal-to-noise (SNR) of an image. The source of this improvement is rooted in the concept of constructive and destructive interference as discussed in Chapter 1. The following diagram of *Figure 62* demonstrates a weak signal in the presence of noise. Note that thermal noise as exists in electronics is completely random. In other words, there is no way of predicting exactly what the noise will be like from one instant to another.

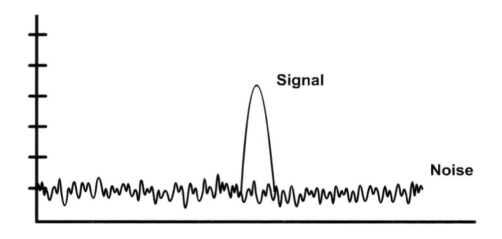

Fig. 62   **Graphical Representation of SNR**

If a second image is taken at a different moment in time, the noise characteristics will have changed, since noise is completely random. In comparison, since the desired signal has a repeatable source, the signal will have the same characteristic as in the first image (signal coherence). If the two images are then added together, the signal from the first image and the signal from the second image will be in phase resulting in constructive interference. The random noise will add only partially constructively. At some points the two noise samples will be in phase, at other points the noise samples will be out of phase, and most of the time, any two samples will be somewhere in between.

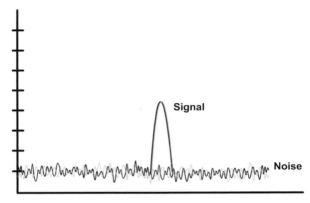

Fig. 63   **Adding Two Image Frames**

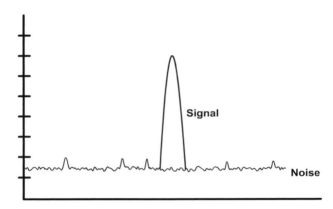

Fig. 64   **Improved SNR from Signal Coherence**

22.1.1 Calculating the Improvement in SNR

Figure 63 demonstrates the advantage of adding two images together. Each successive addition adds the signal constructively and the noise only partially constructively, resulting in increasing improvement in the signal-to-noise ratio. Therefore, if n images are added together, the new signal will be n times larger than the original signal because of the pure constructive interference (signal conherence) *Figure 64*. However, when the same n images are added together, the noise adds up partially constructively and partially destructively, or at a rate of $\sqrt{n}$. Therefore, the SNR increases by:

$$\text{Improvement in SNR} = \frac{n}{\sqrt{n}} = \sqrt{n}.$$

Applying the above rule, if two images are added together, the SNR improves by a factor of 1.4 (the square root of 2). If nine images are averaged together, the SNR improves by a factor of 3.

The following vignette of images demonstrates the improvement achieved in signal-to-noise through averaging. *Figure 65a* is virtually free of all noise. *Figure 65b* has considerable noise. *Figures 65c, 65d,* and *65e* are the resulting images from averaging 2 frames, 9 frames, and 16 frames, respectively. Notice how the noise pattern becomes finer and the signal strength increases relative to the noise strength. In this example, the signal intensity is kept at about the same brightness so that the improvement would be apparent in the decrease in noise amplitude.

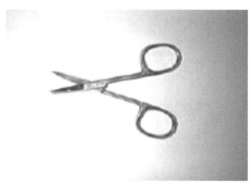

Fig. 65a   **Image of Scissors With No Noise**

Fig. 65b   **Image of Scissors
with Significant Noise**

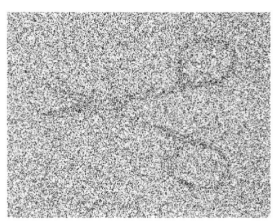

Fig. 65c   **2 Images Averaged
(SNR improved by a factor of 1.4)**

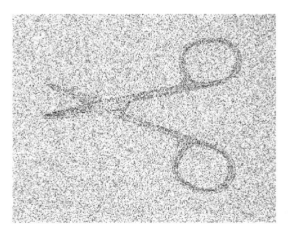

Fig. 65d **9 Images Averaged
(SNR improved by a factor of 3)**

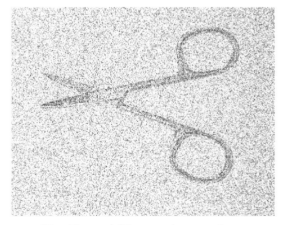

Fig. 65e   **16 Images Averaged
(SNR improved by a factor of 4)**

 **View Animation and Image Library CD**

Chapter 6

22.2 (Spatial) Compound Imaging

The idea of compound imaging is relatively straightforward. Multiple images are created over time and then averaged together to create one image. These multiple images are formed at various angles, as depicted in *Figure 66*. In the early release of compound imaging it was referred to as Sono CT. The generic name is now compound imaging.

22.2.1 Benefits to Compound Imaging

There are two primary benefits to compound imaging. The first advantage, as we have just learned, is an improvement in SNR from adding multiple images together. The second advantage is related to the reduction of specular reflection related artifacts. By creating images at multiple angles, the specular components which cause artifacts, such as reverberation and shadowing, are present in only some of the images. When these images are added together, the specular reflection related artifacts are decreased. Compound imaging tends to reduce the amount of reverberation and shadowing present in an image. *Figure 66* demonstrates how three images might be created at varying angles for compound imaging.

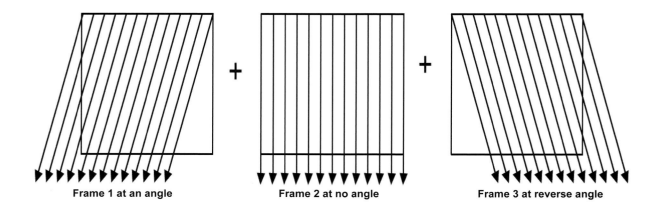

Frame 1 at an angle   **Frame 2 at no angle**   **Frame 3 at reverse angle**

Fig. 66   **Compound Imaging**

Imagine if there were a structure perpendicular to the beams of frame two. This structure would then be a likely source of reverberation artifact. However, in frame 1 and frame 3, since the incident angle to the structure is no longer perpendicular, the specular component is not returned to the transducer, and the artifact is either lessened or weakened. As a result, the artifact will not be as visible in the compounded image as it would in the non-compounded image.

22.2.2 Frame Rate and Temporal Resolution Degradation

Compound imaging is usually performed using between three and nine images. So that the frame time does not degrade, a buffering technique is used such that the last nine frames are used in each new frame displayed. As a new frame is produced, it replaces the oldest frame in the buffer which was taken at the same angle. As a result, there is no change in frame rate. However, this is not to say that there is no degradation in temporal resolution. Anytime averaging is used, short duration events have the potential to be "averaged out" and missed.

Imagine that nine frames are averaged together. Now imagine if a short duration event occurred and was captured in one of the nine frames. In our model above, improvement in SNR came from having the same signal in all frames resulting in a constructive interference (also referred to as signal coherence). In this case, if the signal is only present in one frame, when added with the other eight cases, there will be a destructive interference with the short duration signal, which will diminish the amplitude of the signal. Unless the signal has a very high amplitude, the short duration signal will not be visualized.

22.2.3 Imaging Example

Figure 67a and *Figure 67b* were taken with and without compound imaging. Notice that the conventional imaging of *Figure 67b* has significant reverberation noise, masking the lumen of the vessel. The compound imaging of *Figure 67a*, with compounding, demonstrates a much cleaner image of the lumen. Even more importantly, in this case, there is a thrombus which becomes visible with compound imaging which is not identifiable in the standard image. In this case, the thrombus only became visible when there was enough of an increase in SNR, caused by averaging multiple frames together.

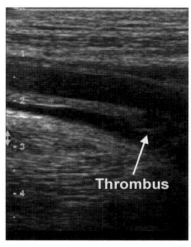
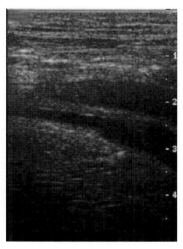

Fig. 67a **Compound Imaging**   *Fig. 67b* **Conventional Imaging**

View Animation and Image Library CD

22.3 Image Persistence

Persistence also refers to an "averaging" technique. Like compound imaging, the goal of persistence is to reduce noise thereby giving the appearance of improved SNR. There are two fundamental differences between a persistence technique and a spatial compounding technique:

- The angle is not changed between frames.
- A weighted average is applied to each frame so that newer frames "count" for more than older frames.

Chapter 6

The word persistence implies a continued presence. The algorithms for persistence can vary significantly from vendor to vendor. There are two main parameters that are varied: how many frames are averaged together and the weighting function applied to each frame. To make this clear, we will consider an example.

$$\text{High persistence} = 0.1 * f_{n-3} + 0.2 * f_{n-2} + 0.3 * f_{n-1} + 0.4 * f_n$$

$$\text{Low persistence} = 0.4 * f_{n-1} + 0.6 * f_n$$

To understand this example, we will need to define a few terms. Each "f" term represents a frame at a given time. The term (f_n) represents the current frame. Therefore, the term (f_{n-1}), represents the frame just previous to the current frame. The multipliers in front express what percentage of the frame to add to the composite frame. In the "high persistence" example, the current frame is being affected by the previous three frames. The displayed frame will be 10% of the frame which existed three frames previously, plus 20% of the frame which existed two frames previously, plus 30% of the frame just previous, plus 40% of the current frame. In comparison, the low persistence example adds 40% of the previous frame to 60% of the current frame.

As mentioned earlier, there are many different algorithms that can be used to create the effect of persistence. It is not likely that any two companies chose to implement persistence in the same manner. Persistence will become a more important topic when color flow is discussed.

22.4 Spatial Averaging
Spatial averaging is another technique which attempts to reduce random noise through averaging. In contrast to the previous techniques which average data from different frames, spatial averaging looks at small local regions within the same frame. *Figure 68* illustrates this concept.

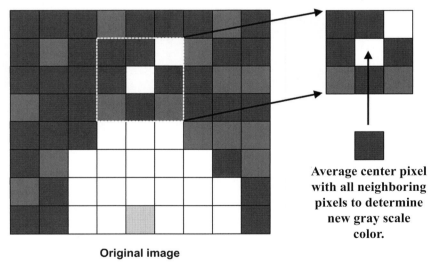

Average center pixel with all neighboring pixels to determine new gray scale color.

Original image

Fig. 68   **"Pre-Smoothed" Original Image**

In *Figure 68*, the "smoothing" algorithm is demonstrated for the pixel in the center of the region enclosed within the dotted white box. The center pixel is averaged with all of the surrounding pixels and re-colorized. Since most of the neighboring pixels are dark, the center pixel is changed from white to a dark gray. This same process is performed pixel-by-pixel across the image, smoothing the image. *Figure 69* represents the smoothed image after averaging is applied on all pixels.

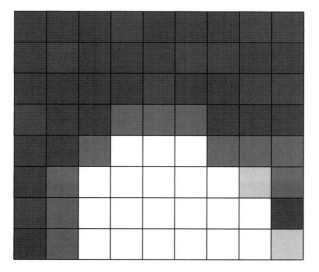

Fig. 69   **Spatially "Smoothed" Image**

The image appears "less noisy" from the fact that averaging tends to reduce noise. In this case, by adding multiple pixels together, the incoherence of the noise tends to add destructively. In comparison, wherever there is signal, the neighboring pixels are also most likely signal, which add constructively. On many systems, this technique is called spatial smoothing, spatial filtering, or spatial averaging. These spatial averaging techniques have been used in ultrasound for many years, although with improved computing power, much more complex algorithms are now employed.

23. Ultrasound Modes

The following is a summary of ultrasound modes and their abbreviations.

A-mode	Amplitude mode
B-mode	Brightness mode
C-mode	Constant depth mode
M-mode	Motion mode

A-mode has already been discussed in Level 1. B-mode has been discussed throughout all of Level 2. However, since 3-D imaging is an advancement of B-mode, a short description of 3-D is included.

23.1 Three-Dimensional (3-D) and Four-Dimensional (4-D) Imaging
To obtain complete structural information, all three dimensions of that structure must be imaged and viewed. One image which could simultaneously display all three dimensions would be ideal. Great strides have been made recently in acquiring and displaying three-dimensional images. 4-D imaging is the presentation of 3-D imaging over time. Acquiring three-dimensional information is difficult because of the increased time requirements to gather information in the third (elevation) dimension. Displaying this information is also difficult because our normal display modes such as prints, films, and monitors really only have two physical dimensions: depth and width, and a third perceived dimension of brightness. For 2-D images, all three of three dimensions are already used. Depth and width

of the image correspond to depth and width in the patient. The third dimension of brightness (hence the name brightness mode) is utilized to demonstrate changes in tissue reflectivity. Using A-mode to display a two-dimensional image has the same difficulty as using a B-mode to display a three-dimensional image: there are not enough display dimensions. The most common current approach to displaying three physical dimensions is to try to develop a perspective and slight rotation of the image. Other approaches include a "wire mesh" presentation, or user determinable 2-D slices. In the future, three-dimensional holograms will probably become the display of choice, but this technology may be long coming.

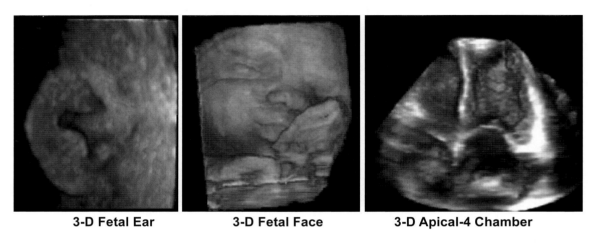

3-D Fetal Ear   **3-D Fetal Face**   **3-D Apical-4 Chamber**

Fig. 70   **Example 3-D Images**

23.2 C-mode (Constant Depth Mode)
For constant depth mode, the ultrasound system electronics employ the distance equation to turn the receiver electronics on and off (gating) as to listen to echoes returning only from a specific depth. This technique can be used to acquire an image slice at a particular depth by moving the transducer back and forth over the patient, and developing the image over time (this technique is rarely used). The most obvious application of a C-mode is PW Doppler. In PW Doppler, the user places the Doppler gate at the specific depth of interest. The system electronics gate out all echoes except those returning from the desired depth.

23.3 M–mode (Motion Mode)
Motion mode (used predominantly for cardiac imaging and fetal heart rate) is a special case of B-mode. In M-mode, a single acoustic line is repeatedly transmitted in the same direction (non-scanned modality). As in B-mode, the returning echo amplitudes are converted to brightness along the line depth. As time passes, these repeated lines are displayed side-by-side, displaying the motion changes over time. Therefore the horizontal axis displays time while the vertical axis displays depth. The motion is determined by your eyes correlating the continuity of certain echoes from one line to the next, as demonstrated in the M-mode of a mitral valve of *Figure 71*.

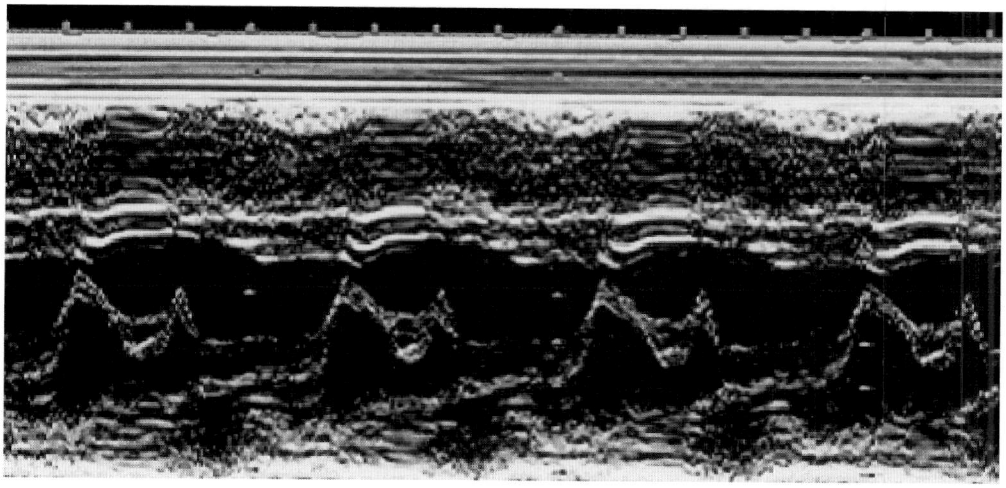

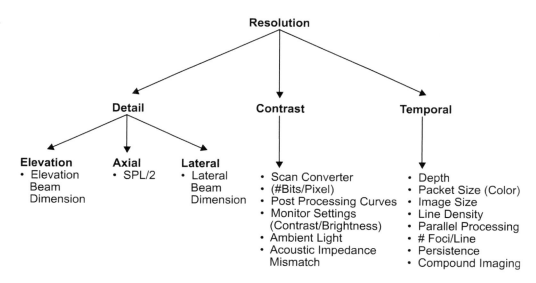

Fig. 71 **Mitral Valve M-mode**

24. Resolution Formally Revisited

Progressing through the various chapters, resolution has been repeatedly discussed and referenced. Since each step has added another level to understanding this multifaceted topic, this section will serve as both a formal review and as a means to integrate the various components into one location.

Resolution

Detail — **Contrast** — **Temporal**

Elevation
- Elevation Beam Dimension

Axial
- SPL/2

Lateral
- Lateral Beam Dimension

Contrast
- Scan Converter
- (#Bits/Pixel)
- Post Processing Curves
- Monitor Settings (Contrast/Brightness)
- Ambient Light
- Acoustic Impedance Mismatch

Temporal
- Depth
- Packet Size (Color)
- Image Size
- Line Density
- Parallel Processing
- # Foci/Line
- Persistence
- Compound Imaging

Fig. 72 **Resolution Chart**

24.1 Detail Resolution

We have already discussed at length the determinants of axial resolution, lateral resolution, and elevation resolution. These three taken together are called detail resolution. As discussed, detail resolution is primarily dependent on transducer characteristics; however, system electronics and the display itself can have an effect. For example, if the system is incapable of producing small enough phase delays, received echoes spaced close in time will be added together, and not kept distinct, thereby reducing resolution. The process of scan conversion can also affect detail resolution as line data is converted into a displayable image format. Also, if the display monitor does not have the adequate number of pixels per area, or not enough horizontal lines, small separations between structures will be lost to pixel size or line density. Furthermore, if the system does not have adequate contrast resolution, two objects that are close together may be visualized as only one object.

24.2 Contrast Resolution

Contrast resolution is the ability to distinguish structures based on variations of brightness. According to most texts and most credentialing exams, the restriction for contrast resolution is the number of bits per pixel in the display (bit depth). In reality, most monitors these days go well beyond what is needed for excellent contrast resolution. The true limit is usually related to one of two parameters, the dynamic range of the human eye, and the non-linear compression necessary to map the enormous signal dynamic range to the smaller dynamic range of the eye. Since most people never change the compression setting while imaging, the chances of missing weak echoes is very real and more common than we would like to admit.

Note: It is conceivable that contrast resolution could be limited by the scan converter. For example, if the scan converter only supported 4 bits/pixel and the display supported 8 bits/pixel, there would still only be 4 bits worth of contrast.

Assume you had a signal with 60 dB of amplitude dynamic range, but the display only supported 4 bits/pixel. In dB, $20 \log(2^4) = 24$ dB. So you have lost 60 - 24 or 36 dB of contrast dynamic range. It may be conceivable that the scan converter is the limiting factor, but it is also conceivable that someone will walk up to you and give you 7.3 million dollars and you won't have to work ever again. The reality is, scan converters used to be a limiting factor, but are not any more with the advances in electronics.

As mentioned, the human eye can only distinguish approximately 64 gray levels simultaneously (6 bits). As a result, increasing the number of bits/pixel of a monitor beyond this limit does not lead to any improvement in contrast resolution. However, having more than 64 shades of gray is useful for a display since more or less contrast may be necessary depending on the lighting in the room. In other words, in a dark room, you would want the display to occupy a lower intensity range, whereas in a bright room you would still need 64 dB of range, but it would need to be at an overall higher intensity. This is why you have a contrast control on your monitors. However, adjusting these controls can be detrimental. Recall that any data storage takes place from the scan converter. If you adjust the contrast on the display monitor, this control does not affect the data you are storing. As a result, what you see on the monitor may not match what you see on replay from your storage device.

Having more bits/pixel is also useful for color. The human eye can see significantly more color shades than gray shades. This fact is easily appreciated by looking at a color photograph of a person's face on a monitor or printed from a printer with fewer than 36 bit color. When more colors exist in a picture than can be presented by a printer or a monitor (too large dynamic range), compression is used. When the compression occurs, there is a loss of "shading" which causes distortion. The result is a very "blotchy" looking image.

 **View Animation and Image Library CD**

24.3 Temporal Resolution

Temporal resolution is the ability to distinguish dynamics, or changes, over time. The principal limit to temporal resolution is the frame rate. Every factor which lowers frame rate lowers temporal resolution. Some examples of these factors are the imaging depth, the imaging frame or sector size, how many foci are being used, the line density, the number of acoustic lines per display line (packet size in color), and whether or not parallel processing is being used. The human eye is capable of discerning the discontinuities associated with data displayed at frame rates somewhere between 15 Hz than 30 Hz. Below 15 Hz, images will definitely appear to "flicker."

As already discussed in Section 17.3, another possible limitation to temporal resolution is the monitor display rate. Recall that the standard United States format has been 30 Hz and that the newer non-interlaced monitors operate at 60 HZ. What happens if you are able to create a scan acoustically at 40 Hz, but the monitor is only capable of displaying 30 Hz? In essence, 10 frames per second are never displayed. This loss of data is one of the reasons why cineloop is so valuable. Cineloop stores all of the frames to be displayed in non-real time. Even when all of the monitors transition to a 60 Hz frame rate, there can still be data lost. However, it is not likely that the monitors will ever go to higher frame rates since 60 Hz is already at or beyond the limit of the human eye.

Finally, techniques which average can deleteriously affect temporal resolution. At times, the degradation is paradoxical in that there is no change in frame rate, yet the temporal resolution is worse. The two "averaging" techniques most commonly used which degrade temporal resolution are persistence and compound imaging. When the ability to perceive short duration events matter, persistence and compound imaging should be reduced or turned off.

25. Real-Time Imaging

Real time imaging implies that all the ultrasound lines are being transmitted, recorded, processed and displayed so as to appear instant and continuous in time. Even though there is a finite amount of time required to build up an entire image, the process happens so fast, that "persistence of vision" makes the image appear continuous. In other words, your eyes do not have the temporal resolution to see the change of one frame to another. Most ultrasound B-mode images have approximately 100 to 400 lines per image. If the image size were increased to say 2,000 lines per image, do you think you could see the frame discordance? What happens when you are using color flow Doppler? (Recall that for color flow, multiple lines are transmitted per packet, lowering the frame rate.)

The advantage of a real time scan mode is improved temporal resolution. Improved temporal resolution minimizes motion artifact caused by patient and sonographer movement, as well as accurately demonstrating structural movements (such as valves).

26. Exercises　Answers Pg. 464-466

1. The _____ determines the initial amplitude, frequency and mode of ultrasound.

   a) receiver
   b) scan converter
   c) recording device
   d) pulser

2. The receiver performs all of the following functions except

   a) amplification.
   b) data storage.
   c) compensation.
   d) compression.
   e) demodulation.
   f) rejection.

3. Amplification is another word for

   a) transmit gain.
   b) receiver gain.
   c) compression.
   d) display contrast.

4. Define each of the following terms

   a) dynamic range
   b) compression
   c) reject
   d) signal-to-noise
   e) noise
   f) signal
   g) preprocessing
   h) post processing

5. Demodulation is a means of signal _____ by removing the initial transmit frequency from the returning echo.

   a) detection
   b) compensation
   c) augmentation
   d) display

6. A compression of 20 dB in amplitude means the range of signals has been compressed or decreased by a factor of _____ .

7.   Give two possible compression algorithms for the following situation.

4 Boxes	**Compression** $\Rightarrow$	**2 Boxes**

Box 1: 2 small white marbles   Box 1: _____

Box 2: 2 large white marbles

Box 3: 2 small black marbles   Box 2: _____

Box 4: 2 large black marbles

8.   In problem #7 how many bits are necessary to display the original uncompressed data? How many after compression?

9.   What is the minimum number of shades necessary to present data? How many bits does this require?

    a) 2, 1
    b) 1, 2
    c) 2, 4
    d) 1, 4

10.   A bi-stable picture is represented by only two shades, black and white, and requires _____ bit(s).

11.   How many bits are necessary to represent 64 gray levels?

12.   How many gray levels can be represented by 10 bits?

13.   Assume 80 dB of amplitude input dynamic range. What is the approximate maximum imaging depth for a frequency of 10 MHz, assuming soft tissue?

14.   Phasing is achieved by _____ shifting the transmit pulses to each of the transducer elements.

15.   Two examples of phasing techniques used with phased array transducers are _____ and _____.

16.   Multiple transmit foci beams have the advantage of _____ and the disadvantage of _____ .

    a) wider display beams, higher frame rates
    b) narrower display beams, higher frame rates
    c) narrower display beams, lower frame rates
    d) wider display beams, lower frame rates

17.   What are the three aspects of detail resolution?

18. Contrast resolution is the ability to distinguish structures based on _____ and is normally dictated by the number of _____ per pixel in the display and the compression mapping.

19. Factors which potentially affect temporal resolution are any factors which lower _____ rate.

27. Conceptual Questions   Answers Pg. 466-467

1. The _____ of an ultrasound system performs five functions: amplification, compensation, compression, demodulation, and rejection.

2. _____ is the process of making small signals larger.

3. _____ is performed by a swept gain control often called time gain control (TGC) or depth gain control (DGC).

4. Compensation is necessary since _____ increases with depth.

5. _____ is a means by which to reduce the signal dynamic range usually through logarithmic amplification.

6. _____ range is a ratio of a maximum to a minimum.

7. _____ is often called signal detection and consists of two stages: rectification and smoothing.

8. _____ is another means by which to limit dynamic range through suppression of smaller, weaker signals.

9. A digital scan converter is effectively a digital _____ block.

10. In the old days, _____ scan converters were used which suffered problems of performance degradation over time, image flicker and fading.

11. The display is most often a _____ (cathode ray tube).

12. The standard CRT in the United States operated with _____ lines at a frame rate of 1/30th of a second.

13. The standard CRT with a frame rate of 1/30th of a second used an interlaced display. First an _____ field of lines 1,3,5,7... is displayed and then an even field of lines 2,4,6,8...is interlaced.

14. More and more non-interlaced monitors are being used which have frame rates twice as fast as an _____ monitor.

15. The smallest division of a display is called a _____.

16.   Better display resolution can be achieved with a higher _____ density.

17.   Each pixel can be represented by multiple _____ which determine how many gray levels a pixel can represent.

18.   Every _____ can represent two shades (black or white).

19.   A 1 bit display is called _____.

20.   A 2 bit display has _____ shades of gray.

21.   A 3 bit display has _____ shades of gray.

22.   A 6 bit display has _____ shades of gray.

23.   _____ is any signal conditioning which cannot be removed or changed once an image is acquired.

24.   _____ is any signal conditioning which can change post data acquisition.

25.   _____ states that all points on a wavefront can be treated as point sources producing spherical secondary wavelets, whose tangential surface predicts the new position of the wavefront over time.

26.   Electronic _____ is achieved by phasing the excitation pulses to each element of the transducer.

27.   Phasing the excitation pulses means that intentional _____ delays are used in exciting transducer elements.

28.   Focusing is also achieved by _____ for electronic transducers.

29.   Multiple transmit focuses improve _____ resolution but decrease temporal resolution (slow frame rates).

30.   _____ resolution includes axial, lateral, and elevation resolution.

31.   _____ resolution is the ability to distinguish between structures based on variations in amplitude or brightness.

32.   Contrast resolution is determined by the scan _____ and the number of bits per pixel in the display.

33.   _____ resolution is the ability to distinguish dynamics or changes over time.

34.   _____ resolution is determined by anything which determines the time it takes to create the image.

28. Video Formats Revisited

28.1 Comparing Line Resolution of Video Formats

The following table compares the line resolution of some of the myriad video formats.

Format	Lines
VHS/VHS-C	220 - 240 lines
BETA	250 lines
8mm	250 - 280 lines
SuperBETA	270 - 280 lines
Analog TV Broadcast	330 lines
Analog Cable TV	330 lines
S-VHS/S-VHSC	400 lines
DVD-R/-RW/+R/+RW	250 - 400+ lines (Depends on recording speed and compression used)
Laserdisc	400 - 425 lines
Hi8	380 - 440 lines
Digital 8	400 - 500 lines
miniDV	400 - 520 lines
microMV	500 lines
ED BETA	500 lines
Commercial DVD	Up to 540 lines

Table 1:   **Comparison of Video Formats**

It is apparent from the above table that there is quite a difference in the detail that different video formats can input into a TV or video display. Basically, VHS is at the bottom of the technology chain in terms of resolution whereas miniDV and DVD represent the best.

28.2 Issues with Analog Videotape

The list of formats can virtually be extended indefinitely. The point is that there are many different "standards" and each standard has benefits and drawbacks. Furthermore, transitioning from one format to another, such as storing data designed to be displayed on a standard U.S. format to VHS, causes degradation in video quality. The problem is further exacerbated by the fact that the U.S. format is considered to be worse than the PAL format or SECAM format because of the poor resolution and extremely poor color variability. These deficits have led to the development of a non-interlaced monitor (60 fps) and high definition, using more horizontal lines to improve resolution (as discussed in Level 2). However, high definition non-interlaced monitors cannot fix the limitations of data already stored in VHS video format. Ultimately the resolution, frame rate, and overall video quality are limited by the "weakest link" in the video processing chain.

The memory requirements to store the real-time data produced by an ultrasound machine (and virtually every medical imaging system) is incredibly enormous. When the data is stored to video, as mentioned above, there is a loss of resolution, since the VHS format is only capable of recording 200 lines of the 525 display lines. Furthermore, a certain amount of noise is introduced by imperfections in the recording process such as, dust, electronic noise, mechanical wear, etc. In addition the color bandwidth of VHS tape is very limited such that a video recording never fully demonstrates the characteristics of the color data as is displayed in the original format.

28.3 Duplication and Conversion Between Formats

The desire to copy data for backup or to convert to another format can present significant issues and potentially cause major degradation in the stored data. There are four possible conversion scenarios:

- Analog to analog (video copying)
- Analog to digital issues (digitizing videotape)
- Digital to digital issues (converting from one digital format to another digital format)
- Digital to analog (not commonly performed so not discussed)

29. Analog to Analog (Video Copying)

As mentioned in Level 2, VHS video has one major advantage over digital formats, the ability to store extremely long records of data. Some of the major disadvantages also discussed include the loss of resolution and color degradation. Depending on the quality of the videotape and the VCR, the color will often "bleed" into surrounding regions as well as distorting the color hue. Using high quality tapes, with a fairly high quality recorder that has been kept free of dust generally results in a fair representation of the original data. However, the videotaped data is never as good as the original data displayed on the ultrasound system monitor. Caution should be exercised when viewing copies of videotapes since each successive copy further degrades the data. In general, for clinical purposes, it is not a good idea to review studies on copied videotape. The following images of *Figure 73* demonstrate the degradation that can occur from videotape copying.

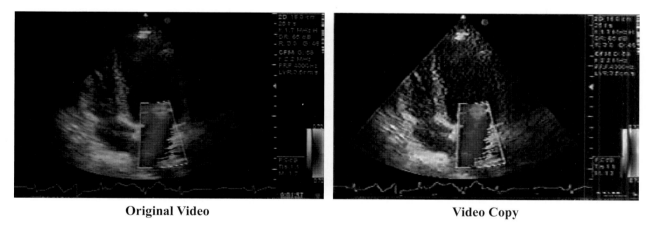

Original Video   **Video Copy**

Fig. 73   **Degradation in Image Quality from Video Duplication**

The images above are of an Apical 4-Chamber view (flow into left ventricle) from an original VHS videotape and from a duplicated VHS video. Notice that the process of video duplication has resulted in a significantly brighter and coarser image than the original videotaped data. The images are also included in color on the animation and image library CD so that the color distortion can be appreciated.

View Animation and Image Library CD

Chapter 6

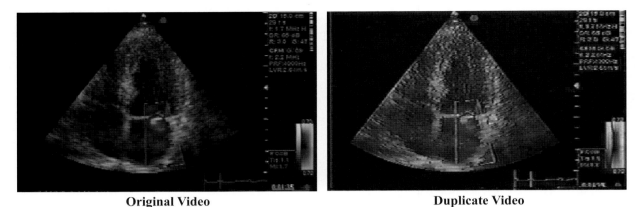

Original Video **Duplicate Video**

Fig. 74   **Dramatic Distortion from Video Duplication**

The two images of *Figure 74* are examples of how significant distortion can occur from video reproduction. In this case there is tremendous distortion of the 2D image with incredible color bleeding. Whenever possible, it is best to review closest to original data as possible.

The images are also included in color on the animation and image library CD so that the color distortion can be appreciated.

30. Analog Data to Digital Data Issues (Digitizing Videotape)

Converting data from analog format to digital format generally requires both hardware and software. At the core of the hardware is the analog to digital converter. The videotape is displayed and the analog signal is input to an A/D converter. The signal is sampled at a rate determined by the clock rate, and the digital output is stored. However, since the converted data requires so much digital memory, the digitally converted data is usually first put through a digital compression scheme before data storage. There are therefore two major drawbacks to data that has been converted from analog to digital.

1. The videotaped data is already not as good as the original data.
2. The compression technique used can further distort the data.

31. Comparison of Digital Memory Devices

Remember that the main issue is how to store enormous amounts of data in limited memory. In time, as memory technologies allow for even larger memory at cheaper costs, this problem may abate but will likely never completely go away. The following table demonstrates how digital memory has changed over recent years and gives an indication of how quickly technology is changing.

Pegasus Lectures, Inc.

Device	Storage capacity	Comments
Floppy Disk	1.4 Megabytes	Almost extinct now
Zip Disks (100)	100 Megabytes	Virtually extinct
Zip Disks (250)	250 Megabytes	Virtually extinct
CD	720 Megabytes	Now making 2 layered to increase capacity
Magneto optical	640 Megabytes	Many systems have MO drives built in
DVD	4.38 Gigabytes	Single side and single layer
	7.95 Gigabytes	Single side, double layer
	8.75 Gigabytes	Double sided, single layer
	15.9 Gigabytes	Double sided, double layer
Hard drives (5 years ago)	2 – 10 Gigabytes	Earliest computers had 128 Kilobytes of memory. Now some computers come with multiple hard drives installed.
Hard Drives (2 years ago)	10 – 40 Gigabytes	
Hard Drives (now)	40-140 Gigabytes	

Table 2: **Comparison of Digital Memory Devices**

With the size of modern digital storage devices you would think that adequate memory would not be a problem. However, a few minutes of pure (uncompressed) video would easily fill up most storage devices. This by itself is a problem, but even getting around the insufficient memory issue leaves the large issue of the ability of the CPU and data bus to move, process, and display such enormous amounts of data. The net result is that virtually all digital data must go through a compression scheme for storage and then a decompression scheme for playback. The software used to perform the compression and decompression is referred to as a CODEC (COmpression and DECompression software).

32. Digital Formats and Compression

32.1 Data Compression and Decompression (CODEC)

A CODEC is a means by which to store data such that less memory is required. Ideally, there would be no loss in data quality with compression. The reality is that there is a significant trade-off: higher compression ratios generally lead to more distortion and loss of data fidelity. There are virtually hundreds of CODECs used today to compress digital data. Each CODEC takes different approaches in an attempt to maximize compression while minimizing loss (a decrease in video quality). Regardless of the approach taken, all video compression schemes result in some video quality degradation. If the loss is not readily apparent during realtime playback, then the degradation is generally considered acceptable. However, with medical applications where the playback may be halted and measurements made from a single frame, the video loss that was not apparent in realtime may now become a significant problem, altering or even rendering the diagnosis incorrect. As a result, the compression used must be very carefully chosen to guarantee that the clinical characteristics necessary for the diagnosis have not been improperly altered.

32.2 Video Formats Versus CODEC

There is so much confusion between what constitutes a video format, what constitutes a video CODEC and variations from format to format and CODEC to CODEC, that it is instructive to briefly discuss the differences.

A video format is actually a standard. Multiple CODEC can belong to an individual format. For example, AVI is actually a format, not a specific compression scheme. It is possible to have video in the AVI format, each that was created using a different CODEC. As a result, two AVI's of the same video, but using different CODEC, will not necessarily be the same. MPEG-4 is another example of a video format that is often confused as being a CODEC.

The following table was modified from a table included in a website article entitled: <u>Digital Video,</u> <u>MPEG and Associated Artifacts,</u> by Shanawaz A. Basith and Stephen R. Done, at the Departments of Computing & Electrical Engineering, Imperial College, London. The table presents some of the video formats that exist, their respective benefits and drawbacks.

32.3 Comparison of Video Formats

Format	Advantages	Disadvantages
Intel Indeo	• Uses an uncompressed audio format that does not need decoding • Inexpensive to compress analog video • Video can be compressed at low frame rates and picture sizes • Supports low data rates	• When using low frame rate, the quality cannot be improved with faster hardware • Frame rates are slow
Cinepak	• Uses an uncompressed audio format that does not need decoding • Better colour resolution than Indeo	• Suffers from the same problems as Indeo • Generally lower frame rates than Indeo
QuickTime	• Uses an uncompressed audio format that does not need decoding • Has the same advantages as Indeo	• Required Apple platform for encoding and editing - new Quicktime for Windows.
MPEG-1	• Higher resolution and frame rates • Better scaling • CD quality audio • Low data rates	• May require extra hardware • High cost encoding
MPEG-2	• Currently the highest resolution and frame rate available • Supports MPEG-1 format	• Higher data rates • Large storage requirements • Requires extra hardware for decoding • Very high cost encoding

Table 3: **Comparisons of Video Formats**

32.4 A Partial List of CODEC

The list of video CODECs could by itself fill a book. We will include the names of a few that may be most recognizable for edification. Some of the most popular CODEC include: DivX, MPEG-4, Cinepak, Microsoft Video 1, Lossless JPEG, ATI Video, etc.

Viewing this list leads to the natural question: "why are there so many CODEC's?". The answer is simple, as already stated, every CODEC leads to some form of loss. Each CODEC has a special ability to handle certain types of graphics, but at a different cost. The bottom line is, each of these CODEC represent a different tradeoff in quality for varying amounts of compression. In other words, a CODEC that is virtually perfect for compression of slow action movies may be terrible for ultrasound data.

To better understand the tradeoffs, it is valuable to review some of the basic theory supporting various compression algorithms.

33. Compression Algorithms and Techniques

To fully appreciate the video degradation that can result from compression algorithms, it is imperative to first develop a rudimentary understanding of the basic theory behind some of the compression approaches. The following is a list of many (but not all) of the theories on which compression algorithms are based.

- Truncation
- Run Length Encoding (RLE)
- Indexing or Lookup Table
- Spatial Interpolation
- Temporal Interpolation
- Mathematical Transforms
- Statistical approaches
- Motion detection

It is instructive to consider the theory of each approach.

33.1 Truncation

Perhaps one of the simplest approaches is based on truncation. Quite simply truncation involves throwing away some data to reduce the data size. Truncation attempts to compress the data by preserving the most significant data and eliminating only the least significant data. However, there is certainly no way for the algorithm to know which information is critical and which is not. The advantage of a truncation scheme is simplicity to develop and implement.

33.2 Run Length Encoding (RLE)

As the name suggests, run length encoding involves looking for repetition of data (runs), measuring the length of the runs, and encoding the length. Perhaps this approach is most easily understood with a simple example. The following data:

2	2	2	A	B	B	B	B	B	1	1	1	1	1	1	1	C	C	C	C

would be encoded as:

2	3	A	1	B	5	1	7	C	4

which is only 10 digits in the compressed form as opposed to the 20 digits in the uncompressed form, or a compression ratio of 2:1.

Note that the run length encoded data really presents the data as paired information in which the first value represents the actual data, and the second value represents the number of pixels (length of the run) that have that same value in a row. So,

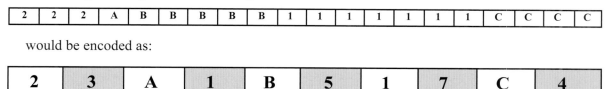

2	3

indicates that the value of 2 was repeated 3 times. Then,

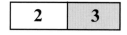

A	1	B	5

indicates that the value of A existed only once before the value of B was repeated 5 times, etc.

From this demonstration, it is clear that RLE can reduce the size for the data needed to represent a frame. The process is then repeated frame by frame so that there is significantly more reduction over the entire video. RLE can also be extended to work in two dimensions (over an array), further improving compression ratios.

However, run length encoding is only truly beneficial when there is significant repetition of values within a data set. When the data varies significantly within a frame, there is very little, if any data reduction. In fact, if the data varies enough, the data size could conceivably become larger (as demonstrated below).

2	1	3	A	B	B	2	B	D

would be encoded to:

2	1	1	1	3	1	A	1	B	2	2	1	B	1	D	1

In this case the compressed data is represented by 16 digits whereas the original data is represented in only 9 digits.

The benefit of RLE is that it is a *lossless* compression scheme, preserving the original video quality. The reality is that RLE by itself rarely results in enough file size reduction to be used in diagnostic ultrasound, since there is significant variance in standard ultrasound signals.

33.3 Indexing (Lookup Table)
The concept behind indexing is that even if data spans a large range of values, not necessarily every value will exist within the data. As a result, the data at each pixel could then be encoded into a smaller value requiring less memory. However, to decipher the code, a table or "index" would be necessary, translating the encoded sequences back to their original values for accurate display. This process is much less than trivial and again has the limitation that if there are many distinct values within the data set, then the compression savings may be minimal or even non-existent.

33.4 Spatial Interpolation
The concept behind spatial interpolation is that each frame can be reduced in size by looking at neighborhoods within the frame. The presumption is that there is some correlation between pixels within a neighborhood, and therefore some of the pixels can be eliminated, reducing the data size. When decompressing the data, the algorithm then makes mathematical attempts to reconstruct the values of the pixels that were decimated to reproduce the entire image. Perhaps an example would best demonstrate this technique:

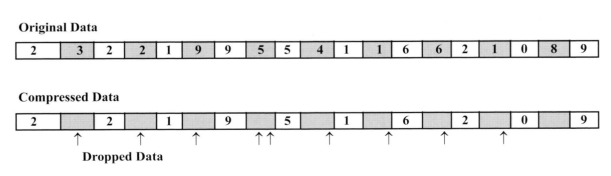

Original Data

2	3	2	2	1	9	9	5	5	4	1	1	6	6	2	1	0	8	9

Compressed Data

| 2 | | 2 | | 1 | | 9 | | 5 | | 1 | | 6 | | 2 | | 0 | | 9 |

Dropped Data

Since the gray squares are skipped, there is half as much data to transmit, in this example, representing a compression ratio of 2:1. For playback, the system then takes the compressed data and attempts to interpolate the missing values as follows:

Interpolated Data

2	2	2	1.5	1	5	9	7	5	3	1	3.5	6	4	2	1	0	4.5	9

Note that this interpolation scheme is not very complex and as a result generates some significant errors (differences between the interpolated values and the original data). More complex non-linear interpolation schemes can be used, but the bottom line is that there will be some amount of error no matter what decompression interpolating algorithm is used. For this simple demonstration case, the error is represented by the difference between the original data and the interpolated data as given in the following array:

Error Data

	1		0.5		4		2		1		2.5		2		0		3.5	

33.5 Temporal Interpolation

The concept behind temporal interpolation is very similar to spatial interpolation except that the data is interpolated over time instead of over physical space. Simplistically viewed, every other frame could potentially be dropped during compression. During decompression, the decompression algorithm would interpolate a frame by looking at the previous and next frame. The interpolated frame would hopefully be close to the original frame that was dropped. Of course non-linear behavior in the data can represent significant problems for this technique. Techniques to overcome the interpolation errors include sending information that tells the decompression algorithm how to reduce the interpolation error in each frame. Of course, the more accurate this correction, the more data is sent, and the smaller the effective compression rate.

33.6 Mathematical Transforms

Another approach is to mathematically transform the data into a complimentary data space. On playback, the inverse transform is applied to try to restore the data. Depending on the data and the transform, this approach can yield large compression ratios. However, there is no one transform that will work well for all different types of video, and the computational power and speed necessary to perform the transformations can become extraordinarily unwieldy. Additionally, there is no guarantee that approximations needed to make the transform solvable do not add significant error into the video. One example of a mathematical transform that can be used is a Discrete Fourier Transform (DFT).

33.7 Statistical Approaches

The use of statistics to characterize data for compressional savings has become a greater reality with faster and more powerful processors. The basic concept is that since some values will occur more frequently in the data than other values, a code can be used to represent the more commonly occurring values. Since the code for the values requires less memory than the actual value, there is a space savings. However, since the codes must be deciphered by the decompression algorithm, the code must also be transferred, somewhat diminishing the space savings.

33.8 Motion Detection

Perhaps one of the most powerful techniques is based on the ability to sense motion and compress accordingly. The basic concept is that from frame to frame, many pixels will have remained static and only objects or structures that are moving need to be encoded. As an example, imagine if there was a video of the trajectory of a ball against a black background. In each of the frames, the black background remains the same and only the position of the ball changes. A motion-based algorithm would look ahead in the frames to see what regions of each frame have changed and encode the data for just those regions. In this example, the only part of the frame that would change is the new location of the ball and the old location of the ball. The data can then be sent as key frames which identify the overall image and motion frames with motion vectors which identify what parts of the image are moving and how much from frame to frame. This technique is extremely powerful and able to achieve significant compression ratios. As a result, this technique is commonly used (in conjunction with other techniques) by most compression algorithms. However, there are certainly a few issues, which become more significant with more complex time variation in the video signal. For example, to detect motion, the algorithm must grid the video into a series of blocks. The algorithm then analyzes each block for changes from frame to frame. If the block is considered "unchanged" then the same block is repeated. When change is identified, the new block is displayed in the new frame. The problem with this technique is two-fold: first, how much of a change constitutes motion, and second, how big or small is the block. When very small changes are recognized within a block, the compression algorithm might decide the changes are not substantial enough to label as motion. This introduces errors into the compressed video. Furthermore, the block size introduces even further quantization errors. As a result, for very well behaved video, this technique achieves impressive compression ratios with no significant video degradation. Conversely, when there is great variation within a frame and from frame to frame, as occurs with ultrasound data, this algorithm can introduce significant errors.

33.9 Combining Algorithms

Most CODEC use a combination of techniques, with various weightings on each. For example, a CODEC designed for simple time transitions with little variation from pixel to pixel within the image can allow the user to very heavily weight spatial, temporal, and motion techniques. If data has significant variance from pixel to pixel but not from frame to frame, then a CODEC which does more temporal encoding will have greater benefits than spatial approaches. Again, the bottom line is that no CODEC is perfect, and all will have losses.

34. Digital to Digital Format Conversion

34.1 Multiple (Iterative) Compressions

Since virtually all digital formats involve compression, converting from one digital format to another digital format implies that the data goes through at least two compressions. Performing multiple (iterative) compressions on the same data (iterative compressions) is a recipe for terrible video loss. People who are trained to process video for a living know that it is critical to preserve the video in its purest form and then experiment with which compression algorithm will yield the best compression ratio while preserving the critical characteristics and quality of the video being processed.

The reason that iterative processing is potentially so catastrophic to video quality is that compression effects are very non-linear. The relatively non-linear errors generated from one compression scheme can grow exponentially when the second compression scheme assumes those errors as actual data. The following two images demonstrate how much distortion can occur from applying multiple digital compression schemes.

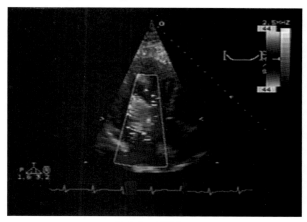 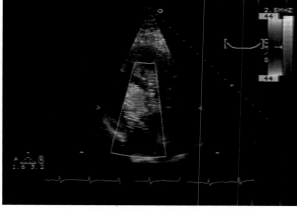

| Original Video | After Analog to Digital Conversion and Iterative Digital Compressions |

Fig. 75   **Distortion from Iterative Digital Conversions**

Note that although these two frames represent the same frame of data, there has been some temporal distortion through the compression scheme such that the flow is no longer representative of the flow actually visualized. It is highly recommended that for clinical review, data never be utilized that has gone through multiple compressions. The rule of thumb should always be to use data that is as close to the source data as possible.

The images of Figure 75 are also included in color on the animation and image library CD so that the color distortion can be better appreciated.

 **View Animation and Image Library CD**

34.2 An "Idealized" Controlled Test

To demonstrate the effects of compression on ultrasound data, a controlled test was performed. An oval filled with a color gradient and overlayed text was inserted into a real ultrasound image and then various compression schemes applied. This test was designed to be intentionally better than real-world situations, since no noise was added to the color box. The following figures demonstrate how much distortion can occur even in this "idealized" situation with various compression schemes applied.

| Original | DivX | DivX Followed by QT | DivX Followed by SVCD |

Fig. 76   **Distortion from Various Compression Schemes for Idealized" Data**

Chapter 6

Notice that the edges of the shape and the text are no longer as well defined as in the original images and that there is a small loss in overall area. Also notice that the color fidelity has been compromised. It is important to realize that this test situation actually represents a situation that is much better than real life since no noise was introduced. Again, the images are also included in color on the animation and image library CD so that the color distortion can be better appreciated.

 **View Animation and Image Library CD**

34.3 A "Closer to Real World" Controlled Test
In the real world, noise is always present in an image. In a follow up test, some noise was added to the color box and the process repeated. The following *Figure 77* demonstrates the results of the controlled test.

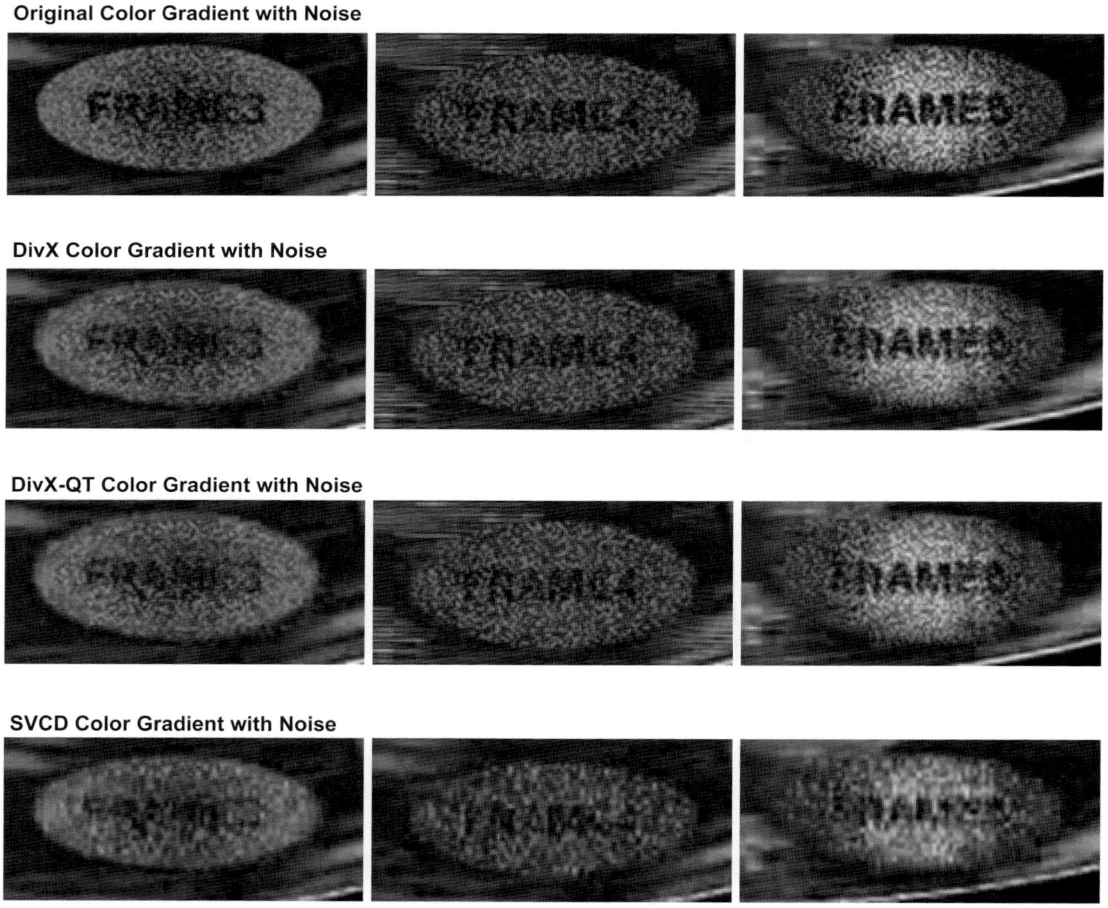

Original Color Gradient with Noise

DivX Color Gradient with Noise

DivX-QT Color Gradient with Noise

SVCD Color Gradient with Noise

Fig. 77   **Distortion with Various Compression Schemes with "Real World" Images**

With the presence of noise in the image, the degradation increases appreciably. Notice again that the edges of the shape and the text are no longer as well defined and that there is a decrease in the color area. Also notice that the color fidelity has been severely compromised in this case. The increased degradation relative to test 2 is expected since the incoherence of the noise presents greater frame-to-frame variance than pure color (as used in test 2). Again, since the DivX CODEC looks for differences (movement) from frame to frame, the noise variance presents a greater challenge. The approximations are obviously less than perfect, and there is obvious color distortion.

Another very noticeable result is the fact that some frames were distorted more than other frames. This increased distortion is most likely the result of the CODEC having recognized a significant enough change in the data to create a new key frame. A key frame attempts to use the current frame with very little compression as a way of "reanchoring" the data back to the actual data.

Again, the images are also included in color on the animation and image library CD so that the color distortion can be better appreciated.

View Animation and Image Library CD

35. DICOM

The purest data is what is seen on the ultrasound system. The only method which currently exists for storing this data uncompressed and unadulterated is through the use of DICOM. DICOM is a standard format agreed upon by ultrasound manufacturers to allow ultrasound images from any system to be viewed on any ultrasound or DICOM reading station. There are three possible methods for storing these DICOM images:
- Store to the ultrasound system's harddrive
- Store to a magneto optical disk
- Store to a external hard drive or computer memory via an Ethernet port

There are two potential disadvantages to DICOM. First, to preserve lossless compression, the compression ratio is not very high, so DICOM data still requires large amounts of memory. As memory is becoming less expensive, this issue is diminishing. Second, DICOM images are only viewable by DICOM readers and not by standard viewing software on laptops or PCs. For viewing on standard laptops and computers without DICOM software, DICOM images are translated into another digital format such as JPEG or Tiff. Once the images are converted from DICOM to any compressed format, there is the potential for some loss of data.

36. Analog Versus Digital Systems

As was mentioned in Level 2, both an analog and a digital system convert the received echoes into digital signals. The primary difference is that a digital system converts the received analog signal much earlier in the processing. The following diagram of *Figure 78* demonstrates the most basic related functions of an analog system.

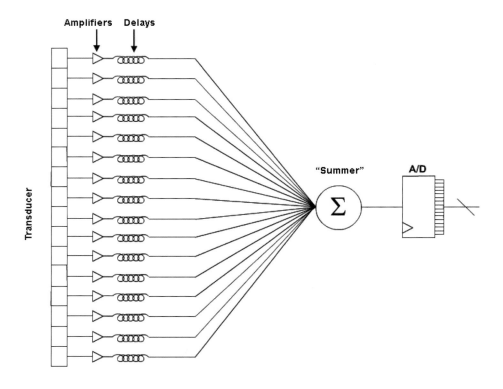

Fig. 78 **Analog Receiver**

Each active transducer element is connected to an amplifier (receiver channel). Since phasing and steering must be performed to make the signals from each channel add correctly, each channel has variable delay lines. Since the signal is still in analog format, the delay lines are analog circuitry. Once the delays have been applied, the signals from each channel can then be added together to yield the appropriately delayed, steered, and focused "beam".

In comparison, the diagram of *Figure 79* indicates the most basic related functions of a digital system. Again every active element is connected to an analog receiver. However, for a digital system, every channel now has a dedicated A/D converter. The signal that arrives at an individual element is converted to digital before delays and summing are applied. Since the signal is now digital, the delays are applied digitally. Digital delays are much easier to implement than the analog delays, allowing for virtually any desired delay profile. Once the signals are delayed, the summing of each channel is also digital. This fact allows the system to easily weight some channels more than others (apodization and windowing functions). The ability to control each channel mathematically introduces incredible processing flexibility that was too costly to design and implement using analog delays and summing.

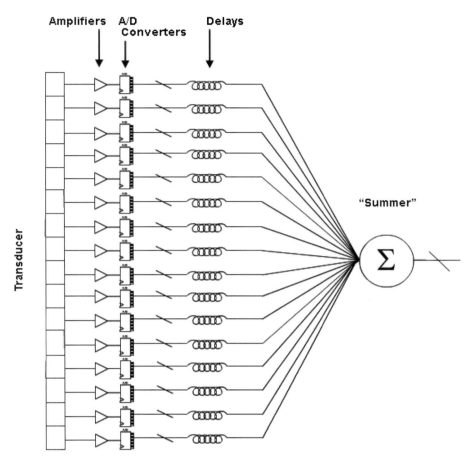

Fig. 79   **Digital Receiver**

In both Figure 78 and 79, we have displayed only the simple block diagrams for the receiver. The transmit beamformer for a digital system also allows greater flexibility than the transmit beamformer for an analog system. Just as the delays for the receiver are digital for a digital system, the delays for the transmit are digital for a digital system. Again, since the delays are now a mathematical process (as opposed to a dedicated hardware design), there is incredible flexibility that allows, opens up the possibility for techniques such as pulse inversion, coded harmonics, and transit apodization to name a few.

System Operation

- It is important to understand terms such as signal, noise, signal-to-noise ratio, and dynamic range.

- Clinically, it is critical that you understand what parameters can be changed to improve signal-to-noise and how to identify good SNR.

- For most exams, the system is divided into two mains subsystems: the receiver (better named the front end) and the scan converter (better named the back end).

- The receiver consists of five basic functions:
    - Amplification
    - Compensation
    - Compression
    - Demodulation
    - Rejection

- The purpose of amplification is to map the very small signals which return from the patient into a higher voltage range which can be visualized on a monitor.

- Compensation is amplification divided into depth regions so that greater amplification can be applied to signals from deeper depths which have experienced greater attenuation than signals from shallower depths.

- The dynamic range of signals returning from the patient span an enormous dynamic range (DNR). To reduce the DNR, a compression scheme is used.

- Since sound is a mechanical wave, as the radio frequency (RF) signal propagates through the body, the interaction with the body changes or modulates the RF signal.

- Demodulation is the process of removing the transmitted radio frequency signal (RF) from the modulated returned echoes.

- The output of demodulation is the early ultrasound mode of amplitude mode (A-mode).

- Rejection is a process by which all levels below a threshold are eliminated.

- The back end of the ultrasound system includes the function of the scan converter which converts the scan of A-mode lines into an interpretable image called brightness mode (B-mode).

- The scan converter aligns the A-mode lines of data into the appropriate image format as well as converting amplitudes into grayscale levels (brightness).

- The principles which are used to interpret an A-mode are the same principles which are used to interpret a B-mode image. Higher amplitude result in brighter pixels, lower amplitudes correspond to darker pixels.

- Transmit power changes SNR and also the potential risk of bioeffects.

- The focus affects power distribution. Adequate SNR may not be achieved if the focus is incorrectly set.

- If appropriate gain settings are not used resulting in apparent poor SNR, higher transmit power than necessary may be used.

- As well as scan conversion, the back end of the system is responsible for data storage.

- The memory in which the image data is stored internally in the system is usually referred to as the cineloop memory.

- Cineloop allows for both real time and non-real time playback of data.

- Analog storage devices such as VHS videotape have the advantage of being able to store very long studies, but have the disadvantage of image quality degradation, poor color, large physical size, and even further degradation with duplication.

- Digital storage devices have the disadvantage of limited study recording time or having to use compression algorithms which degrade the image quality and data fidelity.

- Digital storage quality does not degrade when copied as long as the digital format is not changed. Extreme caution must be exercised to not apply additional compression schemes to already compressed data.

- DICOM is a "lossless" standard digital format agreed upon by the medical device manufacturers.

- The human eye does not have adequate dynamic range to visualize (all at one time) the dynamic range that exists in ultrasound signals returning from the body.

- Additional compression is performed under control of the user in the backend of the system to further compress the dynamic range into the visible range (DNR of the human eye).

- Since all non-lossless compression schemes have the potential for loss of information, care must be taken to verify that disease processes are not missed or misinterpreted.

- Error in two-dimensional measurements can be the result of poor tracing, incorrect angles, or image artifact.

- If the area measurement is generated from a one dimensional radius measurement, care must be taken since any error in the radius is squared in the calculation of the area.

- The same problems exist in three-dimensional measurements as exist in two-dimensional measurements.

- The monitor itself can be the limiting factor in terms of detail resolution, contrast resolution, and temporal resolution.

- You should understand the basic principles of monitors.

- You should know the correct calibration procedure to adjust the brightness and contrast (Gamma curves) of the monitor relative to the ambient light.

- You should know the line resolution of the monitor and the frame rate of the monitor.

- There are many different imaging and processing techniques which tradeoff one imaging parameter to improve another imaging parameter.

- Multiple transmit foci improves lateral resolution at the expense of temporal resolution.

- Parallel processing is a technique to help improve temporal resolution by increasing the acoustic frame rate.

- Compound imaging is a frame averaging technique which reduces noise and artifacts that are generally produced by angle dependent reflection (specular reflection).

- Detail resolution is the collective name for axial resolution, lateral resolution, and elevation resolution.

- Contrast resolution is the ability to distinguish varying tissues based on brightness.

- Contrast resolution can change dramatically with compression settings, gain, transmit, ambient lighting, and monitor settings.

- Temporal resolution is limited by whichever process of image generation, display, or interpretation is the slowest. This can be the acoustic time to scan a frame (acoustic frame time), the time to display the frame (monitor frame rate), or the highest detection rate of the human eye (less than 60 frames per second).

- The advent of digital systems made many new processing techniques economically and technologically feasible. Some of the many techniques facilitated by digital architectures include parallel processing, dynamic receive focusing, many harmonic techniques, and frequency (fusion) compounding.

Note: See Appendix F: Physical Units and Appendix G: Equations for additional review.

Appendix A • Supplemental Exercises

Chapter 1 Mathematics Supplemental Exercises

Answers Pg. 469-474

1. Two quantities are said to be proportional, if an increase in one quantity, leads to a(n) _____ in the other.

2. Two quantities are said to be inversely proportional, if an increase in one quantity leads to a(n) _____ in the other.

3. In the equation $f_{Dop} = \dfrac{2 f_0 v}{c} \cos(\theta)$:

   f_{Dop} is proportional to _____ , _____, and _____.

   f_{Dop} is inversely proportional to _____.

   v is proportional to _____, and _____.

   v is inversely proportional to _____, and _____.

4. Rewrite the equation $f \cdot \lambda = c$

   a)   as $\lambda =$

   b)   as $f =$

   units check $\quad f \cdot \lambda = c \Rightarrow \dfrac{1}{\sec} \cdot m = \dfrac{m}{\sec}$

   Do a unit check for "a" and "b"

   a) $m =$

   b) $\dfrac{1}{\sec} =$

5. If the reciprocal of one over seconds $\left(\dfrac{1}{\sec}\right)$ is seconds, the reciprocal of the reciprocal of one

over seconds $\left(\dfrac{1}{\dfrac{1}{\dfrac{1}{\sec}}}\right)$ is:

6. $\dfrac{3}{2\dfrac{m}{\sec}} = 1.5\left(\dfrac{\sec}{x}\right) : x = ?$

7. $\dfrac{\text{seconds}}{\text{line}} \bullet \dfrac{\text{lines}}{\text{packet}} \bullet \dfrac{\text{packets}}{\text{frame}} =$

8. a) Show graphically how to determine the cos (30°).
   b) Show graphically how to determine the cos (45°).
   c) What is the approximate value of the cos (38°)?

9. a) Show graphically how to determine the sin (30°).
   b) Show graphically how to determine the sin (45°).
   c) What is the approximate value of the sin (38°)?

10. What is the cosine(90°)?

11. What is the cosine(0°)?

12. $\dfrac{1}{\mu \sec} = $ ___ ___ Hz

13. $\dfrac{1}{m \sec} = $ ___ ___ Hz

14. $\dfrac{1}{G \sec} = $ ___ ___ Hz

15. $\dfrac{1}{3n \sec} = $ ___ ___ Hz

16. $\dfrac{1}{\dfrac{1}{3\mu \sec}} = $ ___ ___ $\sec$

17. $\dfrac{1}{Hz} = 1$ ___

18. $\dfrac{2}{Hz} = 2$ _____

19. $(1 \times 10^6) \bullet (1 \times 10^{-2}) =$

20. $(1 \text{ milli}) \bullet (1 \text{ centi}) =$

21. $\dfrac{1 \text{ milli}}{1 \text{ hecto}} =$

22. $(2 \times 10^3) \bullet (1 \times 10^{-3}) =$

23. $(2 \text{ kilo}) \bullet (1 \text{ milli}) =$

24. $\left(\dfrac{2 \text{ kilo}}{1 \text{ milli}} \right) =$

25. Distance = rate • time. Rewrite the equation as:

    a)   rate =

    b)   time =

26. Rate = 1540 m/sec
    Time = 2 μseconds
    Solve for distance.

27. Distance = 60 km
    Rate = 120 km/hr
    Solve for time.

28. a)   How many seconds are in 1 minute?   _____
    b)   How many minutes are in 1 hour?   _____
    c)   How many hours are in 1 day?   _____
    d)   How many days are in 1 week?   _____
    e)   How many seconds are in 1 hour?   _____
    f)   How many seconds are in 1 day?   _____
    g)   How many seconds are in 1 week?   _____

29.   Write out the steps for determining the cosine of an angle.

Step 1: draw the _____ circle.
Step 2: draw the _____.
Step 3: Project the intersection between the angle and the _____ onto the _____ axis.
Step 4: Read the value on the _____ axis.

30.   Repeat number 29 for the sine of an angle.

31.   Calculate the area of a circle if the diameter is 4 cm.

32.   Calculate the volume of a sphere if the radius is 2 mm.

33.   If the radius of a circle is doubled, what change occurs to each of the following parameters?

a)   diameter

b)   circumference

c)   area

d)   volume

34.   If the radius, r, of a vessel decreases by 10%, what is the residual radius percentage?

35.   If the radius, r, of a vessel decreases by 10%, what is the residual area percentage?

36.   If the radius, r, of a vessel decreases by 10%, what is the percentage area change?

Pegasus Lectures, Inc.

Chapter 2 Waves Supplemental Exercises

Answers Pg. 475-488

1. Waves are classified according to whether or not they need a medium in which to propagate. A wave which needs a medium is called a(n) _____ wave, a wave which will work in a vacuum (does not need a medium) is called a(n) _____ wave.

2. A classification within mechanical waves is which way the particles within the medium are displaced relative to the wave direction. These two classifications are called _____ and _____.

3. Sound is a _____ , _____ wave.

4. The classification of waves as _____ indicates that there is a physical interaction between the wave and the _____.

5. Frequency has units of:

6. The period has units of:

7. For a 10 MHz wave, determine the period in

    a)   soft tissue

    b)   bone

    c)   air

    d)   water

8. For a 10 MHz wave, determine the wavelength in

    a)   soft tissue

    b)   bone

    c)   air

    d)   water

9. The period for a 10 MHz wave is _____. Multiplying the frequency times the period yields _____.

10. What determines the frequency?

    a) system and transducer
    b) medium
    c) system and medium
    d) transducer

11. What determines the period?

    a) system and transducer
    b) medium
    c) system and medium
    d) transducer

12. The propagation velocity has units of

    a) distance.
    b) time.
    c) 1/distance.
    d) distance/time.

13. The wavelength has units of _____ .

14. Write the equation which relates frequency, wavelength, and propagation velocity in these different forms.

    a) $f =$
    b) $\lambda =$
    c) $c =$

15. What determines the propagation velocity?

    a) frequency
    b) system, transducer, and properties of medium
    c) system and transducer
    d) properties of medium

16. Since frequency is determined by the system and transducer, and the propagation velocity depends on properties of the medium, and since f, λ, and c are related, what must the wavelength depend on?

    a) system and transducer
    b) properties of medium
    c) just frequency
    d) frequency and propagation velocity

Pegasus Lectures, Inc.

17. Two different ultrasound systems are used for the same view on the same patient. If the wavelength is different, then the _____ must be different.

18. Using the same frequency transducer on two different patients, if the wave length is different then the _____ _____ must be different.

19. If both the frequency and propagation velocity double, the wavelength will _____.

20. As frequency increases, the wavelength _____.

21. The _____ is defined as the maximum variation of a(n) _____ variable.

22. The four acoustic variables are:

    a)   _____
    b)   _____
    c)   _____
    d)   _____

23. The amplitude = max - _____ = mean - _____ = $\dfrac{\text{max - }\rule{2cm}{0.4pt}}{2}$

24. What is the amplitude of the signal defined by
    max = 4 Volts
    min = -4 Volts

25. What is the amplitude of the signal defined by
    mean = 0 Volts
    min = -4 Volts

26. Since Volts is a unit of amplitude, if a voltage ratio is given, the _____ form for decibels must be used.

27. A change in amplitude by a factor of 2 represents a change

    a)   of a factor of _____ in power.

    b)   equal to _____ dB.

28. Intensity $= \dfrac{\rule{2cm}{0.4pt}}{beam\ area}$

29. If the beam area is cut in half and the power remains fixed, the intensity _____.

30. Give the units for power and intensity.

31.	Density equals mass divided by volume. The more particles of a specific medium per volume, the higher the density. How does propagation velocity change with density? (assume no change in stiffness)

32.	A stiff material is very inelastic, or incompressible. How does propagation velocity change with stiffness?

33.	Match the following:

water	331 m/sec
air	500 m/sec
lung	1440 m/sec
liver	1495 m/sec
kidney	1510 m/sec
muscle	1560 m/sec
bone	1560 m/sec
blood	1560 m/sec
brain	1570 m/sec
fat	4080 m/sec

34.	What are the distinctions between infrasound, audible sound, ultrasound, and diagnostic ultrasound?

35.	Using the amplitude form of dB, a factor of 10 equals how many dB?

36.	Using the power form of dB, a factor of 100 equals how many dB?

37.	Looking at your answers from problems - 35 and 36, what difference is there between changing the amplitude by a factor of 10 and the power by a factor of 100?

38. dB stands for decibels and is
    a)   a ratio.
    b)   a power ratio.
    c)   an amplitude ratio.
    d)   a difficult thing to figure out mathematically.

39. Logarithms convert multiplication into _____ and division into _____ .

40. <u>Power factor</u>   <u>dB</u>

    100   =   20 dB
    9.2   =   9.64 dB
    920   =   _____

41. <u>Amplitude factor</u>   <u>dB</u>

    100   =   40 dB
    3   =   9.5 dB
    33.3   =   _____

42. A factor of 1/2 (in power)   =   -3 dB
    A factor of 2 (in power)   =   ____ dB
    A factor of 1/2 (in amplitude) =   ____ dB
    A factor of 2 (in amplitude)   =   ____ dB

Chapter 3 Attenuation Supplemental Exercises

Answers Pg. 481-484

1. Unscramble the following letters to find three wave interactions with media which account for attenuation.

    a)   ptaobrsino

    b)   ctrfleenoi

    c)   ctrfnoarie

2. Of the three factors listed above, which is the dominant factor creating attenuation.

3. Absorption _____ with increasing frequency, decreasing penetration.

4. _____ principle states that all points on a wavefront can be treated as point sources producing spherical secondary wavelets whose tangential surface predicts the new position of the wave over time.

5. What law governs how much refraction occurs?

6. State Snell's law. Make sure to define each term.

7. If the propagation velocities in two interfacing media are equal, the angle of incidence will equal the
    a)   reflection angle.
    b)   transmission angle.
    c)   the angle between the wavefront and the interface.
    d)   b and c.
    e)   a, b, and c.

8. For normal incidence, if the acoustic impedances are identical for medium 1 and medium 2 then there will be
    a)   a small reflection.
    b)   a large reflection.
    c)   a small transmission.
    d)   no reflection.

9. For normal incidence, medium 1 and medium 2 have significantly different propagation velocities and densities. However, the acoustic impedances are identical. Which of the following is true?
    a) There will be a small reflection.
    b) There will be a large reflection.
    c) There will be a small transmission.
    d) There will be no reflection.

10. Since 1- (reflection coefficient) = transmission coefficient, what can be said about answers b and c of question #9?
    a) They are very different answers.
    b) They are the same answers and therefore are not correct.
    c) They make no sense.

11. Given c_t = 4000 m/sec and c_i = 2000 m/sec. For what incident angle will there be total internal reflection (θ_t=90°)?

12. If $c_t > c_i$ what can be said about the incident and transmitted angles?

a) $\theta_i = \theta_t$

b) $\theta_i > \theta_t$

c) $\theta_t > \theta_i$

13. If the density is in units of kg/m³ and c is in units of m/sec, what are the units for acoustic impedance?

    1 Rayl =

14. The approximate acoustic impedance of tissue is 2 MRayls. What can be said about the acoustic impedance of the matching layer and PZT material of a transducer?
    a) PZT < matching layer < 2 MRayls
    b) 2 MRayls < PZT < matching layer
    c) matching layer < 2 MRayls < PZT
    d) 2 MRayls < matching layer < PZT

15. If the incident angle is 30°, the transmitted angle is 60°, and the propagation velocity in the incident medium is 1495 m/sec, what is the propagation velocity in the transmission medium?

16. Whether specular reflection or scattering occurs depends on whether or not the insonified structure looks small or large and smooth or rough with respect to the _____. If the structure looks large and smooth _____ reflection occurs. If the structure looks small or rough, _____ occurs.

17. Which type of reflection returns more acoustic energy to the transducer, if the structure surface is perpendicular to the beam of the transducer?

18. Which type of reflection is responsible for giving the apparent tissue texture?

19. Since scattering increases with frequency, you would expect to see (more / less) tissue texture with a lower frequency transducer. (Circle the correct answer.)

20. Since blood cells tend to be tiny with respect to the wavelength of diagnostic ultrasound, what type of reflection would you expect?

21. Using a 2 MHz transducer, if an ultrasound beam goes through 2 cm of muscle and 15 cm of soft tissue, by how much has the beam been attenuated (in dB)?

22. Using a 5 MHz transducer, how much attenuation would occur to a beam (round trip) to and from a structure 5 cm deep in tissue?

Chapter 4 Pulsed Wave Supplemental Exercises

Answers Pg. 485-489

1. The PRF (pulse repetition frequency) would best be described as

    a) the time between two consecutive pulses.
    b) the frequency within the pulse.
    c) the time between two peaks within a pulse.
    d) the frequency of pulse repetitions.

2. The PRP is the _____ from the start of one pulse to the start of the next.

    a) time
    b) distance
    c) length
    d) frequency

3. State the equation which relates the PRF and the PRP.

4. Which of the following would be a likely PRF in ultrasound?

    a) 1 MHz
    b) 2 MHz
    c) 10 kHz
    d) 10 Hz

5. If you are told the PRF is 20 kHz, what additional information do you need to calculate the PRP?

6. How long does it take for ultrasound to travel in soft tissue a distance of:

    a) 1 cm
    b) 2 cm
    c) 10 cm
    d) to a target 10 cm and back to the transducer.

7. If the maximum imaging depth is 10 cm, and there are 128 lines per frame, how much time does it take to shoot one frame?

8. Convert your answer in #7 into a frame rate.

9. If the maximum imaging depth is 10 cm and there are 4 packets per line and 128 lines, how long does it take to shoot a color frame?

10. If the 2-D (B mode) and color frames are interlaced, how much time does it take between color frames?

11.   Convert your answer from #10 into a frame rate.

12.   Given the above scenario, which of the following changes would increase frame rate the most?

        a)   skip the 2D frame

        b)   cut the color sector in half

        c)   switch to a higher frequency transducer

        d)   change the color packet size from 4 to 3

13.   The operating frequency of a transducer is 2.0 MHz. If a pulse consists of 4 cycles, what is the pulse duration?

14.   The period of a transducer is 0.5 μsec. If a pulse consists of 4 cycles, what is the pulse duration?

15.   Which of the following will not result in a shorter pulse duration?

        a)   using a higher frequency
        b)   using fewer pulses
        c)   using a smaller period
        d)   a lower propagation velocity

16.   Which system would have a short pulse duration?

        a)   system A: 10 MHz, 2 cycles/pulse
        b)   system B: 10 MHz, 4 cycles/pulse
        c)   system C: 2 MHz, 2 cycles/pulse
        d)   system D: 2 MHz, 4 cycles/pulse

17.   If you work 12 hours a day, what is your daily duty cycle?

18.   If you work all day, 5 days per week, what is your weekly duty cycle?

19.   If a pulse has a duration of 4 msec and a pulse repetition period of 10 msec, what is the duty factor?

20.   If a pulse has a duration of 4 msec and a pulse repetition frequency of 0.1 kHz, what is the duty factor?

21.   The operating frequency of a transducer is 2 MHz, and there are 4 cycles per pulse. The pulse repetition period (equivalent to the line time) is 130 μsec. What is the duty cycle?

22.   The operating frequency of a transducer is 2 MHz and there are 4 cycles/pulse. If the maximum imaging depth is 10 cm, what is the duty cycle?

23.   The key word indicating the units for spatial pulse length is the word "length". So spatial pulse length has units of

        a)   time
        b)   distance
        c)   distance/time
        d)   1/time

24.   If the pulse duration = (#cycles/pulse) • (period), the spatial pulse length = (#cycles/pulses) • (_____).

        a)   period
        b)   wavelength
        c)   frequency
        d)   propagation velocity

25.   Since the spatial pulse length is proportional to the wavelength, and the wavelength is proportional to the propagation velocity and inversely proportional to the frequency, what can be said about the spatial pulse length and the frequency? What can be said about the spatial pulse length and the wave length?

26.   For a 4 cycle pulse with an operating frequency of 1.54 MHz, what is the spatial pulse length in soft tissue?

Chapter 5 Transducers Supplemental Exercises

Answers Pg. 490-492

1. In general a transducer converts _____ from one form to another.

2. The principle used by ultrasound transducers is called the _____ effect.

3. Ultrasound transducers actually act as two different types of antennas. On transmit, they convert voltage to _____ energy. On receive, they convert _____ energy back to _____.

4. Quartz is a naturally piezoelectric material.   True or False

5. No material which naturally does not exhibit piezoelectric properties can be made piezoelectric. True or False

6. Materials cannot lose their piezoelectric properties at high temperature.   True or False

7. The Curie temperature for PZT is approximately $300°\,C$.   True or False

8. There are actually 3 planes in ultrasound imaging although only 2 are displayed in real-time 2-D imaging. The axial plane corresponds to the _____, the lateral plane corresponds to the _____ and the elevation plane corresponds to the slice _____.

   (Choices: thickness, depth, width)

9. Draw a single disc shaped transducer and draw the approximate beam profile. (Make certain to label the NZL, focus, 2 • NZL, beamwidth, Fresnel, and Fraunhofer zones.)

10. The use of the name "mechanical" for a transducer implies the means by which it is

    a)   focused.
    b)   steered.
    c)   assembled.
    d)   all of the above.

11. A broad depth of field means that a beam converges and diverges to and from the focus

    a) quickly.
    b) slowly.
    c) more than once.
    d) none of the above.

12. Which transducer style has a variable focus in both the lateral and elevation planes?

13. Which of the following transducers can be <u>electronically</u> <u>steered</u>? (more than one may apply)

    a) Sector phased array
    b) Annular array
    c) Phased linear array
    d) Linear switched array

14. Draw a simple diagram of the major components of a transducer. Explain what function each component serves.

15. The idea of pulsed mode transducer operation is very familiar to you. If you ring a bell or strike a piece of crystal you will hear a ringing sound. The thicker the material, the lower the pitch. For ultrasound transducers, the operating frequency, in a pulsed mode, is given by

    $$f_o =$$

16. In continuous mode the frequency is determined by the excitation or transmit voltage, not the crystal thickness. So, if the thickness of a crystal is increased but the excitation frequency remains constant in CW mode, the operating frequency will _____.

17. Give the equation for the NZL in terms of transducer diameter and frequency.

18. If an unfocused disc-shaped transducer has an aperture of 10 mm, the beamwidth at the focal depth and twice the focal depth is _____ and _____.

19.   Unscramble the four most common means of focusing.

a)   enlsse
b)   vurcde elmeenst
c)   ceeconiltr
d)   rrromis

20.   Focusing can only affect the _____ field.

21.   The resolution, defined as the spatial pulse length divided by 2, is _____ resolution.

22.   Three synonyms for lateral resolution are:

23.   Three synonyms for longitudinal resolution are:

24.   The beamwidth approximately defines the _____ resolution.

25.   What factors can affect the

a)   lateral resolution:

b)   longitudinal resolution:

1. Conventional B-mode imaging spans a dynamic range of approximately

    a)   10 dB
    b)   20 dB
    c)   50 dB
    d)   80 dB
    e)   150 dB

2. The human eye is capable of seeing over a great dynamic range, but not over the entire range at the same time. To choose what range of the overall dynamic range can be viewed, the pupil constricts and dilates. The maximum dynamic range of the human eye at one instance is ___ dB.

3. Since attenuation increases _____ with increasing depth, compensation must be

    _____ .

4. The process of multiplying a signal so that it has a higher amplitude is called _____.

5. A critical process for decreasing the dynamic range of a signal is called _____.

6. Non-linear _____ is necessary in processing diagnostic ultrasound because of the enormous signal dynamic range.

7. A steeper TGC profile is necessary when using a higher frequency transducer since _____ increases with increasing frequency.

8. A flattening of the TGC profile is expected over a region dominated by fluid since fluids tend to be relatively _____ .

9. If a signal spans 80 dB of dynamic range, that is equivalent to saying that the ratio of the largest component of the signal to the smallest component of the signal is _____ to 1.

10. Given that a signal spans a dynamic range of 80 dB and that for a given lighting condition, the eye can only see 10 shades of gray, by what factor would the signal have to be compressed to be visualized?

11.   Given this graphic description of the signal, describe what will happen to the ability to visual-
        ize the mass when compression is applied to make the signal dynamic range match the dynamic
        range of the eye.

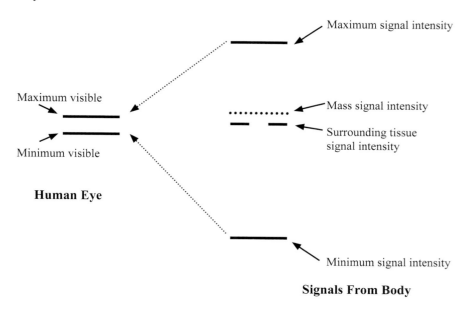

12.   The process of _____ detects the signal "changes" which affect the RF (radio fre-
        quency) transmitted signal.

13.   The early modality of ultrasound which results from the processing stage of demodulation is
        called _____ .

14.   An ultrasound system can be envisioned as a series of processors such as the _____, the
        _____ converter, video display, and signal storage device.

15.   The processes of gray-scaling, performing calculations, tissue colorization, and video compres-
        sion all take place in what part of the ultrasound system?

16.   With a signal to noise ratio of 10:1, if the noise has an amplitude of 1 mV, the signal would have
        an amplitude of _____ .

17.   Increasing the receiver gain improves the signal to noise ratio. (True or False) Explain:

18.   Name at least three ways of potentially increasing the Signal to Noise Ratio of an ultrasound im-
        age at a depth of 6 cm.

19. Name the five basic functions of all ultrasound receivers.

1) _____
2) _____
3) _____
4) _____
5) _____

20. Which receiver function would convert the signal of figure A below, into the signal of Figure B below?

Figure A   Figure B

21. Standard U.S. video format has been an interlaced monitor with a frame rate of _____ and _____ lines. Newer, non-interlaced monitors with a frame rate of _____ and more lines per frame (High Definition) are becoming the new standard.

22. The reason that a higher video monitor frame rate is significant for diagnostic ultrasound is that the _____ resolution can be affected by the monitor frame rate.

23. How many shades of gray can be presented using an 8-bit video display?

24. The range of signal amplitudes a system can process without _____ distortion is called the _____ .

25. Assuming that an ultrasound system has approximately 50 dB of input dynamic range, what is the maximum imaging depth possible using a 5 MHz transducer (assuming soft tissue)?

26. Repeat problem #25 assuming muscle instead of soft tissue.

27.   Referring to problems #25 and #26, assume that the attenuation rate is halfway (in dB) between the attenuation rate of muscle and of soft tissue. What would the maximum imaging depth be?

28.   Using multiple transmit foci improves _____ resolution at the expense of _____ resolution.

29.   Increasing from a single transmit focus to four transmit foci would most likely decrease the frame rate by what factor?

    a)   16
    b)   4
    c)   2.5
    d)   1

    Explain:

30.   Imaging in a bright room, a sonographer increases the monitor brightness so as to adequately visualize the image. While imaging, data are stored to a storage device for later review. The reviewing physician complains that the image is too dark and "contrasty." The reason is:

31.   Which of the following approaches would yield the best imaging results on a large, difficult to image patient?

    a)   4 MHz transmit and receive, 1.2 cm aperture
    b)   2 MHz transmit and receive, 2 cm aperture
    c)   2 MHz transmit and receive, 1 cm aperture
    d)   2 MHz transmit, 4 MHz receive, 2 cm aperture

    Explain:

32. Which of the following approaches would yield the best imaging results on a large, difficult to image patient?

   a) 6 MHz transmit and receive, 0.8 cm aperture
   b) 2.5 MHz transmit and receive, 2 cm aperture
   c) 2 MHz transmit, 4 MHz receive, 1.8 cm aperture
   d) 1.4 MHz transmit, 2.8 MHz receive, 2 cm aperture

   Explain:

33. In A-mode, the vertical axis corresponds to _____, and the horizontal axis corresponds to _____.

Appendix B • Answers to Chapter Exercises

Chapter 1 Mathematics

Section 1.5 Exercises   (Pg. 4)

1. Rounded calculation: round up 24 to 25 so 24 x 6 is approximately 25 x 6 = **150**.
    Actual calculation: 24 x 6 = (25 – 1) x 6 = (25 x 6) – (1 x 6) = 150 – 6 = **144**.

2. Rounded calculation: round up 249 to 250 so 249 x 3 = 250 x 3 = **750**.
    Actual calculation: 249 x 3 = (250 – 1) x 3 = (250 x 3) – (1 x 3) = 750 – 3 = **747**.

3. Rounded calculation: round down 3.1 to 3 so 12 ÷ 3 = **4**.

4. Rounded calculation: round 199 up to 200 so 200 ÷ 5 = **40**.

5. Rounded calculation: round 11 down to 10 so 37 x 11 is approximately 37 x 10 = **370**.
    Actual calculation: 37 x (10 + 1) = 370 + 37 = **407**.

Section 2.1 Exercises   (Pg. 7)

1. $\frac{1}{1} = 1 = \mathbf{100\%}$

2. $\frac{1}{2} = 0.5 = \mathbf{50\%}$

3. $\frac{1}{3} = 0.333 = \mathbf{33.3\%}$

4. $\frac{1}{5} = 0.2 = \mathbf{20\%}$

5. $\frac{1}{6} = 0.1666 = \mathbf{16.7\%}$

6. $\frac{1}{7} = 0.1429 = \mathbf{14.3\%}$

7. $\frac{1}{8} = 0.125 = \mathbf{12.5\%}$

8. $\frac{1}{9} = 0.111 = \mathbf{11.1\%}$

9. $\frac{1}{10} = 0.1 = \mathbf{10\%}$

10. $\frac{1}{11} = 0.0909 = \mathbf{9.1\%}$

11. $\frac{1}{20} = 0.05 = \mathbf{5\%}$

12. $\frac{1}{25} = 0.04 = \mathbf{4\%}$

13. $\frac{1}{30} = 0.0333 = \mathbf{3.3\%}$

14. $\frac{1}{40} = 0.025 = \mathbf{2.5\%}$

15. $\dfrac{1}{50} = 0.02 = \mathbf{2\%}$

21. $\dfrac{2}{1000} = 0.002 = \mathbf{0.2\%}$

16. $\dfrac{1}{100} = 0.01 = \mathbf{1\%}$

22. $\dfrac{2}{50} = 0.04 = \mathbf{4\%}$

17. $\dfrac{2}{100} = 0.02 = \mathbf{2\%}$

23. $\dfrac{2}{500} = 0.004 = \mathbf{0.4\%}$

18. $\dfrac{1}{200} = 0.005 = \mathbf{0.5\%}$

24. $\dfrac{2}{5000} = 0.0004 = \mathbf{0.04\%}$

19. $\dfrac{1}{2000} = 0.0005 = \mathbf{0.05\%}$

25. $\dfrac{4}{5} = 0.8 = \mathbf{80\%}$

20. $\dfrac{1}{1000} = 0.001 = \mathbf{0.1\%}$

Section 3.1 Exercises   (Pg. 8)

1. $\mathbf{\dfrac{1}{3}}$ $\left(since\ 3 \bullet \dfrac{1}{3} = 1\right)$

5. $\mathbf{\dfrac{1}{1.268}}$

2. $\mathbf{\dfrac{1}{110}}$

6. $\mathbf{1{,}024}$

3. $\mathbf{\dfrac{1}{1{,}284}}$

7. $\mathbf{31.926}$

4. $\mathbf{4}$ $\left(since\ \dfrac{1}{4} \bullet 4 = 1;\quad note:\ \dfrac{1}{\left(\dfrac{1}{4}\right)} = 4\right)$

Section 6.1 Exercises   (Pg. 11)

1. The reciprocal of $\dfrac{9}{7}$ is $\mathbf{\dfrac{7}{9}}$.

2. The reciprocal of $\dfrac{32}{689}$ is $\mathbf{\dfrac{689}{32}}$.

3. The reciprocal of $\dfrac{1}{10}$ is $\mathbf{\dfrac{10}{1}}$.

4. The reciprocal of $\dfrac{1}{10{,}000}$ is $\mathbf{\dfrac{10{,}000}{1}}$.

5. The reciprocal of f is $\mathbf{\dfrac{1}{f}}$.

6. The reciprocal of $\dfrac{1}{f}$ is $\mathbf{\dfrac{f}{1}}$.

7. The reciprocal of $(z + 2)$ is $\mathbf{\dfrac{1}{(z+2)}}$.

8. The reciprocal of $\dfrac{1}{\lambda}$ is $\mathbf{\dfrac{\lambda}{1}}$.

9. The reciprocal of π is $\dfrac{1}{\pi}$.

10. The reciprocal of $\dfrac{1}{T}$ is $\dfrac{T}{1}$.

11. The reciprocal of $\dfrac{x}{10,000}$ is $\dfrac{10,000}{x}$.

12. The reciprocal of $\dfrac{10,000}{z^3}$ is $\dfrac{z^3}{10,000}$.

13. The reciprocal of $\dfrac{3x}{\left(z^2+19\right)}$ is $\dfrac{\left(z^2+19\right)}{3x}$.

14. The reciprocal of $\dfrac{meters}{seconds}$ is $\dfrac{seconds}{meters}$.

15. The reciprocal of $\dfrac{1}{seconds}$ is $\dfrac{seconds}{1}$.

16. The reciprocal of $\dfrac{1}{Hz}$ is $\dfrac{Hz}{1}$.

17. The reciprocal of $\dfrac{1}{10\,Hz}$ is $\dfrac{10\,Hz}{1}$.

18. The reciprocal of $\dfrac{3x}{Hz}$ is $\dfrac{Hz}{3x}$.

Section 7.2 Exercises   (Pg. 13)

1. $2^5 = 2 \bullet 2 \bullet 2 \bullet 2 \bullet 2 = \mathbf{32}$

2. $6^2 = 6 \bullet 6 = \mathbf{36}$

3. $9^3 = 9 \bullet 9 \bullet 9 = \mathbf{729}$

4. $10^1 = \mathbf{10}$

5. $10^2 = 10 \bullet 10 = \mathbf{100}$

6. $10^3 = 10 \bullet 10 \bullet 10 = \mathbf{1,000}$

7. $10^4 = 10 \bullet 10 \bullet 10 \bullet 10 = \mathbf{10,000}$

8. $10^5 = 10 \bullet 10 \bullet 10 \bullet 10 \bullet 10 = \mathbf{100,000}$

9. $\left(\dfrac{1}{10}\right)^2 = \dfrac{1}{10} \bullet \dfrac{1}{10} = \dfrac{\mathbf{1}}{\mathbf{100}}$

10. $\left(\dfrac{1}{10}\right)^1 = \dfrac{\mathbf{1}}{\mathbf{10}}$

11. $\left(\dfrac{1}{10}\right)^5 = \dfrac{1}{100,000}$

12. $(3x)^3 = 3x \bullet 3x \bullet 3x = \mathbf{27x^3}$

13. $0^2 = 0 \bullet 0 = \mathbf{0}$

14. $3^5 = 3 \bullet 3 \bullet 3 \bullet 3 \bullet 3 = \mathbf{243}$

Section 7.4 Exercises   (Pg. 14-15)

1. $2^{-2} = \left(\dfrac{1}{2}\right)^2 = \dfrac{1}{2} \bullet \dfrac{1}{2} = \dfrac{\mathbf{1}}{\mathbf{4}}$

2. $3^{-4} = \left(\dfrac{1}{3}\right)^4 = \dfrac{1}{3} \bullet \dfrac{1}{3} \bullet \dfrac{1}{3} \bullet \dfrac{1}{3} = \dfrac{\mathbf{1}}{\mathbf{81}}$

3. $3^4 = 3 \bullet 3 \bullet 3 \bullet 3 = \mathbf{81}$

4. $5^{-1} = \dfrac{1}{5^1} = \dfrac{\mathbf{1}}{\mathbf{5}}$

5. $3^2 = 3 \bullet 3 = \mathbf{9}$

6. $\left(\dfrac{1}{2}\right)^2 = \dfrac{1}{2} \bullet \dfrac{1}{2} = \dfrac{\mathbf{1}}{\mathbf{4}}$

7. $\left(\dfrac{1}{2}\right)^{-2} = \left(\dfrac{2}{1}\right)^2 = 2 \bullet 2 = \mathbf{4}$

8. $\dfrac{1}{3^2} = \dfrac{1}{3 \bullet 3} = \dfrac{\mathbf{1}}{\mathbf{9}}$

9. $\left(\dfrac{2}{3}\right)^2 = \dfrac{2}{3} \bullet \dfrac{2}{3} = \dfrac{\mathbf{4}}{\mathbf{9}}$

10. $\left(\dfrac{3}{2}\right)^{-2} = \left(\dfrac{2}{3}\right)^2 = \dfrac{2}{3} \bullet \dfrac{2}{3} = \dfrac{\mathbf{4}}{\mathbf{9}}$

11. $\left(\dfrac{2}{3}\right)^2 \bullet \left(\dfrac{2}{3}\right)^{-2} = \left(\dfrac{2}{3}\right)^2 \bullet \left(\dfrac{3}{2}\right)^2 = \dfrac{2}{3} \bullet \dfrac{2}{3} \bullet \dfrac{3}{2} \bullet \dfrac{3}{2} = \mathbf{1}$

12. $3^2 \bullet \left(\dfrac{1}{3}\right)^2 = 3 \bullet 3 \bullet \dfrac{1}{3} \bullet \dfrac{1}{3} = \mathbf{1}$

Section 7.6 Exercises   (Pg. 16)

1. $3^3 \bullet 3^4 = 3^{3+4} = \mathbf{3^7}$

2. $4^2 \bullet 4^{-2} = 4^{2-2} = 4^0 = \mathbf{1}$

3. $3^3 \bullet 3^2 = 3^{3+2} = \mathbf{3^5}$

4. $3^{-3} \bullet 3^4 = 3^{-3+4} = 3^1 = \mathbf{3}$

5. $3^{-3} \bullet 3^4 = 3^{-3+4} = 3^1 = \mathbf{3}$

6. $3^{-3} \bullet 3^{-4} = 3^{-3-4} = \mathbf{3^{-7}}$

7. $5^2 \bullet 5^{-2} = 5^{2-2} = 5^0 = \mathbf{1}$

8. $5^2 \bullet 5^{-4} = 5^{2-4} = 5^{-2} = \dfrac{1}{5^2} = \dfrac{\mathbf{1}}{\mathbf{25}}$

9. $\left(\dfrac{2}{3}\right)^2 \bullet \left(\dfrac{2}{3}\right)^{-2} = \left(\dfrac{2}{3}\right)^{2-2} = \left(\dfrac{2}{3}\right)^0 = \mathbf{1}$

10. $\left(\dfrac{x}{y}\right)^3 \bullet \left(\dfrac{x}{y}\right)^{-2} = \left(\dfrac{x}{y}\right)^{3-2} = \left(\dfrac{x}{y}\right)^1 = \dfrac{\boldsymbol{x}}{\boldsymbol{y}}$

11. $\left(\dfrac{x}{y}\right)^{-3} \bullet \left(\dfrac{x}{y}\right)^2 = \left(\dfrac{x}{y}\right)^{-3+2} = \left(\dfrac{x}{y}\right)^{-1} = \dfrac{\boldsymbol{y}}{\boldsymbol{x}}$

12. $2^3 \bullet 10^2 = 8 \bullet 100 = \mathbf{800}$
(Be very careful! The bases are not equal in this problem.)

Section 8.1 Exercises   (Pg. 18)

1. $1 \bullet 10^{-2} = \mathbf{0.01}$

2. $1 \bullet 10^2 = \mathbf{100}$

3. $3 \bullet 10^3 = \mathbf{3,000}$

4. $3 \bullet 10^{-3} = \mathbf{0.003}$

5. $1.68 \bullet 10^9 = \mathbf{1,680,000,000}$

6. $1.68 \bullet 10^{-9} = \mathbf{0.00000000168}$

7. $\dfrac{1.68 \times 10^9}{1.68 \times 10^9} = \mathbf{1}$

8. $0.000016 = \mathbf{16 \bullet 10^{-6}}$

9. $3,200,000 = \mathbf{3.2 \bullet 10^6}$

10. $2.3 \bullet 10^0 = \mathbf{2.3}$

11. $\dfrac{6 \times 10^9}{2 \times 10^6} = 3 \times 10^{9-6} = \mathbf{3 \times 10^3}$

12. $6 \times 10^9 \bullet 0.5 \times 10^{-9} = 3 \times 10^{9-9} = 3 \times 10^0 = \mathbf{3}$

13. $6 \times 10^9 \bullet 0.5 \times 10^{-3} = 3 \times 10^{9-3} = \mathbf{3 \times 10^6}$
$= \mathbf{3,000,000}$

14. $\dfrac{200 \times 10^7}{10 \times 10^2} \bullet 0.5 \times 10^{-3}$
$= 20 \times 10^{7-2} \bullet 0.5 \times 10^{-3}$
$= 10 \times 10^{7-2-3} = \mathbf{10 \times 10^2} = 10^3 = \mathbf{1,000}$

Section 8.3 Exercises   (Pg. 19)

1. $1,600,000 = \mathbf{1.6 \times 10^6}$ **(or 16 x 10⁵, etc.)**

2. $9,000,000,000 = \mathbf{9 \times 10^9}$ **(or 0.9 x 10¹⁰, etc.)**

3. $92,000,000 = \mathbf{92 \times 10^6}$ **(or 9.2 x 10⁷, etc.)**

4. $0.00043 = \mathbf{0.43 \times 10^{-3}}$ **(or 4.3 x 10⁻⁴, etc.)**

5. $0.0000045 = \mathbf{0.45 \times 10^{-5}}$ **(or 4.5 x 10⁻⁶, etc.)**

6. $0.00000000091 = \mathbf{0.91 \times 10^{-9}}$ **(or 9.1 x 10⁻¹⁰, etc.)**

7. $45,000 = \mathbf{45 \times 10^3}$ **(or 4.5 x 10⁴, etc.)**

8. $0.000000046 = \mathbf{46 \times 10^{-9}}$ **(or 4.6 x 10⁻⁸, etc.)**

Section 9.3 Exercises   (Pg. 22)

1.   1.3 k $k = kilo = thousand = 10^3$
        $1.3\ k = 1.3 \times 10^3$
        $1\,.\,3\ 0\ 0\ 0 = \mathbf{1,300.00}$

2.   231 G $G = Giga = billion = 10^9$
        $231\ G = 231 \times 10^9$
        $2\,3\,1\,.\,0\ 0\ 0\ 0\ 0\ 0\ 0\ 0\ 0\ 0\ 0 = \mathbf{231,000,000,000.00}$

3.   0.21 h $h = hecto = hundred = 10^2$
        $0.21\ h = 0.21 \times 10^2$
        $0\,.\,2\ 1\ 0\ 0 = \mathbf{21.00}$

4.   12.2 c $c = centi = hundredths = 10^{-2}$
        $12.2\ c = 12.2 \times 10^{-2}$
        12.2×10^{-2} (notice (⁻²) means 2 places left) = **0.122**

5.   26.2 m $m = milli = thousandths = 10^{-3}$
        $26.2\ m = 26.2 \times 10^{-3}$
        26.2×10^{-3} (notice (⁻³) means 3 places left) = **0.0262**

6.   1.3 μ $\mu = micro = millionths = 10^{-6}$
        $1.3\ \mu = 1.3 \times 10^{-6}$
        1.3×10^{-6} (notice (⁻⁶) means 6 places left) = **0.0000013**

7.   42 n   n = nano = billionths = 10^{-9}

                   42 n = 42 $\times$ 10^{-9}

                   42 $\times$ 10^{-9} (notice ($^{-9}$) means 9 places left) = 0.000000042

8.   0.02 M   M = Mega = millions = 10^{6}

                   0.02 M = 0.02 $\times$ 10^{6}

                   0.02 $\times$ 10^{6} (notice (^{6}) means 6 places right) = **20,000**

Section 9.6 Exercises   (Pg. 24)

1.	2.5 MHz	=	2.5×10^{6} Hz	=	**2,500,000 Hz**
2.	1.6 kHz	=	1.6×10^{3} Hz	=	**1,600 Hz**
3.	1.54 km/sec	=	1.54×10^{3} m/sec	=	**1,540 m/sec**
4.	1.7 µsec	=	1.7×10^{-6} sec	=	**0.0000017 sec**
5.	100 cm	=	100×10^{-2} m	=	**1.00 m**
6.	100 mW/cm^2	=	100×10^{-3} W/cm^2	=	**0.100 W/cm^2**
7.	1.8 ml (convert to liters)	=	1.8×10^{-3} liters	=	**0.0018 liters**
8.	1,400 ml (convert to liters)	=	$1,400 \times 10^{-3}$ liters	=	**1.4 liters**

Section 9.8 Exercises   (Pg. 24)

1. The reciprocal of 2.0 MHz is **0.5 µsec**.

2. The reciprocal of 1.0 kHz is **1 msec**.

3. The reciprocal of 5 µsec is **0.2 MHz**.

4. The reciprocal of 0.1 msec is **10 kHz**.

5. The reciprocal of 10 GHz is **0.1 nsec**.

6. The reciprocal of 10 nsec is **0.1 GHz**.

7. The reciprocal of 0.1 GHz is **10 nsec**.

8. The reciprocal of 0.1 nsec is **10 GHz**.

Section 9.11 Exercises   (Pg. 28)

1. 3 cm = **0.03 m**

2. 3 MHz = **3,000 kHz**

3. 2,000 µsec = **2 msec**

4. 0.006 GHz = **6 MHz**

5. 3,000 msec = **3 sec**

6. 6,000,000 msec = **6 ksec**

7. 920 cm = **0.0092 km**

8. 920 km = **92,000,000 cm**

Section 9.12 Exercises   (Pg. 28-29)

1. $10^3 \bullet 10^2 = 10^{3+2} = 10^5 = \mathbf{100,000}$

2. $10^2 \bullet 10^{-2} = 10^0 = \mathbf{1}$

3. $10^6/10^4 = 10^6 \bullet 10^{-4} = 10^{6-4} = 10^2 = \mathbf{100}$

4. $(2.3 \bullet 10^6) \bullet 10^3 = 2.3 \bullet 10^{6+3} = 2.3 \bullet 10^9 = \mathbf{2,300,000,000}$

5. $(3.6 \bullet 10^3) \bullet 10^{-3} = 3.6 \bullet 10^{3-3} = 3.6 \bullet 10^0 = 3.6 \bullet 1 = \mathbf{3.6}$

6. $2 \bullet (1 \bullet 10^3) = 2 \bullet 10^3 = \mathbf{2,000}$

7. $100 \bullet (1 \bullet 10^2) = 100 \bullet 10^2 = 10^4 = \mathbf{10,000}$ or $10^2 \bullet 1 \bullet 10^2 = \mathbf{10,000}$

8. $10^{17} \bullet 10^{-6} = 10^{17-6} = 10^{11} = \mathbf{100,000,000,000}$

9. $10^{17}/10^6 = 10^{17} \bullet 10^{-6} = 10^{11} = \mathbf{100,000,000,000}$

10. $(3 \bullet 10^4) \bullet (1 \bullet 10^{-2}) = 3 \bullet 1 \bullet 10^{4-2} = 3 \bullet 10^2 = \mathbf{300}$

11. $(3 \bullet 10^4) / (1 \bullet 10^2) = (3 \bullet 10^4) \bullet (1 \bullet 10^{-2}) = (3 \bullet 1 \bullet 10^{4-2}) = 3 \bullet 10^2 = \mathbf{300}$

12. $10^4/10^{-2} = 10^4 \bullet 10^2 = 10^{4+2} = 10^6 = \mathbf{1,000,000}$

13. $10^4 \bullet 10^2 = 10^{4+2} = 10^6 = \mathbf{1,000,000}$

14. $\dfrac{6 \; \cancel{M} \; Hz}{2 \; \cancel{M}} = \mathbf{3 \; Hz}$

15. $\dfrac{12 \; MHz}{4 \; kHz} = \dfrac{12 \times 10^6 \; Hz}{4 \times 10^3 \; Hz} = 3 \times 10^{6-3} = \mathbf{3000}$

16. $\dfrac{(1.54 \; km/sec)}{(1.54 \; cm)} = \dfrac{\left(1.54 \times 10^3 \; m/sec\right)}{1.54 \times 10^{-2} \; m} = \dfrac{(1.54)}{(1.54)} \times 10^{3-(-2)} \bullet \dfrac{m}{m \bullet sec} = \dfrac{1 \times 10^5}{sec}$

$= 0.1 \times 10^6 \bullet \dfrac{1}{sec} = \mathbf{0.1 \; MHz \; or \; 100 \; kHz}$

17. $(13 \; \mu sec) \bullet (1{,}540 \; m/sec)$
    $= (13 \times 10^{-6} \; sec) \bullet (1{,}540 \; m/sec)$
    $= (13 \bullet 1{,}540) \times 10^{-6} \; m$
    $= 0.02 \; m$
    $= \mathbf{2 \; cm}$

18. $0.001540 \ m/\mu sec =$

$$0.001540 \cdot \frac{m}{\mu \, sec} = \frac{0.001540}{1 \times 10^{-6}} \cdot \frac{m}{sec}$$

$$= 0.001540 \cdot 10^6 \ m/sec$$
$$= \mathbf{1{,}540 \ m/sec}$$

19. $1.54 \ mm/\mu sec =$

$$1.54 \cdot \frac{mm}{\mu \, sec} = \frac{1.54 \times 10^{-3}}{1 \times 10^{-6}} \cdot \frac{m}{sec}$$

$$= 1.54 \cdot 10^{-3+6} \ m/sec$$
$$= 1.54 \cdot 10^3 \ m/sec$$
$$= \mathbf{1{,}540 \ m/sec}$$

20. $\dfrac{1}{\left(\dfrac{1}{sec}\right)} = 1 \ sec$

Section 10.4 Exercises   (Pg. 32)

1.   In the equation $z = 3t$, the relationship between z and t is **direct proportionality**.

2.   In the equation $z = 3t$, if t were to double, z would also **double**.

3.   In the equation $z = 3t$, if t were increased by a factor of 36, z would **increase** by a factor of **36**.

4.   In the equation $z = 3t$, if t were decreased by a factor of 4.3, z would **decrease** by a factor of **4.3**.

5.   In the equation $m = 6j$, the relationship between m and j is **direct proportionality (linear proportionality**.

6.   In the equation $m = 6j$, if j were **increased** by a factor of 6, m would increase by a factor of 6.

7.   In the equation $m = \dfrac{5}{j}$, the relationship between m and j is **inverse** proportionality.

8.   In the equation $m = \dfrac{5}{j}$, if j were **increased** by a factor of 3, m would decrease by a factor of **3**.

9.   In the equation $m = \dfrac{5}{j}$, if j were **decreased** by a factor of **19**, m would increase by a factor of 19.

10.   In the equation $y = \dfrac{z}{k}$, if k were increased by a **factor** of **3**, y would decrease by a factor of 3.

11. In the equation $y = \dfrac{z}{k}$, if z were increased by a factor of 2, y would **<u>increase</u>** by a **factor** of **2**.

12. In the equation $y = \dfrac{z}{k}$, $y \propto z$ and $y \propto \dfrac{1}{k}$ (y is proportional to z and inversely proportional to k).

Section 11.1 Exercises   (Pg. 34)

1. $\dfrac{6.5\ \mu sec}{cm} \cdot 2\ cm = \mathbf{13\ \mu sec}$

2. $\dfrac{6.5\ \mu sec}{cm} \cdot 3\ cm = \mathbf{19.5\ \mu sec}$

3. $\dfrac{6.5\ \mu sec}{cm} \cdot 4\ cm = \mathbf{26\ \mu sec}$

4. $\dfrac{6.5\ \mu sec}{cm} \cdot 10\ cm = \mathbf{65\ \mu sec}$

5. $\dfrac{6.5\ \mu sec}{cm} \cdot 1\ cm + \dfrac{6.5\ \mu sec}{cm} \cdot 1\ cm = \dfrac{6.5\ \mu sec}{cm} \cdot 2\ cm = \mathbf{13\ \mu\ sec}$

6. $\dfrac{6.5\ \mu sec}{cm} \cdot 10\ cm + \dfrac{6.5\ \mu sec}{cm} \cdot 10\ cm = \dfrac{6.5\ \mu sec}{cm} \cdot 20\ cm = \mathbf{130\ \mu\ sec}$

Section 12.3 Exercises   (Pg. 37-38)

1. 1/4 of 100 = 100/4 = **25**

2. 1/5 of 100 = 100/5 = **20**

3. 1/3 of 333 = 333/3 = **111**

4. 1/9 of 81 = 81/9 = **9**

5. 1/4 as a percentage = 0.25 = **25%**

6. 1/5 as a percentage = 0.20 = **20%**

7. 1/3 as a percentage = 0.333 = **33.3%**

6.　　1/5 as a percentage = 0.20 = **20%**

7.　　1/3 as a percentage = 0.333 = **33.3%**

8.　　1/9 as a percentage = 0.111 = **11.1%**

9.　　25% of 100 = 0.25 x 100 = **25 (recall 25% = 25/100 = 1/4 = 0.25)**

10.　　20% of 100 = 0.20 x 100 = **20 (recall 20% = 20/100 = 1/5 = 0.20)**

11.　　33.3% of 333 = 333/3 = **111 (recall 33.3% = 33.3/100 = 1/3)**

12.　　11.1% of 81 = 81/9 = **9 (recall 11.1% = 11.1/100 = 1/9)**

13.　　11% less than 81 = 81 - 9 = **72**

14.　　25% less than 100 = 100 - 25 = **75**

15.　　20% less than 100 = 100 - 20 = **80**

16.　　33.3% less than 333 = 333 - 111 = **222**

17.　　Your new salary is 2 x $100 = **$200**.

18.　　Your new salary is $\dfrac{\$100}{2}$ = **$50**.

19.　　Your new salary is 4 x $100 = **$400**.

20.　　Your new salary is **$25**.

21.　　If two variables are directly proportional and one variable doubles, then the related variable **<u>doubles</u>**.

22.　　If two variables are inversely proportional and one variable doubles, then the related variable **<u>halves (reduces by a factor of 2)</u>**.

23.　　If two variables are directly proportional and one variable increases by a factor of 17, then the related variable increases by a factor of **<u>17</u>**.

24.　　If two variables are inversely proportional and one variable decreases by a factor of 17, then the related variable **<u>increases</u>** by a factor of 17.

25.　　If your pay is decreased by 20%, **<u>80%</u>** of your pay is left.

26.　　Given that you are paid hourly, if you work 20% more time, what percentage is the increase in your pay?
Your salary is proportional to the hours you work if you are paid hourly. Therefore, a 20% increase in time worked results in a 20% increase in pay.

27. If you double the speed you drive, by what factor have you reduced the time to drive the same distance?
Since the speed you drive and the time it takes to arrive are inversely proportional, if you double your speed you halve the time (decrease the time by a factor of 2).

28. If you decrease the speed you drive by a factor of 19, by what factor have you increased the time to drive the same distance?
Since the speed you drive and the time it takes to arrive are inversely proportional, if you decrease your speed by a factor of 19, you increase the time by a factor of 19.

29. Which is greater, 10% of 9 or 9% of 10?
Neither. The two quantities are equal since:

$$10\% \text{ of } 9 \Rightarrow 0.1 \bullet 9 = \mathbf{0.9}$$

and

$$9\% \text{ of } 10 \Rightarrow 0.09 \bullet 10 = \mathbf{0.9}$$

30. Which is greater, 25% of 50 or 50% of 25?
Neither. The two quantities are equal since:

$$25\% \text{ of } 50 \Rightarrow 0.25 \bullet 50 = \frac{1}{4} \bullet 50 = \frac{50}{4} = \mathbf{12.5}$$
and
$$50\% \text{ of } 25 \Rightarrow 0.50 \bullet 25 = \frac{1}{2} \bullet 25 = \frac{25}{2} = \mathbf{12.5}$$

31. Answer = **33%**

Section 13.3 Exercises (Pg. 42)

1. *distance = rate • time*
distance = c • t

$$c = 1,540 \frac{m}{sec}$$

$$t = 1 \text{ sec}$$

$$\Rightarrow \text{distance} = 1,540 \frac{m}{sec} \bullet 1 \text{ sec} = \mathbf{1,540 \ m}$$

2. since 1 m ≈ 3.25 ft

$$1,540 \text{ m} \bullet 3.25 \frac{ft}{m} = \mathbf{5,005 \ ft} \approx \mathbf{5,000 \ ft}$$

3. since 1 mile = 5,280 ft
5,005 ft ≈ **1 mile (answer c)**

4.   a)   *distance = rate • time*
              distance = c • t

$$c = 1,540 \frac{m}{sec}$$

distance = 1 cm = 1 • 10⁻² m

Since we want to solve for time, we will rewrite the equation by dividing both sides by c:

$$\Rightarrow \frac{distance}{c} = \frac{c}{c} \bullet t$$

$$so\ t = \frac{distance}{c} = \frac{1 \times 10^{-2}\ m}{1,540 \frac{m}{sec}} = 6.5 \times 10^{-6}\ sec$$

$$= 6.5\ \mu sec$$

       b)   Round-trip would take twice as long or 2 • (6.5 µsec)

$$= \textbf{13 µsec}$$

5.   *distance = c • t*

$$c = 1,540 \frac{m}{sec}$$

t = 130 µsec

$$\Rightarrow depth = (1,540 \frac{m}{sec}) \bullet (130 \times 10^{-6}\ sec) = \textbf{0.20 m or 20 cm}$$

Round-trip, this is equivalent to an imaging depth of **10 cm**.

6.   *distance = c • t*

$$c = 2,000 \frac{m}{sec}$$

t = 130 µsec

$$\Rightarrow distance = 2,000 \frac{m}{sec} \bullet 130\ \mu sec = 0.26\ m = 26\ cm$$

$$imaging\ depth = \frac{distance}{2}(roundtrip) \Rightarrow depth = \frac{26\ cm}{2} = 13\ cm$$

(The system thinks it is imaging to a depth of 10 cm but it is actually imaging to a depth of 13 cm.)

7.   The correct answer is **b**. Objects will appear too shallow because objects at 13 cm in the body are drawn at a depth of 10 cm on the screen.

Section 15.2 Exercises   (Pg. 46)

1.   Since $w \propto q$, increasing q by a factor of 7 **increases w by a factor of 7**.

2.   Since $w \propto q$, decreasing q by a factor of 3 **decreases w by a factor of 3**.

3.   Since $w \propto k$, increasing k by a factor of 2 **increases w by a factor of 2**.

4.   Since $w \propto t^2$, increasing t by a factor of 7 **increases w by a factor of $7^2 = 49$**.

5.   Since $w \propto d^3$, increasing d by a factor of 2 **increases w by a factor of $2^3 = 8$**.

6.   Since $w \propto d^3$, decreasing d by a factor of 3 **decreases w by a factor of $3^3 = 27$**.

7.   Since $w \propto f^4$, increasing f by a factor of 2 **increases w by a factor of $2^4 = 16$**.

8.   Since $w \propto f^4$, decreasing f by a factor of 2 **decreases w by a factor of $2^4 = 16$**.
      (Note that saying decreased by a factor of 2 is the same as saying halved.)
      (Also note that question 8 is the reciprocal of question 7.)

9.   Since $w \propto \dfrac{1}{z}$, increasing z by a factor of 2 **decreases w by a factor of 2**.

10.   This is just another way of stating the exact same question as question number 9. Therefore, the answer is a **decrease in w by a factor of 2, or w is halved**.

11.   Since $w \propto \dfrac{1}{z}$, decreasing z by a factor of 2 (halved) **increases w by a factor of 2**.

12.   This is just another way of stating the exact same question as question number 11. Therefore, the answer is an **increase in w by a factor of 2, or w is doubled**.

13.   Since $w \propto \dfrac{1}{m^3}$, increasing m by a factor of 2 **decreases w by a factor of $2^3 = 8$**.

14.   Since $w \propto \dfrac{1}{m^3}$, increasing m by a factor of 3 **decreases w by a factor of $3^3 = 27$**.

15.   Since $w \propto \dfrac{1}{m^3}$, decreasing m by a factor of 3 **increases w by a factor of $3^3 = 27$**.

      (Of course you noted the fact that question 15 is the reciprocal of question 14!)

Section 15.3 Exercises   (Pg. 47-48)

1.   **a** $f_{dop} \propto f_0$

2.   **b** $f_{dop} \propto 1/c$

3.   **a** $f_{dop} \propto v$

4.   **a** $f_{dop} \propto cos(\theta)$

5.   **c**

6.   **c**   price A = 4 • price B
              price $\propto$ (carats)^2
              carats A = 2 • carats B $\Rightarrow$ price A = $(2)^2$ • price B

7.   **$32,000**
              one carat $\Rightarrow$ $2,000
              four carats $\Rightarrow$ $(4/1)^2$ • $2,000 = 16 • $2,000 = $32,000

8.   **C = ($2,000) • n$^{(2)}$**
               check
               n = 1 carat
                      cost = ($2,000) • 1^2 = $2,000
               n = 4 carats
                      cost = ($2,000) • $(4)^2$ = $32,000

9.   **<u>Increase</u>** power by a factor of **<u>9</u>**.

10.   **Quadruple the intensity**.

11. $\left(intensity = \dfrac{power}{area} \right) \Rightarrow$ *intensity is proportional to power.*

    Increasing intensity by a factor of nine means the power has increased by a factor of nine, but only if the beam area remains fixed.

    Since power is proportional to (amplitude)^2, if the power is increased by a factor of nine, the amplitude is increased by a factor of 3.

12.   Intensity = power/area. If the area is increased by a factor of 2, the intensity is **<u>halved</u>**.

13.   Since intensity equals power divided by area, if the intensity does not change but the beam area increases, the power must also **increase** by a factor equal to the beam area increase.

14.   If the intensity decreases by a factor of 16 for a fixed beam area, the power must have **<u>decreased</u>** by a factor of **<u>16</u>** and the amplitude must have **<u>decreased</u>** by a factor of **<u>4</u>**.

Section 17.2 Exercise   (Pg. 53)

1. $log_{10} x = 2$ $\Rightarrow$ $10^2 = x$
                                        x = 100

2. $log_x 10 = 1$ $\Rightarrow$ $x^1 = 10$
                                        x = 10

3. $\log_{10} 10 = x$ $\Rightarrow$ $10^x = 10$

                                       x = 1

4. $\log_{10} 1,000 = x$ $\Rightarrow$ $10^x = 1,000$

                                       $(1,000 = 10^3)$

                                       $10^x = 10^3$

                                       x = 3

5. $\log_{10} x = 4$ $\Rightarrow$ $10^4 = x$

                                       10,000 = x

6. $\log_6 36 = x$ $\Rightarrow$ $6^x = 36$

                                       $(36 = 6^2)$

                                       $6^x = 6^2$

                                       x = 2

7. $\log_6 x = 2$ $\Rightarrow$ $6^2 = x$

                                       x = 36

8. $\log 100 = x$ $\Rightarrow$ *(note base 10 is assumed)* $\Rightarrow \log_{10} 100 = x$

                                       $10^x = 100$

                                       $100 = 10^2$

                                       $10^x = 10^2$

                                       x = 2

Section 18.3 Exercises   (Pg. 59-60)

1. $\cos(30^0) = $ **0.866**	11. $\sin(30^0) = $ **0.5**
2. $\cos(45^0) = $ **0.707**	12. $\sin(45^0) = $ **0.707**
3. $\cos(60^0) = $ **0.5**	13. $\sin(60^0) = $ **0.866**
4. $\cos(0^0) = $ **1**	14. $\sin(0^0) = $ **0**
5. $\cos(90^0) = $ **0**	15. $\sin(90^0) = $ **1**
6. $\cos(180^0) = $ **-1**	16. $\sin(180^0) = $ **0**
7. $\cos(135^0) = $ **-0.707**	17. $\sin(135^0) = $ **0.707**
8. $\cos(270^0) = $ **0**	18. $\sin(270^0) = $ **-1**
9. $\cos(360^0) = $ **1**	19. $\sin(360^0) = $ **0**
10. $\cos(225^0) = $ **-0.707**	20. $\sin(225^0) = $ **-0.707**

21.

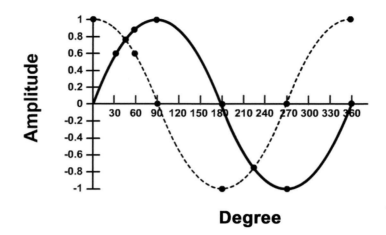

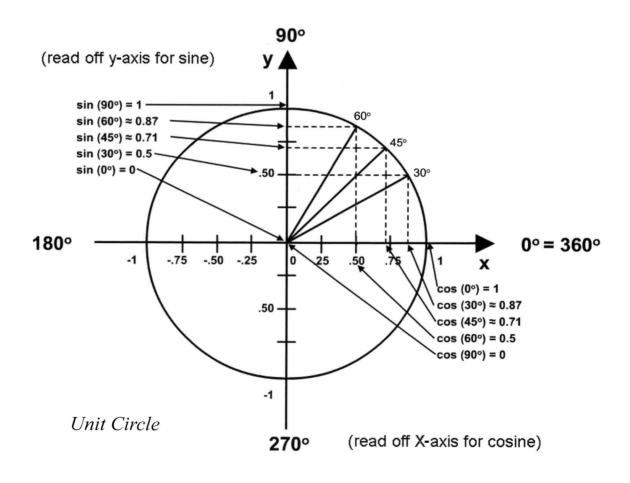

(read off y-axis for sine)

sin (90°) = 1
sin (60°) ≈ 0.87
sin (45°) ≈ 0.71
sin (30°) = 0.5
sin (0°) = 0

cos (0°) = 1
cos (30°) ≈ 0.87
cos (45°) ≈ 0.71
cos (60°) = 0.5
cos (90°) = 0

Unit Circle

(read off X-axis for cosine)

Pegasus Lectures, Inc.

Section 19.2 Exercises   (Pg. 62)

1. 432_8

	8^2	8^1	8^0		
$\Rightarrow$	•	•	•	=	$4 \bullet 8^2 + 3 \bullet 8^1 + 2 \bullet 8^0$
$\Rightarrow$	4	3	2		

$$= \quad 4 \bullet (64) + 3 \bullet (8) + 2 \bullet (1)$$
$$= \quad 256 + 24 + 2$$
$$= \quad \mathbf{282 \text{ or } 282_{10}}$$

2. $2{,}703_8$

	8^3	8^2	8^1	8^0		
$\Rightarrow$	•	•	•	•	=	$2 \bullet 8^3 + 7 \bullet 8^2 + 0 \bullet 8^1 + 3 \bullet 8^0$
	2	7	0	3		

$$= \quad 2 \bullet (512) + 7 \bullet (64) + 0 + 3 \bullet (1)$$
$$= \quad \mathbf{1{,}475}$$

3. 9_{10}

	9	=	$8 + 1 = 1 \bullet (8^1) + 1 \bullet (8^0)$
$\Rightarrow$		=	$8^1 + 8^0$
		=	11 (base 8)
		=	$\mathbf{11_8}$

Section 19.6 Exercises   (Pg. 65)

1. 101_2

	2^2	2^1	2^0		
	•	•	•	=	$1 \bullet (2^2) + 0 \bullet (2^1) + 1 \bullet (2^0)$
	1	0	1		

$$= \quad 1 \bullet (4) + 0 \bullet (2) + 1 \bullet (1)$$
$$= \quad 4 + 0 + 1$$
$$= \quad \mathbf{5}$$

2. $(2_{10})^4$

$\Rightarrow$	=	$1 \bullet 2^4 + 0 \bullet 2^3 + 0 \bullet 2^2 + 0 \bullet 2^1 + 0 \bullet 2^0$
	=	1 0 0 0 0

So $(2_{10})^4$ = $\mathbf{10000_2}$

3. $8 = 2^3$ = $1 \bullet 2^3 + 0 \bullet 2^2 + 0 \bullet 2^1 + 0 \bullet 2^0$
      =   1   0   0   0

So 8   = $\mathbf{1000_2}$

4.   33   =   32 + 1   = $1 \bullet 2^5 + 0 \bullet 2^4 + 0 \bullet 2^3 + 0 \bullet 2^2 + 0 \bullet 2^1 + 1 \bullet 2^0$
                 =   1   0   0   0   0   1

So 33   = $\mathbf{100001_2}$

5. 10111 $=$ $\quad 1 \bullet 2^4 + 0 \bullet 2^3 + 1 \bullet 2^2 + 1 \bullet 2^1 + 1 \bullet 2^0$

    $\quad\quad\quad = \quad 16 + 0 + 4 + 2 + 1$

    $\quad\quad\quad = \quad \mathbf{23}_{10}$

6.
5V	5V	0V	0V	5V	0V	0V	5V
1	1	0	0	1	0	0	1

$\quad = \quad 1 \bullet 2^7 + 1 \bullet 2^6 + 0 \bullet 2^5 + 0 \bullet 2^4 + 1 \bullet 2^3 + 0 \bullet 2^2 + 0 \bullet 2^1 + 1 \bullet 2^0$

$\quad = \quad 128 + \quad 64 + \quad 0 + \quad 0 + \quad 8 + \quad 0 + \quad 0 + \quad 1$

$\quad = \quad \mathbf{201}$

7. The number 1,021 cannot be binary, since binary can only use the digits 0 and 1, and not the digit 2. The lowest possible base the number 1,021 could be in is base 3, which uses the digits 0, 1, and 2.

8.
0000	0001	1
0000	0010	**2**
0000	0011	**3**
0000	**0100**	4
0000	0101	5
0000	0110	**6**
0000	0111	7
0000	**1000**	**8**
0000	1001	**9**

Section 4. Conceptual Questions   (Pg. 84)

1.   Electromagnetic waves
      a)   do not transfer energy
      b)   cannot propagate through a medium
      c)   include sound waves
      d)   none of the above

2.   Mechanical waves must have a **medium** to propagate.

3.   Sound is a **mechanical** wave.

4.   All waves transport **energy**.

5.   A mechanical wave implies an interaction between the wave and the **medium**.

Section 7. Conceptual Questions   (Pg. 90-92)

1.   If a wave needs a medium to propagate, it is a **mechanical** wave.

2.   If a wave does not need a medium to propagate, it is an **electromagnetic** wave.

3.   Which of the following is not an example of an electromagnetic wave?
      a)   x-rays
      b)   light
      c)   sound (sound is a mechanical wave)
      d)   heat
      e)   television signals

4.   All waves are a(n) _____ transfer through cyclical variations.
      a)   particle
      b)   energy (waves are an energy transfer through cyclical variations)
      c)   voltage
      d)   temperature

5.   The naming of waves as mechanical is due to the physical interaction between the wave and the medium. The interaction produces four specific possible changes called **acoustic** variables:
      1)   Pressure
      2)   Density
      3)   Temperature
      4)   Distance

6.	All of the following are acceptable units of pressure except?
	a)	Pa (Pascals)
	b)	lb/in^2
	c)	kg/m^2
	**d)	lb/ft (pressure is a force per area - lb/ft is a force per distance)**
	e)	atm (atmospheres)
	f)	mmHg (millimeters of mercury)

7.	Density is defined as:
	**a)	mass/volume, kg/m^3 (density is mass/volume, kg/m^3)**
	b)	mass/volume, kg/m^2
	c)	volume/mass, m^3/kg
	d)	mass • volume, m^{3}kg

8.	The freezing point of water is at 0° Celsius, what is the freezing point in Fahrenheit?

	0° C = 32° F (freezing point for water)

9.	The boiling point of water is at 212° F, what is boiling the boiling point in Celsius?

	212° F = 100° C (boiling point for water)

10.	**b	Sound is a longitudinal, mechanical wave.**

11.	**d	For a longitudinal wave, the energy is transported by a series of <u>compressions</u> and <u>rarefactions</u> of the medium particles.**

Section 9. Conceptual Questions   (Pg. 105-108)

1.	Repetitious waves are a **<u>cyclical</u>** transfer of **<u>energy</u>.**

2.	**a	Cyclical means periodic or repetitive.**

3.	The major classifications of waves are **<u>electromagnetic</u>** and **<u>mechanical</u>.**

4.	An electromagnetic wave does not need a **<u>medium</u>** to propagate.

5.	**c	Examples of magnetic waves are x-rays, light, and microwaves.**
	(Note: "a" is wrong because sound is mechanical.)

6.	A **<u>mechanical</u>** wave needs a medium to propagate.

7.	There can be no **<u>mechanical</u>** waves in a vacuum.

8.	A vacuum is the absence of a **<u>medium</u>.**

9.	There is no sound in a **<u>vacuum</u>,** since there is no medium.

10. Two classifications of mechanical waves are **transverse** and **longitudinal.**

11. In a **transverse** wave, particle motion is perpendicular or "transverse" to the wave direction.

12. In a **longitudinal** wave, the particle motion is back and forth "longitudinally" or in the same direction as the wave propagation.

13. Sound is a **longitudinal,** mechanical wave.

14. A longitudinal wave has areas of **rarefaction** and compression.

15. An area of **rarefaction** is where the particles are farther apart than the normal state.

16. An area of **compression** is where the particles are closer together than the normal state.

17. Not all waves need a **medium** to propagate; **electromagnetic** waves can operate in a vacuum.

18. **Frequency** is a way of specifying how fast a wave is cyclically varying.

19. The unit for frequency is **Hertz** which is an abbreviation for cycles per **second**.

20. Frequency has units which are the inverse of **time**, or one divided by **seconds,** also called Hz.

21. The number of times a longitudinal wave reaches maximum compression and rarefaction per time is called the **frequency**.

22. The reciprocal of frequency is the **period**.

23. The period has units of **time.**

24. The reciprocal of the **period** is frequency. Frequency has units of Hertz.

25. The **period** is the time between cycles of peak compression in a longitudinal wave such as sound.

26. The **time** between cycles of peak compression is the same as the time between cycles of peak rarefaction.

27. The **period** is the **time** between cycles of peak rarefaction.

28. Frequency and period are **reciprocals**.

29. The units for **frequency** and period are **reciprocals**.

30. Hertz and **time** or seconds are inversely related.

31. Since frequency and period are inversely related, if the frequency increases the period **decreases**.

32. A shorter period means higher **frequency**.

32. A shorter period means higher **frequency**.

33. A lower **frequency** means a longer period.

34. The **wavelength** is the physical measure of distance between wave peaks or similarly wave minima.

35. Wavelength is a measure of **distance** and therefore in the metric system has units of **meters** .

36. The period is a measure of **time** between peaks whereas the **wavelength** is a measure of distance between peaks.

37. Frequency and **wavelength** are related through the wave propagation velocity.

38. The propagation **velocity** has units of meters/second.

39. The **propagation velocity** is a measure of how fast a wave will travel.

40. The propagation velocity, (c), equals the frequency, (f), times the **wavelength** or $f \cdot \lambda = c$.

41. For a given propagation velocity, if the frequency increases, the **wavelength** must decrease.

42. For a given propagation velocity, if the frequency **decreases**, the **wavelength** must increase.

43. Frequency and wavelength have an **inverse** relationship.

44. If the propagation velocity changes, and the frequency is not changed the **wavelength** must change.

45. To determine the **wavelength**, the frequency and the propagation velocity must be known.

46. The frequency, wavelength and propagation velocity are related together by the equation: $\boldsymbol{f \cdot \lambda = c}$.

47. The **amplitude** of a signal is a measure of how big or loud it is.

48. The **amplitude** is determined as the maximum variation from the mean.

49. For a wave, the **mean** is the same as the average.

50. The **_mean_** = $\dfrac{maximum + minimum}{2}$.

51. If the maximum is 20 and the minimum is 10, the mean is **15**.

52. The difference between the maximum and the mean is the same as the difference between the mean and the **minimum**.

53. Since the amplitude equals the difference between the maximum and the mean, the **amplitude** also equals the difference between the **mean** and the minimum.
Or: Amplitude = max - mean = mean - min

54. If the **amplitude** of an ultrasound echo increases, the B-mode image will get brighter.

55.   If the **amplitude** of a Doppler echo **increases,** the Doppler audio will get louder.

56.   Amplitude is used to measure any wave variable. For sound waves, the units of amplitude will be any measure of four **acoustic** variables.

57.   For electrical waves, **amplitude** is used to measure parameters of electric variables such as voltage.

58.   Some possible units of **amplitude** are Pascals, degrees Celsius, meters, kg/m.

59.   A wave which has a physical interaction with the **medium** is called a mechanical wave.

60.   A change within the **medium** caused by a wave is called a variable.

61.   For an acoustic wave, the changes caused to the medium are called **acoustic** variables.

62.   There are **four** acoustic variables.

63.   The four acoustic variables are:

        1)   pressure
        2)   distance (particle displacement)
        3)   temperature
        4)   density

64.   Units of **pressure** are: Pascals, Atmospheres, mmHg, kg/m^2, lbs/in^2.

65.   Units of **distance** are: meters, feet, miles, yards, etc.

66.   Units of **temperature** are: degrees Celsius, degrees Fahrenheit, degrees Kelvin.

67.   Units of **density** are mass/volume such as kg/m^3, and lbs/ft^3.

68.   Changes in acoustic variables are the result of the mechanical interaction of the acoustic wave and the **medium**.

Section 10. Exercises   (Pg. 108-109)

1.   Since 1 minute = 60 seconds,
$$\frac{60\ times}{1\ minute} = \frac{60\ times}{60\ seconds} = \frac{1\ time}{1\ sec} = 1\ Hz$$

2. $$\frac{60\ times}{0.5\ sec} = \frac{120\ times}{1\ sec} = 120\ Hz$$

3. $$\frac{60\ times}{0.1\ sec} = \frac{600\ times}{1\ sec} = 600\ Hz$$

4.   Since 1 hr = 60 minutes = 3,600 seconds

$$\frac{60\ times}{1\ hr} = \frac{60\ times}{3,600\ sec} = \frac{1}{60}\ Hz$$

5.   **b**   (The frequency of operation is determined by the pulser, the electronics which drives the transmitter.)

6.   Frequency will not change. Frequency is determined by the source, not the properties of the medium.

7. $$period = \frac{1}{frequency} = \frac{1}{1\ MHz} = \textbf{\textit{1\ μsec}}$$

8. $$frequency = \frac{1}{period} = \frac{1}{0.5\ μsec} = \frac{1}{0.5}\ MHz = \textbf{\textit{2\ MHz}}$$

9.   **a + c**   (A 10 kHz frequency equals a 0.1 msec period.)

10.   **Unity or 1** (Recall: *freq • period = freq • 1/freq = 1*)

11.   **b**   (Note: Since the period and frequency give the same information, this question is the same as #5.)

12.   The period will not change. (This question is analogous to #6.)

13. $$\frac{662\ m}{2\ sec} = \frac{331\ m}{1\ sec} = 331\frac{m}{sec}$$

14.   *distance = rate • time*

$$distance = \frac{60\ miles}{1\ hr} • 2\ hr = \textbf{120 miles}$$

15.   *distance = rate • time*

$$distance = \left(1,540\frac{m}{sec}\right) • 1\ sec = \textbf{1,540 m}$$ (almost 1 mile)

16. $$distance = rate • time \Rightarrow \frac{distance}{rate} = time$$

$$distance = \frac{45\ miles}{30\frac{miles}{hr}} = 1.5hr$$

17.   (Recall from Chapter 1: we learned that it takes 13 μsec to image a structure at 1 cm which is the equivalent travel distance of 2 cm.)

18.   c   (Speed of sound depends on inertia and elasticity of medium.)

19   d   (Wavelength has units of distance.)

20.   a   (Wavelength is dependent on both frequency and propagation velocity.)

21.   a   (For the same reason as in #20.)

22.   d   (Amplitude does not affect frequency, period, wavelength, propagation velocity, etc.)

Section 13.7 Exercises (Pg. 134-135)

1. $P_f = 1,000$ Watts
      $P_i = 10$ Watts

$$dB \triangleq 10 \bullet log\left(\frac{P_f}{P_i}\right)$$ (Use power form since Watts is a measure of power.)

$$10 \bullet log\left(\frac{1,000}{10}\right) = 10 \bullet log\,(100)$$

Since the log(100) = 2
$10 \bullet log(100) = 10 \bullet (2) =$ **20 dB**

2. $A_i = 1$ mV (Use amplitude form since voltage is a measure of amplitude.)
      $A_f = 100$ mV

$$gain = \frac{100\ mV}{1\ mv} = 100$$

$$dB \triangleq 20 \bullet log\left(\frac{A_f}{A_i}\right)$$

$20 \bullet log(100) = 20 \bullet 2 =$ **40 dB**

3. $A_i = \$2,500$ (Amplitude form)
      $A_f = \$250,000$

$$20 \bullet log\left(\frac{250,000}{2,500}\right) = 20 \bullet log\,(100) = \textbf{40 } dB$$

4. $$\frac{I_f}{I_i} = \frac{1}{1000}$$

$$10 \bullet log\left(\frac{1}{1000}\right) = 10 \bullet (-3) = \textbf{-30 dB}$$

5.

Gain ratio	Power def	Amplitude def
1/1,000	-30 dB	-60 dB
1/100	-20 dB	-40 dB
1/10	-10 dB	-20 dB
1/2	-3 dB	-6 dB
1	0 dB	0 dB
2	3 dB	6 dB
10	10 dB	20 dB
100	20 dB	40 dB
1,000	30 dB	60 dB
10,000	40 dB	80 dB
100,000	50 dB	100 dB
1,000,000	60 dB	120 dB
10,000,000	70 dB	140 dB

6. **3 dB**

7. **-3 dB**

8. **6 dB**

9. **-6 dB**

10. **-30 dB**

11. **40 dB**

Section 14.3 Exercises   (Pg. 136-137)

1.   step 1: write the equation: $f \bullet \lambda = c$

     step 2: put equation into desired form: $\lambda = c/f$

     step 3: write down given information: f = 5 MHz
c = 1,540 m/sec (soft tissue)

     step 4: rewrite information with matching units: $f = 5 \times 10^6$ 1/sec
$c = 1,540$ m/sec (soft tissue)

     step 5: plug into equation and solve equation: $\lambda = \dfrac{1,540 \dfrac{m}{sec}}{5 \times 10^6 \dfrac{1}{sec}}$

     step 6: convert to easy-to-read form $\approx 3 \times 10^{-4}$ m = **0.3 mm**

Pegasus Lectures, Inc.

*<u>Check units and answer</u> - do they both make sense?
(Note that this problem can be solved quickly by realizing that an M in the denominator is equivalent to a μ in the numerator)

$$\lambda = \frac{1540 \text{ m}}{5 \text{ M} \dfrac{1}{\text{sec}} \text{ sec}} = 308 \text{ } \mu m = 0.308 \text{ mm}$$

2. $\lambda = \dfrac{c}{f}$

$f = 5 \text{ MHz} = 5 \times 10^6 \dfrac{1}{sec}$

$c = 4,080 \dfrac{m}{sec} \text{ (bone)}$

$\lambda = \dfrac{4,080 \dfrac{m}{sec}}{5 \times 10^6 \dfrac{1}{sec}} \approx 8 \times 10^{-4} \text{ } m$

$= 0.8 \text{ mm}$

3. $\lambda = \dfrac{c}{f}$

$f = 10 \text{ MHz} = 10 \times 10^6 \dfrac{1}{sec}$

$c = 4,080 \dfrac{m}{sec} \text{ (bone)}$

$\lambda = \dfrac{4,080 \dfrac{m}{sec}}{10 \times 10^6 \dfrac{1}{sec}} \approx 8 \times 10^{-4} \text{ } m$

$= 0.4 \text{ mm}$

4. $c = f \bullet \lambda$
$\lambda = 1 \text{ mm} = 1 \times 10^{-3} \text{ m}$

$f = 2 \text{ } MHz = 2 \times 10^6 \dfrac{1}{sec}$

Solving for c:

$c = 2 \times 10^6 \dfrac{1}{sec} \bullet 1 \times 10^{-3} \text{ m} = 2 \times 10^3 \dfrac{m}{sec}$

$= 2,000 \text{ m / sec or 2 km / sec}$

Do you think this material is stiffer than soft tissue? (probably)
Do you think this material is stiffer than blood? (probably)
How about bone? (probably not)

5. a

$$\left(\begin{array}{l} stiffness \propto \dfrac{1}{compressability} \\[2mm] stiffness \propto \dfrac{1}{elasticity} \\[2mm] stiffness \propto inelasticity \end{array} \right)$$

6. **Decreases**

$$\left(c \propto \dfrac{1}{density} \right)$$

7. If the transmit voltage is increased from 2 to 4 volts, the frequency will **not change**. (Amplitude and frequency are disjoint.)

8.
infrasound	0-20 Hz	(below human hearing)
audible	20-20 kHz	(audible for humans)
ultrasound	>20 kHz	(above human hearing)
diagnostic ultrasound	2 MHz - 10 MHz	(approximate useful diagnostic range)

9. If the amplitude is increased by a factor of nine, the power is **increased** by a factor of **81**, and the intensity is also **increased** by a factor of **81.**

$$\left(intensity = \dfrac{power}{area} \propto \left(amplitude \right)^2 \right)$$

$9^2 = 9 \bullet 9 = \underline{81}$

10. Intensity increases by a factor of 9 since ($3^2 = 9$)
    Recall: (intensity $\propto$ (amplitude)^2)

11. Intensity increases by a factor of 3.
    Recall: (intensity $\propto$ power)

12. Intensity decreases by a factor of 2.

$$Recall \left(intensity \propto \dfrac{1}{area} \right)$$

13. Amplitude has increased by a factor of 2.
    (Increasing amplitude by a factor of 2 increases intensity by a factor of 4.)

Section 15. Conceptual Questions (Pg. 137-139)

1. The frequency is determined strictly by the wave **source**.

2. The period of a wave is determined strictly by the wave **source.**

3. The propagation velocity is determined strictly by the properties of the **medium**.

4. The wave source cannot change the propagation **velocity** which is strictly determined by the properties of the **medium**.

5. The two properties of the medium which determine the propagation velocity are **inertia** (related to density) and **elasticity** (related to compressibility and stiffness).

6. The propagation velocity **decreases** with increased density, assuming no change in stiffness.

7. As the density decreases, the propagation velocity **increases**, assuming no change in stiffness.

8. As the stiffness increases, the propagation velocity **increases**.

9. A stiff material is not very elastic, so stiffness and elasticity are **inversely** related.

10. A material which is inelastic is a stiff material, and therefore has a high **propagation** velocity.

11. Inelasticity and incompressibility are related to **stiffness** .

12. Elasticity and **compressibility** are inversely related to stiffness.

13. A gas is generally more compressible than a **liquid** which is generally more compressible than a solid.

14. Air is more compressible than bone and has a much **lower** propagation **velocity**.

15. **Infrasound** is sound below human hearing.

16. **Audible** sound is sound within human hearing.

17. **Ultrasound** is sound above human hearing.

18. **Diagnostic** ultrasound is approximately from 2 MHz to 10 MHz.

19. All sound waves are **longitudinal** mechanical waves.

20. Human hearing is approximately **20 Hz** to **20 kHz**.

21. Infrasound is below **20 Hz**.

22. Ultrasound is any sound above **20 kHz**.

23.   **Power** is the rate at which energy is transferred.

24.   **Power** is proportional to the (amplitude)^2.

25.   If the amplitude is doubled, the power is **quadrupled**.

26.   If the amplitude is halved, the power is **quartered**.

27.   If the amplitude is increased by a factor of two, the power is increased by a factor of **four.**

28.   If the amplitude is decreased by a factor of two, the power is decreased by a factor of **four**.

29.   Power is measured in units of **Watts**.

30.   The **intensity** is defined as the concentration of energy.

31.   The fundamental unit for **intensity** is power per area.

32.   If power is given in Watts and the area is given in **cm²**, the intensity has units of Watts/cm².

33.   If the area is increased by a factor of two and the power is unchanged, the intensity is decreased by a factor of **two**.

34.   If the power increases by a factor of two and the area is unchanged, the intensity **increases** by a factor of **two**.

35.   If the power **increases** by a factor of two, and the area increases by a factor of two, the intensity does not **change**.

36.   If the amplitude doubles, the power **quadruples**. If the area does not change, the intensity also **quadruples**.

37.   Intensity is proportional to the **power** which is proportional to the **amplitude** squared.

38.   The intensity is inversely proportional to the **area**.

Pegasus Lectures, Inc.

Section 5. Conceptual Questions   (Pg. 159)

1.   **Attenuation** means a diminishing or decrease.

2.   Attenuation is the result of three wave interactions with the medium: **absorption, reflection,** and **refraction.**

3.   In soft tissue, **absorption** is the dominant factor creating attenuation (discussed in Level 2 – but the question is left here to see if you are resourceful.)

4.   **Absorption** is the conversion of energy from sound waves into heat within the medium.

5.   Absorption increases with increasing **frequency.**

6.   The word **refraction** refers to the "bending" of a ray or beam at an interface between two different media.

7.   Refraction is governed by **Snell's** law.

8.   **Snell's** law for refraction depends on the ratio of the propagation **velocities** of two different media at an interface and the incident angle.

9.   The term **normal** in reference to angles means the same as zero degree incidence.

10.   For **normal** incidence there can be no **refraction.**

11.   For normal incidence, the amount of reflection is determined by the acoustic **impedance** mismatch.

12.   The acoustic impedance has units of **Rayls.**

13.   The acoustic impedance equals the **density** times the **propagation velocity.**

14.   Density has units of kg/m^3 and the propagation velocity has units of m/sec. So 1 Rayl equals **1 kg/(m^2 • sec).**

15.   A large impedance mismatch will result in a high percentage of **reflection** or equivalently a **low** percentage of transmission.

16.   No **impedance** mismatch will result in no reflection or equivalently 100% **transmission.**

17.   The amount of refraction is given by **Snell's** law whereas the amount of **reflection** is given by an equation based on the acoustic impedance mismatch.

18.   The acoustic impedance of air is **less** than the acoustic impedance of tissue.

19. **Specular** reflection occurs from surfaces which are large and smooth with respect to the wavelength.

20. A mirror gives a good example of **specular** reflection.

21. **Scattering** occurs from surfaces which are small or rough with respect to the **wavelength**.

22. **Rayleigh scattering** refers to the frequency dependency of scattering. Rayleigh scattering of light through the atmosphere causes the sky to appear blue.

Section 11. Exercises (Pg. 182-183)

1. The three mechanical wave interactions with the medium which constitute attenuation are:
   absorption
   reflection
   refraction

2. Absorption is the conversion of energy from an acoustic wave to **heat.**

3. Absorption **increases** with increasing frequency.

4. Of the three interactions which constitute attenuation, the dominant factor in soft tissue **absorption.**

5. The law which tells at what angle an incident beam will be transmitted is called **Snell's Law.**

6. Snell's Law is defined as: $c_t \sin(\theta_i) = c_i \sin(\theta_t)$

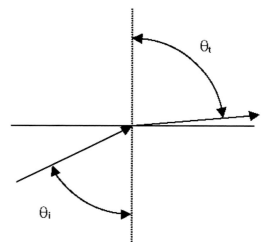

   Where:
   c_t = Speed of sound in transmitted medium
   c_i = Speed of sound in incident medium
   θ_i = incident angle
   θ_t = transmitted (refraction) angle

7. Normal incidence implies that the incident beam direction is **perpendicular** to the media interface.

8. Normal incidence is really just a special case governed by Snell's **Law.** For normal incidence, $\theta_i = 0°$. Since $\sin(\theta_i) = 0$, $\sin(\theta_t) = 0$, implying $\theta_t = 0$ and there is no **refraction.**

9. Given the intensity of a normal incident beam, you would need to know **the acoustic impedances of the two media (mismatch)** to calculate the transmitted intensity.

10. The acoustic impedance is given by the equation: $Z = \rho \cdot c.$

11.   The unit for acoustic impedance is the **Rayl.**

12.   The percentage of a normal incident beam reflected and transmitted at the interface of two media is given by:

$$\% \, reflected = \left[\frac{Z_2 - Z_1}{Z_2 + Z_1} \right]^2$$

$$\% \, transmitted = 1 - \% \, reflected = 1 - \left[\frac{Z_2 - Z_1}{Z_2 + Z_1} \right]^2$$

13.   Percentage transmitted + percentage reflected must equal **1 or 100%**.

14.   **c**   The incident angle is equal to the reflected angle. (Have you ever played pool?)

15.   If the wavelength is small with respect to the structure size and the surface is smooth **specular** reflection should occur.

16.   If the surface is rough and the wavelength is large with respect to the structure size **scattering** reflection should occur.

17.   **Rayleigh** scattering indicates that the amount of scattering changes with wavelength.

18.   For **soft** tissue the attenuation rate is approximately 0.5 dB/(cm-MHz).

19.   For muscle, the attenuation rate is approximately **1 dB/(cm-MHz).**

20.   At a depth of 5 cm, in muscle, the attenuation for a 7.5 MHz beam would be:

f_0 = 7.5 MHz
depth = 5 cm

$$attenuation \; in \; muscle \approx 1 \frac{dB}{(cm \text{-} MHz)}$$

$$attenuation \approx (7.5 \, MHz) \bullet (5 \, cm) \bullet 1 \frac{dB}{(cm \text{-} MHz)} \approx \textbf{37.5 dB}$$

21.   Imaging to a depth of 5 cm, in muscle, the attenuation for a 7.5 MHz beam would be:

f_0 = 7.5 MHz
depth = 5 cm $\Rightarrow$ round trip = 10 cm

$$attenuation \; in \; muscle \approx 1 \frac{dB}{(cm \text{-} MHz)}$$

$$attenuation \approx (7.5 \, MHz) \bullet (10 \, cm) \bullet 1 \frac{dB}{(cm \text{-} MHz)} \approx \textbf{75 dB}$$

(With that much attenuation, you will not see much, if anything, at 5 cm deep.)

Section 13. Exercises   (Pg. 221)

1. $distance = rate \bullet time \Rightarrow time = \dfrac{distance}{rate}$

rate = c_{bone} = 4,080 m/sec = 408,000 cm/sec
distance = 2 • imaging depth = 2 • (2.04 cm) = 4.08 cm (roundtrip)

so time = $\dfrac{4.08\,cm}{\left(408,000\,cm/\sec\right)} = \dfrac{4.08\,cm}{\left(4.08\times10^{5}\,cm/\sec\right)} = 1\times10^{-5}\,sec = 10\times10^{-6}\,sec$

or   **10 μsec**

2. $distance = rate \bullet time$
rate = 1,540 m/sec (soft tissue)

   a)   time = 1 second
distance = (1,540 m/sec) • (1 sec) = 1,540 m =   **1,540 m**

Note: If the question asked for the maximum imaging depth, the answer would be 1/2 of the distance or <u>770 m</u>. (Hopefully, you will not have patients this size.)

   b)   time = 2 seconds
            (shortcut)

$distance = 2 \bullet \left(1,540\,\dfrac{m}{\sec}\right) = 3,080\ m =$ **3,080 m**

   c)   time = 10 seconds

$distance = 10 \bullet \left(1,540\,\dfrac{m}{\sec}\right) = 15,400\ m =$ **15.4 km**

3. c_{air} = 331 m/sec (varies depending on temperature - ok if use 331 m/sec or 347 m/sec)

   a)   distance = 331 m/sec • 1 sec = 331 m
$Imaging\ depth = \dfrac{distance}{2} = \dfrac{331\ m}{2} = 165.5\ m\ (roundtrip)$

   b)   distance = 331 m/sec • 2 sec = 662 m
$Imaging\ depth = \dfrac{distance}{2} = \dfrac{662}{2}\,m = 331\ m$

   c)   distance = 3,310 m
$Imaging\ depth = \dfrac{distance}{2} =$ **1,655 m**

4. Imaging depth $= \dfrac{distance}{2} = 5$ cm $\Rightarrow$ distance $= 2 \bullet 5$ cm $= 10$ cm

c $= 154{,}000$ cm/sec

$$time = \dfrac{10\,\dfrac{cm}{line}}{\left(154{,}000\,\dfrac{cm}{sec}\right)} = 0.65 \times 10^{-4}\,sec = 65\,\dfrac{\mu sec}{line}$$

$$\left(\text{or recalling } \dfrac{13\,\mu sec}{1\,cm} \text{ and scaling}:\ 5\,\dfrac{cm}{line} \bullet \dfrac{13\,\mu sec}{1\,cm} = 65\,\dfrac{\mu sec}{line}\right)$$

PRP = minimum time between lines = 65 μsec

$$PRF = \dfrac{1}{PRP} = \dfrac{1}{65\,\mu sec} = 0.015 \times 10^{6}\ Hz = \mathbf{15\ kHz}$$

5. $frame\ rate = \dfrac{1}{frame\ time}$

1 frame = 100 lines

so $frame\ time = \dfrac{0.1\,msec}{line} \bullet \dfrac{100\,lines}{frame} = \dfrac{10\,msec}{frame}$

and $frame\ rate = \dfrac{1}{frame\ time} = \dfrac{1}{10\,msec} = \mathbf{0.1\ kHz}$ or $\mathbf{100\ Hz}$ or $\mathbf{\dfrac{100\ frames}{sec}}$

6. $frame\ time = \left(\dfrac{time}{line}\right) \bullet \left(\dfrac{\#\,lines}{frame}\right)$

realizing that: $\left(\dfrac{lines}{frame}\right) = \left(\dfrac{lines}{packet}\right) \bullet \left(\dfrac{packets}{frame}\right)$

Given: packet size = 10 lines and frame = 100 packets

so $\left(\dfrac{lines}{frame}\right) = \left(\dfrac{10\,lines}{packet}\right) \bullet \left(\dfrac{100\,packets}{frame}\right) = 1{,}000\,\dfrac{lines}{frame}$

$$\left(\dfrac{time}{line}\right) = \dfrac{\left(2 \times 10\,\dfrac{cm}{line}\right)}{\left(154{,}000\,\dfrac{cm}{sec}\right)} = 0.13\,\dfrac{msec}{line}$$

$$\left(\text{or recalling } \dfrac{13\,\mu \sec}{1\,cm} \text{ and scaling}:\ 10\,\dfrac{cm}{line} \bullet \dfrac{13\,\mu sec}{1\,cm} = 130\,\dfrac{\mu sec}{line} = 0.13\,\dfrac{msec}{line}\right)$$

$$\text{so } \textit{frame time} = \left(\frac{0.13 \, msec}{line} \right) \cdot \left(1,000 \frac{lines}{frame} \right) = \frac{\textbf{0.13 sec}}{\textbf{frame}}$$

$$\text{and frame rate} = \frac{1}{0.13 \frac{sec}{frame}} \approx \textbf{7 Hz}$$

Note: This problem is very important for many reasons. The first important point is that there is not always a one to one correspondence between the number of acoustic lines transmitted and the number of display lines. In color Doppler, each display line is always comprised of a "packet" or "ensemble" of acoustic lines.

The second important point is how dramatically the frame rate decreased as a result of the packet size. Color Doppler always has the risk of low frame rates. If the frame rate is too low, changes which occur may be missed. This is equivalent to our discussions in Chapter 1 about sampling too slowly, thereby causing aliasing. The ability to detect changes in time is called temporal resolution. Low frame rates lead to poor temporal resolution.

There are other modalities which do not have a one to one correspondence between acoustic lines and display lines. Whenever multiple transmit foci are used in B-Mode imaging, there are multiple acoustic lines per display line in the image. The reverse is also possible. If parallel processing is being used, it is possible that there are fewer acoustic lines than display lines. Obviously, parallel processing is an attempt to improve temporal resolution.

7. $PD = (\# \, cycles)(period)$
    $= (8)(0.2 \, \mu sec) = \textbf{1.6 } \mu \textbf{sec}$

8. $period = \dfrac{1}{frequency} = \dfrac{1}{1 \, MHz} = 1 \, \mu sec$

    $PD = (8)(1 \, \mu sec) = \textbf{8 } \mu \textbf{sec}$

9. $period = \dfrac{1}{1 \, kHz} = 1 \, msec$

    $10 \, msec = (\# \, cycles)(1 \, msec)$

    $\# \, cycles = \dfrac{10 \, msec}{1 \, msec} = \textbf{10 } \textbf{\textit{cycles}}$

10. System B as a shorter pulse duration.

    $$\left(PD \propto period \propto \frac{1}{freq} \Rightarrow PD \propto \frac{1}{freq} \right)$$

Pegasus Lectures, Inc.

11. If two systems are operating at the same frequency, then the periods are equal. Since both pulses have the same number of cycles, the pulse durations must be equal.

12. $Duty\ Cycle = \dfrac{PD}{PRP}$ $\left(\dfrac{time\ on\ duty}{total\ time}\right)$

$$= \dfrac{2\ msec}{5\ msec} = 0.4 \Rightarrow \mathbf{40\%}$$

13. $Duty\ Cycle = \dfrac{PD}{PRP}$ $(0.6\% = 0.006)$

$$0.006 = \dfrac{PD}{10\ msec}$$
$$PD = (10\ msec) \cdot (0.006) = \mathbf{0.06\ msec}$$

14. $PRP = \dfrac{1}{PRF} = \dfrac{1}{0.1\ kHz} = 10\ msec$

so this problem is the exact same problem as #2
PD = **0.06 msec**

15. A duty cycle of 100% means that the transmit is continuous, or **continuous wave (CW)**.

Section 16. Conceptual Questions   (Pg. 228-230)

1. The frequency and the **period** are reciprocals.

2. The pulse repetition frequency and the **pulse** repetition **period** are reciprocals.

3. The **PRP**, like the period, has units of **time (seconds).**

4. The **PRF**, like the **frequency**, has units of one over time, which has the name **Hertz**.

5. The **PRP** is the time between pulses repeating.

6. The **PRF** is the frequency at which the pulses repeat.

7. The deeper the imaging depth, the lower the **PRF**, or the more time it takes before repeating a pulse.

8. The frame **time** depends on how much time it takes to shoot one line, and the number of **lines** within the frame.

9. If one line takes 0.1 msec., and there are 120 lines in one frame, the frame time is **12 msec.**

10. The pulse duration has units of **time.**

11. If a pulse has 4 cycles and each cycle lasts 1 msec, the **pulse duration** equals **4 msec.**

12. If a pulse has **6 cycles** and each cycle lasts 2 msec, then the pulse duration equals 12 msec.

13. The time for a cycle to repeat itself is called the **period.**

14. The **pulse duration** equals the number of cycles multiplied by the time for one cycle to occur called the period.

15. The **duty cycle** is the percentage of time the pulse is on divided by the total time between repeating pulses.

16. The time a pulse is "on" is called the **pulse** duration.

17. The "total time" between repeating pulses is called the **pulse repetition period (PRP).**

18. Since the duty cycle is the "on time" divided by the "**total time**", the **duty** cycle equals the pulse **duration** divided by the pulse repetition period.

19. The duty cycle is also called the duty **factor**.

20. The **duty factor** can never be greater than 1 or 100%.

21. A duty factor of **1** means the "pulse" is always on.

22. A duty factor of **0** means there is no pulse.

23. A duty factor of **0.5** means the pulse duration equals one half the pulse repetition period.

24. A duty factor of 50% means the pulse **duration** equals one half the pulse **repetition period**.

25. If the duty cycle is 0.33 and the PRP is 1 msec, then the pulse duration is **0.33 msec**.

26. If the duty cycle is 0.33 and the pulse duration is 0.66 seconds, then the PRP is **2 seconds**.

27. The spatial pulse length has units of **distance** whereas the pulse duration has units of **time**.

28. The **spatial pulse length** equals the number of cycles multiplied by the wavelength (λ).

29. The **pulse duration** equals the number of cycles multiplied by the period.

30. You should notice a similarity between the **spatial pulse length** and the pulse duration. The spatial pulse length has units of distance and is therefore related to the wavelength, which also has units of distance. The **pulse duration** has units of time and is therefore related to the **period** which also has units of time.

31. The operating frequency is the same as the transmit **frequency**.

Pegasus Lectures, Inc.

32. The **bandwidth** is defined as the maximum frequency minus the minimum frequency over which a transducer or system has sensitivity.

33. The **fractional** bandwidth is defined as the bandwidth divided by the operating frequency.

34. The quality factor is the inverse of the **fractional** bandwidth.

35. Since the fractional bandwidth equals the bandwidth divided by the operating frequency, and since the quality factor is the inverse of the fractional bandwidth, the quality factor equals the operating frequency divided by the **bandwidth**.

36. A shorter pulse duration leads to a wider **bandwidth**.

37. An infinitely short pulse duration theoretically creates **infinite** bandwidth.

38. **CW** spectral Doppler requires the least bandwidth.

39. Transmitting at 2 MHz implies that the center frequency of the bandwidth being used is **2 MHz**.

40. A **backing material (damping material)** is used to shorten the ring down of a transducer.

41. Shortening the ring down of a transducer also shortens the **spatial pulse length**, improving the range resolution.

42. The motivation for using a pulsed mode instead of a continuous mode is because CW has no **range** resolution.

Section 11. Exercises   (Pg. 251)

1.   **d**   A transducer is anything which converts one form of **energy** to another.

2.   **b**   Ultrasound transducers convert voltage (electropotential energy) to **acoustic** energy and **acoustic** energy to **voltage.**

True or False

3.   **False**   All transducers use the piezoelectric effect.

4.   **True**   All ultrasound transducers use the piezoelectric effect.

5.   **True**   PZT is a piezoelectric material.

6.   **True**   PZT stands for lead zirconate titanate.

7.   **True**   Some materials can be made piezoelectric through a process called poling.

8.   **True**   The Curie point is the temperature at which a material loses its Piezoelectric properties and is approximately 300° for PZT.

Section 28. Exercises   (Pg. 287-290)

1.   **True**   Blind (Doppler only transducers) have a broad depth of field.

2.   **True**   A phased array transducer must have multiple elements.

3.   **False**   A mechanical system can steer and focus the beam electronically.

4.   **True**   An annular array can be focused electronically but must be steered mechanically.

5.   **c**   An annular transducer has the distinct benefit of variable focus in both elevation and lateral planes. A distinct disadvantage with respect to phased transducers is that an annular transducer **must be steered mechanically.**

6.   **c**   A **linear switched array** has a rectangular image.

7.   **a**   A fundamental difference between a linear switched array and a linear phased array is that a linear switched array **has a fixed focus and can not steer.**

8.   **a**   Sector phased arrays principally create a sector image **for rib access.**

9.   **d**   The "footprint" of a transducer has two dimensions. The beamwidth is associated with the **lateral** dimension and the "slice thickness" is determined by the **elevation** dimension.

10.   Match column B to column A

	A		**B**
a)	Lens	(1):	used to help focus the beam
b)	Matching layer(s)	(3):	lowers acoustic impedance mismatch between the transducer and the patient.
c)	Piezoelectric material	(2):	converts electrical to mechanical energy
d)	Backing material	(5):	used to decrease the spatial pulse length, improving axial resolution,. increases transducer bandwidth, but decreases transducer sensitivity
e)	Wires	(4):	delivers the drive voltage to the crystal, and echo voltage to the receivers

11.   Match column B to column A

	A		**B**
a)	Near field zone	(4):	Fresnel
b)	Far field zone	(5):	Fraunhofer
c)	Focus	(3):	where the beam reaches its minimum diameter
d)	Resolution	(1):	the ability to distinguish changes
e)	Operating frequency	(2):	the transmit frequency

12.   **e**   Axial, longitudinal, depth, and radial are all equivalent names for range or axial resolution. Azimuthal resolution is the same as lateral resolution.

13.   **a**   Angular, azimuthal, and transverse are all equivalent names for lateral resolution. Radial is the same as range or axial resolution.

14.   In pulsed mode, the operating frequency is given by the equation:

$$f_0 = \frac{c\left(of\ crystal\ material\right)}{2 \bullet thickness\left(of\ crystal\right)}$$

15.   In continuous mode, the operating frequency is determined by the **frequency of the "pulser,"** or the transmitter.

16.   **a**   The near zone length is approximately equal to $\dfrac{D^2 f}{6}$. If the frequency doubles, **the NZL increases by a factor of 2**.

17.   **c**   If the diameter of a transducer is increased by a factor of 2, the near zone length **increases by a factor of 2^2, or equivalently, 4**.

18.   **b**   Recall that the focus is at the NZL which is proportional to the diameter of the crystal squared, and proportional to the frequency.

19.   **e**   There is no way to improve the focus in the far field of a transducer since the beam is diffraction limited. If a narrower far field focus is required, a larger diameter transducer would have to be used.

20.   **d**   For an unfocused transducer, the approximate beamwidth at the focal distance and twice the focal distance, given a crystal diameter of 5 mm is **2.5 mm and 5 mm**, respectively.

21.   How thick would a crystal have to be for 2 MHz pulsed mode operation given a propagation velocity through the crystal of 5,000 m/sec?

$$f_0 = \frac{c}{2 \bullet thickness} \Rightarrow thickness = \frac{c}{2 \bullet f_0}$$

$$f_0 = 2 \text{ MHz}$$

$$c = 5,000 \text{ m/sec}$$

$$thickness = \frac{5,000 \ m/sec}{2 \bullet 2 \times 10^6 \ 1/sec} = \frac{5 \times 10^{-3} \ m}{4} =$$

1.25 mm

22.   **b**   If the thickness of a crystal doubles, the frequency of operation for PW mode **halves.**

23.   **b**   Recall that the operating frequency is proportional to the propagation velocity within the crystal.

24.   Radial resolution equals **SPL/2.**

25.   Lateral resolution equals the **beamwidth** and therefore varies with depth since the **beamwidth** varies with depth.

Section 29. Conceptual Questions   (Pg. 290-293)

1.   A transducer is anything which converts **energy** from one form to another form.

2.   An **ultrasound** transducer converts voltage into sound above human hearing and sound into a voltage.

3. An ultrasound transducer converts electropotential **energy** into **mechanical energy** and mechanical energy into electropotential energy.

4. Ultrasound transducers use the **piezoelectric** effect.

5. A commonly used material for ultrasound transducers is **lead** zirconate titanate (PZT).

6. If a transducer is heated above its **Curie** temperature, it will loose its piezoelectric properties.

7. For PZT, the Curie temperature is **300° C.**

8. When a transducer is referred to as "mechanical," it means that the **steering** is performed mechanically.

9. When a transducer is referred to as "**phased,**" it means that the steering is performed electronically.

10. A **lens** is used to help focus a beam in the elevation plane.

11. The **elevation** plane corresponds to the beam thickness.

12. The **matching layer** is used to minimize the acoustic impedance mismatch between the PZT and tissue.

13. Without a matching layer, there would be a large **acoustic impedance** mismatch between the transducer and tissue causing a large **reflection** or equivalently small transmission.

14. The **backing material** is used to shorten the spatial pulse length, improving longitudinal resolutions.

15. The backing material shortens the spatial pulse length by absorbing some of the pulse energy thereby **decreasing** the transducer efficiency.

16. The near field zone is also called the **Fresnel** zone.

17. The near field is the region of the beam shallower than the **focus.**

18. The focus is where the beam reaches its minimum **diameter** and maximum **intensity.**

19. The far field is also called the **Fraunhofer** zone.

20. The far field is the region of the beam **deeper** than the focus.

21. The focal region is also called the **depth** of field and refers to the area of the beam which is most tightly **focused.**

22. **Resolution** is the ability to distinguish between two objects.

23. **Longitudinal** resolution is also known as axial, radial and depth resolution.

24. **Longitudinal** resolution is the ability to distinguish between objects along the beam direction.

25. **Lateral** resolution is also known as angular, azimuthal or transverse resolution.

26. **Lateral** resolution is the ability to distinguish between structures which are side-by-side.

27. The **operating** frequency is the same as the transmit frequency.

28. In **pulsed mode**, the operating frequency is determined by the speed of sound in the crystal and the crystal thickness.

29. In pulsed mode, a thicker crystal will have a **lower** operating frequency.

30. In **continuous mode**, the operating frequency is determined by the frequency of the drive voltage.

31. In **continuous mode,** a thicker crystal will not change the operating frequency.

32. The near zone length (NZL) is the distance from the face of the transducer to the beam **focus.**

33. Any depth shallower than the **focus** is within the near zone.

34. The **near** zone **length** is proportional to the transducer diameter squared.

35. If a transducer diameter is doubled, the near zone length is **quadrupled.**

36. If a transducer diameter is doubled, the focus is **four times** as deep.

37. The near zone length is proportional to the operating **frequency.**

38. If the operating frequency is doubled, the NZL is **doubled**.

39. The **beamwidth** is approximately one half the transducer diameter at the focus.

40. The **beamwidth** is approximately one half the transducer diameter at a distance of one near zone length.

41. The **focus** occurs at a distance of one near zone length.

42. The beamwidth approximately equals the transducer **diameter** at a distance of two near zone lengths.

43. The beamwidth is greater than the transducer diameter at a depth greater than two **near zone** lengths.

44. **Focusing** can be achieved by lenses, curved elements, **electronically**, or with mirrors.

45. A phased array transducer uses **electronic** focusing in the lateral dimension and a **lens** for focusing in the elevation dimension.

46. The curvature of an image produced by a **curved** linear transducer matches the curvature of the transducer face.

47.   Mechanical transducers use lenses, and/or mirrors for focusing but cannot be focused **electronically.**

48.   Focusing can only affect the **near field**, never the far field.

49.   Beyond the Fresnel zone, the beam is said to be **diffraction** limited.

50.   In **continuous** mode, transmit and receive occur simultaneously, continuously.

51.   For a **CW** mode the operating frequency equals the drive voltage frequency.

52.   In a **pulsed mode**, transmit and receive alternate, intermittently.

53.   B-mode is an example of a **pulsed** wave mode.

54.   Color flow is an example of a **pulsed** wave mode.

55.   CW Doppler is an example of a **continuous** wave mode.

56.   In **pulsed mode**, the operating frequency equals the propagation velocity within the crystal divided by two times the **thickness**.

57.   **Longitudinal** (axial, radial, depth) resolution is the ability to distinguish between structures along the beam direction.

58.   The longitudinal resolution is determined by one half the **spatial pulse length**.

59.   **Lateral** resolution, (angular, transverse, azimuthal) is the ability to distinguish between structure which lie side by side.

60.   The lateral resolution is determined by the **beamwidth.**

Section 7. Exercises   (Pg. 322)

1.   Increasing the **transmit** gain increases the SNR.

2.   Increasing the **receiver** gain may affect the apparent SNR, but not the true SNR.

3.   The five receiver functions are:
   1)   **amplification**
   2)   **compensation**
   3)   **compression**
   4)   **demodulation**
   5)   **rejection**

4.   **Compression** is a technique to reduce the dynamic range of a signal.

5.   For deeper imaging depths **lowering** the operating frequency will most likely increase the SNR.

6.   For a system with 10 TGC sliders, if the imaging depth is set to 20 cm, each slider represents **2 cm**.

7.   Both increasing the overall gain by 20 dB and increasing all of the TGCs by 20 dB have the same effect on the image.

8.   If the largest signal is 10 volts and the dynamic range is 10,000 to 1, the smallest signal would be:

$$\frac{10 \text{ volts}}{x} = \frac{10,000}{1}$$
$$10 \text{ volts} = 10,000x$$
$$\frac{10 \text{ volts}}{10,000} = x$$
$$x = 1 \times 10^{-3} \text{ volts}$$
$$= \underline{1 \ mV}$$

Section 26. Exercises   (Pg. 374-376)

1.   d   The **pulser** determines the initial amplitude, frequency and mode of ultrasound.

2.   b   The receiver performs all of the following functions except **data storage.**

3.   b   Amplification is another word for **receiver gain.**

4.   Define each of the following terms: (See description in chapter for answers.)

5.   a   Demodulation is a means of signal **detection** by removing the initial transmit frequency from the returning echo.

6. A compression of 20 dB in amplitude means the range of signals has been compressed or decreased by a factor of **10**.

$$\text{compression of 20 dB} \Rightarrow \text{a factor of 10}$$

$$\text{since 20 dB} = 20 \bullet log_{10}\left(\frac{A_1}{A_2}\right)$$

$$\frac{20}{20} = 1 = log_{10}\left(\frac{A_1}{A_2}\right) \Rightarrow \left(\frac{A_1}{A_2}\right) = 10$$

7. **One possible scheme (by color):**
   Box 1: 4 white marbles (2 small + 2 large)

   Box 2: 4 black marbles (2 small + 2 large)

   Another possible scheme (by size):
   Box 1: 4 large marbles (2 black + 2 white)

   Box 2: 4 small marbles (2 black + 2 white)

   (A compression of 2:1 or 6 dB)

8. To represent 4 states (boxes) you need 2 bits since $2^2 = 2 \cdot 2 = 4$ (00, 01, 10, 11), or 4 choices. To represent 2 states (boxes) you need 1 bit since $2^1 = 2$ (0, 1), or 2 choices.

9. **a** To present data, you must have at least 2 shades which can be represented by 1 bit.

10. A bi-stable picture is represented by only two shades, black and white, and requires **1** bit.

11. **6 bits** are necessary to represent 64 gray levels since $2^6 = 64$.

12. **1024** gray levels can be represented by 10 bits since $2^{10} = 1,024$.

13.
Amplitude input DNR	=	80 dB
f_o	=	10 MHz
attenuation	=	0.5 dB / (cm-MHz) (soft tissue one way)
	=	1 dB / (cm-MHz) (soft tissue roundtrip)
max depth	=	X (cm)

$$80 \ dB = \left(10 \ MHz\right)\left(x \ cm\right)\left(\frac{1 \ dB}{cm \times MHz}\right)$$

$$x = 8 \ cm$$

Note: Do you think the assumption for the attenuation rate is realistic? Can you typically penetrate to 8 cm with a 10 MHz transducer?

14. Phasing is achieved by **time** shifting the transmit pulses to each of the transducer elements.

15. Two examples of phasing used with phased array transducers are **steering** and **focusing**.

16.   c   Multiple transmit foci beams have the advantage of **narrower display beams** and the disadvantage of **lower frame rates.**

17.   There are three aspects of detail resolution: **axial, lateral,** and **elevation resolution.**

18.   Contrast resolution is the ability to distinguish structures based on **brightness** and is normally dictated by the number of **bits** per pixel in the display and the compression mapping.

19.   Factors which potentially affect temporal resolution are any factors which lower **frame** rate.

Section 27. Conceptual Questions   (Pg. 376-377)

1.   The **receiver** of an ultrasound system performs five functions: amplification, compensation, compression, demodulation, and rejection.

2.   **Amplification** is the process of making small signals larger.

3.   **Compensation** is performed by a swept gain control often called time gain control (TCG) or depth gain control (DGC).

4.   Compensation is necessary since **attenuation** increases with depth.

5.   **Compression** is a means by which to reduce the signal dynamic range usually through logarithmic amplification.

6.   **Dynamic** range is a ratio of a maximum to a minimum.

7.   **Demodulation** is often called signal detection and consists of two stages rectification and smoothing.

8.   **Rejection** is another means by which to limit dynamic range through suppression smaller, weaker signals.

9.   A digital scan converter is effectively a digital **memory** block.

10.   In the old days, **analog** scan converters were used which suffered problems of performance degradation over time, image flicker and fading.

11.   The display is most often a **CRT** (cathode ray tube).

12.   The standard CRT in the U.S. operated with **525** lines at a frame rate of 1/30th of a second.

13.   The standard CRT with a frame rate of 1/30th of a second used an interlaced display. First an **odd** field of lines 1,3,5,7... is displayed and then an even field of lines 2,4,6,8...is interlaced.

14.   More and more non-interlaced monitors are being used which have frame rates twice as fast as an **interlaced** monitor.

15.   The smallest division of a display is called a **pixel**.

16.   Better display resolution can be achieved with a higher **pixel or line** density.

17.   Each pixel can be represented by multiple **bits** which determine how many gray levels a pixel can represent.

18.   Every **bit** can represent two shades (black or white).

19.   A 1 bit display is called **bi-stable**.

20.   A 2 bit display has **four** shades of gray.

21.   A 3 bit display has **eight** shades of gray.

22.   A 6 bit display has **sixty-four** shades of gray.

23.   **Preprocessing** is any signal conditioning which can not be removed or changed once an image is acquired.

24.   **Post processing** is any signal conditioning which can change post data acquisition.

25.   **Huygen's Principle** states that all points on a wavefront can be treated as point sources producing spherical secondary wavelets, whose tangential surface predicts the new position of the wavefront over time. (Just because this principle was discussed in Chapter 5 – doesn't mean you can forget it, or anything else for that matter!)

26.   Electronic **steering** is achieved by phasing the excitation pulses to each element of the transducer.

27.   Phasing the excitation pulses means that intentional **time** delays are used in exciting transducer elements.

28.   Focusing is also achieved by **phasing** for electronic transducers.

29.   Multiple transmit focuses improve **lateral** resolution but decrease temporal resolution (slower frame rates).

30.   **Detail** resolution includes axial, lateral and elevation resolution.

31.   **Contrast** resolution is the ability to distinguish between structures based on variations in amplitude or brightness.

32.   Contrast resolution is determined by the scan **converter** and the number of bits per pixel in the display.

33.   **Temporal** resolution is the ability to distinguish dynamics or changes over time.

34.   **Temporal** resolution is determined by anything which determines the time it takes to create the image.

Appendix C • Answers to Supplemental Exercises

Chapter 1 Mathematics   (Pg. 395-398)

1.   Two quantities are said to be proportional, if an increase in one quantity, leads to an **increase** in the other.

2.   Two quantities are said to be inversely proportional, if an increase in one quantity leads to a **decrease** in the other.

3.   In the equation $f_{Dop} = \dfrac{2 f_0 v}{c} \cos(\theta)$:

   f_{Dop} is proportional to the **operating frequency (f_0), velocity (v),** and **cos(θ).**

   f_{Dop} is inversely proportional to **the propagation velocity (c).**

   v is proportional to **c**, and f_{Dop}.

   v is inversely proportional to **(f_0)**, and **cos(θ).**

4.   Rewrite the equation $f \bullet \lambda = c$

   a)   as $\lambda = \dfrac{c}{f}$

   b)   as $f = \dfrac{c}{\lambda}$

   units check $f \bullet \lambda = c \Rightarrow \dfrac{1}{\sec} \bullet m = \dfrac{m}{\sec}$ ✔

   Do a unit check for "a" and "b"

   a) $m = \dfrac{m}{\sec * \dfrac{1}{\sec}} = m$ ✔

   b) $\dfrac{1}{\sec} = \dfrac{m}{\sec * m} = \dfrac{1}{\sec}$ ✔

5. If the reciprocal of one over seconds $\left(\dfrac{1}{\sec}\right)$ is seconds, the reciprocal of the reciprocal of one

over seconds $\left(\dfrac{1}{\dfrac{1}{\dfrac{1}{\sec}}}\right)$ is: $\left(\dfrac{1}{\sec}\right)$

6. $\dfrac{3}{2\dfrac{m}{\sec}} = 1.5\left(\dfrac{\sec}{x}\right) = 1.5\left(\dfrac{\sec}{m}\right);$ so $x = m$

7. $\dfrac{\text{seconds}}{\text{line}} \bullet \dfrac{\text{lines}}{\text{packet}} \bullet \dfrac{\text{packet}}{\text{frame}} = \dfrac{\text{seconds}}{\text{frame}}$

8. a) Show graphically how to determine the cos (30°).
    b) Show graphically how to determine the cos (45°).
    c) What is the approximate value of the cos (38°)?

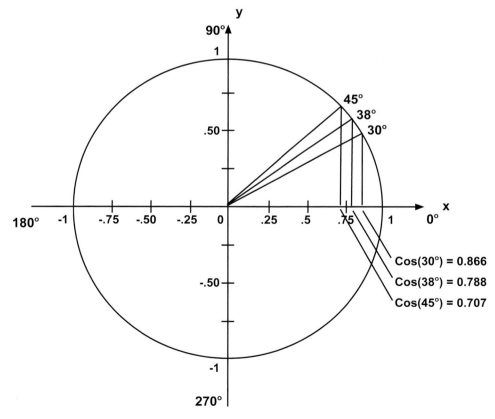

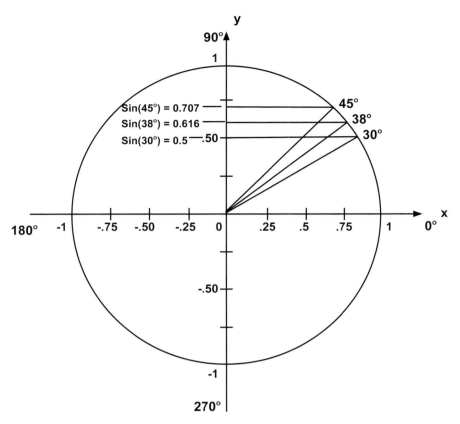

9. a) Show graphically how to determine the sin (30°).
    b) Show graphically how to determine the sin (45°).
    c) What is the approximate value of the sin (38°)?

10. What is the cosine(90°)? **cosine(90°) = 0**

11. What is the cosine(0°)? **cosine(0°) = 1**

12. $\dfrac{1}{\mu\,\text{sec}} = \underline{1}\ \underline{M}\ Hz$

13. $\dfrac{1}{m\,\text{sec}} = \underline{1\ kHz}$

14. $\dfrac{1}{G\,\text{sec}} = \underline{1}\ \underline{n}\ Hz$

15. $\dfrac{3}{n\,\text{sec}} = \underline{0.33}\ \underline{GHz}$

16. $$\frac{1}{\dfrac{1}{3\ \mu sec}} = 3\ \underline{\mu sec}$$

17. $$\frac{1}{Hz} = \frac{1}{\dfrac{1}{sec}} = 1\ \underline{sec}$$

18. $$\frac{2}{Hz} = \frac{2}{\dfrac{1}{sec}} = 2\ \underline{sec}$$

19. $(1 \times 10^6) \bullet (1 \times 10^{-2}) = 1 \times 10^{6-2} = 1 \times 10^4$

20. $(1\ milli) \bullet (1\ centi) = (1 \times 10^{-3}) \bullet (1 \times 10^{-2}) = 1 \times 10^{-3-2} = 1 \times 10^{-5}$

21. $\dfrac{1\ milli}{1\ hecto} = \dfrac{(1 \times 10^{-3})}{(1 \times 10^2)} = (1 \times 10^{-3}) \bullet (1 \times 10^{-2}) = 1 \times 10^{-3-2} = 1 \times 10^{-5}$

22. $(2 \times 10^3) \bullet (1 \times 10^{-3}) = (2 \times 10^{3-3}) = 2 \times 10^0 = 2 \times 1 = 2$

23. $(2\ kilo) \bullet (1\ milli) = (2 \times 10^3) \bullet (1 \times 10^{-3}) = (2 \times 10^{3-3}) = 2 \times 10^0 = 2 \times 1 = 2$

24. $\left(\dfrac{2\ kilo}{1\ milli}\right) = \dfrac{(2 \times 10^3)}{(1 \times 10^{-3})} = (2 \times 10^{3+3}) = 2 \times 10^6$

25. Distance = rate • time. Rewrite the equation as:

a) $\qquad rate = \dfrac{distance}{time}$

b) $\qquad time = \dfrac{distance}{rate}$

26. Rate = 1540 m/sec
Time = 2 μseconds
Solve for distance.

$$distance = rate * time = \frac{1540\ m * 2\ \mu \cancel{sec}}{\cancel{sec}} = 3080\ \mu m$$

27. Distance = 60 km
Rate = 120 km/hr
Solve for time.

$$time = \frac{distance}{rate} = \frac{60 \, km}{120 \frac{km}{hr}} = 0.5 \, hr$$

28. a) How many seconds are in 1 minute?　**60 seconds / minute**
b) How many minutes are in 1 hour?　**60 minutes / hour**
c) How many hours are in 1 day?　**24 hours / day**
d) How many days are in 1 week?　**7 days / week**

e) How many seconds are in 1 hour?　$\dfrac{60 \, seconds}{minute} * \dfrac{60 \, minutes}{hour} = \dfrac{3600 \, seconds}{hour}$

f) How many seconds are in 1 day?　$\dfrac{3600 \, seconds}{hour} * \dfrac{24 \, hours}{day} = \dfrac{86,400 \, seconds}{day}$

g) How many seconds are in 1 week?　$\dfrac{86,400 \, seconds}{day} * \dfrac{7 \, days}{week} = \dfrac{604,800 \, seconds}{week}$

29. Write out the steps for determining the cosine of an angle.
Step 1: draw the **unit** circle.
Step 2: draw the **angle**.
Step 3: Project the intersection between the angle and the **circle** onto the **x**-axis.
Step 4: Read the value on the **x**-axis.

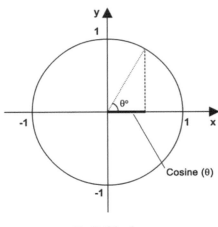

Unit Circle

30. Repeat number 29 for the sine of an angle.
Step 1: draw the **unit** circle.
Step 2: draw the **angle**.
Step 3: Project the intersection between the angle and the **circle** onto the **y**-axis.
Step 4: Read the value on the **y**-axis.

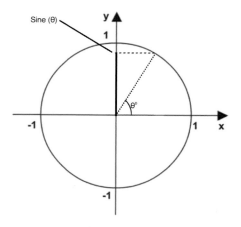

Unit Circle

31. Calculate the area of a circle if the diameter is 4 cm.

$$\text{Area of a circle} = \pi * \left(\frac{d}{2}\right)^2 = \pi * \left(\frac{4\ cm}{2}\right)^2 = \pi * (2\ cm)^2 = 3.14 * 4\ cm^2 = 12.56\ cm^2$$

32. Calculate the volume of a sphere if the radius is 2 mm.

$$\text{Volume of a sphere} = \frac{4\pi\ r^3}{3} = \frac{4\pi\ (2\ mm)^3}{3} = \frac{4\pi * 8\ mm^3}{3} = \frac{4 * 3.14 * 8\ mm^3}{3} = 33.49\ mm^3$$

33. If the radius of a circle is doubled, what change occurs to each of the following parameters?

a) diameter $\propto$ radius $\Rightarrow$ ***so doubling the radius is the same as doubling the diameter***

b) circumference $\propto$ radius $\Rightarrow$ ***so doubling the radius is the same as doubling the circumference***

c) area $\propto$ radius^2 $\Rightarrow$ ***so doubling the radius is the same as quadrupling the area***

d) volume $\propto$ radius^3 $\Rightarrow$ ***so doubling the radius is the same as increasing the volume by a factor of eight***

34. If the radius, r, of a vessel decreases by 10%, what is the residual radius percentage?
The residual radius = 100% - 10% = 90%

35. If the radius, r, of a vessel decreases by 10%, what is the residual area percentage?

$$\text{area} \propto \text{radius}^2 \Rightarrow \left(\frac{9}{10}r\right)^2 = \left(\frac{81}{100}\right)r^2 = 81\%$$

36. If the radius, r, of a vessel decreases by 10%, what is the percentage area change?

$$\text{area} \propto \text{radius}^2 \Rightarrow \left(\frac{9}{10}r\right)^2 = \left(\frac{81}{100}\right)r^2 = 81\% \Rightarrow \textit{residual} = 81\%$$

$$\Rightarrow \textit{percentage change} = 19\%$$

Chapter 2 Waves (Pg. 399-403)

1. Waves are classified according to whether or not they need a medium in which to propagate. A wave which needs a medium is called a **mechanical** wave, a wave which will work in a vacuum (does not need a medium) is called an **electromagnetic** wave.

2. A classification within mechanical waves is which way the particles within the medium are displaced relative to the wave direction. These two classifications are called **transverse** and **longitudinal**.

3. Sound is a **longitudinal, mechanical** wave.

4. The classification of waves as **mechanical** indicates that there is a physical interaction between the wave and the **medium**.

5. Frequency has units of: **Hertz abbreviated Hz = cycles/second or 1/sec**

6. The period has units of: **Time or seconds**

7. For a 10 MHz wave, determine the period in
   The frequency (and hence the period) is determined by the source and is independent of the medium. $T = \dfrac{1}{frequency} = \dfrac{1}{10\ MHz} = \dfrac{1}{10} * \dfrac{1}{M} * \dfrac{1}{Hz} = 0.1\ \mu\mathrm{sec}$

   a) soft tissue $0.1\ \mu\,\mathrm{sec}$
   b) bone $0.1\ \mu\,\mathrm{sec}$
   c) air $0.1\ \mu\,\mathrm{sec}$
   d) water $0.1\ \mu\,\mathrm{sec}$

8. For a 10 MHz wave, determine the wavelength in
   a) soft tissue
   $$\lambda = \frac{c}{f} = \frac{1540\ m}{10\ MHz * \sec} = \frac{1540\ m}{10\ M\dfrac{1}{\sec} * \sec} = \frac{1540\ \mu m}{10} = 154\ \mu m \text{ (which is the same as 0.154 mm)}$$

   b) bone
   $$\lambda = \frac{c}{f} = \frac{4080\ m}{10\ MHz * \sec} = \frac{4080\ m}{10\ M\dfrac{1}{\sec} * \sec} = \frac{4080\ \mu m}{10} = 408\ \mu m \text{ (which is the same as 0.408 mm)}$$

   c) air
   $$\lambda = \frac{c}{f} = \frac{331\ m}{10\ MHz * \sec} = \frac{331\ m}{10\ M\dfrac{1}{\sec} * \sec} = \frac{331\ \mu m}{10} = 33.1\ \mu m \text{ (which is the same as 0.0331 mm)}$$

d) water

$$\lambda = \frac{c}{f} = \frac{1495\ m}{10\ MHz * \sec} = \frac{1495\ m}{10\ M \frac{1}{\sec} * \sec} = \frac{1495\ \mu m}{10} = 149.5\ \mu m \text{ (which is the same as 0.1495 mm)}$$

9. The period for a 10 MHz wave is **0.1 μsec**. Multiplying the frequency times the period yields **unity or 1**.

10. What determines the frequency?
    a) **system and transducer**
    b) medium
    c) system and medium
    d) transducer

11. What determines the period?
    a) **system and transducer**
    b) medium
    c) system and medium
    d) transducer

12. The propagation velocity has units of
    a) distance.
    b) time.
    c) 1/distance.
    d) **distance/time.**

13. The wavelength has units of **distance or meters** .

14. Write the equation which relates frequency, wavelength, and propagation velocity in these different forms.

    a) $f = \dfrac{c}{\lambda}$

    b) $\lambda = \dfrac{c}{f}$

    c) $c = f * \lambda$

15. What determines the propagation velocity?
    a) frequency
    b) system, transducer, and properties of medium
    c) system and transducer
    d) properties of medium

16. Since frequency is determined by the system and transducer, and the propagation velocity depends on properties of the medium, and since f, λ, and c are related, what must the wavelength depend on?
    a) system and transducer
    b) properties of medium
    c) just frequency
    d) frequency and propagation velocity

17. Two different ultrasound systems are used for the same view on the same patient. If the wavelength is different, then the **(operating) frequency** must be different.

18. Using the same frequency transducer on two different patients, if the wave length is different then the **propagation velocity** must be different.

19. If both the frequency and propagation velocity double, the wavelength will **remain the same**.

$$\lambda = \frac{c}{f} = \frac{\cancel{2}\,c}{\cancel{2}\,f} = \frac{c}{f}$$

20. As frequency increases, the wavelength **decreases.**

21. The **amplitude** is defined as the maximum variation of an **acoustic** variable.

22. The four acoustic variables are:
    a) **pressure**
    b) **density**
    c) **temperature**
    d) **particle motion (distance)**

23. The amplitude = max - **mean** = mean - **min** = $\dfrac{max - min}{2}$

24. What is the amplitude of the signal defined by
    max = 4 Volts
    min = -4 Volts

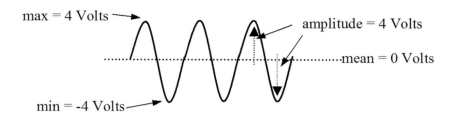

25.   What is the amplitude of the signal defined by
        mean = 0 Volts
        min = -4 Volts

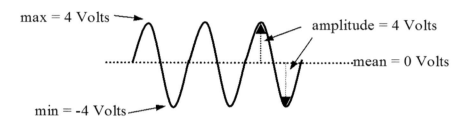

26.   Since Volts is a unit of amplitude, if a voltage ratio is given, the **amplitude** form for decibels must be used.

27.   A change in amplitude by a factor of 2 represents a change
        a)   of a factor of **four** in power,
        b)   equal to **6** dB.

                20*log(2) = 20*0.3 = 6 dB
                or
                10*log(4) = 10*[log(2)+log(2)] = 10*[0.3+0.3] = 10*0.6 = 6 dB

28.   Intensity = $\dfrac{\textbf{power}}{\text{beam area}}$

29.   If the beam area is cut in half and the power remains fixed, the intensity **doubles**.

$$\frac{\text{power}}{\frac{1}{2}\text{beam area}} = \frac{2*\text{Power}}{\text{beam area}} = 2*\text{Intensity}$$

30.   Give the units for power and intensity.
                Power has units of: **Watts**
                Intensity has units of: **Watts/cm²**

31. Density equals mass divided by volume. The more particles of a specific medium per volume, the higher the density. How does propagation velocity change with density? (Assume no change in stiffness)

For a given material, as the density increases the propagation velocity decreases.

32. A stiff material is very inelastic, or incompressible. How does propagation velocity change with stiffness?

For a given material, as the stiffness increases the propagation velocity increases.

33. Match the following:

water	**1495 m/sec**
air	**331 m/sec**
lung	**500 m/sec**
liver	**1560 m/sec**
kidney	**1560 m/sec**
muscle	**1570 m/sec**
bone	**4080 m/sec**
blood	**1560 m/sec**
brain	**1510 m/sec**
fat	**1440 m/sec**

34. What are the distinctions between infrasound, audible sound, ultrasound, and diagnostic ultrasound?
   - ➢ **Infrasound is sound below human hearing or less than 20 Hz.**
   - ➢ **Audible sound is the human hearing range of 20 Hz to 20 kHz.**
   - ➢ **Ultrasound is sound above human hearing or greater than 20 kHz.**
   - ➢ **Diagnostic ultrasound is between 2 MHz and 10 MHz for conventional transcutaneous imaging. (Higher and lower frequencies are sometimes used.)**

35. Using the amplitude form of dB, a factor of 10 equals how many dB?

A factor in amplitude of 10 implies that: $\left(\dfrac{A_f}{A_i}\right) = 10$

$$x \, dB = 20 * \log\left(\dfrac{A_f}{A_i}\right)$$

$$dB = 20 * \log(10) = 20 * 1 = 20 \; dB$$

36. Using the power form of dB, a factor of 100 equals how many dB?

A factor in power of 100 implies that: $\left(\dfrac{P_f}{P_i}\right) = 100$

$$x \, dB = 10 * \log\left(\dfrac{P_f}{P_i}\right)$$

$$x \, dB = 10 * \log(100) = 10 * 2 = 20 \; dB$$

37. Looking at your answers from problems 33 and 34, what difference is there between changing the amplitude by a factor of 10 and the power by a factor of 100?
Since power is proportional to the amplitude squared (Power α Amplitude$^{2)}$ a factor of 10 in amplitude is equivalent to a factor of 100 in power. Therefore converting the amplitude factor of 10 and the power factor of 100 into decibels, should yield the same result.

38. dB stands for decibels and is
    a)   a ratio   (true but not the right answer)
    b)   **a power ratio**   **(true and more specific than choice a)**
    c)   an amplitude ratio   (Not true: dB is always a power ratio, the amplitude form has an extra factor of 2, which converts the ratio into a power ratio.)
    d)   a difficult thing to figure out mathematically.

39. Logarithms convert multiplication into **addition** and division into **subtraction**.

40.

Power factor		dB	
100	=	20 dB	$10*\log(100) = 20$ dB
x 9.2	=	+9.64 dB	$10*\log(9.2) = 9.64$ dB
920	=	**29.64 dB**	

$10*\log(920) = 10*\log(9.2 \times 10) =$
$10[\log(9.2) + \log(10)] =$
$10*\log(9.2) + 10*\log(10) =$
9.64 dB $+ 20$ dB $=$
29.64 dB

Note that this problem can be solved simply by recognizing the fact that logarithms convert multiplication into addition. Since decibels are logarithmic, the same rules apply.

41.

Amplitude factor		dB	
100	=	40 dB	$20*\log(100) = 40$ dB
÷ 3	=	-9.5 dB	$20*\log(3) = 9.5$ dB
33.3	=	**30.5 dB**	

$20*\log(33.3) = 10*\log(100 \div 3) =$
$20 [\log(100) - \log(3)] =$
$20*\log(100) + 20*\log(3) =$
40 dB $- 9.5$ dB $=$
30.5 dB

Note that this problem can be solved simply by recognizing the fact that logarithms convert division into addition. Since decibels are logarithmic, the same rules apply.

42.

A factor of 1/2 (in power)	=	-3 dB
A factor of 2 (in power)	=	**+3** dB
A factor of 1/2 (in amplitude)	=	**-6** dB
A factor of 2 (in amplitude)	=	**+6** dB

Chapter 3 Attenuation (Pg. 404-406)

1. Unscramble the following letters to find three wave interactions with media which account for attenuation.
    a) ptaobrsino   **absorption**
    b) ctrfleenoi   **reflection**
    c) ctrfnoarie   **refraction**

2. Of the three factors listed above, which is the dominant factor creating attenuation.
    The dominant factor of attenuation is absorption (in soft tissue). Since no medium is mentioned you would have to presume soft tissue to be able to answer this question.

3. Absorption **increases** with increasing frequency, decreasing penetration.

4. **Huygen's Principle** states that all points on a wavefront can be treated as point sources producing spherical secondary wavelets whose tangential surface predicts the new position of the wave over time.

    (note that Huygen's is covered later in the book – but every once in a while it is good to see how resourceful a person will be)

5. What law governs how much refraction occurs?
    Snell's Law

6. Give Snell's Law. Make sure to define each term.
    $$c_t \ \sin\left(\theta_i\right) = c_i \ \sin\left(\theta_t\right)$$
    where:
    c_t = Speed of sound in transmitted medium
    c_i = Speed of sound in incident medium
    θ_i = incident angle
    θ_t = transmitted (refraction) angle

7. If the propagation velocities in two interfacing media are equal, the angle of incidence will equal the
    a) reflection angle.
    b) transmission angle.
    c) 90° minus the angle of insonification.
    d) b and c.
    e) **a, b, and c.**

    (The incident angle always equals the angle of reflection. If there is no change in propagation speed between two media, there is no refraction hence the incident angle equals the refraction angle. By definition incident angle equals 90° minus the angle of insonification.)

Pegasus Lectures, Inc.

Appendix C

8. For normal incidence, if the acoustic impedances are identical for medium 1 and medium 2 then there will be
   a)   a small reflection.
   b)   a large reflection.
   c)   a small transmission.
   d)   no reflection.

   For normal incidence there is no refraction. Since the acoustic impedances are equal, there is also no reflection.

9. For normal incidence, medium 1 and medium 2 have significantly different propagation velocities and densities. However, the acoustic impedances are identical. Which of the following is true?
   a)   there will be a small reflection
   b)   there will be a large reflection
   c)   there will be a small transmission
   d)   there will be no reflection

   For normal incidence there is no refraction. Since the acoustic impedances are equal, there is also no reflection. This question is identical to question #8. You should realize that it is possible for two media to have different densities and propagation velocities and still have equal (or nearly equal) acoustic impedances. (For example 2 x 4 = 1 x 8)

10. Since 1- (reflection coefficient) = transmission coefficient, what can be said about answers b and c of question #9.
    a)   they are very different answers
    b)   they are the same answers and therefore are not correct
    c)   they make no sense

11. Given c_t = 4000 m/sec and c_i = 2000 m/sec. For what incident angle will there be total internal reflection (θ_t=90°)?

    $$c_i = 2000 \text{ m/sec}$$
    $$c_t = 4000 \text{ m/sec}$$
    $$\theta_t = 90° \Rightarrow \sin(90°) = 1$$

    $$c_i * \sin\left(\theta_t\right) = c_t * \sin\left(\theta_i\right) \qquad \sin\left(\theta_i\right) = \frac{c_i * \sin\left(\theta_t\right)}{c_t}$$

    $$\sin\left(\theta_i\right) = \frac{c_i * \sin\left(\theta_t\right)}{c_t} = \frac{2000 \ \text{m/sec} * 1}{4000 \ \text{m/sec}} = \frac{2}{4} = 0.5$$

    $$\sin\left(\theta_i\right) = 0.5 \Rightarrow \theta_i = 30^0$$
    $$\sin\left(\theta_i\right) = 0.5 \Rightarrow \theta_i = 30^0$$

12. If $c_t > c_i$ what can be said about the incident and transmitted angles?
    a) $\theta_i = \theta_t$
    b) $\theta_i > \theta_t$
    c) $\theta_t > \theta_i$

$$\frac{c_t}{c_i} = \frac{\sin(\theta_t)}{\sin(\theta_i)} \Rightarrow \frac{\sin(\theta_t)}{\sin(\theta_i)} > 1 \Rightarrow \sin(\theta_t) > \sin(\theta_i)$$

since the angle θ_t increases, the sine increases, $\theta_t > \theta_i$

Notice that there are two ways of determining the answer, the graphical approach on the right and the mathematical approach on the left.

13. If the density is in units of kg/m³ and c is in units of m/sec, what are the units for acoustic impedance?

$$z = p * c \Rightarrow \frac{1\ kg}{m^3} * \frac{1\ m}{\sec} = \frac{1\ kg}{m^2 * \sec} = 1\ Rayl$$

14. The approximate acoustic impedance of tissue is 2 MRayls. What can be said about the acoustic impedance of the matching layer and PZT material of a transducer?
   a)   PZT < matching layer < 2 MRayls
   b)   2 MRayls < PZT < matching layer
   c)   matching layer < 2 MRayls < PZT
   d)   **2 MRayls < matching layer < PZT**

   By design, the matching layer has an acoustic impedance less than the crystal material but higher than the tissue so as to improve transmission efficiency.

15. If the incident angle is 30°, the transmitted angle is 60°, and the propagation velocity in the incident medium is 1495 m/sec, what is the propagation velocity in the transmission medium?

   c_i = 1495 m/sec
   c_t = ?
   θ_i = 30° $\Rightarrow$ sin(30°) = 0.5
   θ_t = 60° $\Rightarrow$ sin(60°) = 0.867

   $$c_i * \sin(\theta_t) = c_t * \sin(\theta_i) \Rightarrow c_t = \frac{c_i * \sin(\theta_t)}{\sin(\theta_i)}$$

   $$c_t = \frac{1495\,\frac{m}{\sec} * 0.867}{0.5} \approx 3000\,\frac{m}{\sec} * 0.867 \approx 2550\,\frac{m}{\sec}$$

   Note that dividing by 0.5 is the same as multiplying by 2. By rounding 1495 up to 1500 you get 3000 m/sec multiplied by 0.867. If you round of 0.867 to 0.85, you can again do the math in your head by performing:

   *3000 * 0.8 = 2400 m/sec*
   *3000 * 0.9 = 2700 m/sec*
   *so   3000 * 0.85 = 2550 m/sec (half way between 2400 and 2700)*

   The actual answer without any rounding off is 2589 m/sec. So our back of the envelope calculation gave us only 1.5% error. The point is you don't really need a calculator to answer these questions.

16. Whether specular reflection or scattering occurs depends on whether or not the insonified structure looks small or large and smooth or rough with respect to the **wavelength (λ)**. If the structure looks large and smooth **specular** reflection occurs. If the structure looks small or rough, **scattering** occurs.

17. Which type of reflection returns more acoustic energy to the transducer, if the structure surface is perpendicular to the beam of the transducer?
    Given that the beam is perpendicular to the structure, <u>specular reflection</u> would return the most energy back to the transducer. Recall that for specular reflection, the angle of incidence equals the angle of reflection. Therefore, if the beam were not perpendicular to the structure, the reflection may not return to the transducer. Always remember that specular reflection is highly angularly dependent.

18. Which type of reflection is responsible for giving the apparent tissue texture?
    Scattering is what creates apparent tissue texture

19. Since scattering increases with frequency, you would expect to see more /(**less**) tissue texture with a lower frequency transducer.

20. Since blood cells tend to be tiny with respect to the wavelength of diagnostic ultrasound, what type of reflection would you expect?
    Rayleigh Scattering

21. Using a 2 MHz transducer, if an ultrasound beam goes through 2 cm of muscle and 15 cm of soft tissue, by how much has the beam been attenuated (in dB)?

    $$attenuation \approx \frac{0.5 \ dB}{cm * MHz} \text{ in soft tissue}$$

    $$attenuation \approx \frac{1 \ dB}{cm * MHz} \text{ in muscle}$$

    $$attenuation = \left(\frac{1 \ dB}{cm * MHz} * 2 \ MHz * 2 \ cm \right) + \left(\frac{0.5 \ dB}{cm * MHz} * 2 \ MHz * 15 \ cm \right)$$

    $$= 4 \ dB + 15 \ dB = 19 \ dB$$

22. Using a 5 MHz transducer, how much attenuation would occur to a beam (round trip) to and from a structure 5 cm deep in tissue?

    $$attenuation = \left(\frac{0.5 \ dB}{cm * MHz} * 5 \ MHz * 10 \ cm \right) = 25 \ dB$$

Pegasus Lectures, Inc.

1. The PRF (pulse repetition frequency) would best be described as:
   a) the time between two consecutive pulses
   b) the frequency within the pulse
   c) the time between two peaks within a pulse
   d) the frequency of pulse repetitions

2. The PRP is the _____ from the start of one pulse to the start of the next.
   a) time
   b) distance
   c) length
   d) frequency

3. Give the equation which relates the PRF and the PRP.

4. Which of the following would be a likely PRF in ultrasound?
   a) 1 MHz
   b) 2 MHz,
   c) 10 kHz
   d) 10 Hz
   Typical PRF's in ultrasound are in the kHz range. Calculating a PRP for a standard imaging depth easily shows this fact. For example, imaging to a depth of 8 cm takes 8 cm * 13 μsec/cm = 104 μsec $\approx$ 100 μsec = 0.1 *m*sec which yields a PRF of 10 kHz.

5. If you are told the PRF is 20 kHz, what additional information do you need to know the PRP?
   No additional information is necessary, the PRP is the reciprocal of the PRF.

6. How long does it take for ultrasound to travel in soft tissue a distance of:
   a) 1 cm   **6.5 μsec**
   b) 2 cm   **13 μsec**
   c) 10 cm   **65 μsec**
   d) to a target 10 cm and back to the transducer.   **130 μsec**

   Since distance is linearly related to time, a change in one of the variables results in the same rate of change in the other variable. As a result, we can calculate the time for sound to travel 1 cm and then scale accordingly.

   d = 1 cm
   r = 1540 m/sec
   t = ?

   $$d = r*t \Rightarrow t = \frac{d}{r} = \frac{1\ cm}{1540\frac{m}{sec}} = \frac{0.01\ \cancel{m}}{1540\frac{\cancel{m}}{sec}} = \frac{0.01\ sec}{1540} = 0.00000649\ sec \approx 6.5\ \mu\ sec$$

   Make certain to always pay attention to the round trip aspect. Imaging implies roundtrip. So to image 1 cm is the same as traveling 2 cm.

7. If the maximum imaging depth is 10 cm, and there are 128 lines per frame, how much time does it take to shoot one frame?

$$\frac{time}{frame} = \frac{13\ \mu\sec}{cm} * \frac{10\ cm}{line} * \frac{128\ lines}{frame} = 16640 * \frac{\mu\sec}{frame} = 16.64 * \frac{m\sec}{frame}$$

8. Convert your answer in #7 into a frame rate.

$$frame\ rate = \frac{1}{frame\ time} = \frac{1}{16.64\ \dfrac{m\sec}{frame}} \approx 0.06\ \frac{kframes}{sec} = 60\ \frac{frames}{sec} = 60\ Hz$$

9. If the maximum imaging depth is 10 cm and there are 4 packets per line and 128 lines, how long does it take to shoot a color frame?

$$\frac{time}{frame} = \frac{13\ \mu\sec}{cm} * \frac{10\ cm}{packet} * \frac{4\ packets}{line} * \frac{128\ lines}{frame} = 66,560\ \frac{\mu\sec}{frame} = 66.56\ \frac{m\sec}{frame}$$

Note that you could also just take the answer from number 7 and multiply by four.

10. If the 2-D (B mode) and color frames are interlaced, how much time does it take between color frames?

$$66.56\ \frac{m\sec}{frame} + 16.64\ \frac{m\sec}{frame} = 83.2\ \frac{m\sec}{frame}$$

11. Convert your answer from #10 into a frame rate.

$$frame\ rate = \frac{1}{frame\ time} = \frac{1}{83.2\ \dfrac{m\sec}{frame}} \approx 0.012\ \frac{kframes}{sec} = 12\ \frac{frames}{sec} = 12\ Hz$$

Note that you could have done this calculation in your head since the time to create the color and the B-mode is 5 times longer than to create just the B-mode. Therefore, the frequency for color with B-mode is 1/5 the frequency of B-mode alone. (60 Hz * 1/5 = 12 Hz)

12. Given the above scenario, which of the following changes would increase frame rate the most?
    a)   skip the 2D frame   (Saves 16 msec)
    b)   cut the color sector in half   (Saves 32 msec)
    c)   switch to a higher frequency transducer   (no effect)
    d)   change the color packet size from 4 to 3   (Saves 16 msec)

13. The operating frequency of a transducer is 2.0 MHz. If a pulse consists of 4 cycles, what is the pulse duration?

$$P = \frac{1}{2\ MHz} = 0.5\ \mu\ sec$$

$$PD = 0.5\ \mu\ sec * 4 = 2.0\ \mu\ sec$$

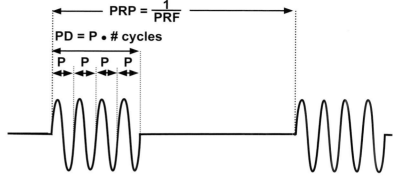

14. The period of a transducer is 0.5 μsec. If a pulse consists of 4 cycles, what is the pulse duration? **This is the same problem as number 13 since a period of 0.5 μsec is the same as a frequency of 2 MHz.**

$$P = \frac{1}{2\ MHz} = 0.5\ \mu\ sec$$

$$PD = 0.5\ \mu\ sec * 4 = 2.0\ \mu\ sec$$

15. Which of the following will not result in a shorter pulse duration?
    a) using a higher frequency
    b) using fewer pulses
    c) using a smaller period
    d) a lower propagation velocity

    "Using a higher frequency" and "using a shorter period" are the same answer. Some authors use the word "pulses" to refer to cycles in the pulse. The use of the word "pulses" here is intended to teach students to pay attention to the intent since there is no guarantee that questions are well written or written using the same language to which they are accustomed. The propagation speed would affect the wavelength and spatial pulse length, but does not affect the period or the pulse duration.

16. Which system would have a short pulse duration?
    a) system A: 10 MHz, 2 cycles/pulse
    b) system B: 10 MHz, 4 cycles/pulse
    c) system C: 2 MHz, 2 cycles/pulse
    d) system D: 2 MHz, 4 cycles/pulse

    The pulse duration is proportional to the period and the number of cycles in the pulse. A high frequency results in a short period. So the shortest PD will occur with the highest frequency and fewest cycles, or choice "a".

17. If you work 12 hours a day, what is your daily duty cycle?

$$Duty\ Cycle = \frac{time\ worked}{total\ work\ time} = \frac{12\ hours}{24\ hours} = 0.5\ or\ 50\%$$

18. If you work all day, 5 days per week, what is your weekly duty cycle?

$$Duty\ Cycle = \frac{time\ worked}{total\ work\ time} = \frac{5\ days}{7\ days} = 0.71\ or\ 71\%$$

19. If a pulse has a duration of 4 msec and a pulse repetition period of 10 msec, what is the duty factor?

$$Duty\ Cycle = \frac{PD}{PRP} = \frac{4\ msec}{10\ msec} = 0.4\ or\ 40\%$$

20. If a pulse has a duration of 4 msec and a pulse repetition frequency of 0.1 kHz, what is the duty factor?

This question is really the same as question #19. Since the PRP is the reciprocal of the PRF, if the PRF is 0.1 kHz, the period is 10 msec.

$$PRP = \frac{1}{PRF} = \frac{1}{0.1\ kHz} = 10\ msec$$

$$Duty\ Factor = \frac{PD}{PRP} = \frac{4\ msec}{10\ msec} = 0.4 = 40\%$$

21. The operating frequency of a transducer is 2 MHz, and there are 4 cycles per pulse. The pulse repetition period (equivalent to the line time) is 130 μsec. What is the duty cycle?

$$P = \frac{1}{f} = \frac{1}{2\ MHz} = 0.5\ \mu sec$$

$$PD = P * \#\ cycles = 0.5\ \mu sec * 4 = 2\ \mu sec$$

$$Duty\ cycle = \frac{PD}{PRP} = \frac{2\ \mu sec}{130\ \mu sec} = \frac{1}{65} = 0.015 = 1.5\%$$

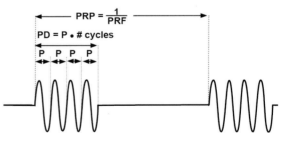

22.   The operating frequency of a transducer is 2 MHz and there are 4 cycles/pulse. If the maximum imaging depth is 10 cm, what is the duty cycle?

This problem is identical to question # 21. Recall that it takes 13 μsec per cm of imaging depth. A 10 cm line takes 130 μsec, and there is no difference between this question and the last question.

23.   The key word indicating the units for spatial pulse length is the word "length". So spatial pulse length has units of
a)   time.
b)   distance.
c)   distance/time.
d)   1/time.

24.   If the pulse duration = (#cycles/pulse) • (period), the spatial pulse length = (#cycles/pulses) • (_____).
a)   period.
b)   wavelength.
c)   frequency.
d)   propagation velocity.

25.   Since the spatial pulse length is proportional to the wavelength, and the wavelength is proportional to the propagation velocity and inversely proportional to the frequency, what can be said about the spatial pulse length and the frequency? What can be said about the spatial pulse length and the wave length?

The spatial pulse length is proportional to the wavelength and the wavelength is proportional to the propagation speed and inversely proportional to the frequency. Therefore, the SPL is also proportional to the propagation speed and inversely proportional to the frequency. These relationships are important since the SPL determines the axial resolution.

$$SPL \propto \lambda \propto c \text{ and } SPL \propto \lambda \propto \frac{1}{f}$$

26.   For a 4 cycle pulse with an operating frequency of 1.54 MHz, what is the spatial pulse length in soft tissue?

$$SPL = \# \, cycles * \lambda$$

$$\lambda = \frac{c}{f} = \frac{1540 \frac{m}{sec}}{1.54 \, MHz} = \frac{1540 \frac{m}{sec}}{1.54 \, M \frac{1}{sec}} = 1000 \, \mu m = 1 \, mm$$

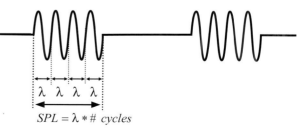

$$SPL = \lambda * \# \; cycles$$

$$SPL = 1 \, mm * 4 = 4 \, mm$$

Chapter 5 Transducers (Pg. 411-413)

1. In general a transducer converts **energy** from one form to another.

2. The principle used by ultrasound transducers is called the **piezoelectric** effect.

3. Ultrasound transducers actually act as two different types of antennas. On transmit, they convert voltage to **acoustic (mechanical, sound)** energy. On receive, they convert **acoustic (mechanical, sound)** energy back to **voltage**.

4. Quartz is a naturally piezoelectric material. **True**

5. No material which naturally does not exhibit piezoelectric properties can be made piezoelectric. **False** (This question is an excercise in dealing with multiple negatives in a sentence.)

6. Materials cannot lose their piezoelectric properties at high temperature. **False**

7. The Curie temperature for PZT is approximately 300°C. **True**

8. There are actually 3 planes in ultrasound imaging although only 2 are displayed in real-time 2-D imaging. The axial plane corresponds to the **depth**, the lateral plane corresponds to the **width** and the elevation plane corresponds to the slice **thickness**.

   (Choices: thickness, depth, width)

9. Draw a single disc shaped transducer and draw the approximate beam profile. (Make certain to label the NZL, focus, 2 • NZL, beamwidth, Fresnel, and Fraunhofer zones.)

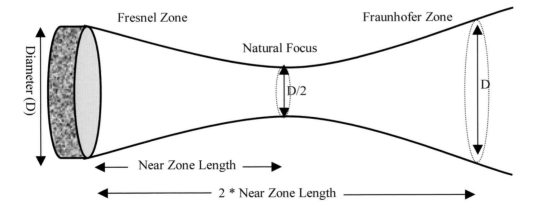

10. The use of the name "mechanical" for a transducer implies the means by which it is
    a) focused
    b) steered
    c) assembled
    d) all of the above

11.   A broad depth of field means that a beam converges and diverges to and from the focus
    a)   quickly.
    b)   slowly.
    c)   more than once.
    d)   none of the above.

12.   Which transducer style has a variable focus in both the lateral and elevation planes?
    There are now two possible answers: annular arrays (which are almost extinct), and 2-D arrays (which are still relatively rare).

13.   Which of the following transducers can be <u>electronically steered</u>? (more than one may apply)
    a)   Sector phased array
    b)   Annular array
    c)   Phased linear array
    d)   Linear switched array

14.   Draw a simple diagram of the major components of a transducer. Explain what function each component serves.

Piezoelectric crystals: ***Convert electropotential (voltage) into acoustic waves and acoustic waves back into voltage***

Backing material: ***Shortens spatial pulse length improving longitudinal resolution***

Matching layer: ***Minimizes the acoustic impedance mismatch from crystal to tissue and tissue back to crystal***

Wires: ***Transmit - delivers voltage to crystal.***
Receive - delivers echo voltage to system receivers.

Lens: ***Helps to focus beam in elevation plane***

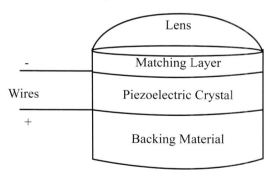

15.   The idea of pulsed mode transducer operation is very familiar to you. If you ring a bell or strike a piece of crystal you will hear a ringing sound. The thicker the material, the lower the pitch. For ultrasound transducers, the operating frequency, in a pulsed mode, is given by

$$f_0 = \frac{c}{2 * thickness}$$

16. In continuous mode the frequency is determined by the excitation or transmit voltage, not the crystal thickness. So, if the thickness of a crystal is increased but the excitation frequency remains constant in CW mode, the operating frequency will **not change**.

17. Give the equation for the NZL in terms of transducer diameter and frequency.

$$NZL_{(mm)} \approx \frac{D^2_{(mm)} \cdot f_{(MHZ)}}{6}$$

18. If an unfocused disc-shaped transducer has an aperture of 10 mm, the beamwidth at the focal depth and twice the focal depth is **5 mm** and **10 mm**.

19. Unscramble the four most common means of focusing.
    a) enlsse   **lenses**
    b) vurcde elmeenst   **curved elements**
    c) ceeconiltr   **electronic**
    d) rrromis   **mirrors**

20. Focusing can only affect the **near** field.

21. The resolution, defined as the spatial pulse length divided by 2, is **axial (longitudinal, depth, range)** resolution.

22. Three synonyms for lateral resolution are:
    azimuthal
    side-by-side
    transverse
    angular
    (The fourth term is included as a bonus.)

23. Three synonyms for longitudinal resolution are:
    radial
    axial
    depth
    range
    (The fourth term is included as a bonus.)

24. The beamwidth approximately defines the **lateral** resolution.

25. What factors can affect the
    a) lateral resolution:
    Any factor which affect the beamwidth such as: the frequency, the aperture, the focus, multiple transmit foci, parallel processing, etc.
    b) longitudinal resolutioin:
    Any factor which affect the spatial pulse length such as: the frequency, the wavelength, the propagation speed, the backing or damping material, the excitation pulse driving the crystal, etc...

1. Conventional B-mode imaging spans a dynamic range of approximately
   a) 10 dB
   b) 20 dB
   c) 50 dB
   d) 80 dB
   e) 150 dB

2. The human eye is capable of seeing over a great dynamic range, but not over the entire range at the same time. The pupil constricts and dilates to determine the specific range within the entire synamic range. The maximum dynamic range of the human eye at one instance is ≈ **36 dB**.

3. Since attenuation increases **exponentially** with increasing depth, compensation must be **logarithmic**.

4. The process of multiplying a signal so that it has a higher amplitude is called **amplification**.

5. A critical process for decreasing the dynamic range of a signal is called **compression**.

6. Non-linear **compression** is necessary in processing diagnostic ultrasound because of the enormous signal dynamic range.

7. A steeper TGC profile is necessary when using a higher frequency transducer since **attenuation** increases with increasing frequency.

8. A flattening of the TGC profile is expected over a region dominated by fluid since fluids tend to be relatively **homogenous**.

9. If a signal spans 80 dB of dynamic range, that is equivalent to saying that the ratio of the largest component of the signal to the smallest component of the signal is **10,000** to 1.

$$20 * \log\left(\frac{A_f}{A_i}\right) = 80 \ dB$$

$$\log\left(\frac{A_f}{A_i}\right) = \frac{80}{20}$$

$$\log\left(\frac{A_f}{A_i}\right) = 4$$

$$\left(\frac{A_f}{A_i}\right) = 10^4$$

$$\text{Since A}_i = 1, \Rightarrow \left(\frac{A_f}{1}\right) = 10^4 \Rightarrow A_f = 10^4 = 10,000$$

10.   Given that a signal spans a dynamic range of 80 dB and that for a given lighting condition, the eye can only see 10 shades of gray, by what factor would the signal have to be compressed to be visualized?

From question 9 we learned that 80 dB is a ratio of 10,000 to 1. If for a given lighting condition the eye were only capable of detecting 10 shades of gray, the 10,000 levels would have to be compressed to 10 levels, or: $\dfrac{10,000}{10} = 1,000$ **. So the signal would need to be compressed by a factor of 1,000.**

11.   Given this graphic description of the signal, describe what will happen to the ability to visualize the mass when compression is applied to make the signal dynamic range match the dynamic range of the eye.

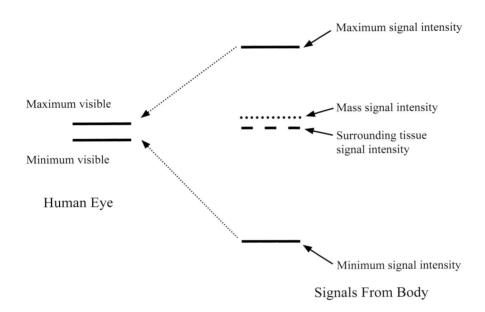

Since there is so much compression necessary to map the signal dynamic range to the dynamic range of the human eye, the ability to distinguish the mass from the surrounding tissue may be compromised. In essence the difference in signal intensity between the mass and the surrounding tissue is compressed and the mass may not be visualized.

12.   The process of **demodulation** detects the signal "changes" which affect the RF (radio frequency) transmitted signal.

13.   The early modality of ultrasound which results from the processing stage of demodulation is called **A-mode**.

14.   An ultrasound system can be envisioned as a series of processors such as the **receiver**, the **scan** converter, video display, and signal storage device.

15. The processes of gray-scaling, performing calculations, tissue colorization, and video compression all take place in **the scan converter.**

16. With a signal to noise ratio of 10:1, if the noise has an amplitude of 1 mV, the signal would have an amplitude of **10 m V.**

17. Increasing the receiver gain improves the signal to noise ratio. (True or **False**) Explain: **Increasing the receiver gain increases both the noise and the signal equally, thereby leaving the signal to noise ratio unaffected.**

18. Name at least three ways of potentially increasing the Signal to Noise Ratio of an ultrasound image at a depth of 6 cm.
   1. **increase the transmit power**
   2. **use a lower frequency transducer**
   3. **move the transmit focus to 6 cm or a little deeper than 6 cm**
   4. **use a transducer with a larger aperture**

19. Name the five basic functions of all ultrasound receivers.
   1. **amplification**
   2. **compensation**
   3. **compression**
   4. **demodulation**
   5. **reject**

20. Which receiver function would convert the signal of figure A below, into the signal of Figure B below?

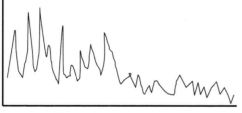

Figure A   Figure B

Compensation (TGC's): Note how the signals later in time have been amplified more than the signals which returned earlier in time.

21. Standard U.S. video format has been an interlaced monitor with a frame rate of <u>**30 Hz**</u> and <u>**525**</u> lines. Newer, non-interlaced monitors with a frame rate of <u>**60 Hz**</u> and more lines per frame (High Definition) are becoming the new standard.

22. The reason that a higher video monitor frame rate is significant for diagnostic ultrasound is that the <u>**temporal**</u> resolution can be affected by the monitor frame rate.

23. How many shades of gray can be presented using an 8-bit video display?
$$2^8 = 256$$

24.   The range of signal amplitudes a system can process without **harmonic** distortion is called the **dynamic range**.

25.   Assuming that an ultrasound system has approximately 50 dB of input dynamic range, what is the maximum imaging depth possible using a 5 MHz transducer (assuming soft tissue)?

$$\frac{0.5 \ dB}{cm * MHz} * 5 \ MHz * 2 * imaging \ depth \ (cm) = 50 \ dB$$

$$5 * imaging \ depth \ (cm) = 50$$

$$imaging \ depth \ (cm) = \frac{50}{5} = 10 \ cm$$

So the maximum imaging depth would be 10 cm

26.   Repeat problem #25 assuming muscle instead of soft tissue.

$$\frac{1 \ dB}{cm * MHz} * 5 \ MHz * 2 * imaging \ depth \ (cm) = 50 \ dB$$

$$10 * imaging \ depth \ (cm) = 50$$

$$imaging \ depth \ (cm) = \frac{50}{10} = 5 \ cm$$

So the maximum imaging depth would be 5 cm

27.   Referring to problems #25 and #26, assume that the attenuation rate is halfway in dB between the attenuation rate of muscle and of soft tissue. What would the maximum imaging depth be?

$$\frac{0.75 \ dB}{cm * MHz} * 5 \ MHz * 2 * imaging \ depth \ (cm) = 50 \ dB$$

$$7.5 * imaging \ depth \ (cm) = 50$$

$$imaging \ depth \ (cm) = \frac{50}{7.5} = 6.67 \ cm$$

So the maximum imaging depth would be 6.67 cm (if you are surprised – this question points out that attenuation is non-linear – most people would assume the answer to be 7.5 cm)

Pegasus Lectures, Inc.

28.   Using multiple transmit foci improves **lateral** resolution at the expense of **temporal** resolution.

29.   Increasing from a single transmit focus to four transmit foci would most likely decrease the frame rate by what factor?
      a.   16
      b.   4
      c.   2.5
      d.   1

      Explain:
      When using multiple transmit foci, multiple acoustic lines are transmitted and then spliced together to create a single, narrower, display line. Although multiple acoustic lines are transmitted, not all of the lines are of equal length. For the acoustic line with the shallowest transmit, there is no need to receive data from deeper depths since that data will never be used. Similarly, the second focus acoustic line will be a little longer than the first, but still shorter than the third line, etc. As a result, with four transmit foci, the frame rate will be slower than for a single transmit but higher than four full lines. The only choice which meets these requirements is slower by a factor of 2.5

30.   Imaging in a bright room, a sonographer increases the monitor brightness so as to adequately visualize the image. While imaging, data are stored to a storage device for later review. The reviewing physician complains that the image is too dark and "contrasty." The reason is:

      Monitor display controls affect the contrast and brightness of the image on the screen but not the data being stored to the storage device. When the monitor is adjusted for a bright room it is no longer "calibrated." When "calibrated" the data on the monitor is supposed to appear the same as data which has been stored. In this case, since the monitor is not calibrated, the stored data will have a different intensity than the data on the screen.

      This is a very common problem, especially at sites where machines are used for mobile testing or in the OR. In both cases it is often not practical to make the room dark.

31.   Which of the following approaches would yield the best imaging results on a large, difficult to image patient?
      a)   4 MHz transmit and receive, 1.2 cm aperture
      b)   2 MHz transmit and receive, 2 cm aperture
      c)   2 MHz transmit and receive, 1 cm aperture
      d)   2 MHz transmit, 4 MHz receive, 2 cm aperture

      Explain:
      For a large, difficult to image patient sensitivity will be very important. To achieve the maximum sensitivity, the lowest frequency should be used for both transmit and receive. This fact eliminates choices "a" and "d". To achieve higher intensities at greater depths, a deep focus is desired. Recall that a larger aperture results in a deeper focus. In this case, since both transducers are operating at the same frequency, the transducer with a 2 cm aperture would have a natural focus four times deeper than the transducer with the 1 cm aperture.

32.　Which of the following approaches would yield the best imaging results on a large, difficult to image patient?

a)　　6 MHz transmit and receive, 0.8 cm aperture
b)　　2.5 MHz transmit and receive, 2 cm aperture
c)　　2 MHz transmit, 4 MHz receive, 1.8 cm aperture
d)　　**1.4 MHz transmit, 2.8 MHz receive, 2 cm aperture**

Explain:
As with question 31, higher frequencies can be immediately eliminated, leaving choices "b" and "d". Transmitting at 1.4 MHz will have significantly better penetration than transmitting at 2.5 MHz. Receiving at 2.8 versus 2.5 MHz will not have nearly as much impact as the difference in transmit frequencies. Therefore, the best solution would be using the harmonic imaging with the fundamental at 1.4 MHz and the receive at 2.8 MHz.

33.　In A-mode, the vertical axis corresponds to **amplitude (acoustic impedance mismatch, reflectivity, etc.)** and the horizontal axis corresponds to **depth (or time)**.

Appendix D • Resources

ACCREDITATION AND CREDENTIALING RESOURCES

INDIVIDUAL

American Registry of Diagnostic Medical Sonographers (ARDMS)   www.ardms.org
51 Monroe Street
Plaza East One
Rockville, Maryland 20850-2400
Telephone 1.301.738-8401
Fax 1.301.738-0312

American Registry of Radiologic Technologists (ARRT)   www.arrt.org
1255 Northland Drive
St. Paul, Minnesota 55120-1155
Telephone 1.651.687.0048

Cardiovascular Credentialing International (CCI)   www.cci-online.org
1500 Sunday Drive, Suite 102
Raleigh, NC 27607
Telephone 1.800.326.0268 or 919.861.4539
Fax 919.787.4916

ACCREDITATION

American College of Radiology Commission on Standards and Accreditation (ACR)   www.acr.org

American Institute of Ultrasound in Medicine (AIUM)   www.aium.org

Intersocietal Commission for the Accreditation of Echocardiography Laboratories (ICAEL)   www.icael.org

Intersocietal Commission for the Accreditation of Magnetic Resonance Laboratories (ICAMRL)   www.icamrl.org

Intersocietal Commission for the Accreditation of Nuclear Medicine Laboratories (ICANL)   www.icanl.org

Intersocietal Commission for the Accreditation of Vascular Laboratories (ICAVL)   www.icavl.org

Joint Commission on Accreditation of Health Organizations (JCAHO)   www.jcaho.org

Appendix D

EDUCATION

American College of Radiology Programs (ACR)   www.acr.org

Association of Educators in Imaging and Radiologic Sciences (AERS)   www.aers.org

Accreditation Council for Continuing Medical Education (ACCME)   www.accme.org

Accrediting Bureau of Health Education Schools (ABHES)   www.abhes.org

Canadian Medical Association (CMA)   www.cma.ca

Commission on Accreditation of Allied Health Education Programs (CAAHEP)   www.caahep.org

Educational Credential Evaluators, Inc. (ECE)   www.ece.org

Joint Review Committee on Education in Cardiovascular Technology (JRCCVT)   www.jrccvt.org

Joint Review Committee on Education in Diagnostic Medical Sonography (JRCERT)   www.jrcdms.org

OTHER RESOURCES

Accreditation Consultants

Inside Ultrasound, Inc.   www.insideultrasound.com
KRP Accreditation Specialists, Inc.   www.krpaccreditation.com

Industry Resources

Aloka   www.aloka.com
ATS Laboratories   www.atslaboratories.com
Agfa   www.agfa.com/healthcare/us
Advanced Technological Laboratories   www.medical.philips.com/main/products
B-K Medical   www.bkmed.com
Baxter Medical   www.baxter.com
Biomedix   www.biomedix.com
Biosound Esaote   www.biosound.com
Boston Scientific   www.bostonscientific.com
Bracco Diagnostics   www.bdi.bracco.com
CIRS   www.cirsinc.com
Civco Medical Instruments   www.civcomedical.com
Data Star Systems- Datacheck   www.datastarsystems.com
Dynatek Dalta   www.dynatekdalta.com
Fluke Biomedical   www.flukebiomedical.com/rms
Gammex-RMI   www.gammex.com
GE Medical Systems   www.gemedicalsystems.com
Hitachi Medical Systems   www.hitachimed.com
J.R. Associates   www.1jra.com
JJ&A   www.jja-instruments.com

Kodak	www.kodak.com
Medison Medical Systems	www.medisonusa.com
Onda Corporation	www.ondacorp.com
Parker Laboratories	www.parkerlabs.com
Parks Medical Electronics	www.parksmed.com
Philips Medical Systems	www.medical.philips.com
Precision Acoustics, Inc.	www.acoustics.co.uk/
Siemens Medical Systems (Acuson)	www.siemensultrasound.com
Shimadzu Medical Systems	www.shimadzu.com
Sonosite	www.sonosite.com
Sonus Pharmaceuticals	www.sonuspharma.com
Sound Ergonomics	www.soundergonomics.com
Toshiba Ultrasound	www.toshiba.com
Unetixs, Inc.	www.unetixs.com

Organizations

Alliance of Cardiovascular Professionals (ACP)	www.acp-online.org
American Academy of Family Physicians (AAFP)	www.aafp.org
American Academy of Neurology (AAN)	www.aan.com
American Association for Vascular Surgery (AVS)	www.vascularweb.org
American College of Obstetrics and Gynecologist (ACOG)	www.acog.org
American College of Cardiology (ACC)	www.acc.org
American College of Chest Physicians (ACCP)	www.chestnet.org
American College of Emergency Physicians (ACEP)	www.acep.org
American College of Obstetricians and Gynecologists (ACOG)	www.acog.org
American College of Phebology (ACP)	www.phebology.org
American College of Radiology (ACR)	www.acr.org
American Emergency Ultrasonographic Society (AEUS)	www.aeus.org
American Hospital Association (AHA)	www.aha.com
American Institute of Ultrasound in Medicine (AIUM)	www.aium.org
American Medical Association (AMA)	www.ama-assn.org
American Osteopathic College of Radiology (AOCR)	www.aocr.org
American Roentgen Ray Society (ARRS)	www.arrs.org
American Society of Echocardiography (ASE)	www.asecho.org
American Society of Neurology (ASN)	www.aan.com/professionals
American Society of Neuroimaging (ASN)	www.asnweb.org
American Society of Neuroradiology (ASNR)	www.asnr.org
American Society of Opthalmologic Ultrasound (ASOU)	www.asou.us
American Society of Radiologic Technologists (ASRT)	www.asrt.org
American Urological Association (AUA)	www.auanet.org
Canadian Society of Diagnostic Medical Sonographers (CSDMS)	www.csdms.org
European Society for Vascular Surgery (ESVS)	www.esvs.org
Health Professions Network	www.healthpronet.org
International Society of Radiographers and Radiologic Technologists	www.isrrt.org
Musculoskeletal Ultrasound Society	www.musoc.com
North American Society of Pacing and Electrophysiology (NASPE)	www.naspe.org
North Carolina Ultrasound Society (NCUS)	www.ncus.org
Peripheral Vascular Surgery Society (PVSS)	www.pvss.org
Radiological Society of North America (RSNA)	www.rsna.org
Society of Breast Imaging (SBI)	www.sbi-online.org
Society of Diagnostic Medical Sonography (SDMS)	www.sdms.org

Society of Interventional Radiology (SIR)   www.sirweb.org
Society of Invasive Cardiovascular Professionals (SICP)   www.sicp.com
Society of Nuclear Medicine (SNM)   www.snm.org
Society of Radiologists in Ultrasound (SRU)   www.sru.org
Society for Vascular Medicine and Biology (SVMB)   www.svmb.org
Society for Vascular Surgery (SVS)   www.vascularweb.org
Society for Vascular Ultrasound (SVU)   www.svunet.org
Society of Pediatric Echocardiography (SOPE)   www.sope-online.com
Society of Pediatric Radiology (SPR)   www.pedrad.org
Society of Radiologists in Ultrasound (SRU)   www.sru.org
Vascular Disease Foundation (VDF)   www.vdf.org
World Federation for Ultrasound in Medicine and Biology (WFUMB)   www.wfumb.org

Government Resources

Agency for Health Care Policy and Research Practice Guidelines (AHCPR)   www.ahcpr.gov
Center for Devices and Radiological Health (CDRH/FDA)   www.fda.gov
ClinicalTrials.gov   www.clinicaltrials.gov
National Council on Radiation Protection and Measurement (NCRP)   www.ncrp.com
National Electrical Manufacturers Association (NEMA)   www.nema.org
National Library of Medicine (NLM)   www.nlm.nih.gov
U.S. Department of Health and Human Services   www.os.dhhs.gov
World Federation for Ultrasound in Medicine and Biology (WFUMB)   www.wfumb.org

Index

Index

Index

Index

Appendix F • Abbreviations

Abbreviations: Physical Units

Related to time:

P or T	Period (seconds)
PD	Pulse duration (the time for which the transmit pulse lasts)
PRP	Pulse repetition period (the time to transmit and receive an acoustic line of data)
Frame time	The time required to build up a frame = the time per acoustic line multiplied the total number of lines in the frame.

Related to frequency:

f	Frequency (Hz)
f_o	Operating or transmit frequency of a transducer (for diagnostic ultrasound 2-12 MHz common)
PRF	Pulse repetition frequency = 1/PRP (typically less than 10 kHz)
Frame rate	The reciprocal of the frame time (typically less than 100 Hz)
Hz	Hertz = 1 cycle/second

Various parameters that have units of amplitude:

V	Volts: unit of electromotive force
m	Meters: unit of distance (metric system)
Z	Rayls: unit of acoustic impedance
R	Resistance, either electrical or to fluid flow
P	Pressure: mmHg, atm, dynes/cm^2, kg/m^2, etc....,: unit of pressure (*not to be confused with P for period or P for power)

Related to power:

P	Power: units of Watts (*not to be confused with P for period or P for pressure)
W	Watts
I	Intensity = power/area = W/m^2
dB	Decibels: a logarithmic power ratio

Related to distance:

d	distance (*not to be confused with D or d for diameter)
λ	Lambda: wavelength which has units of distance
SPL	Spatial Pulse Length
NZL	The distance from the transducer face to the focus of the transducer

Related to measure or circular dimensions:

ρ	Density = mass/volume = kg/ m^3
r	Radius of a circle: units of distance
d	Diameter of a circle = 2*radius: units of distance
A	Area: units of m^2
Vol	Volume: units of m^3
Q	Volumetric flow: volume per time, or m^3/sec

Related to motion:

r	the general term usually used in the distance equation for the velocity. (*not to be confused with r for radius)
v	velocity of blood: units of m/sec
c	propagation speed of sound: units of m/sec

Related to hemodynamics:

P	Pressure: mmHg, atm, dynes/cm², kg/m², etc…,: units of pressure (*not to be confused with P for period or P for power)
ΔP	Pressure gradient (change in pressure = $P_2 - P_1$ where P_2 is the distal pressure and P_1 is the proximal pressure): units as above
Q	Volumetric flow: volume per time, or m³/sec
R	Resistance, either electrical or to fluid flow

Note: Caution must be used since many letters can stand for more than one physical quantity. Also pay attention as to whether the letter is uppercase or lower case, since in some cases a capitalized letter indicates a different parameter than a lower case letter.

Appendix G • Equations

Related to Time and Frequency:

1. $Period\ (P) = \dfrac{1}{frequency\ (f)}$

2. $PD = P * (\#\ of\ cycles\ in\ pulse)$

3. $PRP = \dfrac{13\ \mu\ sec}{cm} * imaging\ depth\ (cm) = \dfrac{1}{PRF}$

4. $Frame\ time = PRP * \dfrac{\#\ lines}{frame} = \dfrac{1}{frame\ rate}$

5. $Duty\ Factor = \dfrac{PD}{PRP} * 100\% = \dfrac{Temporal\ Average\ Intensity\ (TA)}{Pulse\ Average\ Intensity\ (PA)} * 100\%$

Related to Amplitude and Power:

1. $Amplitude = max\text{ - }mean = mean - \min = \dfrac{max\text{ - }min}{2}$

2. $Power \propto (Amplitude)^2$

3. $Intensity = \dfrac{Power}{Beam\ Area}$

4. a) $dB \triangleq 10 * \log\left(\dfrac{P_f}{P_i}\right)$ where $\left(\dfrac{P_f}{P_i}\right)$ is the power ratio (power gain factor)

   b) $dB \triangleq 20 * \log\left(\dfrac{A_f}{A_i}\right)$ where $\left(\dfrac{A_f}{A_i}\right)$ is the amplitude ratio (amplitude gain factor)

Related to Distance (Physical Dimension):

1. $d = r * t$

2. $\lambda = \dfrac{c}{f}$

3. $SPL = \lambda * (\#\ cycles\ in\ pulse)$

Related to Circular Dimensional Measurement:

1. $Circle\ circumference = 2\pi\,r = \pi\,d$

2. $Circle\ area = \pi\,r^2$

3. $Circle\ volume\ (sphere) = \dfrac{4\pi\,r^3}{3}$

Related to Resolution:

1. $Axial\ Resolution = \dfrac{SPL}{2}$

2. $Lateral\ Resolution = lateral\ beamwidth$

3. $Elevation\ Resolution = elevation\ beamwidth$

4. $Temporal\ Resolution$ is determined by the acoustic frame rate and the monitor frame rate

5. $Nyquist\ Limit:\ Maximum\ detectable\ frequency = \dfrac{Sample\ frequency}{2}$

6. $Contrast\ resolution\ of\ a\ monitor = 2^n$:
           $Where\ n = number\ of\ bits\ assigned\ to\ greyscale\ of\ monitor$

Related to Transducers:

1. $NZL = \dfrac{D^2}{4\lambda} \approx \dfrac{D^2 f}{6}\ (D\ must\ be\ in\ mm\ and\ f\ must\ be\ in\ MHz\ to\ use\ the\ approximate\ form)$

2. $Beamwidth \approx \dfrac{D}{2}$ (at the focal depth, the beam is approximately half the crystal diameter)

3. $Beamwidth \approx D$ (at twice the focal depth, or $2*NZL$)

4.   a) $f_0 =$ (frequency of the drive Voltage for CW)

           b) $f_0 = \dfrac{C_{crystal}}{2*thickness_{crystal}}\ \left(for\ PW\right)$

5. $Bandwidth\ (BW) = upper\ frequency\ corner - lower\ frequency\ corner$

6. $FBW\ \% = \dfrac{BW}{f_0}*100\%$

7. $Quality\ (Q)\ factor = \dfrac{1}{FBW}$

8. $BUF\ \left(beam\ uniformity\ factor\right) = \dfrac{Spatial\ Peak\ Intensity\,(SP)}{Spatial\ Average\ Intensity\,(SA)}$

Related to Properties of Material and Attenuation:

1. $\rho = \dfrac{mass}{volume}$

2. $Z = \rho * c$

3. $\% \text{ reflection} + \% \text{ transmission} = 100\%$

4. $\% \text{ reflection} = \left[\dfrac{Z_2 - Z_1}{Z_2 + Z_1}\right]^2$

5. $R = \dfrac{8\ell\eta}{\pi r^4}$

6. $c_i * \sin\left(\theta_t\right) = c_t * \sin\left(\theta_i\right)$

7. $Attenuation\ rate: \quad \approx \dfrac{0.5\ dB}{cm \times MHz}\left(soft\ tissue\right)$

    $\approx \dfrac{1\ dB}{cm \times MHz}\left(muscle\right)$

Related to Hemodynamics and Doppler:

1. $f_{Dop} = \dfrac{2 f_o v * \cos\left(\theta\right)}{c}$

2. $f_{Dop}\left(max\right) = \dfrac{PRF}{2}\left(without\ aliasing\ by\ Nyquist\right)$

3. $\Delta P = Q * R \left(simplified\ law\ of\ hemodynamics\right)$

4. $Q = \overline{v} * area \left(continuity\ equation\right)$

5. $R = \dfrac{8\ell\eta}{\pi r^4}$

6. $Q = \dfrac{\Delta P \pi r^4}{8\ell\eta}\left(Poiseiulle's\ Law\right)$

7. $K.E. = \dfrac{1}{2}\rho v^2 \Rightarrow \Delta P \approx 4\left(v_2^2 - v_1^2\right) \approx 4\left(v_2^2\right) if\ v_2 \gg v_1$

8. $Hydrostatic\ pressure = mgh \approx 2\dfrac{mmHg}{inch}$

Pegasus Lectures, Inc.

Your resource for a lifetime of learning in ultrasound.

Pegasus Lectures offers a wide array of educational materials:

<u>**Exam Sim Suite CD-ROMs**</u>

<u>**Case Study CD-ROMs**</u>

<u>**Tutorial CD-ROMs**</u>

<u>**Videos**</u>

<u>**Texts**</u>

<u>**Seminars**</u>

<u>**e-courses**</u>

- Ultrasound Physics and Instrumentation
- Vascular Physics and Instrumentation
- Cardiovascular Physics and Instrumentation
- Abdomen
- Adult Echocardiography

- Breast Ultrasound
- Musculoskeletal Imaging
- Obstetrics and Gynecology
- Pediatric Echocardiography
- Vascular Technology

For additional information regarding Pegasus Lectures, Inc., please visit our website at

www.PegasusLectures.com

or call/write us at

Pegasus Lectures, Inc.
P.O. Box 157
Forney, Texas 75126
pegasuslectures@aol.com

Tel: 972.564.3056
Fax: 972.552.9186

NOTES:

NOTES:

NOTES:

<u>NOTES:</u>

NOTES: